Peptide Self-Assembly and Engineering

Peptide Self-Assembly and Engineering

Fundamentals, Structures, and Applications

Volume 2

Edited by Xuehai Yan

WILEY VCH

Editor

Prof. Xuehai Yan
Institute of Process Engineering, CAS
Zhongguancun
Haidian District
Beijing, 100190
China

Library of Congress Card No.: applied for

British Library Cataloguing-in-Publication Data
A catalogue record for this book is available from the British Library.

Bibliographic information published by the Deutsche Nationalbibliothek
The Deutsche Nationalbibliothek lists this publication in the Deutsche Nationalbibliografie; detailed bibliographic data are available on the Internet at http://dnb.d-nb.de.

Print ISBN: 978-3-527-35196-1
ePDF ISBN: 978-3-527-84124-0
ePub ISBN: 978-3-527-84125-7
oBook ISBN: 978-3-527-84126-4

Typesetting: Straive, Chennai, India
Printing and Binding: CPI Group (UK) Ltd, Croydon, CR0 4YY

C9783527351961_240124

Contents

Preface

It is with great pleasure that I introduce this book, which marks the 30th anniversary of the discovery of the first peptide building block capable of self-assembly. Over the past three decades, this field has undergone remarkable growth in scientific understanding and technical expertise. The materials and techniques derived from this research have not only expanded our knowledge but also provided us with innovative tools to address the challenges faced in the development of our modern society. The use of peptide-based materials with biocompatibility, biodegradability, and biorecyclability holds immense potential for promoting healthy, green and sustainable development on our planet.

In celebration of this significant milestone, I propose the publication of a comprehensive book that provides an overview of the advancements and future directions in peptide self-assembly and engineering. One particularly captivating area of exploration is the recent discovery of amino acid and peptide glasses, which exist in a thermodynamically metastable state. This finding opens up exciting avenues for the creation of dynamic, complex, and metastable glassy structures and materials that closely resemble biological systems. I firmly believe that more fascinating discoveries and groundbreaking achievements in the field of peptide self-assembly and engineering are yet to come, making this an ideal time to compile a book that presents a summary of the latest scientific findings from the past decades.

This book covers a wide range of topics related to peptide self-assembly and engineering, including self-assembly principles, assembled structures and functions, and materials engineering and applications. As such, it will cater to a diverse readership, comprising individuals with backgrounds in chemistry, materials science, nanotechnology, molecular engineering, biomedicine, and life science. Whether you come from academia, industry, or the education sector, I am confident that you will find valuable insights and information within the pages of this book.

Finally, I would like to express my deepest gratitude to my mentors, colleagues, collaborators, and students, as well as family members, whose unwavering support has been instrumental in my academic journey. I extend my heartfelt appreciation to the contributors of each chapter for accepting my invitation and sharing their expertise to make this book a reality.

Xuehai Yan
Beijing, China
August 2023

14

Functional peptide coatings

Xingcen Liu[1] and Junbai Li[2]

[1] *Key Laboratory of Colloid and Interface Chemistry, Ministry of Education, Shandong University, Jinan, 250100, China*
[2] *Beijing National Laboratory for Molecular Sciences (BNLMS), CAS, Key Lab of Colloid, Interface and Chemical Thermodynamics, Institute of Chemistry, Chinese Academy of Sciences, Beijing 100190, China*

14.1 Introduction

Coating is the process of depositing a thin coating of a material onto a substrate. Coatings are generally made of functional materials, as they can control or dictate the interactions with the surrounding environment, including air, dust, water, oil, chemicals, bacteria, viruses, fungi, and so on. Therefore, coatings are applied to surfaces to offer protection, decoration, recognition, and other special functions. In certain complex cases, coating may better to have multiple properties, which makes some of them multilayer. Multilayer coatings usually consist of different layers, such as the intermediate coat, the primer coat, and the top coat, each contributing different functions. For example, when the intermediate coat offers adhesion properties, the primer coat endows specific functions, and the top coat offers antifouling or superhydrophobic properties. Moreover, one important advantage of functional coatings is that a small amount of material can form into thin layers to change and functionalize the substrate as desired.

Peptide coatings are layers of peptide deposition with various properties. Over the past one hundred years, different types of peptides, including self-assembled, zwitterionic, peptidomimetics, hydrogels, PEGylated, and polymer-grafted, have been suggested as coatings. It is because of their ease of synthesis, tunable structures, versatile properties, biocompatibility, low toxicity profiles, and desirable proteolytic stability. Furthermore, some specific peptide sequences have been designed to exhibit properties such as preventing microbes and/or proteins and identifying/targeting specific proteins. This is why peptide coatings are chosen for different applications.

Advanced functional peptide coatings also require appropriate deposition methods. The coating strategies are designed or modified to meet different requirements,

Peptide Self-Assembly and Engineering: Fundamentals, Structures, and Applications, First Edition.
Edited by Xuehai Yan.

such as coating thickness, velocity, patterns, and properties. Various strategies and techniques have been developed for coating peptides onto different types of materials. In this chapter, we will provide brief introductions to several deposition methods used for peptide coatings and describe some of their applications.

14.2 Peptide coating techniques

Over the past decades, different strategies and methods have been developed for the preparation of peptide coatings on various substrates. Here, we briefly discuss the most common techniques for peptide coating, including drop-casting, dip-coating, spin-coating, lay-by-layer assembly, physical vapor deposition (PVD), and chemical vapor deposition (CVD). It is difficult to determine which technique is the best, as each has its own advantages and drawbacks. They all can be used to prepare coatings of varying thicknesses by changing some parameters. The common advantages of drop-casting, dip-coating, and spin-coating are great simplicity, controllable speed, low cost, simple device, and scalability. However, dip-coating is possible for cross-contamination in multilayers and is inapplicable for non-planar substrates. Dip-coating and spin-coating can also be time-consuming, as they only offer one substrate at a time, while the size of the substrates is limited by the spinning device. The PVD and CVD techniques show excellent uniformity, high deposition rate, and high density, and are easily fabricated for industrial-scale applications. Vapor deposition techniques are available for various substrates, but they require high voltage or sophisticated reactors to offer the needed vapor. Moreover, these techniques can affect the quality of products. Thus, it is important to choose the proper technique to obtain the desired properties.

14.2.1 Drop-casting

Drop-casting is the easiest strategy for peptide coatings. In this strategy, a drop of peptide solution is first deposited ("drop-casted") on the substrate. Once the drop is casted, it must spread to achieve equilibrium, and at the same time, evaporation happens, leaving a coating in the end (Figure 14.1a) [1]. When considering the wetting, spreading, and evaporating processes, a simple drop becomes a quite complex system.

For a drop on a solid surface, the wetting area is restrained by the contact line or the gas–liquid–solid three-phase line. According to the contact angle θ, the wetting situations can be divided into three cases: non-wetting with $\theta > 90°$, partial wetting with $0 < \theta < 90°$, and complete wetting with $\theta \rightarrow 0$. At the three-phase line, the famous Neumann-Young rule describes the connection of solid–solid, solid–gas, and liquid–gas interfacial tensions, and the contact angle [2]. It depends on the nature of the substrate and the solution. The density, viscosity, surface tension, surface wettability, and drop volume can affect the wetting/spreading dynamics [1].

For a drop-casting of the peptide solution, it goes through two main stages: stage I, a short but fast wetting/spreading process; stage II, where the evaporation dominates and the volume decreases greatly. The spreading and evaporation of the droplet on

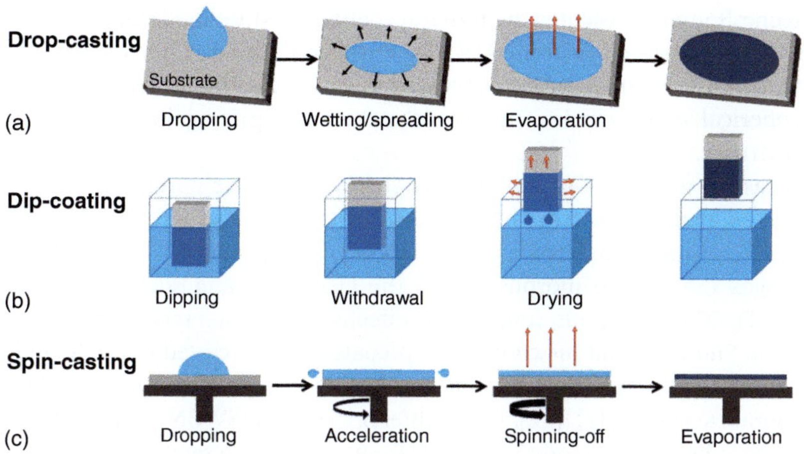

Figure 14.1 The drop-casting, dip-coating, and spin-coating techniques.

substrates are accompanied by the flow inside the droplet. During these stages, the concentration changes with spreading/evaporation, causing concentration gradients, which further lead to surface tension gradients. The concentration gradients cause capillary flow, a radially outward flow of the solution toward the contact line from the center of the drop [3]. The surface tension gradients cause Marangoni flow, which drives the liquid in the opposite direction to the capillary flow [4]. Marangoni flow is usually less in aqueous drops than in volatile nonaqueous solvents. Temperature gradients can also enhance the Marangoni flow by adjusting the substrate temperature [5]. The highness of the drop may cause non-negligible buoyancy convection, especially with high drops, where gravity may dominate the dynamics equilibrium.

The deposition of solutions after evaporation can form a ring-like pattern, called coffee ring, which can be observed by the eyes. The coffee ring originates from the pinning of the contact line after wetting/spreading reaches equilibrium [6]. Due to the large free space at the edge of the drop, the evaporation near the contact line is the greatest. The higher evaporation rate causes greater solvent loss, leading to more active capillary flow and Marangoni flow there [3]. The competition between capillary flow and Marangoni flow results in the pattern of the coffee ring, especially when the Marangoni flow is weak [7]. Therefore, when controlling the surface tension by changing the surface hydrophobicity/hydrophilicity, such as introducing surfactants, the coffee ring effect can be ameliorated [8], which will help obtain a uniform distribution by drop-casting.

Hydrophobic dipeptides have been introduced to assemble into interfacial aggregates by a drop-casting method. Clegg's group reported the self-assembly of Nap-diphenylalanine (NapFF) at the air–water interface by drop-casting [9]. NapFF assembled into a thin film via diffusion in the high-pH solvent and then drop-casting onto the low-pH subphase. The drop-casting procedure is only successful when the NapFF concentration is high enough and the subphase pH is well below the pK_a. The interfacial film acts like an elastic sheet and can stabilize air bubbles for days. Reches's group presented an antiviral coating via drop-casting of the tripeptide L-3,4-dihydroxyphenylalanine (DOPA)-Phe-Phe-Ome [10]. This tripeptide solution is drop-casted onto the glass surface repeatedly, resulting in three uniform layers of spherical nanoparticles. Importantly, the coating is against DNA- and RNA-based viruses.

The drop-casting method of peptide-based hybrids plays an important role in the fabrication of biomaterials. Kraatz et al. presented the modification of gold electrodes by drop-casting of the ferrocene-Glu-Cys-Gly-OH (Fc-ECG) [11]. The drop-casting changes the surface morphology of the electrodes and succeeds in the deposition of Fe. The Fc-peptide conjugate is effective as a redox mediator for glucose oxidation. Shoseyov and his co-workers prepared a drop-casted reusable optical biosensor for gaseous acetic acid using peptide-encapsulated single-walled carbon nanotubes (SWCNTs) [12]. Five different peptide/SWCNTs were drop-casted onto the substrate, and only YK-SWCNTs succeeded as a sensor.

14.2.2 Dip-coating

Among the available coating techniques, dip-coating is the most widely used due to its simple process, high coating quality, low processing temperature, and inexpensive setup. In recent years, dip-coating has been successfully used to fabricate, inorganic–organic hybrid material depositions and obtain homogeneous crack-free composite coatings on various implants.

Dip-coating is available to create complex patterns and shapes on both flat and heterogeneous substrates. A general dip-coating process is described by three simple steps: dipping, withdrawal, and drying (Figure 14.1b). Dipping can be explained as immersion and stabilization. The substrates for dip-coating can be cylindrical rollers, planar plates, or fibers. In the beginning, the substrate is immersed in the coating solution and waited a certain amount of time for its stabilization. The next step is withdrawal. By withdrawing the substrate from the solution with a fixed or changing velocity, a thin layer of the solution is retained, which will evaporate in the third step. During the drying process, the liquid evaporates along with the various deposition processes, forming complex patterns and shapes. The patterns or shapes are closely connected to the inherent properties of the coating solution, including viscosity, density, and surface tension. Besides, the roughness and substance of substrates, the concentration of the solution, the withdrawal speed, and the experimental conditions (such as temperature and humidity) are all related to the deposition results.

Although these steps appear to be simple, more details need to be understood, especially during the latter two steps. The analysis of dip-coating was first started in the case of the theoretical film thickness by dip-coating from a Newtonian liquid in the pioneering work of Landau and Levich [13]. They developed an analytical model by defining the film thickness h, the capillary length l, the capillary number Ca, the substrate withdrawal speed v, the viscosity η, the gravity g, the density ρ, and the surface tension σ. They predicted the film thickness as $h = 0.945 l Ca^{2/3}$, while $l = \sqrt{\sigma/\rho g}$ and $Ca = \eta v/\sigma$ [14]. This equation only fits in the case of $Ca << 1$, according to plenty of experimental and numerical tests [15, 16]. With larger capillary numbers, gravity dominates capillary forces, leading to a new law as $h \propto lCa^{1/2}$ [17]. Then it was extended for the stripes formed during dip-coating as $h' = 0.356WCa^{1/3}$, here h' is the film thickness at the half-width of the wetting stripe and W is the width of the wetting stripe [18].

The Landau–Levich model is based on the Newtonian and non-evaporating fluid for the dip-coating process. However, most solutions used in the dip-coating technique are non-Newtonian fluids. Then it has been extended to non-Newtonian liquid, with the kinetics of evaporation at the meniscus modeled. In these models, the thickness is also through the concentration of the solution, which is always changing due to the evaporating solute/solvent system [19]. There are several distinct regimes for different ranges of withdrawal speed. The draining/evaporation regime (which is also called Landau–Levich regime) is based on the higher speed described by the Landau–Levich model. The capillary/evaporation regime (or short evaporation regime) fits the low speed, in which the thickness is inversely proportional to the speed.

Over the last few years, dip-coating has been widely utilized to fabricate peptide coatings. Li et al. developed a controllable dip-coating procedure for the fast fabrication of ultralong-aligned diphenylalanine single crystals [20]. The diphenylalanine/NH_4OH binary solution was introduced in their dip-coating system. Diphenylalanine was negatively charged because of the deprotonation of the ammonium in the NH_4OH aqueous solution. The evaporation is strongest near the three-phase line, and the local concentration of diphenylalanine will exceed the saturation degree. The nucleation then starts there, and the subsequent substrate withdrawal leads to the continuously oriented growth of crystals from the solution. The structures of crystals could be controlled by the parameters of the dip-coating process. Li et al. investigated the growth of diphenylalanine during the dip-coating process from NH_4OH solution in detail (Figure 14.2) [21]. They show how different parameters lead to different assemblies or arrangements. These parameters are the initial diphenylalanine concentration, the initial NH_4OH concentration, the withdrawal speed, and the evaporation rate (which is varied by the external gas flow at the meniscus region). It turns out that under changing parameters, diphenylalanine can form into microfibers/nanofibers with different densities or stripes with different widths and

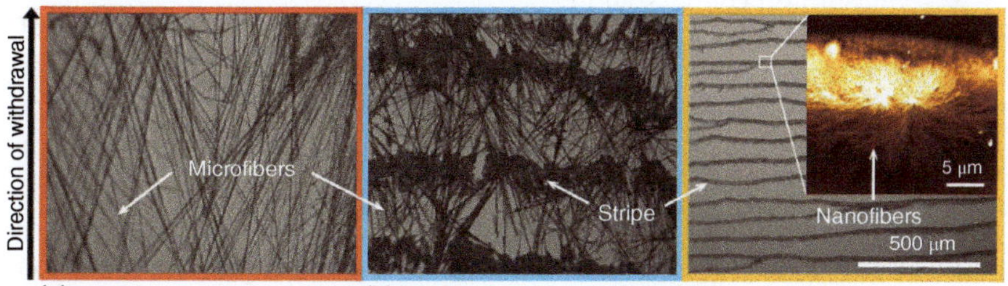

Figure 14.2 Scheme of the different types of FF aggregates by dip-coating.
Source: Reprinted with permission from Ref. [21]; © 2022 American Chemical Society.

spaces. The formation mechanism of various assemblies depends on local diphenylalanine concentration at the meniscus. Then they tried to change these parameters of dip-coating in the diphenylalanine/acid (acetic, propanoic, formic acid, and HCl) solutions [22]. For low diphenylalanine concentrations and low acidity, microfibers/nanofibers or stripes are assembled. For higher acidity, closed smooth films without fibrous structures are found. The thickness of films is controllable and explained by the evaporation regime.

Abell et al. presented a novel dip-coating procedure to fabricate optical fiber sensors [23]. The fiber coating is carried out by a one-step or two-step process, both involving submersion of the optical fiber tip in the aqueous solution of silk fibroin and functionalized silk-binding peptide. The silk coating is stable under long-term exposure to water and repeated washing.

14.2.3 Spin-coating

Spin-coating is another simple method for producing uniform thin films on flat substrates. As a low-cost, easily controllable technique, spin-coating is easily used to fabricate different materials on different surfaces. Spin-coating has been used for biomedical and microelectronic applications, such as drug delivery devices, wound dressings, production of coatings, and cell culture substrates [24].

The machine used for spin-coating is called a spin coater. The spin-coating technique generally consists of four steps, as shown in Figure 14.1c. First, a small quantity of the liquid resource is dropped onto the middle of the substrate. Then, the substrate starts to rotate to a certain speed. At the same time, the increasing centrifugal force and the surface tension induce the liquid to spread onto a flat surface. The liquid is evaporated during the entire procedure, especially after the spreading step. Heat or other drying treatments may be needed for certain materials in the final evaporation step. In the end, a thin film is left on the substrate.

Among these four steps of a spin-coating procedure, several factors affect the final film thickness. The material and smoothness of the substrate lay good foundation. The inherent properties of the liquid (including the solution viscosity, the surface tension, and the drying rate) and the parameters during the rotation (such as the angular speed, acceleration, and spin time) all determine the thickness and properties of the final films [25].

The spin-coating technique was first reported in the 1920s for the application of paint coatings [26]. many attempts have been done to get a mathematical model of the spin-coating process until 1958, when Emslie's group offered the EBP model for the prediction of final thickness [27]. In the EBP model, the thinning rate is $\frac{dh}{dt} = -2\frac{\rho\omega^3}{3\eta}h^3$, where h is the layer thickness, t is the time, ρ is the liquid density, ω is the rotation rate, and η is the liquid viscosity [28, 29]. However, when evaporation dominates the last step, the model needs to be fixed as $\frac{dh}{dt} = -2\frac{\rho\omega^3}{3\eta}h^3 - e$, where e is added as the evaporation rate [30–32]. Since then, this model has been modified by taking more factors into account according to different conditions.

Spin-coating technology used to modulate peptide assembly is of significant interest. Fakhraai's group systematically investigated the surface effects on amyloid-β peptide aggregation by using spin-coating to rapidly dry the samples [33]. The simple but reliable spin-coating method was chosen because it is available to control the assembly formation rates and the final morphologies. Under a longer subsequent incubation time, the self-assembled fibrils grew longer. With the same technique, they examined the influence of different drying processes on the final morphology later [34]. They demonstrated that a low spinning rate can restrain drying artifacts on the surface, while a fast rate without incubation results in larger fibrils. Therefore, by choosing the proper drying procedure, one can obtain the desired structures of peptides.

Take short peptide molecules as an example. Spin-coating was utilized to prepare a variety of diphenylalanine self-assembled architectures by Verma et al. [35]. By simultaneously changing the spinning rate and the solution concentrations, various structures were obtained, ranging from long fibrils to short fibers, globules, and finally nanodots. The combination of different interactions (centrifugal force, capillary, Marangoni flow during evaporation, and interfacial van der Waals interaction) and the assembling property leads to versatile morphologies with the same molecule.

Ree's group fabricated a well-ordered molecular assembly using the polypeptide (PBCL20) solution spin-coating method [36]. PBCL20 was dissolved in *N,N*-dimethylformamide (DMF) or tetrahydrofuran, and then the solution was spin-coated onto silicon substrates. After drying, the resulting PBCL20 films were of 80–100 nm thickness and composed thin fibrils with micro- or nanometer scale in both solvents. The larger fibrils formed with the DMF solution of PBCL20 were due to the additional mobility of the PBCL20 chains offered by the DMF solvent.

However, spin-coating has several obvious drawbacks. First, it has low efficiency as it has process only one substrate at a time. The size of the substrate is also one of the main drawbacks of spin-coating. Especially, high-speed spinning is much more challenging as the size increases since film thinning becomes more challenging [37]. Another limit of spin-coating is that more than 90% of resources are thrown off and wasted while only a small amount of material is coated onto the substrate. Spin-coating is usually employed in labs to prepare small-sized materials, as it is not appropriate for producing materials on a large scale for practical applications.

14.2.4 Layer-by-layer Assembly

Since the 1950s, two coating techniques, self-assembled monolayers and Langmuir–Blodgett deposition, have dominated the area of thin film, although both of them have considerable drawbacks [38]. Therefore, layer-by-layer (LBL) assembly, as their alternative, was first introduced to create multilayers of oppositely charged nanoparticles by Iler [39]. Moreover, in 1992, Decher and his co-workers promoted the LBL assembly by fabricating oppositely charged polyelectrolyte multilayers [40]. Since then, LBL assembly has been an effective strategy to fabricate versatile functional coatings for biosensors, tissue engineering, implant coatings, drug delivery, fiber optics, and food packaging [41].

LBL assembly is a cyclic deposition of layers that starts with the adsorption of a charged material onto a substrate. And then, after washing, the oppositely charged material will be adsorbed on the first layer [42]. With these cyclic depositions, the multilayers are formed on the substrates. The changing of the repeating time can decide the thickness or specific functions. The structures, thickness, and other properties can be well controlled by designing suitable raw materials and adjusting the parameters.

Electrostatic interactions are usually the main driving forces for LBL assembly. The mechanism based on overcompensation was proposed by Schlenoff and his co-workers [43]. They explained that the intrinsic compensation from a pair of materials with opposing charges coexists with the extrinsic compensation of ion pairing from charged counterions. When the intrinsic compensation dominates the process, the growth of the polyelectrolyte multilayers follows the linear growth model. When the two compensations are both weak, the growth of multilayers fits an exponential growth model [44, 45]. Ionic strength and pH are the key factors for the assembly, which can change the thickness by a thousand times. Based on this mechanism, besides polyelectrolytes, most charged biomolecular species can be successfully used as raw materials for LBL assembly, including polypeptides, proteins, polysaccharides, nucleic acids, and viruses [46–49].

The requirement for LBL assembly is an appropriate substrate to support the multilayer assembly. Various substrates have been developed for good behavior, including metals, carbon, glass, quartz crystals, mica, silicon wafers, and different polymers [50]. Among them, some metals, glass, and silicon wafers have negative charges in solutions due to surface oxidation and possible hydrolysis, which may be helpful for the next steps [38]. According to specific requirements, some modifications on the substrates are introduced, like nanoparticles, which are usually used to increase the surface roughness to improve the wettability of the films [51]. Substrates also have different alternatives in their shapes, including one-dimensional substrates (nanowires, nanotubes, and particle surfaces), two-dimensional substrates (planar surfaces and plates), and three-dimensional surfaces (porous surfaces). In many cases, the multilayers can be removed from the substrates perfectly for specific applications.

Peptides and oligosaccharides are widely used as interacting pairs for LBL assembly, which is a benefit of adding peptide-based functions into the system [52]. Elbert and Picart successfully prepared poly(L-lysine) (PLL)/alginate and PLL/hyaluronan multilayers, respectively [53, 54]. Then, more researchers have been working on this area. Porcel's group systematically studied the influence of molecular weight changes on the PLL/hyaluronan system [55]. They found that the higher molecular weight of PLL limited the PLL diffusion in the upper layers. Crouzier and Picart investigated more details on the mechanism of polypeptide/polysaccharides multilayers [56]. They compared different films prepared with PLL as a polycation, and three polysaccharides with different charge densities (heparin > chondroitine sulfate > hyaluronan) as polyanions. They found out that the net charge of films directly depends on the charge density of polyanions. For PLL/hyaluronan, 46% of PLL was unpaired and simultaneously compensated with Cl^-, while PLL/heparin presented an excess negative charge with compensation by Na^+.

The combination of peptides and polymers is another common strategy in LBL assembly. Zhang and his co-workers used a heparin/peptide-polyethylene glycol system to build tailored multilayer biomatrices by LBL assembly [57]. The first layer of the first negatively charged heparin was immobilized on the oppositely charged substrate, and then positively charged peptide-polyethylene glycol was adsorbed onto heparin as the second layer. Subsequently, the multilayers were grown by the cyclic deposition steps.

Besides electrostatic interactions, other LBL assembly-based driving forces (donor/acceptor, covalent bonding, hydrogen bonding, hydrophobic interaction, and biological recognition) have also been developed [58]. Overall, combining multi-interactions can dramatically change the properties of the multilayers, even under crucial conditions. One can design the appropriate system to fabricate multilayers with the desired properties and functions.

14.2.5 Physical Vapor Deposition

In the first sections of this chapter, the most common coating production techniques we talked about were all solution processes. In contrast, we will introduce dry processes in the next two sections, physical vapor deposition (PVD) and chemical vapor deposition (CVD). The distinguishing feature between them is the vapor. For PVD, the vapor is composed of condensed atoms and molecules on the substrate, while in CVD, the vapor originates from a chemical reaction [59].

The PVD technique includes the formation of condensed vapor by physical process and then the deposition of vapor onto a solid surface as coatings [60]. PVD can produce coatings with designed structures, controlled morphology, homogeneous layers, excellent adhesion, graduated properties, and diverse materials [61]. PVD is commonly applied for thin films, very thick deposits, multilayer deposition coatings, graded composition deposits, free-standing structures, and in combination with other techniques [62, 63]. All these results obey three basic steps: the creation of vapor from the source (or target), movement from the source to the substrate, and deposition growth on the substrate (Figure 14.3) [64, 65]. Among them, the formation of the physical vapor is through a phase transition from a liquid or solid phase to a gas or plasma phase. Physical vapor can be simply created by evaporation, sputtering, or ion bombarding.

During the evaporation process, the vapor is created by heating the target to a high temperature and then transported to a substrate through a vacuum environment, ending by condensation on the substrate and the formation of a coating. The vacuum environment creates a safe condition to reduce gaseous contaminants during the entire process and helps the vapor undergo collisionless transport. Thermal evaporation is generally produced at a low background pressure (about 10^{-4} Pa), making sure to transport the evaporated atoms to the substrates without collision. The evaporated atoms then condense on the substrates at a suitable temperature. And this temperature needs to be below a certain value to control the supercooling of the material. However, material degradation is a key challenge that restrains this method in some cases.

For sputtering, the source is created by ion impact on the target instead of thermal evaporation. In the sputtering process, a target is bombarded by high-energy atoms or

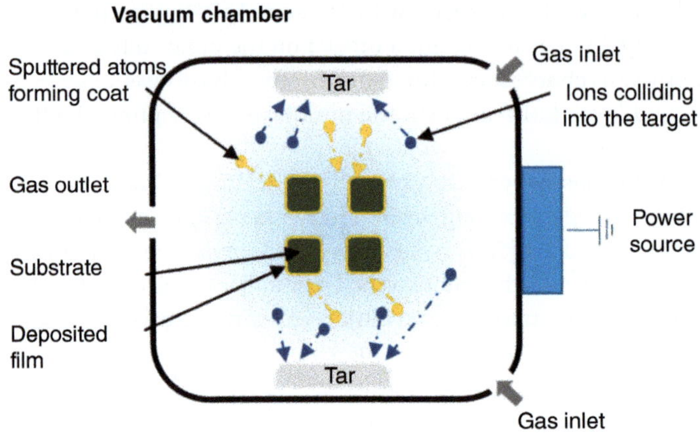

Figure 14.3 PVD technique. Source: Ref. [64]; © 2018 by the authors. Licensee MDPI, Basel, Switzerland.

ions, producing single atoms, clusters, or molecules that are deposited on the wall of a vacuum chamber [66]. During the sputtering process, the high-energetic particles are initially ionized in a chemically inert gas environment and subsequently bombard the target to form coatings [67]. The ionization is typically from a glow discharge, a cost-effective source of ions. The discharge is formed by the separated but parallel cathode and anode pair. The gap between the electrodes is a few centimeters long and filled with a certain working gas (most often argon). The atoms of the working gas are excited, ionized, accelerated, and bombarded there to maintain the discharge for the sputtering deposition [68]. As a clean coating technique, sputtering ensures better coating densification and a more friendly condition of a low or medium temperature [69]. Sputtering has been a generic name for various sputtering techniques, which are also named by their sources and orientations, such as diode sputtering, ion-beam sputtering, bias sputtering, magnetron sputtering, and reactive sputtering [70].

For an effective PVD process, a series of parameters must be taken into account, including the selection of the source, target, vapor, and substrate, and the adjustment of temperature, depositing rate, and bombardment efficiency [71]. As the PVD technique improved in the past decades, the deposition process can be under a gaseous, plasma, or electrolytic environment. The sputtering process utilizes low vacuum pressure and low deposition rate, while evaporation needs low atomic energy. Therefore, it is important to choose the appropriate PVD technique to fabricate desired depositions with different structural features, mass density, composition, surface roughness, optical and electrical properties, and so on.

Peptide nanotubes can be prepared by PVD to avoid using solvents and complex chemical synthesis routes. Gazit and Rosenman demonstrated the formation of large arrays of the aromatic dipeptide with the PVD technique for the first time [72]. The PVD process starts by heating a metal holder within the dipeptide monomer powder to about 220 °C, and after a certain time, the powder is evaporated onto a substrate surface [73]. This method makes it possible to control the size and density of nanotubes by accurately tuning the initial amount of the building monomers in the gas phase. Rosenman's group also fabricated dense and homogeneous dipeptide nanotubes by PVD [74]. They next studied the growth mechanism according to their molecular composition, fine morphological and packing structure, and physical and chemical properties, proving that the PVD technique can enable a controllable deposition method for fabricating peptide nanotubes.

14.2.6 Chemical Vapor Deposition

CVD is a generic name for depositions that involve homogeneous chemical reactions and/or dissociation of gaseous reactants in the gas phase, as well as heterogeneous chemical reactions that occur near the surfaces (Figure 14.4) [75]. The CVD reactions involve reduction, oxidation, pyrolysis, disproportionation, compound formation, and reversible transfer [62]. Whether the reactions could happen or not depends on the reactant gas and/or the by-products. The general process of CVD involves the following steps [76–78]: (i) generation of the active gaseous reactants, (ii) transport of the reactants to the surface, (iii) adsorption of the reactants onto the surface, (iv) diffusion of the reactants to the growth sites, (v) nucleation and growth of coating, and (vi) desorption of gaseous by-products and unreacted precursors.

The original application of CVD is reported in 1893, when de Lodyguine deposited W onto the filaments by the reduction of WCl_6 [79]. In the next 100 years, CVD has expanded rapidly to versatile techniques. According to the activated source of the chemical reactions, CVD can be categorized as thermally activated, plasma-assisted, and laser-assisted CVD. Depending on the chamber pressure, there are low-pressure (0.01–1.33 kPa), atmospheric pressure, and ultrahigh-vacuum (less than 10^{-4} kPa) CVD. Considering the plasma characteristics, there are plasma-enhanced, remote plasma-enhanced, microwave plasma-assisted, and magneto-microwave plasma CVD. More specifically, metal–organic CVD is one of the thermal CVD with metal–organic precursors [80].

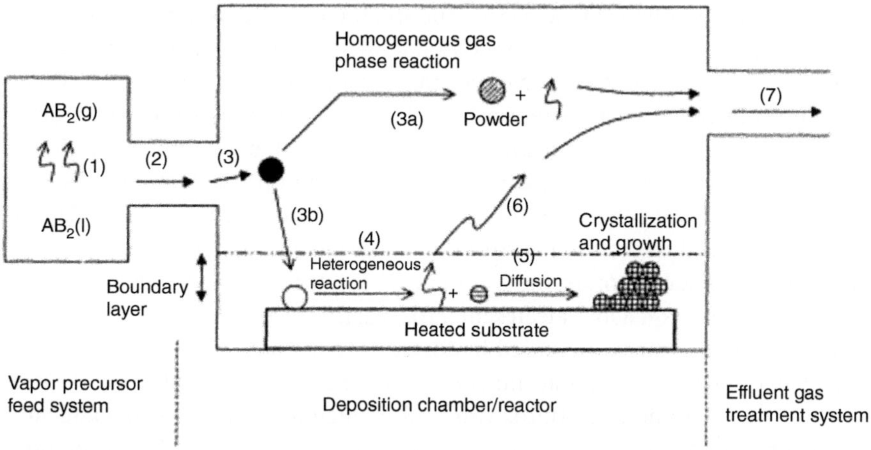

Figure 14.4 CVD technique. Source: Ref. [75]; Reproduced with permission Elsevier Science Ltd.

For example, thermal CVD utilizes heating lamps or using inorganic chemical precursors to heat the substrates quickly and activate enough energy for reactions. The thermal energy could be from infrared radiation, radio frequency (rf) heating, or resistive heating. The rate of heating or cooling changes, leading to concise control of coating formation. Thermal CVD is widely applied, from low-temperature deposition of thin films to high-temperature deposition for coating applications.

Laser-assisted homogeneous and heterogeneous CVD is called laser CVD [81]. In laser CVD, a focused laser beam is used to heat the substrate of several volatile precursors, which react on the surface. The high-energy beam can be used to drive CVD reactants for the deposition of film or coating. As the distance over which the gas transport may occur is only one beam diameter, the reaction rates of laser CVD are consequently very fast [82].

Another example is plasma-enhanced CVD. It utilizes an electrical source of energy to create plasma and sustain the whole reaction process. The electrical power is supplied at a sufficiently high voltage to the gas, leading to the breaking down of the gas and generating a glow discharge plasma, including ions, electrons, and electronically excited species [75]. The electrical energy can initiate homogeneous reactions to create chemically active radicals and ions for subsequent heterogeneous reactions, which result in layer formation on the substrate [62]. The advantage of plasma-enhanced CVD is that it needs a much lower temperature (close to ambient) and allows materials sensitive to temperature changes to be operated [83]. Therefore, the plasma-enhanced CVD requires a series of new reaction paths to achieve ambient temperature coating.

Single amino acids and simple peptides can be deposited by CVD due to their similar structure to chemical monomers. Monomers are exposed to a high-energy plasma zone in an inert atmosphere, allowing the chemical reactions of the radicals to occur there, as they are polymerized into a network during the deposition process [84]. Tsukruk's group did much research in this field. They fabricated conformal, uniform, and ultrathin synthetic peptide coatings onto a series of practical surfaces via plasma-enhanced CVD [85]. The smooth tyrosine films were fabricated with plasma-polymerized tyrosine monomer, which proved to consist of polytyrosine molecules, but more densely packed, more complete, and highly crosslinked than the films by other solution deposition. Then they used the histidine monomer for the formation of robust and uniform coatings capable of fabricating titania nanostructures on different substrates [86]. Tsukruk's group also demonstrated that plasma-enhanced CVD can be used for simultaneous copolymerization and deposition of the biological molecule (L-tyrosine) with inorganic or organic monomers to form a robust and stable composite coating [87, 88]. Since plasma-enhanced CVD has been widely used on a lot of different surfaces, this technique will be accessible and can be applied to many enhanced biological interfaces.

Naik et al. used plasma-enhanced CVD for the formation of dipeptide nanostructures [89]. The dipeptide without a solvent sublimated into a plasma area and subsequently deposited vertically aligned nanotubes on the substrate. The formation, morphologies, crystalline nature, and mechanical stability of peptide nanotubes depend on the plasma-enhanced CVD processing conditions, which differ from the

PVD-deposited dipeptide nanotubes. It has been proven that CVD can be used to synthesize various peptide nanostructures.

14.3 Applications

Due to the exceptional characteristics of the peptide coatings prepared in this chapter, plenty of applications are envisaged, including antifouling coatings, antimicrobial coatings, implant coatings, cell adhesion, drug delivery, and sensors.

14.3.1 Antifouling Coating

Biofouling is the undesired accumulation of organisms and relevant by-products such as bacteria, barnacles, algae, bryozoans, sponges, and fungi on surfaces [90]. It has become a serious issue in many fields of daily life, including health, water, food, and energy. One of the solutions is to coat the surfaces with suitable materials that resist biofouling by preventing adhesion to the surface (such as antifouling coatings) or killing the organisms (such as antimicrobial coatings discussed in the next section). Various peptides have been developed as antifouling coatings due to their biodegradability, biocompatibility, and low toxicity.

Short peptides can easily be self-assembled into desired coating structures and properties. For example, a kind of self-assembly tripeptide (DOPA-Phe-Phe-OMe) nanosphere has the antifouling property [91]. Within a DOPA moiety in the peptide, it could adhere to the surfaces and endow the antifouling properties to the surfaces. Then they reported that another short peptide, DOPA-Phe-Phe-Arg-Gly-Asp, was coated on the surface to resist fouling attachments by the combination of peptide and topography [92].

The amphiphilic peptides coated onto titanium (Ti) surfaces show resistance to the adhesion of Gram-positive and Gram-negative bacteria [93]. Moreover, the coating could reduce the bacterial growth in the solution. Guler et al. prepared a bioactive coating by assembling the peptide amphiphiles into nanofibers [94]. This coating could prevent bacterial colonization and prevent mammalian cells from settling on surfaces.

An ionic complementary peptide, EAR16-II, could form an amphipathic film in the presence of methylcellulose (MC) or *n*-dodecyl-β-D-maltoside (DDM) as additives [95]. Then, EAR16-II/MC and EAR16-II/DDM coatings on the microchip channels remarkably reduced the adsorption of bovine serum albumin (BSA) and lysozyme.

Zwitterionic peptides can also work as antifouling coatings (Figure 14.5) [90]. Su et al. reported a zwitterionic peptide (CRERERE) covalently coated onto a gold substrate with an ultralow or low protein adhered to it [96]. The strong surface hydration of the zwitterionic peptide contributed to its high antifouling ability by impeding interactions with single proteins. Zhang et al. fabricated a multifunctional coating of zwitterionic polypeptide KE and DOPA, which have antifouling and anchoring roles, respectively [97]. This coating could anchor atop surfaces of

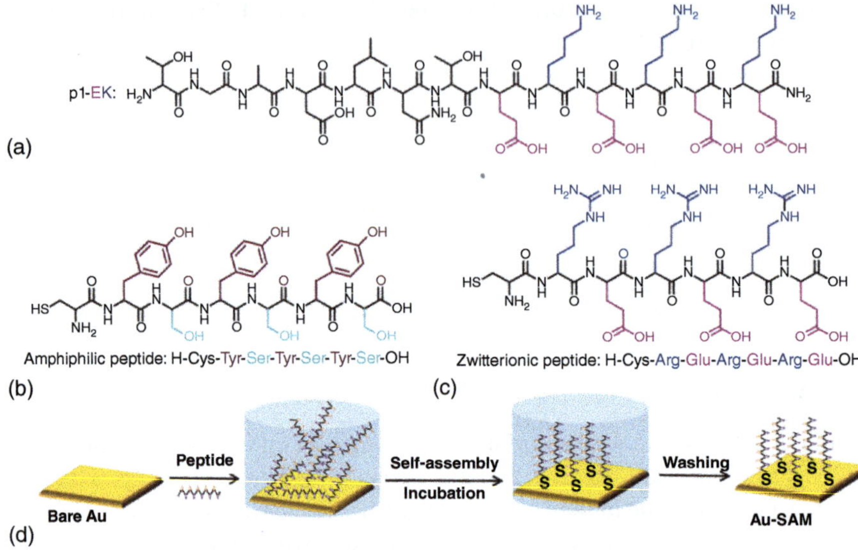

Figure 14.5 The formation of antifouling coating by a zwitterionic peptide. Source: Reprinted with permission from Ref. [90]; © 2018 John Wiley and Sons.

various substrates and exhibit superior antifouling properties, such as repelling BSA-FITC, *Staphylococcus aureus*, and *Escherichia coli*.

Polyethylene glycol (PEG) is a hydrating steric barrier to foulants on surfaces. PEGylation of biomolecules is a powerful tool in several applications, including antifouling. PEGylated peptides as coatings have been proven to be one of the powerful materials mentioned before. The PEGylation peptide (HKH) coated on the Ti surface was fabricated via a facile one-step modification reported by Grinstaff et al. [98]. This coating showed both nonspecific protein adsorption and bacterial colonization. They also reported the assembly of another PEGylated peptide (TBP_4-PEG) on Ti to obtain a surface coating that could restrain serum protein adsorption and *S. aureus* adhesion [99].

Furthermore, Bellassai reported an oligopeptide-PLL-coated gold substrate used to reduce the adsorption of bovine serum albumin [100]. The coating exhibited excellent antifouling properties with the highest concentration of protein solution.

14.3.2 Antimicrobial Coating

The accumulation of bacteria on surfaces is always one of the vital concerns for safety and health management. The adhesion of polysaccharides or proteins later supports the attachment of bacteria onto the surface. Therefore, antimicrobial coatings come into existence. Among them, peptide-based coatings occupy an important place. Antimicrobial peptides (AMPs) are the most suitable building blocks owing to their scalability, versatile design, environmentally friendly features, and excellent ability to resist growth, inactivate, or kill different microbes [101].

Rodriguez et al. prepared smooth Ti samples coated with lactoferrin-derived hLf1-11 peptide [102]. The antibacterial features were verified by two oral strains showing an outstanding reduction. They compared the effects of the coatings prepared with two different techniques, including silanization and polymer brush, suggesting that the polymer method decreased bacterial attachment due to the larger immobilization amounts of peptides. Leong et al. demonstrated that a potent AMP (Lasio-III) was immobilized on a silicone catheter to resist urinary tract infection pathogens [103]. The N-terminal of Lasio-III was modified with a cysteine residue to attach onto the silicone catheter surface via chemical coupling with the allyl glycidyl ether and PEG. The Lasio-III-coated catheter exhibited great antimicrobial features against Gram-negative and positive bacteria and inhibited the biofilm growth of *Enterococcus faecalis* and *E. coli*. Reis et al. reported that the commercial silk sutures were coated with AMP (6mer-HNPA) by dip-coating to prevent bacterial attachment [104]. The coated sutures significantly prevented bacterial adherence and biofilm formation while maintaining cell viability and blood compatibility.

Reches's group has conducted an extensive research work in the antimicrobial coating area. They reported two peptides, DOPA-Phe(4F)-Phe(4F)-OMe and DOPA-Phe-Phe-OMe, which can self-assemble into nanospheres with antiviral activity [10]. By drop-casting, the peptide spheres adhered onto the surface and formed an antiviral coating against DNA- and RNA-based viruses. They presented a novel short peptide, NH_2-DOPA-$(Phe)_2$-$(His)_6$-OH, with DOPA providing adsorption ability, $(Phe)_2$ inducing self-assembly, and $(His)_6$ contributing strong affinity with metal ions [105]. Therefore, this peptide successfully coated various surfaces (such as Cu(II) ion and SiO_2 surfaces) and provided them with antiviral and antibacterial activity.

In addition, multi-layer surface modification is widely designed and applied on various implanted materials, including silicon, glass, PDMS, and other silicon-/silica-based substrates. Wang and his colleagues demonstrated a self-assembled peptide-based interface with triple layers to significantly improve the tissue self-healing and prevent biofilm-mediated inflammation (Figure 14.6) [106]. This biointerface is composed of a cell-adhesive peptide (Arg-Gly-Asp), an infectious-environment-responsive peptide, and an antifouling hexaethylene glycol layer. The three-layer interface coated onto prosthetic replacements is capable of smartly responding to the surrounding pathological or physiological microenvironment.

14.3.3 Implant Coating

Implants or other medical devices associated with infections not only threaten patients' health but also cause increased hospitalization costs. One of the ways to prevent implant-associated infections is by coating implants with infection-resistant layers on the surface [107]. AMPs have been applied as coatings on implants or other medical devices to fight infections. Compared to antibiotics, AMP coatings can enhance bacterial specificity, minimize toxicity to host cells, and reduce the risks of drug resistance [108]. The key point is the safe and efficient immobilization of the antimicrobial peptides onto the appropriate substrates. Generally, there are

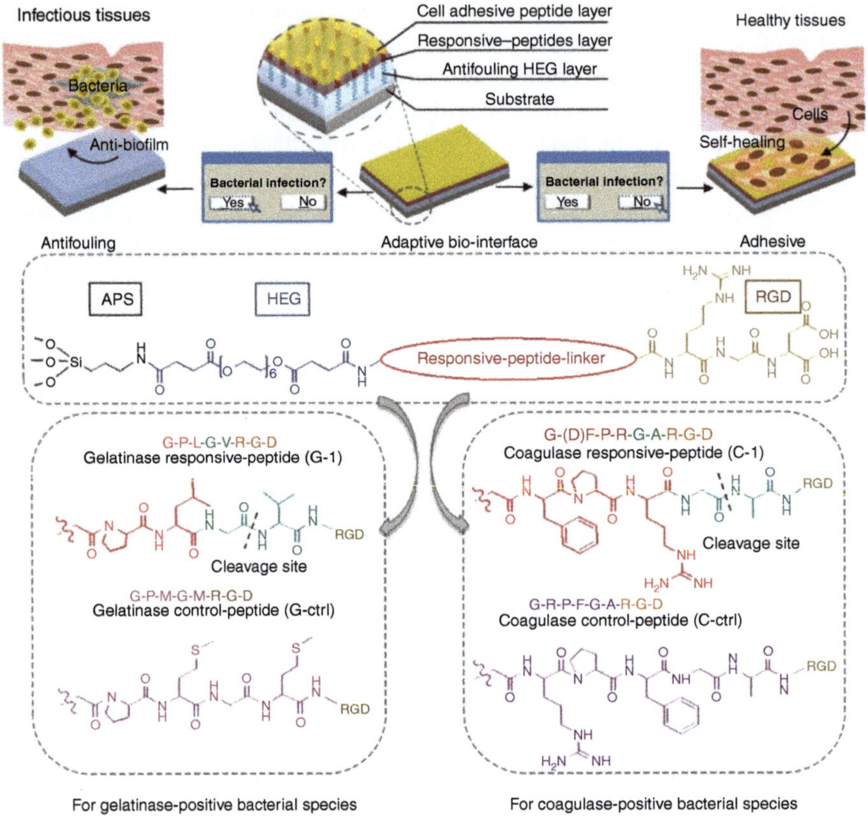

Figure 14.6 The formation and antiviral activity of a peptide-coated surface. The self-assembled peptide surface includes three layers: a cell-adhesive peptide layer (Arg-Gly-Asp), an infectious-environment-responsive peptide, and an antifouling HEG layers. Source: Reprinted with permission from Ref. [106]; © 2015 John Wiley and Sons.

three methods for immobilization (shown in Figure 14.7) [109]. The first is a primary coating, meaning that the peptides are directly coated on the substrates. The second involves covalently linking the peptides onto the functional group of a pre-prepared layer. The third method is embedding the peptides into the matrix scaffold and then releasing them.

Titanium (Ti) and alloys are the main metallic materials for implants. Aparicio's group developed a novel Ti coating with a homogeneous, strongly anchored, and highly hydrophobic peptide, GL13K [110]. The GL13K coatings had an antibacterial effect and good cytocompatibility, which made them appropriate for metallic and orthopedic implants. Another study used SESB2V AMP to coat the Ti substrate to improve the antibacterial effect and tested it on rabbit corneas [111]. There was less infection and lower incidence on rabbit corneas with the AMP-coated Ti implants than those without AMP protection. The bactericidal efficiency of AMP was greater against *S. aureus* than *Pseudomonas aeruginosa*. These results prove that SESB2V AMP can be efficiently functionalized in rabbit cornea models to prevent infections.

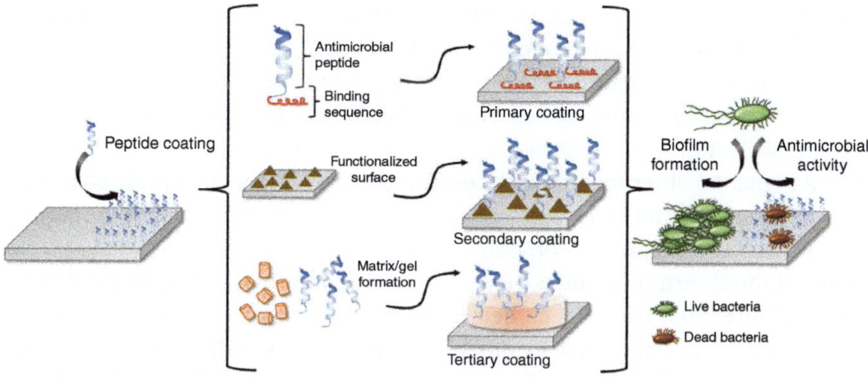

Figure 14.7 Strategy for the antimicrobial peptide coating on the implants [109]. 2021 by the authors. Licensee MDPI, Basel, Switzerland.

The peptide arginine-glycine-aspartic acid (RGD) has also been immobilized onto the Ti surface as a coating to promote implant osseointegration. Ryu's group demonstrated physically stable RGD coating onto anodized Ti surfaces [112]. They proved that the physical adsorption method provided more stable peptide coatings by comparing it to the chemical grafting method.

Recently, a hybrid peptide, P1-SAP, consisting of two peptide sequences have been used to form a surface-immobilized multifunctional coating on hydroxyapatite/tricalcium phosphate surfaces [113]. The coating is formed by a dip-coating or spraying approach and is stable for over one month. Thanks to the synergistic effects of cationic peptides between surface hydrophobic groups and superhydrophilic surfaces, the P1-SAP coating performs threefold antimicrobial efficiency against bacteria/biofilm and exhibits twofold antifouling properties compared to bare groups. Moreover, these P1-SAP-coated implants show significant efficacy against subcutaneous infections.

In many cases, a peptide-involved hybrid coating is popular for implants or other medical devices. As bacterial infections are the most common cause of orthopedic implant failure, antimicrobial peptide coatings are widely improved. Cogan et al. demonstrated a novel short peptide utilized to coat Ti with hydroxyapatite [114]. The peptides consist of a Ti-binding peptide and a hydroxyapatite-binding peptide. Therefore, a peptide-hydroxyapatite coating was formed on the Ti surface by dip-coating creating a Ti-peptide-hydroxyapatite sandwich. This method performed fast deposition on the Ti surface and had excellent initial biocompatibility compared to the standard commercial methods. Moreover, this coating method costs less money and requires low temperature/pressure. Another example is the use of PEGylated Ti binding peptides (TBP) on Ti substrate to obtain a bacteriophobic coating that can successfully resist protein and *S. aureus* adsorption [99]. The coating performance can be improved by the repeat number of TBP, with TBP_4-PEG being the best version in all assays. Especially, the TBP_4-PEG formed a serum-resistant coating that is capable of restraining *S. aureus* colonization and biofilm formation. Furthermore, another AMP Tet123-linked collagen IV (AMPCol), as a multilayer coating, was assembled onto smooth Ti surfaces by the LBL technique [115]. The coating with controlled AMP release decreased the growth of the Gram-negative anaerobes and Gram-positive aerobes for up to one month. A chimeric peptide with functionality can form a solid-surface coating [116]. The antimicrobial property of this coating on the implant was demonstrated by reducing the bacterial colonization on the implant below detectable limits.

Besides implants, other medical devices also take advantage of peptide coatings, such as catheters. Nizhakkedathu et al. investigated an effective surface tethering approach to form AMP coatings on polyurethane [117]. The AMP was labeled with a cysteine at the C-terminus and coated with an anti-adhesive hydrophilic polymer onto the polyurethane used for catheter manufacture. The AMP-coated catheter was tested in a rat urinary catheter model and demonstrated the ability to significantly reduce bacterial adhesion. Park et al. reported a peptide WKYMVm coated onto cobalt chromium stents in the porcine restenosis model [118]. The WKYMVm coating can improve endothelial healing and prevent restenosis effectively.

14.3.4 Cell Adhesion

Cell adhesion is common in multifarious natural phenomena, including embryogenesis, wound healing, metastasis, immune response, maintenance of tissue structure, and tissue integration of biomaterials [119]. Surface characteristics of materials, such as their topography, chemical energy, and surface energy, are of great significance in cell adhesion to biomaterials. Therefore, it is necessary for an appropriate coating on the material's surface to connect with tissues.

Some bone proteins have adhesive properties because they have the Arg-Gly-Asp (RGD) sequence. RGD is specific to the capture of cell membrane receptors (Figure 14.8) such as integrin, osteopontin, fibronectin, thrombospondin, type I collagen, and bone sialoprotein [119, 120]. Another advantage of grafting RGD onto a surface is that it has less accessible molecular arrangements.

Guillemot et al. introduced the grafting of two RGD-containing peptides (cyclo-DfKRG and linear RGD) onto the Ti surface of a new hybrid material [121]. They claimed that RGD-grafted biomaterials can be successfully associated with autologous bone marrow stroma cells to promote cell colonization through the development of hybrid materials. It was not long before Pallu and co-workers demonstrated the cyclo-DfKRG peptide coating on Ti using different anchors (phosphonate or thiol) [122]. After 10 days of cell seeding, this peptide coating with a phosphonate anchor succeeded in higher cell adhesion and strong mRNA expression, while that with a thiol anchor stimulated it within 3 days. Li et al. fabricated RGD-containing collagen/hyaluronic acid polyelectrolyte membrane coatings onto the Ti surface by the LBL technique [123]. Adding RGD to this hybrid coating promoted the stability and tunable biodegradability of the coating. *In vitro* evaluation proved the coating could significantly improve the pre-osteoblast's adhesion, proliferation, and differentiation. Webster et al. compared four peptides for their efficiency of cell adhesion

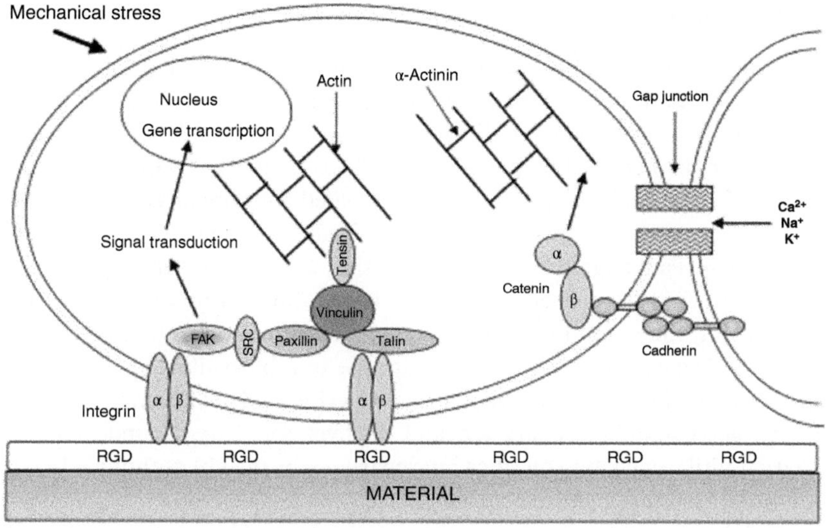

Figure 14.8 The mechanism of RGD for cell adhesions. Source: Reprinted with permission from Ref. [119]; © 2000 Elsevier Science B.V.

as nanotubular Ti coatings by a molecular plasma deposition method [124]. They found out that the arginine-glycine-aspartic-serine (RGDS) and lysine-arginine-serine-arginine (KRSR) coatings increased osteoblast density.

The bone morphogenetic protein (BMP) peptides are another type of widely studied adhesive peptide. Zouani et al. evaluated the differentiation of pre-osteoblastic cells when the BMPs and GRGDSPC peptides were grafted on polyethylene terephthalate surfaces [125]. As a result, in the cases of grafted surfaces, the thickness of the extracellular matrix was remarkably increased when the mineralization of pre-osteoblastic cells and the osteogenic differentiation were enhanced. Another work about BMP peptides is a P1 and P2-coated bone mineral prepared by Chung et al. [126]. These two BMP peptides could increase osteoblastic differentiation. Especially, P1-coated bone minerals promoted new bone regeneration more than the non-peptide control.

Recently, Kakinoki et al. demonstrated a peptide Leu-Asp-Val (LDV) coating on the expanded polytetrafluoroethylene (ePTFE) surface by one-pot oxidation method and a Tyr-Lys-Tyr-Lys-Tyr-Lys (YK3) anchor [127]. The LDV-involved coating showed enhanced endothelial cell adhesion on ePTFE and improved neointima-like tissue regeneration. At the same time, the YK3 anchor stabilized the peptide coating on the ePTFE surface, avoiding a complex process. Rapaport's group designed a novel peptide, DapSer, with multiple glutamic acid residues that could induce calcium/phosphate mineralization [128]. The DapSer-coated TiO_2 alloy bone implants improved protein adsorption, calcium/phosphate mineralization, and further cell adhesion.

14.3.5 Drug Delivery

Cell-penetrating peptides (CPPs) are peptides capable of transporting micromolecules and macromolecules across cell membranes [129]. CPPs are mostly amphiphilic and/or cationic peptides and are rich in several basic amino acids such as lysine, arginine, and leucine. Lee et al. designed Tat CPP-coated peptide nanoribbons for use as intracellular nanocarriers [130]. These Tat-coated nanoribbons can carry two different molecules simultaneously and selectively to the nucleus and the cytoplasm, respectively. Panchagnula et al. reported that CPP-coated solid lipid nanoparticles could be used for oral administration of insulin as a promising per-oral carrier [131]. Later, Chen and his co-workers prepared novel nanostructured lipid carriers with CPP-coated tripterine to facilitate the oral bioavailability of tripterine [132]. This new kind of CPP could act as a superior choice of carrier, as it has high stability, good lipophilic character, and no hygroscopicity. Neundorf et al. investigated a multilayer coating on silica microparticles by the LbL technique [133]. For the multilayer coating, a positively charged CPP was coated atop the biopolymer protamine and dextran sulfate surface as the outmost layer. This coating facilitated effective and fast endocytotic uptake. CPP (R8) could also be coated onto liposomes for doxorubicin delivery across the blood–brain barrier [134]. It was found that the R8-coated oleic acid-modified liposomes were capable of drug delivery for glioma.

Nuclear localization signaling (NLS) peptides are another widely used peptide for the nuclear-targeted delivery system for nanocarriers such as quantum dots (QDs), nanoparticles, gold nanorods, and metallic nanoclusters, because they can promote the transportation of these carriers across the membrane into the nucleus. Chen et al. demonstrated that a new type of NLS peptide-coated QDs can successfully enter the cell nucleus, and 25% of them were in the cytoplasm as a result of aggregation [135]. Lo et al. fabricated a nuclear-targeted delivery platform of NLS peptide-coated nanodiamonds (NDs) [136]. The cationic NLS peptide coating was confirmed not to increase the size of the carrier. They helped to effectively enhance cellular uptake and cargo delivery to the nucleus.

It is worth mentioning that RGD or other peptides have also been utilized as cargo delivery systems. Lee et al. synthesized cyclic RGD-coated peptide nanoribbons that could encapsulate hydrophobic molecules and deliver them to cells [137]. These cRGD-coated 1D β-ribbons could be specific to a cancer cell as well as a multivalent drug carrier. Fu et al. designed a peptide, Phe^{11}-protonetin, as a recognition reagent [138]. Phe^{11}-protonetin-coated magnetic spheres could be used as carriers to isolate Gram-positive bacteria with acceptable selectivity and high efficiency. Pan and co-workers reported micellar nanoparticles covalently coated with CLL1-targeting peptides as nanotherapeutics [139]. The CCL1-targeting peptides promoted binding and targeted delivery of more daunorubicin into leukemia stem cells for better leukemia therapy.

Metallic nanoparticles exhibit great potential for drug delivery and therapeutic applications. Peptide coatings as one common protection for metallic nanoparticles have been investigated for decades. Peptide coatings can not only bestow significant biocompatibility of nanoparticles but also endow them with biologically specific

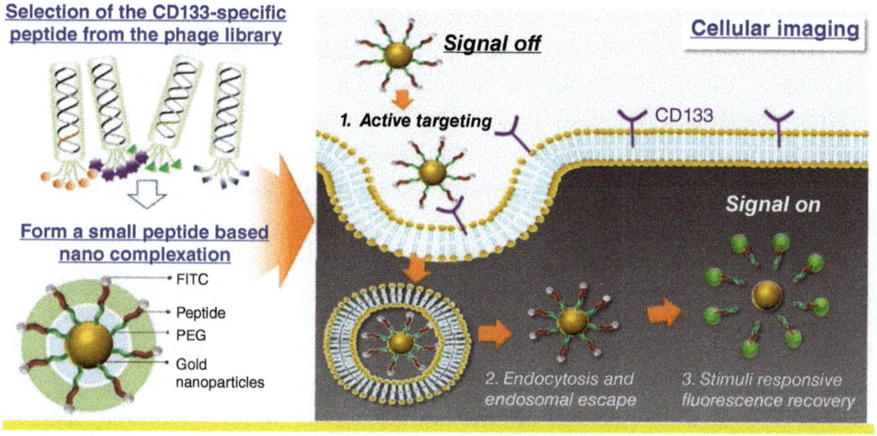

Figure 14.9 A small peptide CBP4 coated onto gold nanoparticles (GNPs) to prepare an imaging agent with stimuli-responsive properties. Source: Ref. [140]; Reproduced with permission Elsevier Science Ltd.

functionalities. For example, nine tridecapeptides coated gold nanocluster ($Au_{25}peptide_9$) had shown an efficient ability to bind and inhibit thioredoxin reductase 1, leading to tumor cell apoptosis [141]. Another novel small peptide, CBP4, was coated onto gold nanoparticles (GNPs) to prepare an imaging agent with stimuli-responsive properties (Figure 14.9) [140]. The CBP4-coated GNPs could provide an accurate diagnosis of glioblastoma and further carry drugs for therapeutic applications. Han et al. fabricated peptide-coated platinum nanoparticles (TPP-Pt) for precise near-infrared photothermal therapy and excellent tumor inhibitory effects [142]. TPP-Pt could be delivered to the mitochondrial site with minimal side effects due to the mitochondrial targeting of TPP. Moreover, the TPP coating endowed ultrasmall PtNPs with high stability, monodispersity, and biosafety. Furthermore, Fe_3O_4 nanoparticles coated with the tumor-targeting peptide WSG were biomineralized for imaging and targeting ovarian cancer cells [143].

14.3.6 Sensors

One of the important ways to ensure the accuracy and sensitivity of sensors is by using various responsive and repeatable approaches to deposition or immobilization [144]. Specific peptides can be designed, synthesized, and deposited on the surface of sensors as excellent sensing materials. Especially, sensitive, effective, convenient, precise, and rapid assays in biological media can promote early prediction, prognostic evaluation, and therapeutic efficacy, which require biomarkers or simple peptide coatings as protection [145].

The pH sensors are quite common analytical instruments. A silk peptide was coated onto a pencil graphite electrode as a pH sensor (PSPG) in a zero-current potentiometry system for the first time by Ma et al. [146]. The PSPG sensor works based on the protonation and deprotonation of the PSPG surface.

The detection of heavy metal ions is necessary for multiple applications, such as waste management, environmental monitoring, clinical toxicology, and developmental biology. Coating the plasmon resonance sensor surface with the peptides NH_2-(His)$_6$-COOH and NH_2-Gly-Gly-His-COOH proved to be an excellent method to detect Cu^{2+} and Ni^{2+} [147]. The detection is available in the ppt–ppb range due to the combination of high-resolution plasmon resonance and highly selective peptides as recognition elements.

Different responsive coatings are generated on materials in the blood for enzyme targeting and even relevant cell microenvironments. Jiang et al. developed the peptide-coated gold nanoclusters (AuNCs) as a label-free sensor for the protein post-translational modification (PTM) enzymes [148]. The peptide coating could protect the AuNCs from O_2-mediated fluorescence quenching. When the PTM enzyme deacetylates the peptide, destroying the coating and exposing the AuNCs outside, O_2 will quench their fluorescence and oxidize them into non-fluorescence clusters. Another FTIC-combined peptide, FITC-Cys-Ala-Leu-Asn-Asn, was coated on palladium nanoparticles to prepare a highly sensitive fluorescent sensor for trypsin in urine samples [149]. The peptide coating provided excellent stability and high biocompatibility.

It has been proven that many diseases are caused by or induced by specific proteins; thus, the recognition of these proteins makes it possible to diagnose diseases. Weiss et al. developed a colloidally stable and monodisperse peptide-coated CdSe/ZnS luminescent probe for live cell imaging [151]. The synthetic α-peptide-coated CdSe/ZnS nanocrystals were accessible to target live Hela cells specifically via catching av-CD14 proteins, which made them suited for the detection of single proteins and live cell imaging. Shimoni et al. developed a screening test for celiac disease by peptide-coated AuNPs [152]. The peptide sequence was derived from the gliadin proteins, which could induce the release of autoantibodies and trigger celiac disease. At the same time, the aggregation of AuNPs performed a shift in wavelength, proving the screening celiac disease. Luo et al. developed a low-fouling sensor for alpha-fetoprotein (AFP) based on the self-assembled aptamer and peptide-coated Au substrate [153]. The zwitterionic peptides were densely immobilized to form an antifouling layer, and the attached aptamer as a recognizing layer achieved target binding. This aptasensor performed excellent feasibility in the quantitative assay of AFP in real serum samples. Another work involves the use of an arthritis-specific peptide-coated carbon nanotube as an immunosensor for the assay of the specific autoantibodies in serum [154]. This label-free biosensor avoided the pre-treatment of serum and exhibited greater accuracy and speed as an effective drug screening tool in the pharmaceutical industry. Moreover, a combinational reactive oxygen species (ROS)-responsive activatable NIR-II sensor was constructed based on the kidney targeting peptide (KTP), which is helpful in *in vitro* urine analysis and *in vivo* long-term kidney monitoring (Figure 14.10) [150]. This peptide-based sensor is capable of monitoring early kidney injuries and reporting on kidney dysfunctional progression, such as detecting renal dysfunction.

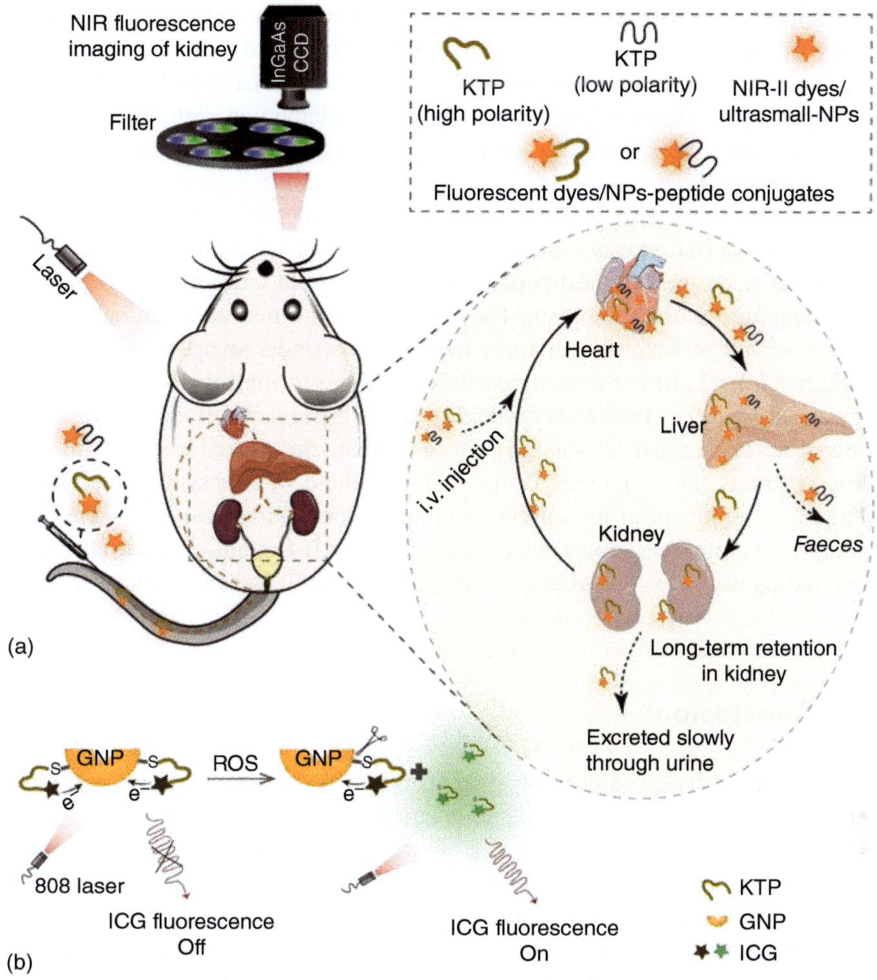

Figure 14.10 A ROS-responsive activatable NIR-II sensor based on the kidney targeting peptide for the detection of kidney diseases. Source: Reproduced with permission Ref. [150]; © 2021 John Wiley and Sons.

14.3.7 Other Applications

Food safety has been a growing concern worldwide, especially when foodborne pathogens cause such a great number of diseases and deaths. Food packaging plays an important role in ensuring food safety and quality. Peptides with antimicrobial features and biocompatibility are great choices for food packaging and preservation. Shemesh et al. used a tripeptide coating on a stainless steel surface to prevent bacterial species from dairy products without affecting their technological properties [155]. More antimicrobial peptides widely used in food packaging, including nisin, pediocin, and polylysine, usually coated together with chitosan or some safe polymers [156]. Li et al. combined ε-polylysine and nisin with chitosan coating to inhibit the white blush and maintain the quality of fresh-cut carrots [157]. Recently, Kulawik developed chitosan/furcellaran coatings implemented with different antimicrobial peptides, which almost completely decreased the total viable counts in the pork loins [158].

Ice formation on surfaces has an obvious influence on safety and other potential problems. One alternative way to minimize ice information is by using anti-icing coatings. Wang et al. designed a short peptide immobilized onto solid surfaces as an anti-icing coating for the first time [159]. The 12-amino acid α-helical peptide with high antifreeze activity performed great anti-icing properties under an open environment.

Lithium-sulfur (Li-S) batteries are widely used due to their generation of high energy density, but they have poor cyclability due to the loss of sulfur. Therefore, the coating of sulfur nanoparticles is introduced to maintain the active sulfur amount and then increase the cyclability. Dutta et al. presented various synthetic peptides used as a coating for sulfur nanoparticles [160]. Three different peptides were chosen, and two of them were successfully coated on sulfur. In the end, only poly(leucine-lysine) coating was proven to effectively restrain the sulfur loss in the electrolyte.

14.4 Conclusion

In this chapter, we reviewed the typical and common techniques for the preparation of peptide coatings, together with their abundant applications. Generally, coating peptides onto the substrates can be achieved by two types of approaches: solvent-based techniques and non-solvent techniques. The solvent-based techniques like drop-casting, dip-coating, spin-coating, and LBL assembly all share the same advantages: ease of use, quick method, high reproducibility, low cost, and high controllability. These advantages allow researchers to obtain peptide coatings with the desired thickness, structures, and functions. The non-solvent techniques mainly include PVD and CVD, both of which have high growth rates and good reproducibility. Understanding these descriptions of different techniques helps to choose a suitable method to prepare a certain coating. Modifying and changing the surface properties by peptide coating to meet the specific requirements for various applications have a great influence on modern life and industry. For now, peptide coatings have been widely applied as antifouling and antimicrobial coatings, as well as implant coatings and food packaging. Moreover, peptide coatings have been fabricated for use in sensing, targeting, and imaging in medical, optical, or electrical fields due to their specific sequences, biocompatibility, and other relevant properties.

In particular, the outbreak of the COVID-19 global pandemic posed enormous challenges to human health and even the entire humanity. It has devastated the world economy and threatened people's lives and safety. The COVID-19 pandemic acted as "a wake-up call" that researchers needed to develop new strategies to overcome viral transmission. The virus can live for hours or even days on metal, glass, cloth, fur, and other materials, greatly increasing the risk of transmission. Therefore, Coronavirus can be spread by touching surfaces contaminated with them. Touching the face or body (for example, eyes, mouth, nose, and hand) is considered one of the main routes of transmission. The good news is that there has been some research on using peptides as antiviral coatings, but more research is still needed to industrialize this kind of biomaterial.

However, there is still much progress to be made to improve strategies and choose original peptides to obtain coatings with better properties and abundant applications by a more efficient process. Moreover, it is still challenging to develop peptide coatings with simple/stronger immobilization and more multifunctions for commercial production. Up to now, most peptide coatings are lab-only; the widespread application of these materials will need further breakthroughs and provide fundamental improvements to our daily lives in the future.

References

1 Brutin, D. and Starov, V. (2018). Recent advances in droplet wetting and evaporation. *Chem. Soc. Rev.* 47: 558–585.

2 Starov, V. (2010). Surface forces action in a vicinity of three phase contact line and other current problems in kinetics of wetting and spreading. *Adv. Colloid Interface Sci.* 61 (1–2): 139–152.

3 Kumar, A.K.S., Zhang, Y.F., Li, D.L., and Compton, R.G. (2020). A mini-review: how reliable is the drop casting technique? *Electrochem. Commun.* 121: 106867.

4 Erbil, H.Y. (2012). Evaporation of pure liquid sessile and spherical suspended drops: a review. *Adv. Colloid. Interface. Sci.* 170: 67–86.

5 Ta, V., Carter, R., Esenturk, E. et al. (2016). Dynamically controlled deposition of colloidal nanoparticle suspension in evaporating drops using laser radiation. *Soft Matter* 12: 4530–4536.

6 Kuang, M., Wang, L., and Song, Y. (2014). Controllable printing droplets for high-resolution patterns. *Adv. Mater.* 26: 6950–6958.

7 Hu, H. and Larson, R.G. (2006). Marangoni effect reverses coffee-ring depositions. *J. Phys. Chem. B* 110 (14): 7090–7094.

8 Li, P., Li, Y., Zhou, Z.K. et al. (2016). Evaporative self-assembly of gold nanorods into macroscopic 3D plasmonic superlattice arrays. *Adv. Mater.* 28: 2511–2517.

9 Li, T., Kalloudis, M., Cardoso, A.Z. et al. (2014). Drop-casting hydrogels at a liquid interface: the case of hydrophobic dipeptides. *Langmuir* 30: 13854–13860.

10 Hu, T., Agazani, O., Nir, S. et al. (2021). Antiviral activity of peptide-based assemblies. *ACS Appl. Mater. Interfaces* 13: 48469–48477.

11 Zhan, T., Feng, X.Z., An, Q.Q. et al. (2022). Enzyme-free glucose sensors with efficient synergistic electro-catalysis based on a ferrocene derivative and two metal nanoparticles. *RSC Adv.* 12: 5072–5079.

12 Shumeiko, V., Malach, E., Helman, Y. et al. (2021). A nanoscale optical biosensor based on peptide encapsulated SWCNTs for detection of acetic acid in the gaseous phase. *Sensor. Actuat. B. Chem.* 327: 128832.

13 Landau, L. and Levich, B. (1942). Dragging of a liquid by a moving plate. *Acta Physicochim.* 17: 42–54.

14 Zhang, H.K., Yin, Y.R., Zhang, X.M. et al. (2021). Numerical simulation of the hydrodynamics of yield stress fluids during dip coating. *J. Non-Newtonian Fluid* 298: 104675.

15 White, D.A. and Tallmadge, J.A. (1965). Theory of drag out of liquids on flat plates. *Chem. Eng. Sci.* 20: 33–37.

16 Javidi, M., Pope, M.A., and Hrymak, A.N. (2016). Investigation on dip coating process by mathematical modeling of non-Newtonian fluid coating on cylindrical substrate. *Phys. Fluids* 28: 063105.

17 Jeong, D.H., Lee, M.K.H., Thiévenaz, V. et al. (2022). Dip coating of bidisperse particulate suspensions. *J. Fluid Mech.* 936: A36(1–25).

18 Gupta, S. and Tiwari, N. (2017). Dip coating in the presence of an opposing Marangoni stress. *Eur. Phys. J. E* 40: 9–6.

19 Faustini, M., Louis, B., Albouy, P.A. et al. (2010). Preparation of sol-gel films by dip-coating in extreme conditions. *J. Phys. Chem. C* 114: 7637–7645.

20 Sun, B.B., Li, Q., Riegler, H. et al. (2017). Self-assembly of ultralong aligned dipeptide single crystals. *ACS Nano* 11: 10489–10494.

21 Liu, X.C., Danglad-Flores, J., Eickelmann, S. et al. (2022). Controlled-alignment patterns of dipeptide micro- and nanofibers. *ACS Nano* 16: 10372–10382.

22 Liu, X.C., Riegler, H., and Hao, J.C. (2022). Diphenylalanine deposition by dip-coating from acidic solutions: fibers and closed homogeneous films. *Langmuir* 38: 13055–13064.

23 Capon, P.K., Horsfall, A.J., Li, J.W. et al. (2021). Protein detection enabled using functionalised silk-binding peptides on a silk-coated optical fibre. *RSC Adv.* 11: 22334.

24 Moreira, J., Vale, A.C., and Alves, N.M. (2021). Spin-coated freestanding films for biomedical applications. *J. Mater. Chem. B* 9: 3778–3799.

25 Chtouki, T., Mrabet, M.E., Tarbi, A. et al. (2021). Comprehensive review of the morphological, linear and nonlinear optical characterization of spin-coated NiO thin films for optoelectronic applications. *Opt. Mater.* 118: 111294.

26 Walker, P. and Thompson, J. (1922). *Proceedings of the 25 Annual Meeting*, 22.

27 Emslie, A.G., Bonner, F.T., and Peck, L.G. (1958). Flow of a viscous liquid on a rotating disk. *J. Appl. Phys.* 29 (5): 858–862.

28 Toolan, D.T.W. and Howse, J.R. (2013). Development of in situ studies of spin coated polymer films. *J. Mater. Chem. C* 1: 603–616.

29 Fong, P.W.K. and Li, G. (2021). The challenge of ambient air–processed organometallic halide perovskite: technology transfer from spin coating to meniscus blade coating of perovskite thin films. *Front. Mater.* 8: 635224.

30 Meyerhofer, D. (1978). Characteristics of resist films produced by spinning. *J. Appl. Phys.* 49: 3993–3997.

31 Lawrence, C.J. (1988). The mechanics of spin coating of polymer films. *Phys. Fluids* 31 (10): 2786–2795.

32 van Hardeveld, R.M., Gunter, P.L.J., van Ijzendoorn, L.J. et al. (1995). Deposition of inorganic salts from solution on flflat substrates by spin-coating: theory, quantifification and application to model catalysts. *Appl. Surf. Sci.* 84 (4): 339–346.

33 Lin, Y.C., Petersson, E.J., and Fakhraai, Z. (2014). Surface effects mediate self-assembly of amyloid-β peptides. *ACS Nano* 8: 10178–10186.

34 Lin, Y.C., Repollet-Pedrosa, M.H., Ferrie, J.J. et al. (2017). Potential artifacts in sample preparation methods used for imaging amyloid oligomers and protofibrils due to surface-mediated fibril formation. *J. Phys. Chem. B* 121: 2534–2542.

35 Bhandaru, N., Kaur, G., Panjlab, A., and Verma, S. (2021). Spin coating mediated morphology modulation in self-assembly of peptides. *Nanoscale* 13: 8884–8892.

36 Kim, G., Yoon, J., Kim, J.S. et al. (2008). Molecular fibers based on the honeycomb-like self-assembly of an r-helical polypeptide. *J. Phys. Chem. B* 112: 8868–8870.

37 Butt, M.A. (2022). Thin-film coating methods: a successful marriage of high-quality and cost-effectiveness—a brief exploration. *Coatings* 12: 1115(1–22).

38 Tang, Z.T., Wang, Y., Podsiadlo, P., and Kotov, N.A. (2006). Biomedical applications of layer-by-layer assembly: from biomimetics to tissue engineering. *Adv. Mater.* 18: 3203–3224.

39 Iler, R.K. (1966). Multilayers of colloidal particles. *J. Colloid Interface Sci.* 21 (6): 569–594.

40 Decher, G., Hong, J.D., and Schmitt, J. (1992). Buildup of ultrathin multilayer films by a self-assembly process: III. Consecutively alternating adsorption of anionic and cationic polyelectrolytes on charged surfaces. *Thin Solid Films* 210–211: 831–835.

41 Zhang, X.H., Ou-yang, S.B., Wang, J.L. et al. (2018). Construction of antibacterial surface via layer-by-layer method. *Curr. Pharm. Design* 24: 926–935.

42 Richardson, J.J., Björnmalm, M., and Caruso, F. (2015). Technology-driven layer-by-layer assembly of nanofilms. *Science* 348: aaa2491.

43 Schlenoff, J.B., Ly, H., and Li, M. (1998). Charge and mass balance in polyelectrolyte multilayers. *J. Am. Chem. Soc.* 120: 7626–7634.

44 Schlenoff, J.B. and Dubas, S.T. (2001). Mechanism of polyelectrolyte multilayer growth: charge overcompensation and distribution. *Macromolecules* 34: 592–598.

45 Porcel, C., Lavalle, P., Ball, V. et al. (2006). From exponential to linear growth in polyelectrolyte multilayers. *Langmuir* 22: 4376–4383.

46 Mueller, M. (2001). Orientation of α-helical poly(l-lysine) in consecutively adsorbed polyelectrolyte multilayers on texturized silicon substrates. *Biomacromolecules* 2: 262–269.

47 Lvov, Y., Ariga, K., Ichinose, I., and Kunitake, T. (1995). Assembly of multicomponent protein films by means of electrostatic layer-by-layer adsorption. *J. Am. Chem. Soc.* 117: 6117–6123.

48 Richert, L., Lavalle, P., Vautier, D. et al. (2002). Cell interactions with polyelectrolyte multilayer films. *Biomacromolecules* 3: 1170–1178.

49 Yoo, P.J., Nam, K.T., Qi, J. et al. (2006). Spontaneous assembly of viruses on multilayered polymer surfaces. *Nat. Mater.* 5: 234–240.

50 Rawtani, D. and Agrawal, Y.K. (2014). Emerging strategies and applications of layer-by-layer self-assembly. *Nanobiomedicine* 1: 8.

51 Wu, L.M. and Baghdachi, J. (2015). *Functional Polymer Coatings: Principles, Methods, and Applications*. Hoboken, New Jersey: John Wiley & Sons, Inc. ISBN: 978-1-118-88292-4.

52 Boudou, T., Crouzier, T., Ren, K.F. et al. (2010). Multiple functionalities of polyelectrolyte multilayer films: new biomedical applications. *Adv. Mater.* 22: 441–467.

53 Elbert, D.L., Herbert, C.B., and Hubbell, J.A. (1999). Thin polymer layers formed by polyelectrolyte multilayer techniques on biological surfaces. *Langmuir* 15: 5355–5362.

54 Picart, C., Lavalle, P., Hubert, P. et al. (2001). Buildup mechanism for poly(l-lysine)/hyaluronic acid films onto a solid surface. *Langmuir* 17: 7414–7424.

55 Porcel, C., Lavalle, P., Decher, G. et al. (2007). Influence of the polyelectrolyte molecular weight on exponentially growing multilayer films in the linear regime. *Langmuir* 23 (4): 1898–1904.

56 Crouzier, T. and Picart, C. (2009). Ion pairing and hydration in polyelectrolyte multilayer films containing polysaccharides. *Biomacromolecules* 10: 433–442.

57 Thomas, A.K., Wieduwild, R., Zimmermann, R. et al. (2018). Layer-by-layer assembly of heparin and peptide-polyethylene glycol conjugates to form hybrid nanothin films of biomatrices. *ACS Appl. Mater. Interfaces* 10: 14264–14270.

58 Qiu, X.Q., Li, Z.W., Li, X.H., and Zhang, Z.J. (2018). Flame retardant coatings prepared using layer by layer assembly: A review. *Chem. Eng. J.* 334: 108–122.

59 Elshabini, A., Elshabini-Riad, A.A., and Barlow, F.D. (1998). *Thin Film Technology Handbook*. McGraw-Hill Professional.

60 Rossnagel, S.M. (2003). *J. Vac. Sci. Technol. A* 21: S74–S87.

61 Baptista, A., Silva, F., Porteiro, J. et al. (2018). Sputtering physical vapour deposition (PVD) coatings: a critical review on process improvement and market trend demands. *Coatings* 8: 402.

62 Abegunde, O.O., Akinlabi, E.T., Oladijo, O.P. et al. (2019). Overview of thin film deposition techniques. *AIMS Mater. Sci.* 6 (2): 174–199.

63 Ricciardi, S. (2012). *Surface Chemical Functionalization based on Plasma Techniques*. Lamberts Academics Publishing.

64 PintoG., Silva F., Porteiro J., Míguez J., Baptista A. (2018). Numerical simulation applied to PVD reactors: an overview. *Coatings* 8: 410.

65 Martin, P. (2011). *Introduction to surface engineering and functionally engineered materials*. John Wiley & Sons.

66 Reichelt, K. and Jiang, X. (1990). The preparation of thin films by physical vapour deposition methods. *Thin Solid Films* 191: 91–126.

67 Wang, Y.C., Jeong, H., Chowdhury, M. et al. (2018). Exploiting physical vapor deposition for morphological control in semi-crystalline polymer films. *Polym. Cryst.* 1: e10021.

68 Gudmundsson, J.T., Anders, A., and von Keudell, A. (2022). Foundations of physical vapor deposition with plasma assistance. *Plasma Sources Sci. Technol.* 31 (8): 083001.

69 Karabacak, T., Senkevich, J.J., Wang, G.C., and Lu, T.M. (2005). Stress reduction in sputter deposited fifilms using nanostructured compliant layers by high working-gas pressures. *J. Vac. Sci. Technol. A* 23: 986–990.

70 Seshan, K. (2012). *Handbook of Thin Film Deposition*. William Andrew.

71 Wang, B., Fu, X.H., Song, S.G. et al. (2018). Simulation and optimization of film thickness uniformity in physical vapor deposition. *Coatings* 8: 325.

72 Adler-Abramovich, L., Aronov, D., Beker, P. et al. (2009). Self-assembled arrays of peptide nanotubes by vapour deposition. *Nat. Nanotechnol.* 4: 849–854.

73 Amdursky, N., Koren, I., Gazit, E., and Rosenman, G. (2011). Adjustable photoluminescence of peptide nanotubes coatings. *J. Nanosci. Nanotechnol.* 11 (10): 9282–9286.

74 Bank-Srour, B., Becker, P., Krasovitsky, L. et al. (2013). Physical vapor deposition of peptide nanostructures. *Polym. J.* 45: 494–503.

75 Choy, K.L. (2003). Chemical vapour deposition of coatings. *Prog Mater Sci* 48: 57–170.

76 Choy, K.L. (2000). *Handbook of Nanostructured Materials and Nanotechnology. vol. 1: Synthesis and Processing* (ed. H.S. Nalwa), 533. San Diego (CA): Academic Press.

77 Hitchman, M.L. and Jensen, K.F. (1993). *Chemical Vapor Deposition—Principles and Applications*. London: Academic Press.

78 Tjong, S.C. and Chan, H. (2004). Nanocrystalline materials and coatings. *Mater Sci Eng R* 45: 1–88.

79 De Lodyguine J.S. Illuminant for incandecent lamps. US patent 575002 1893.

80 Martín-Palma, R.J. and Lakhtakia, A. (2013). *Engineered Biomimicry*. Waltham, MA: Elsevier.

81 Herman, I.P. (1989). Laser-assisted deposition of thin films from gas-phase and surface-adsorbed molecules. *Chem Rev.* 89: 1323–1357.

82 Osgood, R.M. and Deutsch, T.F. (1985). Laser-induced chemistry for microelectronics. *Science* 227: 709–714.

83 Li, Y., Mann, D., and Rolandi, M. (2004). Preferential growth of semiconducting single-walled carbon nanotubes by a plasma enhanced CVD method. *Nano Lett.* 4: 317–321.

84 Zubavichus, Y., Shaporenko, A., Grunze, M., and Zharnikov, M. (2007). NEXAFS spectroscopy of homopolypeptides at all relevant absorption edges: polyisoleucine, polytyrosine, and polyhistidine. *J. Phys. Chem. B* 111: 9803–9807.

85 Anderson, K.D., Slocik, J.M., McConney, M.E. et al. (2009). Facile plasma-enhanced deposition of ultrathin crosslinked amino acid films for conformal biometallization. *Small* 5 (6): 741–749.

86 Anderson, K.D., Marczewski, K., Singamaneni, S. et al. (2010). Plasma amino acid coatings for a conformal growth of titania nanoparticles. *ACS Appl. Mater. Interfaces* 2 (8): 2269–2281.

87 Anderson, K.D., Young, S.L., Jiang, H. et al. (2012). Plasma-enhanced copolymerization of amino acid and synthetic monomers. *Langmuir* 28: 1833–1845.

88 Singamaneni, S., Kharlampieva, E., Jang, J.-H. et al. (2010). Metalized porous interference lithographic microstructures via biofunctionalization. *Adv. Mater.* 22: 1369–1373.

89 Vasudev, M.C., Koerner, H., Singh, K.M. et al. (2014). Vertically aligned peptide Na nanostructures using plasma-enhanced chemical vapor deposition. *Biomacromolecules* 15: 533–540.

90 Sakala, G.P. and Reches, M. (2018). Peptide-based approaches to fight biofouling. *Adv. Mater. Interfaces* 5: 1800073.

91 Nir, S., Zanuy, D., Zada, T. et al. (2019). Tailoring the self-assembly of a tripeptide for the formation of antimicrobial surfaces. *Nanoscale* 11: 8752–8759.

92 Dolid, A., Gomes, L.C., Mergulhao, F.J., and Reches, M. (2020). Combining chemistry and topography to fight biofilm formation: fabrication of micropatterned surfaces with a peptide-based coating. *Colloids Surf. B Biointerfaces* 196: 111365.

93 Saha, A., Nir, S., and Reches, M. (2020). Amphiphilic peptide with dual functionality resists biofouling. *Langmuir* 36: 4201–4206.

94 Ceylan, H., Tekinay, A.B., and Guler, M.O. (2011). Selective adhesion and growth of vascular endothelial cells on bioactive peptide nanofiber functionalized stainless steel surface. *Biomaterials* 32: 8797–8805.

95 Yu, X.L., Xiao, J.Z., and Dang, F.Q. (2015). Surface modification of poly(dimethylsiloxane) using ionic complementary peptides to minimize nonspecific protein adsorption. *Langmuir* 31 (21): 5891–5898.

96 Ye, H.J., Wang, L.B., Huang, R.L. et al. (2015). Superior antifouling performance of a zwitterionic peptide compared to an amphiphilic, non-ionic peptide. *ACS Appl. Mater. Interfaces* 7: 22448–22457.

97 Qi, H., Zheng, W.W., Zhou, X. et al. (2018). A mussel-inspired chimeric protein as a novel facile antifouling coating. *Chem. Commun.* 54: 11328–11331.

98 Khoo, J., Hamilton, P., O'Toole, G.A. et al. (2009). Directed assembly of PEGylated-peptide coatings for infection-resistant Titanium metal. *J. Am. Chem. Soc.* 131 (31): 10992–10997.

99 Khoo, J., O'Toole, G.A., Nair, S.A. et al. (2010). *Staphylococcus aureus* resistance on titanium coated with multivalent PEGylated-peptides. *Biomaterials* 31 (35): 9285–9292.

100 Bellassai, N., Marti, A., Spoto, G., and Huskens, J. (2018). Low-fouling, mixed-charge poly-l-lysine polymers with anionic oligopeptide side-chains. *J. Mater. Chem. B* 6: 7662–7673.

101 Freitas, E.D., Bataglioli, R.A., Oshodi, J., and Beppu, M.M. (2022). Antimicrobial peptides and their potential application in antiviral coating agents. *Colloids Surf. B Biointerfaces* 217: 112693.

102 Godoy-Gallardo, M., Mas-Moruno, C., Yu, K. et al. (2015). Antibacterial properties of hLf1-11 peptide onto titanium surfaces: a comparison study between silanization and surface initiated polymerization. *Biomacromolecules* 16: 483–496.

103 Mishra, B., Basu, A., Chua, R.R.Y. et al. (2014). Site specific immobilization of a potent antimicrobial peptide onto silicone catheters: evaluation against urinary tract infection pathogens. *J. Mater. Chem. B* 2: 1706–1716.

104 Franco, A.R., Fernandes, E.M., Rodrigues, M.T. et al. (2019). Antimicrobial coating of spider silk to prevent bacterial attachment on silk surgical sutures. *Acta Biomater.* 99: 236–246.

105 Boas, D. and Reches, M. (2021). A novel copper-binding peptide that self assembles into a transparent antibacterial and antiviral coating. *Front. Bioeng. Biotechnol.* 9: 736679.

106 Li, L.L., Qi, G.B., Yu, F. et al. (2015). An adaptive biointerface from self-assembled functional peptides for tissue engineering. *Adv. Mater.* 27: 3181.

107 Ahmadabadi, H.Y., Yu, K., and Kizhakkedathu, J.N. (2020). Surface modification approaches for prevention of implant associated infections. *Colloids Surf. B Biointerfaces* 193: 111116.

108 Zhang, B.G.X., Myers, D.E., Wallace, G.G. et al. (2014). Bioactive coatings for orthopaedic implants—recent trends in development of implant coatings. *Int. J. Mol. Sci.* 15: 11878–11921.

109 Drexelius, M.G. and Neundorf, I. (2021). Application of antimicrobial peptides on biomedical implants: three ways to pursue peptide coatings. *Int. J. Mol. Sci.* 22: 13212.

110 Holmberg, K.V., Abdolhosseini, M., Li, Y.P. et al. (2013). Bio-inspired stable antimicrobial peptide coatings for dental applications. *Acta Biomater.* 9: 8224–8231.

111 Tan, X.W., Goh, T.W., Saraswathi, P. et al. (2014). Effectiveness of antimicrobial peptide immobilization for preventing perioperative cornea implant-associated bacterial infection. *Antimicrob. Agents Chem.* 58 (9): 5229–5238.

112 Huh, J.B., Lee, J.Y., Jeon, Y.C. et al. (2013). Physical stability of arginine-glycine-aspartic acid peptide coated on anodized implants after installation. *J. Adv. Prosthodont.* 5: 84–91.

113 Yang, X., Lou, F., Yuan, W.H. et al. (2022). Polypeptide coatings on biominerals with superior antimicrobial and antifouling properties inspired by human salivary proteins. *Appl. Mater. Today* 27: 101446.

114 Kelly, M., Williams, R., Aojula, A. et al. (2015). Peptide aptamers: novel coatings for orthopaedic implants. *Mat. Sci. Eng. C Mater.* 54: 84–93.

115 Shi, J., Liu, Y., Wang, Y. et al. (2015). Biological and immunotoxicity evaluation of antimicrobial peptide-loaded coatings using a layer-by-layer process on titanium. *Sci. Rep.* 5: 16336.

116 Yazici, H., O'Neill, M.B., Kacar, T. et al. (2016). Engineered chimeric peptides as antimicrobial surface coating agents toward infection-free implants. *ACS Appl. Mater. Interfaces* 8: 5070–5081.

117 Yu, K., Lo, J.C.Y., Yan, M. et al. (2017). Anti-adhesive antimicrobial peptide coating prevents catheter associated infection in a mouse urinary infection model. *Biomaterials* 116: 69–81.

118 Jang, E.J., Lee, S.Y., Bae, I.H. et al. (2020). Comparison between basic and inverse dual drug and peptide-coated stents in a porcine restenosis model. *Appl. Chem. Eng.* 31 (5): 502–508.

119 Anselme, K. (2000). Osteoblast adhesion on biomaterials. *Biomaterials* 21: 667–681.

120 Grzesik, W.J. and Robey, P.G. (1994). Bone matrix RGD glycoproteins: immunolocalization and interaction with human primary osteoblastic bone cells in vitro. *J. Bone Miner. Res.* 9: 487–496.

121 Porte-Durrieu, M.C., Guillemot, F., Pallua, S. et al. (2004). Cyclo-(DfKRG) peptide grafting onto Ti–6Al–4V: physical characterization andinterest towards human osteoprogenitor cells adhesion. *Biomaterials* 25: 4837–4846.

122 Pallu, S., Bourget, C., Bareille, R. et al. (2005). The effect of cyclo-DfKRG peptide immobilization on titanium on the adhesion and differentiation of human osteoprogenitor cells. *Biomaterials* 26: 6932–6940.

123 Huang, Y., Luo, Q.J., Li, X.D. et al. (2012). Fabrication and in vitro evaluation of the collagen/hyaluronic acid PEM coating crosslinked with functionalized RGD peptide on titanium. *Acta Biomater.* 8: 866–877.

124 Balasundaram, G., Shimpi, T.M., Sanow, W.R. et al. (2011). Molecular plasma deposited peptides on anodized nanotubular titanium: An osteoblast density study. *J. Biomed. Mater. Res. A* 98A (2): 192–200.

125 Zouani, O.F., Chollet, C., Guillotin, B., and Durrieu, M.C. (2010). Differentiation of pre-osteoblast cells on poly(ethylene terephthalate) grafted with RGD and/or BMPs mimetic peptides. *Biomaterials* 31: 8245–8253.

126 Lee, J.Y., Choo, J.E., Park, H.J. et al. (2008). Synthetic peptide-coated bone mineral for enhanced osteoblastic activation in vitro and in vivo. *J. Biomed. Mater. Res. Part A* 87 (3): 688–697.

127 Kakinoki, S., Nishioka, S., Arichi, Y., and Yamaoka, T. (2022). Stable and direct coating of fibronectin-derived Leu-Asp-Val peptide on ePTFE using one-pot tyrosine oxidation for endothelial cell adhesion. *Colloids Surf. B Biointerfaces* 216: 112576.

128 Povimonsky, A.G. and Rapaport, H. (2017). Peptide coating applied on the spot improves osseointegration of titanium implants. *J. Mater. Chem. B* 5: 2096–2105.

129 Bolhassani, A. (2011, 1816). Potential efficacy of cell-penetrating peptides for nucleic acid and drug delivery in cancer. *Biochim. Biophys. Acta.* 2: 232–246.

130 Lim, Y.B., Lee, E., and Lee, M. (2007). Cell-penetrating-peptide-coated nanoribbons for intracellular nanocarriers. *Angew. Chem. Int. Ed.* 46: 3475–3478.

131 Varma, M.V. and Panchagnula, R. (2005). Enhanced oral paclitaxel absorption with vitamin E-TPGS: effect on solubility and permeability in vitro, in situ and in vivo. *Eur. J. Pharm. Sci.* 25 (4–5): 445–453.

132 Chen, Y., Yuan, L., Zhou, L. et al. (2012). Effect of cell-penetrating peptide-coated nanostructured lipid carriers on the oral absorption of tripterine. *Int. J. Nanomed.* 7: 4581–4591.

133 Reibetanz, U., Lessig, J., Hoyer, J., and Neundorf, I. (2010). Surface functionalized colloidal microparticles for fast endocytotic cell uptake. *Adv. Eng. Mater.* 12: 488–495.

134 Yuan, B., Zhao, Y.R., Dong, S.Y. et al. (2019). Cell-penetrating peptide-coated liposomes for drug delivery across the blood–brain barrier. *Anticancer Res.* 39 (1): 237–243.

135 Kuo, C.W., Chueh, D.Y., Singh, N. et al. (2011). Targeted nuclear delivery using peptide-coated quantum dots. *Bioconjugate Chem.* 22: 1073–1080.

136 Leung, H.M., Chan, M.S., Liu, L.S. et al. (2018). Dual-function, cationic, peptide-coated nanodiamond systems: facilitating nuclear-targeting delivery for enhanced gene therapy applications. *ACS Sustain. Chem. Eng.* 6: 9671–9681.

137 Lim, Y.B., Kwon, O.J., Lee, E. et al. (2008). A cyclic RGD-coated peptide nanoribbon as a selective intracellular nanocarrier. *Org. Biomol. Chem.* 6: 1944–1948.

138 Fan, E., Peng, J.X., Shi, Y.L. et al. (2020). Quantification of live Gram-positive bacteria via employing artificial antibacterial peptide-coated magnetic spheres as isolation carriers. *Microchem. J.* 154: 104643.

139 Zhang, H.Y., Luo, J.T., Li, Y.P. et al. (2012). Characterization of high-affinity peptides and their feasibility for use in nanotherapeutics targeting leukemia stem cells. *Nanomedicine.* 8: 1116–1124.

140 Cho, J.H., Kim, A.R., Kim, S.H. et al. (2017). Development of a novel imaging agent using peptide-coated gold nanoparticles toward brain glioma stem cell marker CD133. *Acta Biomater.* 47: 182–192.

141 An, D.Y., Su, J.G., Weber, J.K. et al. (2015). A peptide-coated gold nanocluster exhibits unique behavior in protein activity inhibition. *J. Am. Chem. Soc.* 137: 8412–8418.

142 Ma, Z.Y., Zhang, Y.F., Zhang, J. et al. (2020). Ultrasmall peptide-coated platinum nanoparticles for precise NIR-II photothermal therapy by mitochondrial targeting. *ACS Appl. Mater. Interfaces* 12: 39434–39443.

143 Wei, Y., Yin, G.F., Ma, C.Y. et al. (2013). Synthesis and cellular compatibility of biomineralized Fe3O4 nanoparticles in tumor cells targeting peptides. *Colloids Surf. B Biointerfaces* 107: 180–188.

144 Wasilewski, T., Szulczy'nski, B., Kamysz, W. et al. (2018). Evaluation of three peptide immobilization techniques on a QCM surface related to acetaldehyde responses in the gas phase. *Sensors* 18: 3942.

145 Cui, M., Ma, Y.H., Wang, L. et al. (2020). Antifouling sensors based on peptides for biomarker detection. *Trends Anal. Chem.* 127: 115903.

146 Ma, M.M. and Wen, Z.T.Y. (2012). Poly silk peptide film pH sensor based on zero current potentiometry. *Adv. Mater. Res.* 450–451: 554–556.

147 Forzani, E.S., Zhang, H.Q., Chen, W., and Tao, N.J. (2005). Detection of heavy metal ions in drinking water using a high-resolution differential surface plasmon resonance sensor. *Environ. Sci. Technol.* 39: 1257–1262.

148 Wen, Q., Gu, Y., Tang, L.J. et al. (2013). Peptide-templated gold nanocluster beacon as a sensitive, label-free sensor for protein post-translational modification enzymes. *Anal. Chem.* 85: 11681–11685.

149 Zhou, G.H., Jiang, H.M., Zhou, Y.F. et al. (2018). Peptide-coated palladium nanoparticle for highly sensitive bioanalysis of trypsin in human urine samples. *Nanomater. Nanotechnol.* 8: 1–8.

150 Chen, Y., Pei, P., Lei, Z.H. et al. (2021). A promising NIR-II fluorescent sensor for peptide-mediated long-term monitoring of kidney dysfunction. *Angew. Chem. Int. Ed.* 60: 15809–15815.

151 Pinaud, F., King, D., Moore, H.P., and Weiss, S. (2004). Bioactivation and cell targeting of semiconductor CdSe/ZnS nanocrystals with phytochelatin-related peptides. *J. Am. Chem. Soc.* 126: 6115–6123.

152 Kaur, A., Shimoni, O., and Wallach, M. (2018). Novel screening test for celiac disease using peptide functionalised gold nanoparticles Basic Study. *World J. Gastroenterol.* 24 (47): 5379–5390.

153 Cui, M., Wang, Y., Jiao, M.X. et al. (2017). Mixed self-assembled aptamer and newly designed zwitterionic peptide as antifouling biosensing interface for electrochemical detection of alpha-fetoprotein. *ACS Sens.* 2: 490–494.

154 Drouvalakis, K.A., Bangsaruntip, S., Hueber, W. et al. (2008). Peptide-coated nanotube-based biosensor for the detection of disease-specific autoantibodies in human serum. *Biosen. Bioelectron.* 23: 1413–1421.

155 Friedlander, A., Nir, S., Reches, M., and Shemesh, M. (2019). Preventing biofilm formation by dairy-associated bacteria using peptide-coated surfaces. *Front. Microbiol.* 10: 1405.

156 Liu, Y.W., Sameen, D.E., Ahmed, S. et al. (2021). Antimicrobial peptides and their application in food packaging. *Trends Food Sci. Technol.* 112: 471–483.

157 Song, Z.Y., Li, F., Guan, H. et al. (2017). Combination of nisin and ε-polylysine with chitosan coating inhibits the white blush of fresh-cut carrots. *Food Control* 74: 34–44.

158 Kulawik, P., Jamr'oz, E., Janik, M. et al. (2022). Biological activity of biopolymer edible furcellaran-chitosan coatings enhanced with bioactive peptides. *Food Control* 137: 108933.

159 Zhang, Y.F., Liu, K., Li, K.Y. et al. (2018). Fabrication of anti-icing surfaces by short α-helical peptides. *ACS Appl. Mater. Interfaces* 10: 1957–1962.

160 Jewel, Y., Yoo, K., Liu, J., and Dutta, P. (2016). Self-assembled peptides for coating of active sulfur nanoparticles in lithium–sulfur battery. *J. Nanopart. Res.* 18: 54.

15

Self-assembling Peptide Amyloids: From Structure to Function in Nanotechnology

Hao Kong and Gang Wei

Qingdao University, College of Chemistry and Chemical Engineering, Qingdao 266071, P. R. China

15.1 Introduction

Supramolecular self-assembly that originates from biology is a bottom-up method to form functional nanostructures and nanomaterials [1]. It is well known that self-assembly can promote the initial monomers into complex systems through fine-tunable intermolecular interactions [2]. Many biological nanostructures and nanomaterials in nature come from the self-assembly of biomolecules [3], among which peptides and proteins are a kind of natural compounds composed of amino acids, and their self-assembly components have unique functions in biological processes [4, 5]. In the past, the studies on peptide and protein self-assembly mainly focused on the mechanisms of amyloid aggregation and the induced factors of amyloid disease in human body, such as the Alzheimer's disease, Parkinson's disease, Huntington's disease, and type II diabetes [6]. These diseases are often associated with misfolding of peptides and proteins and their subsequent transformation into intractable aggregates and the formation of amyloids, typical of which is the production of amyloid fibers. In recent years, nanomaterials formed by the supramolecular self-assembly of peptides and proteins have also attracted wide attention all over the world due to their controllable synthesis and easy modification as well as facile functional regulation.

In the process of peptide self-assembly in solution, amyloid nanostructures are usually formed by internal interactions, such as the hydrogen bonding, electrostatic interaction, hydrophobic interaction, and π–π conjugation [7]. At the same time, the change in external conditions, such as pH, temperature, concentration, ionic strength, and solvent type, also affects the self-assembly of peptide nanomaterials [8, 9]. By adjusting appropriate self-assembly conditions, many unique amyloid nanostructures and nanomaterials with excellent biological activities can be obtained, including zero-dimensional (0D) nanoparticles and nanospheres, one-dimensional (1D)

Peptide Self-Assembly and Engineering: Fundamentals, Structures, and Applications, First Edition.
Edited by Xuehai Yan.

nanofibers and nanotubes, two-dimensional (2D) nanosheets and nanoribbons, and three-dimensional (3D) hydrogels [10, 11]. Therefore, the amyloid nanomaterials formed by peptide self-assembly have superior and unique physical and chemical properties, such as high mechanical strength, stability, biocompatibility, and customizable functions [12–14]. These excellent properties encourage a wide range of applications for self-assembled peptide amyloid materials in biomedicine, biosensors, tissue engineering, and energy and environmental science [15].

Many reviews on the self-assembly of peptide molecules and the formation of functional amyloids have been released. For instance, Luan et al. summarized the structure and function of peptide nanomaterials in the field of cancer therapy [16]. Wei et al. discussed the relationship between disease and the aggregation mechanism of amyloid proteins and summarized the progress in the design, synthesis, and application of materials based on amyloid proteins [17]. In this chapter, we summarize briefly the peptide amyloid nanomaterials from controllable structure to functional adjustment and their applications in the fields of biomedicine, biosensors, tissue engineering, and energy and environmental science. We mainly focus on the functional regulation of various dimensions of peptide amyloid nanomaterials and the hybridization of other nanomaterials to peptide nanomaterials. We believe that this chapter will be valuable to guide the methodology and structural control of various peptide-based nanomaterials and promote the optimal design and construction of peptide-based functional materials and their advanced applications.

15.2 Structure of Self-assembled Peptide Amyloids

15.2.1 0D Peptide Amyloids

0D peptide amyloids are uniform nanomaterials with nanoscale morphology, including the peptide nanoparticles, peptide nanospheres, and peptide nanocages. Peptide molecules designed by various sequences can have multifunctional properties after the self-assembly into 0D nanomaterials, so they can adapt to a variety of applications in a variety of scenarios. For example, Wu et al. developed a well-designed multifunctional peptide nanospheres for drug delivery [18]. As shown in Figure 15.1a, the multifunctional 51-amino acid peptide P51 is composed of two peptide chains connected by disulfide bonds. Among them, RGD is a good targeting peptide of integrin $\alpha_v\beta_3$, which is overexpressed in many kinds of cancer cells. The SEEDP with negative charge can combine with the positively charged drug pirarubicin through electrostatic interaction. Disulfide bond and the PVGLIG correspond to the cleavage sites of reductant (DTT) and enzyme (MMP2). As shown in Figure 15.1b–d, P51 contains an α-helix that wraps pirarubicin by electrostatic and hydrophobic interactions to form stable spherical nanoparticles. In the acidic environment of tumor, DTT and MMP2 stimulate the release of pirarubicin from peptide nanoparticles.

In another case, Du et al. reported a kind of spherical micellar nanoparticle (EYPN) self-assembled by amphiphilic egg yolk peptides from food sources [19].

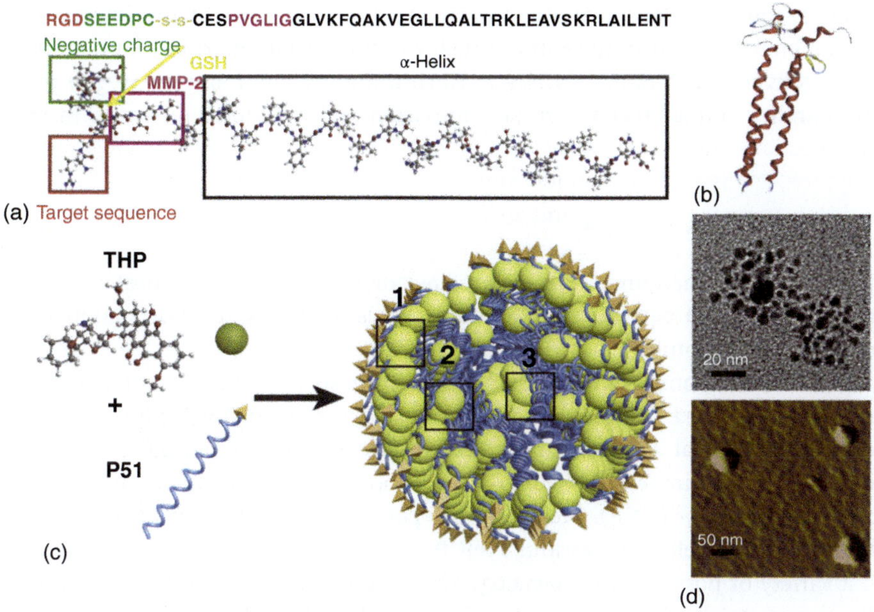

Figure 15.1 (a) Secondary structure of P51. (b) 3D structure of P51. (c) Self-assembly schematic diagram of P51-THP nanoparticles. (d) TEM and AFM images of P51-THP nanoparticles. Source: Ref. [18]. Reproduced with permission of Elsevier 2019.

Amphiphilic bioactive peptides can be obtained from defatted yolk protein by enzymatic hydrolysis. These amphiphilic EYPs can be self-assembled into micellar nanostructures from bottom-up method under water conditions. The formed nanoparticles are stable, monodispersed, and controllable. Meanwhile, as natural nanoparticles based on peptides, EYPN has the characteristics of small particles, moderate wettability, high surface activity, and interface deformability. In a similar study, Morris et al. reported the design and synthesis of a self-assembling peptide cage (SAPE) [20]. SAPE is made from the *ab initio* α-helical coiled helical peptide. Specifically, a group of homotrimer (CC-Tri3) and heterodimer (CC-Di-A and CC-Di-B) peptides are linked by disulfide bonds to form two complementary centers. When they are mixed in aqueous solution, these hubs are assembled into a hexagonal lattice and finally folded into spherical particles with about 100 nm in diameter. Ideally, each CC-Tri3 unit is oriented in the peptide lattice, so that its N-terminal faces the outside of the particle, and its C-terminal faces the interior, while CC-Di-An and CC-Di-B have a greater degree of freedom around the disulfide bond.

In addition to single-form nanomaterials, 0D peptide nanomaterials can also achieve morphological transformation under some conditions. For instance, Sun et al. developed the synthesis of pH-responsive transformable peptide nanoparticles [21]. A peptide–porphyrin conjugate was designed by coupling pH-responsive dipeptide tryptophan-glycine (WG) with hydrophobic porphyrin (P) by amidation. The peptide–porphyrin coupling (PWG) self-assembled into nanoparticles under physiological conditions. When the nanoparticles reach the acidic condition of the tumor, the protonation of PWG promotes the formation of intermolecular hydrogen bonds, which induces the transformation of nanoparticles to nanofibers. The conversion of nanoparticles to fibril improved their singlet oxygen production ability and achieved high accumulation and long-term retention in the tumor site.

15.2.2 1D Peptide Amyloids

1D peptide amyloid nanomaterials inspired by amyloid fibrils are the most common and commonly used peptide-based nanomaterials, including peptide nanofibers, nanowires, and nanotubes.

Collier et al. demonstrated the design and synthesis of supramolecular peptide nanofibers assembled from a self-designed short synthetic peptide [22]. In the absence of additional adjuvants, peptide nanofibers can be immunized to break B-cell tolerance and improve the protective antibody response to mouse autologous tumor necrosis factor (TNF). Moreover, the peptide nanofibers can be assembled with exogenous T-cell epitopes and TNF B-cell epitopes to form long nanofibers with a variety of possible stoichiometry. This result is different from the peptide–carrier conjugate which contains only a fixed number of T-cell epitopes. In another case, Tekinay et al. reported the synthesis of self-assembled amyloid nanofiber based on biotinylated peptide amphiphile (Biotin-PA) [23]. The periphery of nanofibers presents biotin groups as noncovalent binding sites of antigens. Streptavidin (SA)–biotin affinity is a strong interaction. Using SA as the linker between nanofibers and biotinylated antigens, a variety of biotinylated functional molecules such as antigens are attached to nanofibers.

In addition, Tang and colleagues designed and developed four-domain self-assembled peptide nanowires [24]. The peptide sequence contains a self-assembled peptide domain Q11, cytotoxic peptide melittin, peptidase substrate, and polyanion sequence. The Q11 domain is a short-fibrillated peptide that can be self-assembled into lamellar-rich nanowires to provide a structural carrier for therapeutic diagnostic probes. Melittin is an amphoteric cationic peptide composed of 26 amino acids, which is used as a therapeutic agent for surface display of nanowires. MMP2 is overexpressed in extracellular matrix (ECM) of various tumors and acts as an activable tumor targeting module.

Besides, peptide molecules can also be assembled into 1D tubular nanostructures, which have inherent semiconductor properties and extraordinary electrical properties, so they have potential applications in the field of energy and sensing. Khanra and colleagues reported a composite of diphenylalanine (FF)-based self-assembled nanotubes and cobalt ferrite (CFO) magnetic nanoparticles [25]. The antispinel junction site of CFO has Fe and Co ions, which can provide electrons to the amine groups in FF nanotubes, so CFO nanoparticles are uniformly dispersed on peptide nanotubes. The combination of Co_3O_4 nanoparticles and vertically arranged FF nanostructures opens up the possibility of peptide-based nanomaterials for organic energy storage.

15.2.3 2D Peptide Amyloids

Different from 0D and 1D peptide nanomaterials, 2D peptide-based amyloid nanomaterials, including peptide nanoribbons and nanosheets, have higher specific surface area and more functional groups exposed to the surface.

Stevens and colleagues combined amphiphilic peptides (F6C11) into ultrathin 2D Janus nanosheets and slender nanoribbons by controlling and adjusting cosolvent and solvation effects (Figure 15.2) [26]. The molecular dynamics model study further shows the control of solvation-directed self-assembly (SDSA). The preferential solvation of the aromatic and alkyl domains on the surface of the peptide skeleton and fibril leads to the volume exclusion effect and limits the peptide association between the hydrophobic walls. For solvents with lower polarity, it is easy to selectively interact with alkyl and Phe6 fragments of peptide amphiphiles, which leads to volume exclusion effect and peptide binding between hydrophobic walls, thus preventing β-lamellar stacking. For polar solvents, the abovementioned volume exclusion effect is more limited, and then these hydrophobic walls may be combined. In another case, Dai et al. demonstrated that a key amyloid-forming fragment derived from Aβ was self-assembled into a 2D nanosheet wider than 200 nm [27]. Combined with a variety of biophysical and calculation methods, it is shown that the nanosheet structure model is formed by the accumulation of

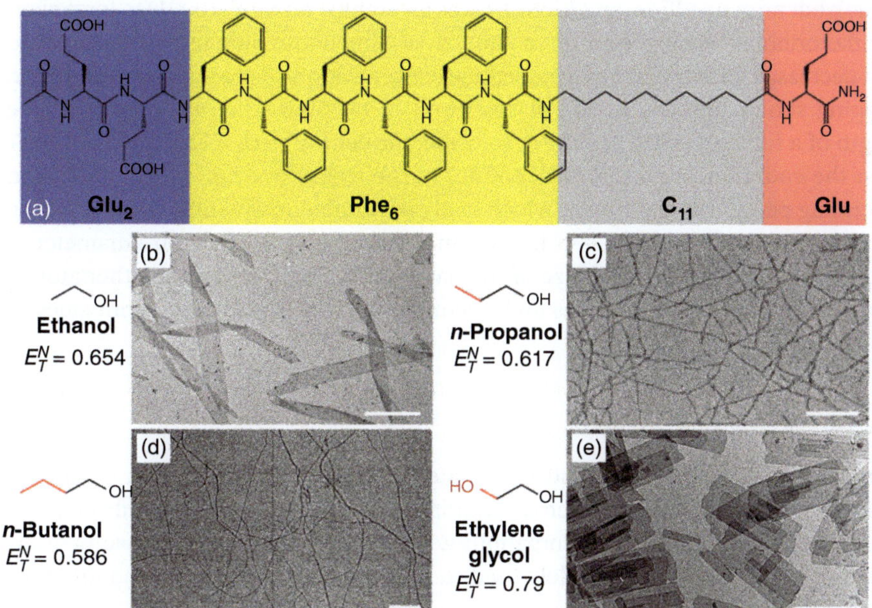

Figure 15.2 (a) Molecular formula of asymmetric peptide (F6C11). TEM images of F6C11 self-assembles (0.25 mM) in the presence of different alcohols: (b) ethanol, (c) *n*-propanol, (d) *n*-butanol, and (e) ethylene glycol. Source: Ref. [26]. American Chemical Society/CC BY 4.0.

amyloid fibril spine perpendicular to the fiber axis. Different from 1D fibril, nanosheet is a 2D extended structure with flat surface and higher density of functional groups. In addition, the morphology of peptide nanosheets is mainly determined by sequence-specific side-chain interactions, and amyloid peptides with different compositions and amino-acid combinations can potentially self-assemble into different structures.

In addition to 2D peptide nanosheets and nanoribbons formed in solution, peptide molecules can also form 2D peptide nanomaterials at the gas–liquid interface and on the surface of inorganic materials. For example, Lee et al. introduced a tyrosine-rich peptide YYACAYY that can be assembled into huge nanowires at the air/water interface [28]. 2D peptide nanostructure has a strong driving force, which can flatten the top of water droplets into a plane. At the same time, it also has redox activity and cross-linking phenolic groups. The spin-coated peptide nanomembrane was immersed in potassium permanganate solution to induce tyrosine cross-linking and manganese oxide hybrid. Peptide/MnO_x hybrid nanofilms have the advantages of uniformity, large scale, room temperature treatment, thickness control, and expansibility to other peptide sequences. In addition, peptide/MnO_x hybrid nanomembrane can transport protons effectively, and its proton conductivity is about 18.6 $mS\,cm^{-1}$ at room temperature, which is much higher than that of biomaterials. It is a promising new type of proton conductor.

In another case, Chen et al. chose YSATFTY (named MoSBP1), a peptide bound to molybdenum disulfide, and MoSBP1 was assembled on MoS_2 (0001) to form slender nanoribbons arranged in three equivalent directions, showing an aspect ratio that decreased with the increase in peptide concentration [29]. Molecular resolution imaging shows that the length of each unit is 1.7 times the maximum possible length of a fully extended MoSBP1 molecule; the central part of each unit is higher than the end, indicating that the peptides in the region overlap; there is no chain extending parallel to the dimer, which leads to variable row width, thus excluding the association of N—C or C—N in the dimer. The ring structure with a diameter of about 0.5 nm is similar to the size of the flat benzene ring reported in other atomic force microscopy (AFM) studies and is symmetrically distributed on both sides of the row.

15.2.4 3D Peptide Amyloids

Most of the 3D peptide amyloid nanomaterials are peptide hydrogels, which are formed by physical or chemical cross-linking of strongly interacting peptide nanofibers. Because of their high biocompatibility, controllable gelation, and macroporous network structure, they are widely used in targeted drug loading, wound dressing, and adsorption.

Schneider and colleagues reported the design and synthesis of a polyphasic peptide hydrogel [30]. The peptide sequence containing seven lysine residues is protonated under neutral pH, keeping the peptide in a dissolved and unfolded monomer state. In the syringe, the peptide can initiate the sol–gel phase transition and quickly self-assemble into a fibrous hydrogel network by triggering the peptide to amphiphilic β-folding in which each fiber is composed of double-layer β-folds. These folds can be cut and thinly transported to the lumen of collapsed blood vessels along the long-axis intermolecular hydrogen bond of a given fiber. Eventually, light is used to initiate a gel–sol phase transition, destroying the hydrogel network, causing the gel to be removed and restoring blood flow.

Yang et al. developed a method for the fabrication of a hybrid peptide hydrogel loaded with adriamycin and melittin (Figure 15.3) [31]. In the solution of 0.9% NaCl, the amphiphilic peptides with synthetic sequence RADARADARADARADA were gelled at a concentration of 0.5–2% at pH $4.0 \leq 7.5$ but did not produce hydrogel in the absence of NaCl, indicating that the peptides are the building blocks of peptide hydrogels under physiological conditions. By this method, melittin and doxorubicin were successfully encapsulated in peptide hydrogel scaffolds. Hydrogel has interwoven nanofiber structure, good biocompatibility, controlled drug release *in vivo* and *in vitro*, and enhanced killing effect on melanoma cells. Saiani et al. controlled the final properties of materials by designing and controlling fiber–fiber interactions and adjusting the topology of hydrogel networks [32]. High-strength hydrogel networks were constructed based on the design characteristics of β-sheet-forming peptides with alternating hydrophobic and hydrophilic residues and the ability of arginine guanidine side groups to interact with themselves and other

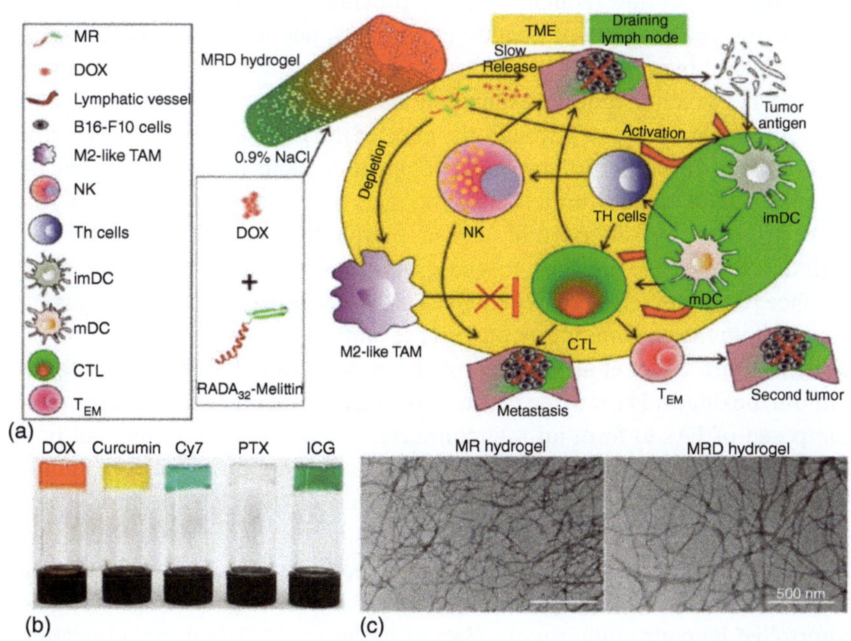

Figure 15.3 (a) Mechanism of peptide hydrogel-mediated antitumor effects against melanoma. (b) Photographs of peptide hydrogels loaded with various agents. (c) TEM images of peptide hydrogel. Source: Ref. [31]. Reproduced with permission of American Chemical Society 2018.

amino-acid side groups. The interaction between nanofibers is mainly controlled by hydrophilic residues, especially arginine containing guanidine side groups, which can interact strongly with other amino-acid side groups and with various configurations of themselves, including hydrogen bonds and electrostatic interactions. The introduction of this amino acid will lead to the increase in fiber–fiber interaction, thus affecting the topology of the formed network and the final mechanical properties of the hydrogels.

15.3 Functional Regulation of Self-assembled Peptide Amyloid Nanomaterials

15.3.1 Functional Regulation with Metal NPs

There is a unique interaction between self-assembled peptide nanomaterials and metal materials [33]. Self-assembled peptide nanomaterials can not only be wrapped on the surface of metal nanoparticles as a protective end, it can also bind metal nanoparticles closely by means of loading and *in situ* growth. This chapter briefly introduces the combination of nanomaterials such as metals and their oxides and sulfides with peptide nanomaterials, which can provide excellent catalytic, electronic, and semiconductor properties for peptide nanomaterials.

The flexibility of peptide sequence design provides great convenience for the development and construction of peptide nanosheets, peptide nanorods, and peptide nanoparticles. Lin et al. designed and synthesized a special amphiphilic peptide sequence F6C11, which contains hexamethyl alanine, hydrophobic alkyl tail, and hydrophilic glutamic acid [34]. Through the force of the groups on the side chain of amino acids, the hydrophilic and lipophilic polypeptide nanosheets were formed by self-assembly. Due to the multifunctional properties of different groups, amphiphilic nanosheets formed by self-assembly can accept many guest components, including metals and their compounds. In this study, it is found that the catalytic activity of the surface restriction enzyme assembled on the nanosheet has been improved, which can imitate the enzymatic reaction on the biofilm system.

In another report, Guler et al. used atomic layer deposition (ALD) technology to coat titanium dioxide and zinc oxide on the surface of an organic nanonetwork template composed of PAs to form an interconnected nanotube system that can promote electron transfer, making it possible to make anode materials on self-assembled peptide amphiphilic templates by ALD [35]. Because of the high specific surface area of these multiempty network templates, the adhesion sites of photosensitizers on semiconductor materials are increased. The deposition thickness of titanium dioxide and zinc oxide on amphiphilic peptide nanonetwork template can be indirectly controlled by controlling the number of cycles of ALD, and the adsorption number of sensitizer molecules can be effectively regulated. At the same time, it is also found that 100-cycle ZnO devices have excellent device performance based on material efficiency ratio and high filling factor.

Through computational design, it is possible to create self-assembled peptide nanostructures with desired shape and constitution, and the templates of these peptide structures allow metal nanomaterials to grow on them in a certain way. As a result, various templated metal nanostructures can be synthesized. For example, Tian et al. used computationally designed peptide sequences to show an efficient ability to bind to gold nanoparticles under the modification of cysteine, resulting in organized and regular 1D and 2D gold nanoparticle arrays (Figure 15.4a) [36]. Peptide templates play an important role in the growth of these gold nanoparticle arrays. At the same time, the growth pathways of different gold nanoparticles in the process of *in situ* solution–peptide template synthesis and the adsorption of special gold colloidal nanocrystals on the precursor of peptide template were studied. The successful synthesis, growth pathway, and adsorption of these gold nanoparticle arrays explain the template effect of peptide nanostructures, which provides a new idea for the formation of specific metal nanostructures.

The combination of metals or their compounds with peptides promotes the formation of functional hybrid nanomaterials. Peptides can affect the growth shape and spatial arrangement of metal nanoparticles, and metal nanoparticles affect the function of peptides. Luo et al. used a specific peptide sequence (CGGEVSALEK) to functionalize the gold nanopolyhedron to form a chiral gold nanopolyhedron [39]. In their study, by designing the chirality of the peptide sequence, the chirality of the

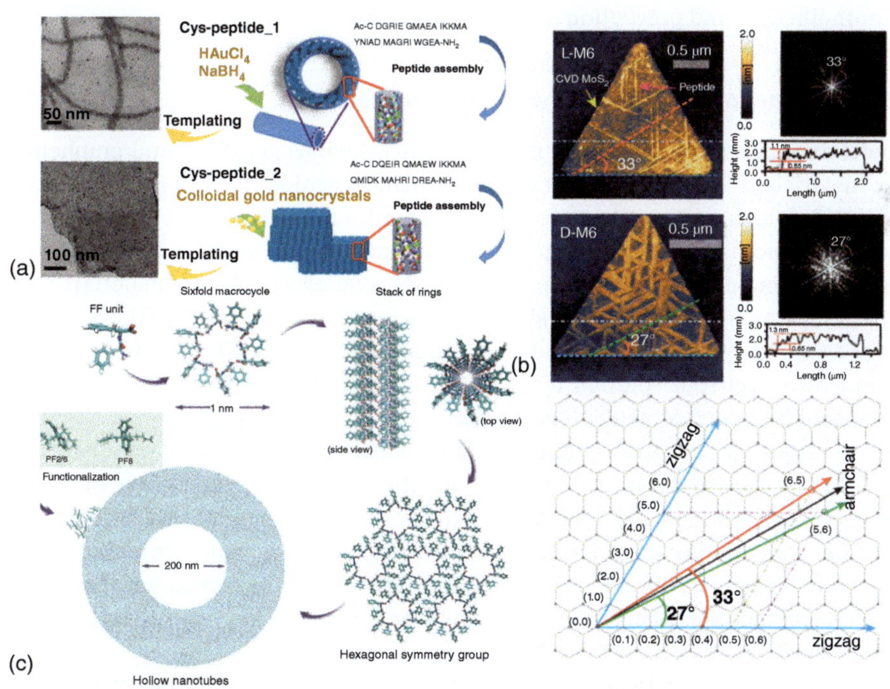

Figure 15.4 (a) Synthesis diagram and transmission electron microscope images of peptide–gold nanoparticle composites. Source: Ref. [36]. Copyright American Chemical Society 2018. (b) Chiral recognition of peptides in the process of self-assembly on MoS_2 surface. Source: Ref. [37]. Copyright American Chemical Society 2021. (c) Schematic diagram of layered self-assembly and polycyclopentene modification in FF components. Source: Ref. [38]. Reproduced with permission of Wiley 2015.

peptide sequence was transferred to gold nanoparticles by the method of chiral transfer. The development of 3D chiral gold nanostructures with the size of several hundred nanometers has been successfully realized, and the controllable synthesis of asymmetric gold nanopolyhedrons has been achieved. In addition, due to the flexibility of peptide sequence design, the chirality of the designed peptides is more diverse, which provides a wealth of options for subsequent chiral transfer. At the same time, it provides a novel method for the synthesis of materials with unique optical properties and special chiral drugs.

Hou et al. developed a multipurpose genetically engineered polypeptide hydrogel (PC10ARGD), which can be combined with chemotherapeutic drugs (DOX) and immunoadjuvant drug to transport drugs for synergistic treatment of breast cancer [40]. At the same time, the hydrogel is loaded with near-infrared (NIR) Ag_2S QDs, which has good photothermal properties and can greatly improve the sustained release ability of chemotherapeutic drug DOX, thus reducing multiple injections and improving the overall therapeutic effect. In addition, the loaded drug enhances the immune effect after treatment by enhancing the function of T lymphocytes. The injectable Ag_2S QD/DOX/Bestatin@PC10ARGD hydrogel developed in this study showed high tumor cell inactivation activity and inhibition of tumor cell metastasis *in vivo* and *in vitro*, which provided a new treatment way for tumor immunotherapy and prevention of tumor recurrence.

15.3.2 Functional Regulation with 2D Nanomaterials

There are many members of 2D material family, such as graphene and graphene-like materials, MXene, and transition-metal dichalcogenide (TMD) [41]. Large specific surface area and excellent electronic properties are the common properties of most 2D nanomaterials [42]. When 2D nanomaterials are used to combine with peptide nanomaterials to form composites, the two excellent nanomaterials will fully complement each other and show unique functions in synergy [43].

For example, Wu et al. prepared diphenylalanine-graphene (FF-G) self-assembled nanowires in aqueous solution by a simple one-step method [44]. FF can be self-assembled into peptide nanowires in aqueous solution. When graphene dispersion is used instead of aqueous solution, the high density and intertwined nanowires of FF-G can be clearly observed. Hemoglobin (Hb) was further immobilized on FF-G nanocomposites as a model molecule to construct an H_2O_2 biosensor. Thanks to the good biocompatibility and charge transfer ability of FF-G nanocomposite nanowires, the biosensor shows excellent performance; especially compared with other graphene composite control samples, its linear range is wider, and the detection limit is lower.

As shown in Figure 15.4b, Sun et al. studied the chiral recognition of the self-assembled structure of peptides on molybdenum disulfide (MoS_2) surface using *in situ* AFM [37]. Using the edge of the facet of MoS_2 as a marker to determine the crystal orientation of its ordered structure, it is found that the peptide enantiomers form mirror symmetrical nanowires on the surface of MoS_2. These peptide nanowires are composed of ordered and repetitive molecular units with specific size and period, so they show obvious lattice matching in the longitudinal and transverse direction of the nanowires. The size of the unit cell in the self-assembled structure was measured by *in situ* atomic force microscope, and the lattice matching model between peptide and MoS_2 lattice was proposed. In another case, Park and colleagues combined Fmoc-FF peptide nanofibers with g-C_3N_4 nanosheets to synthesize self-assembled peptide (Fmoc-FF)/graphitized carbonitride (g-C_3N_4) hydrogels for light harvesting and biomimetic photosynthesis [45]. The composite hydrogel is formed by the π–π interaction between the aromatic ring in the Fmoc-FF nanofiber and the g-C_3N_4 nanosheet. The photocurrent density of the obtained hydrogel used as biomimetic photosynthesis is 1.8 times higher than that of the single g-C_3N_4 hydrogel (0.82 $\mu A\,cm^{-1}$). This is mainly due to the effective stripping of g-C_3N_4 nanowires in the Fmoc-FF/g-C_3N_4 network, which promotes the photoinduced electron transfer. Fmoc-FF/g-C_3N_4 hydrogel reduced NAD^+ to NADH with enzyme activity under light and drove photoresponsive redox biocatalysis. In addition, Fmoc-FF/g-C_3N_4 hydrogels also have the function of wrapping key photosynthetic components, such as electronic media, cofactors, and enzymes.

Nie et al. designed chimeric polypeptide functional titanium carbide MXenes (PEP-Ti_3C_2) to bind to carboxypeptidase Y (CPY)-mediated peptide cleavage to determine the activity of posttranslational modification (PTM) enzymes [46]. The modification of MXene by soybean phospholipids not only stabilizes the Ti_3C_2 MXenes but also provides a scaffold for the functional peptides of the trailing membrane insertion sequence. Peptides (MIP) are anchored on the lipid bilayers on the surface of MXene and act as fluorescent nanoprobes for PTM enzyme sensing. In the presence of PTM enzyme, with the digestion of peptides by CPY, the modified groups in the peptide probe are removed, resulting in the release of labeled fluorescent groups, so PEP-Ti_3C_2 can be used for fluorescence analysis of PTM enzymes including deacetylase and protein phosphatase at low concentrations.

15.3.3 Functional Regulation with Polymers

There are great similarities between peptides and polymers in terms of the structure and composition. Peptides are composed of small molecular amino acids by dehydration and condensation, and polymers are polymerized by small molecular monomers. The idea of combining the two provides a research direction for many researchers. Peptide nanomaterials and polymers are compounded to form new composites, which are widely used in the fields of electrochemical cell sensors, biodegradable biological films, drug delivery carriers, and medical devices [47, 48].

Lian et al. dispersed a dipeptide monomer in the aqueous solution of chitosan to make it self-assembled to form peptide nanotube–chitosan (PNT-CS) composites [49]. The structure and properties of PNT-CS composites were characterized, and it was found that the composites had 3D nanostructure, high specific surface area, good stability, and excellent hydrophilic properties. In addition, electrochemical characterization shows that PNT-CS composites have good electrical conductivity. In the follow-up development and application, PNT-CS is used to prepare electrochemical cell sensors. The composite combines the advantages of peptide nanotubes and chitosan, and the detection of cancer cells is superior to the traditional nanomaterial cell sensor. PNT-CS is an ideal platform for the next generation of cell sensors because of its good biocompatibility, easy preparation, and excellent electrochemical properties.

In another work, Khanra et al. found that polyfluorene (PF) was compounded on diphenylalanine (FF)-based nanostructures to obtain FF-PF polymer nanocomposites with good biocompatibility and biodegradability (Figure 15.4c) [38]. Due to the conjugation effect on polymers, the electron transfer properties of FF-PF polymer nanocomposites with polyfluorene were improved, and the ability of FF nanotubes to extract charge was enhanced, which greatly increased the photoelectric effect of nanocomposites and opened up a new way for the development of conductive luminescent polymer materials. In addition, it was also found that the composite polymer had good biodegradability, and the biodegradability of nanocomposites under enzymatic catalysis was significantly improved compared with the traditional polyfluorene. The composite of conductive polymers and peptide nanomaterials shows excellent application prospects in the field of organic electronics and provides an idea to solve the pollution problem of organic polymer materials.

Alves et al. studied the fabrication of hybrid material of PCL/FF-MNTs, which is composed of electrospun polycaprolactone (PCL) fiber and L-L-diphenylalanine micronanotubes (FF-MNTs), and has excellent properties and can be used as biomimetic scaffolds, and the strength of the scaffolds can be adjusted, which increases the application range of the hybrid materials [50]. The results show that with the increase in FF-MNTs content, the mechanical properties of the materials are constantly changing; the strength of the scaffold changes from brittleness to toughness; and the Young's modulus of polymer fiber increases. In addition, in the *in vitro* penetration experiment, the study also found that the stability of the composite mixed with polycaprolactone in releasing benzocaine was much higher than that of the traditional commercial aerogel.

15.4 Applications of Peptide Amyloids

In this section, various applications of self-assembled peptide amyloid nanomaterials for biosensors, bioimaging, cancer therapy, antibacterial materials, tissue engineering, and energy and environmental science are presented.

15.4.1 Biosensors

Because peptides have flexible self-assembly structure and good biocompatibility, functional customized biosensors made of self-assembled peptide nanomaterials can sensitively detect a variety of biomolecules and biomarkers [14]. In the work of Cui et al., an electrochemical biosensor with high sensitivity and selectivity was proposed [51]. Amphoteric peptides were self-assembled into monolayer carriers (SAM) on the surface of gold electrodes. It was found that SAM had good antifouling properties by impedance method. Through the covalent connection between carboxyl and amino groups, oligonucleotides are modified on SAM. Oligonucleotides can form a double-helix structure with the target DNA through base pairing, which changes the impedance of the electrode to achieve the purpose of detection.

In the work of Wang and colleagues, an amphoteric peptide was also used to construct an antifouling sensing interface which can sensitively detect immunoglobulin E (IgE) in biological samples by making use of its unique antifouling properties and the ability to reduce nonspecific adsorption [52]. The amphoteric peptides and IgE aptamers self-assembled on macroporous Au substrates, while the macroporous Au substrates self-assembled on glassy carbon electrodes with the help of multilayer polystyrene nanospheres. Because of the large specific surface area and high specificity of nucleic acid aptamers, the fabricated electrochemical biosensors exhibited high sensitivity and selectivity to IgE. Meanwhile, due to the existence of zwitterionic peptides, the biosensor interface can reduce nonspecific adsorption and pollution effects. Therefore, the biosensors have been successfully applied to the detection of IgE in complex biological samples, indicating that the peptide-based sensing interface has a broad application prospect in antifouling detection.

Peptide hybrid materials can be utilized to achieve antifouling applications. For instance, Chen and coworkers developed a self-assembled light surface plasmon resonance biosensor (FO-SPR), which has great application potential in resisting nonspecific adsorption and high sensitivity detection of platelet-derived growth factor (PDGF-BB) [53]. Among them, the addition of antipollution peptide shows a strong ability to resist the negative side of nonspecific adsorption. The gold layer was coated on the surface of bare optical fiber by thermal evaporation, and the combination of nucleic acid aptamer and polypeptide with optical fiber was realized through the interaction of gold–sulfur bond. Subsequently, the weak nucleic acid aptamers and peptides were removed by 6-Mercapto-1-hexanol (MCH) binding; the stability of nonspecific binding sites was blocked; and the antifouling properties were enhanced. In the process of PDGF-BB detection, nucleic acid aptamer, PDGF-BB, and nucleic acid aptamer-functionalized AuNPs complex are formed on the surface of optical fiber (FO) probe, which can significantly amplify FO-SPR signal.

In the work of Lian et al., the enzyme horseradish peroxidase (HRP) was directly encapsulated to form a hydrogel through the self-assembly of peptides with sequence Fmoc-FF [54]. In the test, it is found that the formed hydrogel retains the biological activity of HRP and can realize the transfer of electrons in the hydrogel. The Fmoc-FF hydrogel electrochemical hydrogen peroxide biosensor has high selectivity and low detection limit. The preparation process has the characteristics of low cost and environmentally friendly, which is a potential method to integrate biological cells or enzymes and other active substances together.

15.4.2 Bioimaging

The functionality of peptide nanomaterials has been enriched by the modification of organic luminophores and quantum dot materials and thus contributed to the applications in the bioimaging [55].

Wang et al. developed a self-assembled multicolor fluorescent peptide nanoparticle. In this study, tetrapeptide Trp-Trp-Trp-Trp (WWWW) and Zn^{2+} self-assembled into polychromatic fluorescent nanoparticles (TPNPs) under π–π stacking, Zn^{2+} coordination, and hydrogen-bonding forces. Due to the Zn^{2+} coordination to a certain extent, its fluorescence intensity is enhanced; the emission wavelength of tryptophan is long; and the straight- and long-chain structures of WWWW provide more possibilities for its self-assembly. Therefore, this nanoparticle has four emission wavelengths of blue (421 nm), green (530 nm), red (635 nm), and near-infrared (824 nm). It breaks the limitations of monochromatic fluorescent nanomaterials, has better biocompatibility and photostability, and at the same time exhibits excellent biological cell imaging capabilities, which has good prospects in biomedical applications. Since integrin receptors have been widely studied as good diagnostic targets, for example, the cyclic RGD peptide targeting $\alpha_V\beta_3$ integrin has been widely used for targeted tumor bioimaging.

Recently, Fluksman and coworkers developed self-assembling peptide nanocarriers targeting integrin $\alpha_2\beta_1$. In their work, they prepared integrin-targeted self-assembled nanocarriers (ITNCs) based on Lys (Arg)-Thr-Ser [K(R)TS] cyclic peptide as a targeting agent. At the same time, the near-infrared dye indocyanine green (ICG) is encapsulated. Active targeting of $\alpha_2\beta_1$ integrin was finally achieved. ITNCs have high aggregation and fluorescence intensity at tumor sites, and have good biocompatibility, with little toxic side effects on normal organ systems. This system provides a good platform for tumor imaging in the near-infrared region.

To effectively assist nanoparticles to achieve intracellular escape, Guo et al. designed a self-assembling peptide nanoparticle. The nanoparticles are self-assembled by the small-molecular-weight dipeptide Try-Phe. The aptamer AS1411 of human breast cancer cells (MCF-7) and the influenza hemagglutinin peptide were used as cell licenses to enhance the specificity of cell drug delivery capabilities and improve endosome escape. In addition, the three drugs of Clolar, siRNA, and DOX can be delivered at the same time. This multidrug combination therapy has better tumor treatment effect than single drug therapy. This peptide nanoparticle can not only specifically deliver a variety of drugs but also promote the accumulation of drugs in the tumor site on the basis of visualizing the morphological details of tumor cells, effectively inhibiting the growth of tumors. This combination therapy has great potential for application in cancer treatment.

Because of the complexity of tumor, it is an arduous task to develop a highly sensitive tumor imaging probe. As shown in Figure 15.5a, Zhao et al. constructed an NIR probe based on peptides, which can react to fibroblast activating protein-α (FAP-α) and specifically form nanofibers on the surface of cancer-associated fibroblasts (CAF) [56]. The probe has enhanced tumor imaging ability and can show small tumors about 2 mm in diameter.

15.4.3 Phototherapy

Traditional clinical treatment of cancer, such as chemotherapy and radiotherapy, will not only cause certain damage to the human body itself, reduce human

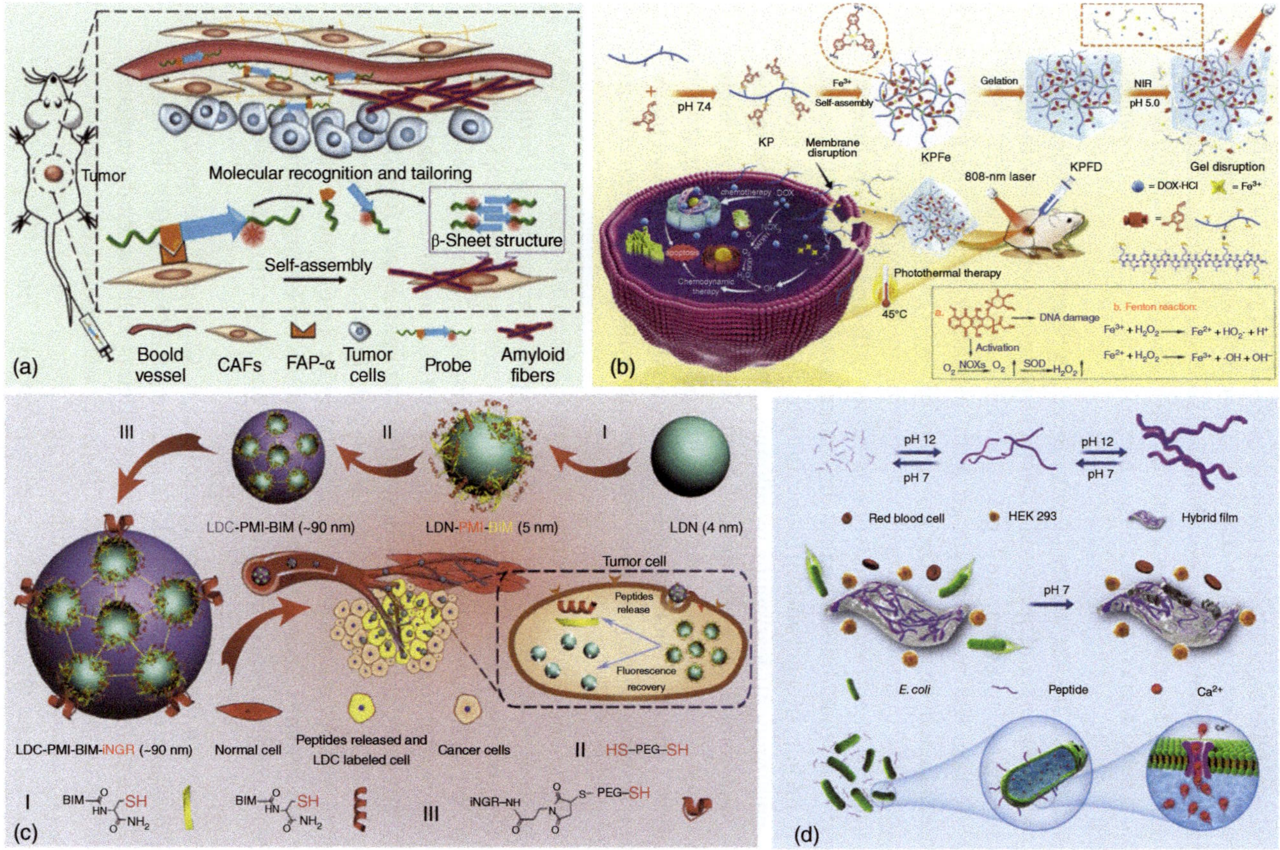

Figure 15.5 (a) Schematic illustration of CAF-instructed self-assembly of nanofibers *in situ* for enhanced tumor imaging. Source: Ref. [56]. Copyright Wiley 2019. (b) Schematic illustration of the self-assembly process of the anticancer peptide of KL. Source: Ref. [57]. Copyright Royal Society of Chemistry 2022. (c) Schematic diagram of LDC-PMI-BIM-iNGR serving as peptide delivery platform for targeted cancer therapy. Source: Ref. [58]. Copyright American Chemical Society 2018. (d) Self-assembly synthesis and antibacterial mechanism of two antibacterial peptides $K_3(FA)_4K_3$ and $K_6(FA)_4$. Source: Ref. [59]. Reproduced with permission of American Chemical Society 2020.

immunity, but also will be accompanied by a high recurrence rate. As a more advanced diagnosis and treatment technology, photothermal therapy has the advantages of simple operation, less trauma, short treatment time, and quick recovery [60]. Phototherapy includes photothermal therapy (PTT) and photodynamic therapy (PDT), which brings dawn to targeted therapy. The principle of PTT is to target photosensitizers or nanomaterials near the tumor tissue and then use the tissue penetration characteristics of infrared light to induce and excite the photosensitizers to convert light energy into heat energy to kill cancer cells [61, 62].

In order to improve the sensitivity of anticancer peptides to protein degradation, Liu et al. designed and prepared injectable peptide hydrogels with drug release, near-infrared response, and pH sensitivity (Figure 15.5b) [57]. The formed peptide hydrogel was synthesized from anticancer peptide (KL), Fe^{3+}, and protocatechualdehyde through the formation of Fe(III)–catechol complex in the gel network. The obtained hydrogel has near-infrared absorption properties and can be used for photothermal ablation of tumor cells and remote photocontrol of drug release. In addition, the unstable imine bond of pH between KL and PCA endows the injection gel with pH sensitivity to slow release of KL in moderately acidic environment, leading to membrane instability and promoting cell uptake of DOX in combined chemotherapy. *In vitro* and *in vivo* experiments show that the injectable hydrogel has a synergistic therapeutic effect on tumor growth by photothermal combined chemotherapy. Therefore, this work provides a promising attempt for the development of therapeutic hydrogels from anticancer peptides.

PDT is a new technique that uses photodynamic effect to diagnose and treat diseases. It has a good application prospect in the field of biomedicine. In order to improve the shortcomings of traditional nanoengineering methods, such as drug leakage, premature release, and inaccurate release, Chen et al. developed novel acid-activated self-assembly nanophotosensitizers based on amphiphilic peptide derivatives [63]. The peptide derivative was synthesized from fluorescein molecule FL by thermally activated delayed fluorescence (TADF). This self-assembled nanophotosensitizer can specifically enter tumor cells and decompose in lysosomes, accompanied by "on" fluorescence and photodynamic therapy. This nanophotosensitizer will open up new opportunities for cancer treatment.

In order to improve the efficiency of tumor therapy, Chen et al. designed a self-transitive phototherapy chimeric peptide (C_{16}-Cypate-RRKK-PEG_8-COOH, designated as CCP) for the combination of highly efficient cell membrane-targeted hypothermic low-temperature PTT and PDT [64]. The self-assembled CCP nanoparticles showed significant tumor accumulation after systemic administration without additional carriers, which avoided the carrier-related side effects. CCP can produce reactive oxygen species (ROS) and low fever (<45 °C) in the cell membrane, and can quickly induce immunogenic cell death, thus realizing the effective binding of low-temperature PTT/PDT.

15.4.4 Drug Delivery

The main goal of traditional cancer treatment, such as chemotherapy, is to provide enough drugs to tumor cells on the premise of reducing contact with normal cells. Previous studies have shown that under physiological conditions, drugs may encounter problems such as biological barriers and targeting phenomena in the process of drug delivery, and the efficacy of drugs will be weakened due to changes in the environment. In contrast, peptide-based nanopharmaceuticals have advantages, such as better permeability, easier synthesis, and lower cost [65]. The functional customization and self-assembly of peptide sequences provide a convenient strategy for the creation of new nanodrugs for pharmaceuticals. Compared with antibody–drug conjugates (ADCs), polypeptide molecular drugs have higher specificity and fewer side effects, so they can break the biological barrier, can be used for drug delivery, and provide powerful resources for targeted drug delivery.

As shown in Figure 15.5c, Yan et al. prepared 90 nm nanospheres, which are self-assembled from rare earth-doped nanoparticles (5 nm), two anticancer peptides with different targets (BIM and PMI), and a cyclopeptide targeting cancer cells [58]. Rare earth peptide nanoclusters (LDC-PMI-BIM-iNGR) enhance the resistance of peptide drugs to protein decomposition, decompose under the reduction conditions existing in tumor microenvironment, and inhibit the growth of cancer cells *in vitro* and *in vivo*. In addition, LDC-PMI-BIM-iNGR showed very low systemic toxicity and side effects *in vivo*.

The intratumoral administration of chemotherapeutic drugs can make the drug localize in the tumor, reduce the nonspecific targeting, and improve the curative effect. pH-responsive peptide hydrogel is considered to be a suitable carrier for intratumoral injection of chemotherapeutic drugs. Therefore, Raza and colleagues conducted a study to develop a paclitaxel (PTX) drug delivery system using pH-responsive FER-8 peptide hydrogel (HG-PTX) for tumor targeting [66]. The sensitive nature of pH triggers the drug in the acidic pH environment of the tumor site and provides continuous delivery of the drug. HG-PTX provides an attractive strategy and potential carrier for effective anticancer drug delivery. The carrier can enhance tumor targeting, prolong retention time, reduce systemic side effects, and increase drug accumulation at the tumor site.

Fu et al. proposed and prepared tryptophan–tryptophan–tryptophan tripeptide self-assembled nanoparticles (TPNPs1) with high fluorescence intensity, uniform size, and low cytotoxicity by means of π–π stacking and zinc coordination [67]. In addition, there is fluorescence resonance between TPNPs1 and doxorubicin, which has been successfully applied to real-time cell imaging and drug-release monitoring. In addition, in order to enhance the tumor targeting of peptide nanoparticles, Fan et al. constructed bifunctional peptides that enhance tumor targeting and apoptosis by fusing hepatitis A virus with classical tumor targeting RGD motifs and aspartic NGR motifs into apoptosis-inducing peptide sequence AVPIAQK. Furthermore, it was used as a nanocarrier to encapsulate the hydrophobic drug docetaxel (DOC) [68]. Bioimaging analysis shows that polypeptide nanoparticles can penetrate into transplanted tumor cells, and have significant tumor retention time and high tumor targeting, thereby revealing broad application prospect in the treatment of lung cancer.

15.4.5 Tissue Engineering

Peptide-based nanomaterials, especially peptide hydrogels, have become important candidates for tissue culture and regeneration because of their high biocompatibility [69]. Hydroxyapatite biomineralized on peptide nanomaterials also has potential applications in dental and bone tissue engineering. Ribeiro et al. modified multidomain peptides (MDPs) with the bioactive motifs of mineralization protein, cell adhesion protein (fibronectin, FN), and bone synthesis factor (osteogenic growth peptide, OGP) [70]. MDPs membrane with intrinsic mineralization, cell adhesion, and bone induction was successfully synthesized by electrostatic interaction between redesigned HA-MDP and hyaluronic acid (HA). In the experiment of cell culture *in vitro*, under the condition of serum-free, the HA-MDP membrane can support the adhesion of primary human periosteal cells, showing the potential to deliver specific cell groups *in vivo*.

Li et al. used peptides with the sequence of LLVFGAKMLPHHGA to self-assemble peptide nanosheets (PNSs) in 2,2,2-trifluoroethanol (TFE) [71]. 3D graphene foam (GF) with continuous macropores was synthesized by pyrolysis of polyurethane foam (PUF) coated with GO. Furthermore, PNS is adsorbed on GF by π–π stacking interaction to form 3D GF-PNSs hybrid scaffolds for hydroxyapatite (Hap) mineral growth. The MLPHHGA sequence of peptides provides many functional groups, such as carboxyl groups, which can specifically promote the biomimetic mineralization of HAp. In the experiment, GF-PNSs hybrid scaffolds were immersed in SBF and mineralized to form GF-PNSs-HAp minerals as potential bone graft scaffolds. L-929 cells showed high activity in the study of cytocompatibility of the new GF-PNSs-HAp mineral, which proved the high biocompatibility of GF-PNSs-HAp mineral.

In another study, Deidda et al. designed RGDSGAITIGC peptide, a bifunctional self-assembled amyloid peptide [72]. RGD sequence motifs and cysteine residues were incorporated into the N- and C-terminal of the peptide, respectively, and the characteristics of cell adhesion and potential cysteine-mediated functionalization were added. The total solvent accessibility of RGD sequence motifs is a key factor in determining cell adhesion. On the other hand, the existence of cysteine-exposed-SH functional groups plays an important role in selective binding to metals or surfaces and possible coupling with signal molecules. The designed peptides can be self-assembled into nanofibers, and the bifunctional properties of nanofibers can be used to prepare new biomaterials with good biomedical applications.

Tran et al. constructed scaffolds using RADA-16I peptides, which can be self-assembled to form hydrogels according to the change in pH value [73]. Because of the permissibility of RADA-16I peptide stent to axon growth and its ability to support vascularization, RADA-16I peptide stent can form microvascular connection at the blood spinal cord barrier (BSCB) to reduce inflammation and scar formation at the injured site and promote the increase in axon growth after spinal cord injury (SCI). In the experiment of injecting different concentrations of RADA16I peptide stent into rat spinal cord contusion, it was found that the combination of peptide stent formed microvessels, reduced the formation of inflammation and glial scar, and increased the axon growth density of the injured graft site. These results suggest that RADA-16I peptide stent microvascularization has potential application value in the treatment of spinal cord injury.

15.4.6 Antibacterial Materials

Cationic antimicrobial peptides destroy the negatively charged bacterial cell membrane through electrostatic interaction, thus playing a bactericidal and antibacterial role [74]. At the same time, because of the high biocompatibility of peptide-based nanomaterials, the antibacterial properties of wound dressings can also be satisfied.

For example, Feng et al. combined RADA16 peptides that can be self-assembled into nanofibrils with antimicrobial peptides (AMPs) to form RA-AMPs [59]. The synthesized RA-AMPs can not only retain the antibacterial activity of AMPs but also self-assemble to form fibril nanostructures. Hydrogel was prepared by RA-AMPs and thermosensitive polymer (PNIPAM) with critical temperature of 32–34 °C, and MGFE peptide which can promote the growth of human cells was inserted into the hydrogel. Finally, an antibacterial hydrogel (PNI/RA-AMPs/E) with good thermal response, biocompatibility, and mechanical properties was formed and significantly promoted wound healing. Due to the thermosensitive phase transition properties of PNI/RA-AMPs/E hydrogels, MGFE peptides can be continuously released to about 65% within 24 hours when the temperature is raised to 37 °C. In addition, because the 3D network structure formed by the staggered fibril of RA-AMPs peptide nanofibers limits the escape of water molecules, PNI/RA-AMPs/E has a more sustained drug release. PNI/RA-AMPs/E hydrogel showed good biocompatibility in cytotoxicity and blood compatibility *in vitro*. In further *in vivo* experiments, the liver model of mice injected with PNI/RA-AMPs/E hydrogel almost stopped bleeding at 30 s. In the full-thickness skin detection model of hydrogel wound dressing, the wound-healing effect of PNI/RAAMPs/E hydrogel treatment group was the best, and the wound-healing rate was about 80%. The above experiments fully proved the good application effect of PNI/RA-AMPs/E hydrogel as wound dressing.

In another case, Malhotra et al. designed α/γ hybrid peptides, Boc-D-Phe-γ^4-L-Phe-PEA (NH007) and Boc-L-Phe-γ^4-L-Phe-PEA (NH009). The two designed dipeptides can be self-assembled into hydrogels in aqueous DMSO solution [75]. The hydrogel has good stability. Because γ-amino acids enter the peptide sequence as nonprotein amino acids, the two kinds of hydrogels show excellent antiprotease hydrolysis. The degradation rates of NH007 peptides in 24 and 36 hours were 23% and 40%, respectively, while those of NH009 peptides were 77% and 94%, respectively, at the same time, which were better than those reported in the literature. More importantly, both hydrogels have good antibacterial effects. The inhibition rates of NH007 and NH009 gels on *Escherichia coli*, *Bacillus subtilis*, *Pseudomonas aeruginosa*, and *Staphylococcus aureus* were 59% and 66%, 65% and 67%, 51% and 71%, 40% and 60%, respectively. It has broad-spectrum antibacterial activity against *E. coli*, *P. aeruginosa*, *B. subtilis*, and *S. aureus*.

In addition, Chen et al. proposed a strategy of using synthetic multidomain peptides (MDPs) as a molecule to construct self-assembled antibacterial nanofibers (self-assembling antimicrobial nanofibers, SAANs) [76]. The cytocompatibility of AMP was improved by attaching natural AMP to nanofiber scaffolds. Melittin (Mel) was selected as the natural AMP model, and Mel was combined with the C-terminal of MDP peptide with sequence HHHQLQLQLQLQLQLQLQLQL to form $(QL)_6$-Mel. The MDP peptide with sequence WKKQLQLQLQLQLQLKK was selected and named as $(QL)_6$-K. $(QL)_6$-Mel and $(QL)_6$-K can be co-assembled into nanofibers with controllable Mel metrology. In the process of self-assembly, the hydrophobic residue of Mel is constrained for embedding into nanofibers, which reduces the hydrophobic interaction between Mel and lipid membrane, which leads to the decrease in Mel permeability of mammalian cell membrane than that of bacterial cell membrane. In subsequent cytotoxicity experiments, compared with free Mel, Mel-integrated SAN showed a significant reduction in cytotoxicity. Both SAANs (Mel-30%) and SAANs (Mel-50%) showed inhibitory effect on *E. coli* while reducing cytotoxicity. This design idea of limiting AMP to supramolecular polymer scaffolds with rigid conformation has an obvious effect on reducing its biological cytotoxicity.

Sha et al. proposed a new antimicrobial peptide design strategy, self-assembly to construct peptide-based nanomaterials to improve its stability, through the disassembly of nanostructures to release antimicrobial peptides to make them play a role (Figure 15.5d) [77]. Two new types of AMPsK3 $(FA)_4K_3$ and $K_6(FA)_4$ were designed in the experiment. Two kinds of AMPs can be self-assembled to form peptide nanofibers under the condition of pH 12. Then, under the condition of pH 7, the two AMP nanofibers were decomposed into $K_3(FA)_4K_3$ and $K_6(FA)_4$ monomers, respectively, to exert antibacterial activity. After the two kinds of AMPs are decomposed into monomers, they will destroy the bacterial membrane and induce calcium efflux to exert antibacterial activity. Two kinds of AMP fibrils have long-term antibacterial properties. After three rounds of bacterial injection culture, AMP fibrils still show excellent antibacterial properties. In addition, $K_3(FA)_4K_3$ and $K_6(FA)_4$ fibers were added to the Agar membrane to obtain AMP–Agar hybrid film. AMP–Agar hybrid film has excellent antibacterial activity against *E. coli* and low hemolysis rate, indicating that the hybrid membrane has good biocompatibility.

15.4.7 Energy Materials

15.4.7.1 Optoelectronic Materials

Because some self-assembled peptide nanomaterials have certain photosensitivity and electrical activity, they also have great advantages in the process of light capture and electron transfer, showing great potential application in optoelectronic.

As shown in Figure 15.6a, Liu et al. reported the voltage-regulated photoconductive and reverse photoconductive ring tyrosine–tyrosine (cyclo-YY) self-assembled nanofibers and further demonstrated the voltage-regulated persistent negative photoconductive (PNPC) and transient positive photoconductive (TPPC) behaviors obtained in the nanofibers [78]. The peptide nanofibers were cyclically heated, and the resistance was observed to increase sharply with the increase in temperature. When the temperature increases from 25 °C to 110 °C, the resistance of cyclo-YY nanofibers increases by 10,000 times. Benefiting from the synergistic effect of TPPC

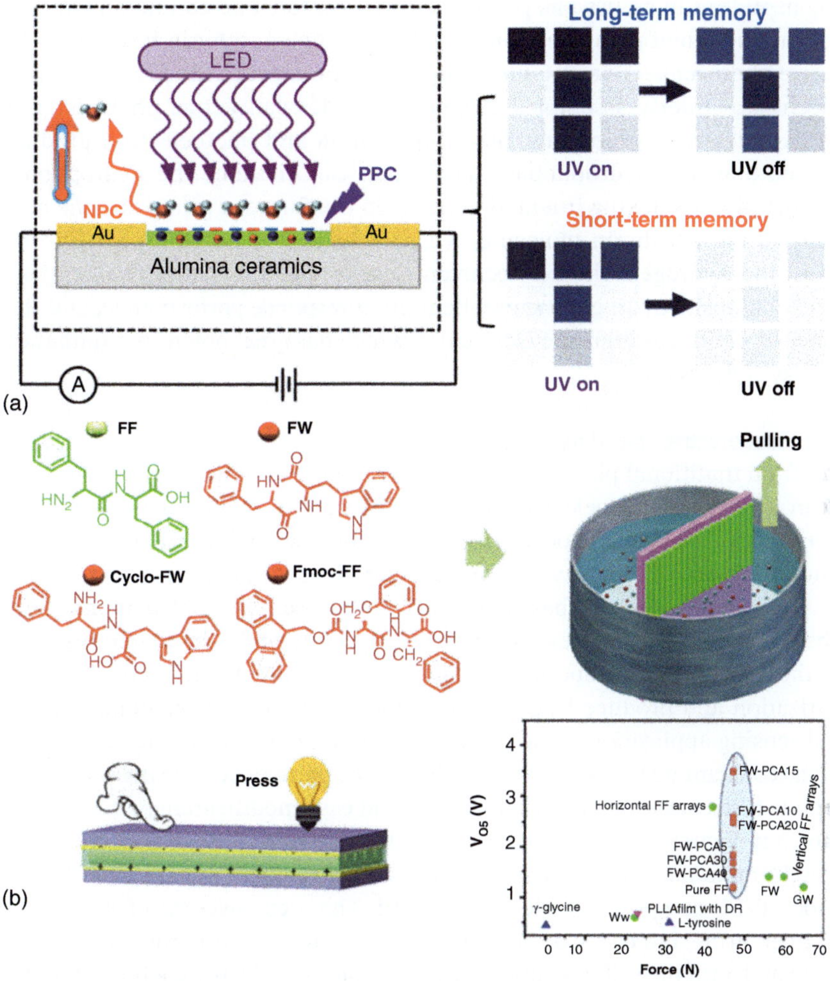

Figure 15.6 (a) The electrodes based on peptide nanomaterials with continuous PNPC and TPPC can be observed under ultraviolet light. Source: Ref. [78]. Copyright American Chemical Society 2020. (b) Self-assembly and piezoelectric diagrams of FF peptides and their derived peptides. Source: Ref. [79]. Reproduced with permission of American Chemical Society 2022.

and PNPC, peptide nanofibers can switch back and forth through a bias voltage to simulate biosensors in artificial vision and storage devices. Because of the inherent biocompatibility of peptide materials, reversible photoconductive nanofibers have a wide range of applications in the sensing and storage of biological and abiotic interfaces.

In the work of Feng et al., photocapture hybrid hydrogels were prepared by self-assembled aromatic peptides (Fmoc-L_3-OMe) doped with porphyrins, and effective solar-electron energy conversion was achieved [80]. The ordered assembly of aromatic peptides can be used as photoelectron acceptors and conductors to promote the production of photoelectrons by photoantenna porphyrin molecules. As an effective photoconversion antenna, porphyrin can improve the productivity of photoelectrons. Orderly assembled aromatic peptides can act as photoelectron receptors and transfer, promoting charge separation and photoelectron production. In addition, the hydrophobic Fmoc group can enhance the hydrophobic interaction and π–π stacking interaction between the fluorene group and the aromatic ring in the porphyrin molecule, which is helpful for the porphyrin to be trapped in the hydrogel. The photocurrent test results show that the peptide/porphyrin composite hydrogel has excellent photoresponse performance, and the photoelectron yield is as high as 672 nA cm^{-2}, which has great potential to enhance solar energy conversion.

15.4.7.2 Piezoelectric Materials

Different from traditional piezoelectric materials, self-assembled peptide nanomaterials can be used as piezoelectric devices to be used in related nanogenerators *in vivo* because of their high biocompatibility and biodegradability. Hutchison and colleagues proposed an innovative method for thin, flexible, and amorphous organic piezoelectric devices based on oligopeptide self-assembled monolayers [81]. These piezoelectric devices are simple in structure and easy to manufacture because the self-assembly properties of oligopeptides eliminate the need for electrical polarization and produce large voltage responses that are very important for potential sensing applications. The piezoelectric device exhibits a huge piezoelectric voltage constant up to 2 V mN^{-1}. In addition, the piezoelectric devices based on oligopeptide films have high biocompatibility and easy modification.

As shown in Figure 15.6b, Yang et al. found that different ratios of FW, cyclo-FW, and Fmoc-FF monomers were added to FF solution to assemble FW/FF, cyclo-FW/FF, and Fmoc-FF/FF complex peptide crystals [79]. The area coverage of horizontal FW/FF fiber array increases at first and then decreases with the increase in FW. Compared with the self-assembled FF alone, the piezoelectric coefficient of the co-assembled peptides of FF and FW increased by 38%, and the open-circuit voltage output of the resulting collection device increased nearly three times. The effective piezoelectric coefficient of the co-assembled peptide array along the vertical direction is significantly improved, and the 15% FW-based nanogenerator produces the highest output.

15.4.8 Environmental Science Applications

15.4.8.1 Absorption of Pollutants

Peptide nanofibers and hydrogels have high adsorption capacity for pollutants because of their physical and chemical interactions. Brar et al. studied the self-assembled morphology of dipeptides in different solvents [82]. Using the self-assembled fibril network of dipeptide Fmoc-L-Phe-L-Trp-OMe (Fmoc-FW-OMe) to specifically adsorb cationic dyes, the adsorption of different cationic dyes was explored. The results showed that the hydrogel network composed of peptide nanofibers can easily adsorb and trap small molecular cationic dyes such as methylene blue (MB) and crystal violet (CV) within the fibrils. This recyclable peptide hydrogel has excellent biocompatibility and has great application potential in environmental remediation.

Chen et al. developed a green and sustainable graphene oxide/peptide nanofiber/cellulose nanofiber (GO/PNF/CNF) membrane for fluorine removal in water [83]. The EDC/NHS-functionalized GO nanosheets were connected with cellulose nanofibers and self-assembled peptide nanofibers through amide bonds; $ZrOCl_8 \cdot H_2O$ was added as a precursor; and ZrO_2 was biomimetically mineralized on GO nanosheets by adjusting the pH. The hydrogen bond interaction between GO and CNF can effectively enhance the mechanical properties of the film, so that it can maintain its original shape in water and is easy to recover after filtration. The added Zr^{4+} can bind to the carboxyl group of GO/PNF/CNF nanohybrids through electrostatic interaction and generate ZrO_2 nanoparticles under the adjustment of pH. After testing, when the concentration of F^- is lower than 200 mg L^{-1}, the fluorine-removal efficiency of the nanohybrid membrane can reach 96–99%, and its adsorption capacity can reach 11.63 mg/g.

As shown in Figure 15.7a, Yang et al. utilized self-assembled peptide nanofibers as templates for biomimetic mineralization of hydroxyapatite (HA) and introduced GO as a carrier and polyvinyl alcohol (PVA) as a cross-linking agent [84]. The YWYAF sequence has many benzene rings, which can be connected with GO nanosheets through π–π conjugation, while a large number of hydroxyl groups on PVA can be connected with GO and PNF through hydrogen bonds to form a stable 3D structure. The freeze-dried PVA/PNF/GO hybrid aerogel was soaked in SBF solution, and the carboxyl group on PNF would act as the nucleation site of HA, continuously attracting Ca^{2+} to aggregate and grow. Finally, flower-like nanospheres with a size of about 2 μm were formed after 5 days. This nanohybrid aerogel with HA has a strong adsorption capacity for MB. In addition, the adsorption capacity of the metal ion Pb^{2+} has been greatly improved. When the Pb^{2+} is 400 mg/L, the saturated adsorption capacity of the hybrid aerogel can reach 113.88 mg/g.

In another case, Yang et al. reported a self-assembled microporous peptide-polysaccharide aerogel with excellent oil–water separation ability [86]. The lipophilic peptide nanofibers formed by the self-assembly of diphenylalanine peptide (Fmoc-FF) were co-assembled with the hydrophilic polysaccharide konjac glucomannan (KGM) to form a hydrogel. The aerogel with microporous structure is finally obtained by freeze-drying. The pore structure of the aerogel can be adjusted by changing the ratio of Fmoc-FF and KGM. This aerogel has both the lipophilicity of peptide and the hydrophilicity of KGM, so it can absorb oil from water to achieve the effect of oil–water separation.

15.4.8.2 Photocatalytic Degradation of Pollutants

The D-A structure composed of peptides and other materials is a promising organic semiconductor with potential application in photocatalytic degradation of pollutants. Tong et al. developed a simple ionic self-assembly method and synthesized a hybrid submicron sphere composed of Weakley-type polyoxometalates $Na_9[EuW_{10}O_{36}] \cdot 32H_2O$(EuW10) and cationic peptides (K8) [87]. The side-chain

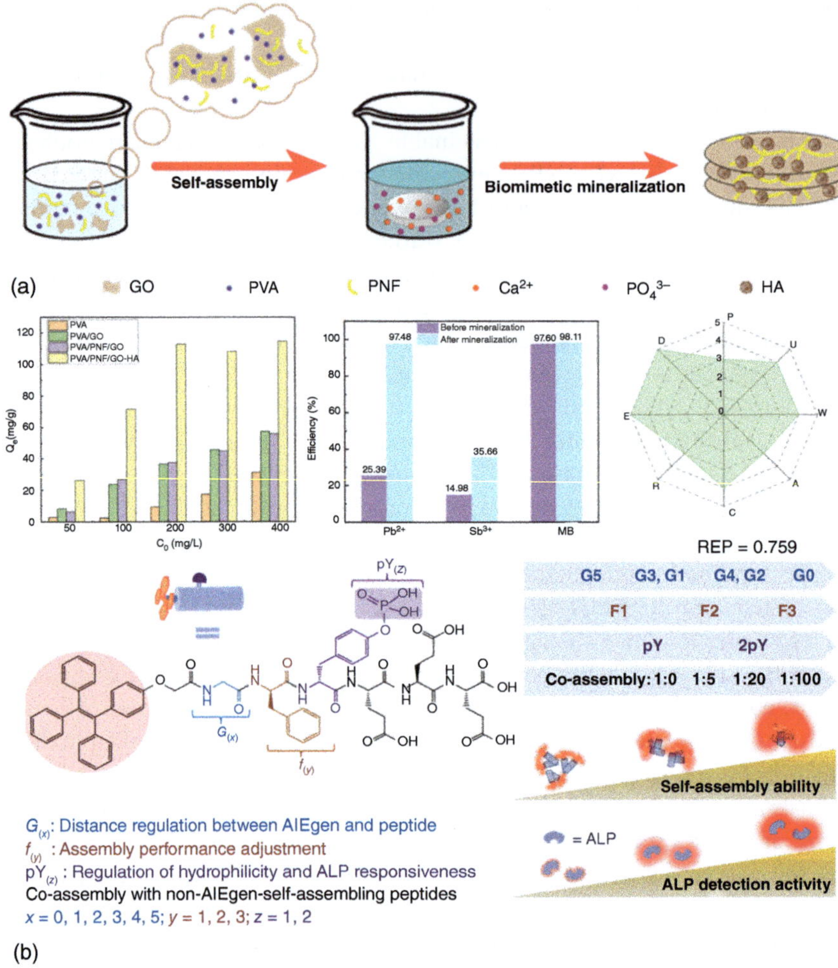

Figure 15.7 (a) Schematic diagram of synthesis and adsorption of pollutants of PVA/PNF/GO-HA hybrid aerogels. Source: Ref. [84]. Copyright Royal Society of Chemistry 2022. (b) Molecular structures of the AIEgen–peptides and the correlation between the structure and the ability of detecting ALP. Source: Ref. [85]. Reproduced with permission of American Chemical Society 2022.

amino group of the K8 peptide can form hydrogen bonds with the oxygen atoms between EuW10, combined with electrostatic interactions, and further form the nanostructure of submicron spheres. Due to the effect of the noncovalent interaction between K8 and EuW10, this submicron sphere can expose the photocatalytic active facet, and EuW10 can act as an electron acceptor to accept electrons from K8. In addition, W—O can also act as an active material to attract H_2O_2 to the surface of the catalyst for catalytic degradation. Therefore, this K8/EuW10 hybrid submicron sphere can be used as an excellent photocatalyst for the degradation of organic dyes in wastewater.

In the work of Li et al., a series of peptide-based enzyme mimics were designed inspired by the "catalytic triad" in serine proteases [88]. Enzyme mimics are artificial biocatalysts with the advantages of good stability, low cost, and high efficiency, while self-assembling peptides can be used as enzyme mimics with excellent performance. The activity of peptide-based enzyme mimics is mainly affected by rational design principles such as the hydrophobic backbone of the peptide, amino-acid sequence, species, and periodic distribution. The peptide sequence designed to simulate the active site of the catalytic center amino acid of serine protease is self-assembled and synthesized as an enzyme mimic, which has a good catalytic degradation effect on di(2-ethylhexyl) phthalate DEHP. Therefore, self-assembling peptide-based enzyme mimics are expected to be put into use as a promising detoxification biomaterial in the future.

15.4.8.3 Detection of Pollutants

Electrochemical sensing technology has been used as a variety of detection applications due to its high sensitivity, low cost, and portability. Among them, self-assembled peptide nanostructures can be used as electrochemical sensors because they have more active sites.

For example, Yang et al. developed a self-assembling peptide-based metalloenzyme mimic for the detection of organophosphorus pesticides in the environment [89]. The metal active site on the self-assembled peptide is combined with Zn^{2+}. On the one hand, Zn^{2+} can polarize the P=O bond of paraoxon and increase the electrophilicity of the phosphorus center. On the other hand, the hydrolyzed molecules can be activated by Zn^{2+} and initiate a nucleophilic attack on paraoxon, and finally, the negative charge of the leaving group of the broken P—O bond can be neutralized by Zn^{2+}. After testing, this Zn^{2+}-binding peptide can effectively detect OP quantitatively, and the detection limit can reach 0.08 μM. Bolat et al. designed a method to synthesize peptide nanotubes (PNTs) on modified pencil graphite electrodes (PGEs), and adsorbed two-dimensional peptide nanotubes self-assembled by diphenylalanine peptides on pencil graphite electrodes [90]. The average diameter of the tubes is approximately 50 nm, which increases the overall surface area. This graphite electrode deposited with peptide nanotubes has a good detection effect on organophosphorus pesticide fenitrothion pesticide.

Aggregation-induced emission luminogens (AIEgens) are widely used in biological tracer, detection, and imaging because of their good light stability and sensitivity [91]. At the same time, AIEgen can turn on fluorescence after aggregation or assembly, which makes them become ideal luminescent molecules for the construction of supramolecular peptide nanoprobes [92]. However, the highly distorted or helical molecular conformation of AIEgen often hinders the assembly of AIEgen–peptides. In order to develop highly efficient self-assembled AIEgen–peptide, Zhang et al. studied the effect of peptide sequence on the detection activity of alkaline phosphatase (ALP) of AIEgen–peptide conjugates (Figure 15.7b) [85]. By increasing the number of enzyme reaction sites or the hydrophilicity of the probe precursor molecule, maintaining an appropriate distance between the AIEgen–peptide and maintaining a certain conformation, the ability of the probe to assemble and detect ALP can be enhanced.

15.5 Conclusions

In summary, the chapter introduced and discussed in detail the progress in structural control, functional regulation, and various applications of self-assembled peptide materials. Based on the above introduction, it can be concluded that the sequence design of peptide molecules is the basis of the structure and function construction of self-assembled peptide nanomaterials. To some extent, external stimulation conditions change the function of peptide nanomaterials by promoting the transformation of structure. Not limited to the functional regulation caused by the structural change of peptide nanomaterials, other functional nanomaterials, such as metal NPs, 2D nanomaterials, and polymers, can also increase or promote their functions by doping or cross-linking. Finally, the carefully designed and functionally regulated peptide nanomaterials have enhanced applications in the fields of biosensor, bioimaging, phototherapy, drug delivery, tissue engineering, antibacterial, and energy and environmental science.

Here, we put forward some views and prospects for the future development of self-assembled peptide nanomaterials. First of all, we should explore and discover natural biological peptides and explore their unique physical and chemical properties and self-assembly morphology and behavior. It inspires the sequence design and self-assembly synthesis of synthetic peptide nanomaterials. Secondly, computer simulation technology should be effectively used to study the driving force and unique mechanism of peptide self-assembly and further guide the optimal design of peptide sequences and the synthesis of peptide nanomaterials with specific functions. Third, the development of supramolecular nanomaterials combining peptides with fluorescent molecules and drugs and exploring their self-assembly and decomposition *in vivo* can promote their application in biological imaging and disease treatment. Finally, the improvement in the electrochemical properties and stability of peptide nanomaterials with unique structure and function will help to further expand their potential applications in the field of energy and environmental science.

Acknowledgments

The author thanks the financial support from the National Natural Science Foundation of China (No. 51873225), the Taishan Scholars Program of Shandong Province (No. tsqn201909104), and the High-Grade Talents Plan of Qingdao University.

References

1 Cao, X.H., Gao, A.P., Hou, J.T., and Yi, T. (2021). Fluorescent supramolecular self-assembly gels and their application as sensors: a review. *Coord. Chem. Rev.* 434: 213792.

2 Yao, Q.X., Huang, Z.T., Liu, D.D. et al. (2019). Enzyme-instructed supramolecular self-assembly with anticancer activity. *Adv. Mater.* 31 (45): 1804814.
3 Levin, A., Hakala, T.A., Schnaider, L. et al. (2020). Biomimetic peptide self-assembly for functional materials. *Nat. Rev. Chem.* 4 (11): 615–634.
4 Tao, K., Levin, A., Adler-Abramovich, L., and Gazit, E. (2016). Fmoc-modified amino acids and short peptides: simple bio-inspired building blocks for the fabrication of functional materials. *Chem. Soc. Rev.* 45 (14): 3935–3953.
5 Razak, M.A., Begum, P.S., Viswanath, B., and Rajagopal, S. (2017). Multifarious beneficial effect of nonessential amino acid, glycine: a review. *Oxid. Med. Cell. Longev.* 2017: 1716701.
6 Knowles, T.P.J., Vendruscolo, M., and Dobson, C.M. (2014). The amyloid state and its association with protein misfolding diseases. *Nat. Rev. Mol. Cell Biol.* 15 (6): 384–396.
7 Mendes, A.C., Baran, E.T., Reis, R.L., and Azevedo, H.S. (2013). Self-assembly in nature: using the principles of nature to create complex nanobiomaterials. *WIREs Nanomed. Nanobiotechnol.* 5 (6): 582–612.
8 Versluis, F., Marsden, H.R., and Kros, A. (2010). Power struggles in peptide-amphiphile nanostructures. *Chem. Soc. Rev.* 39 (9): 3434–3444.
9 Wang, L., Gong, C.C., Yuan, X.Z., and Wei, G. (2019). Controlling the self-assembly of biomolecules into functional nanomaterials through internal interactions and external stimulations: a review. *Nanomaterials* 9 (2): 285.
10 Sinha, N.J., Langenstein, M.G., Pochan, D.J. et al. (2021). Peptide design and self-assembly into targeted nanostructure and functional materials. *Chem. Rev.* 121 (22): 13915–13935.
11 Hu, X.Z., Liao, M.R., Gong, H.N. et al. (2020). Recent advances in short peptide self-assembly: from rational design to novel applications. *Curr. Opin. Colloid Interface Sci.* 45: 1–13.
12 Delfi, M., Sartorius, R., Ashrafizadeh, M. et al. (2021). Self-assembled peptide and protein nanostructures for anti-cancer therapy: targeted delivery, stimuli-responsive devices and immunotherapy. *Nano Today* 38: 101119.
13 Xing, P.Y. and Zhao, Y.L. (2016). Multifunctional nanoparticles self-assembled from small organic building blocks for biomedicine. *Adv. Mater.* 28 (34): 7304–7339.
14 Puiu, M. and Bala, C. (2018). Peptide-based biosensors: from self-assembled interfaces to molecular probes in electrochemical assays. *Bioelectrochemistry* 120: 66–75.
15 Zhang, W.S., Yu, X.Q., Li, Y. et al. (2018). Protein-mimetic peptide nanofibers: motif design, self-assembly synthesis, and sequence-specific biomedical applications. *Prog. Polym. Sci.* 80: 94–124.
16 Luan, X., Kong, H., He, P. et al. (2023). Self-assembled peptide-based nanodrugs: molecular design, synthesis, functionalization, and targeted tumor bioimaging and biotherapy. *Small* 19 (3): 2205787.
17 Wei, G., Su, Z.Q., Reynolds, N.P. et al. (2017). Self-assembling peptide and protein amyloids: from structure to tailored function in nanotechnology. *Chem. Soc. Rev.* 46 (15): 4661–4708.

18 Jiang, X.L., Fan, X.B., Xu, W. et al. (2019). Self-assembled peptide nanoparticles responsive to multiple tumor microenvironment triggers provide highly efficient targeted delivery and release of antitumor drug. *J. Control. Release* 316: 196–207.

19 Du, Z.Y., Li, Q., Li, J.G. et al. (2019). Self-assembled egg yolk peptide micellar nanoparticles as a versatile emulsifier for food-grade oil-in-water pickering nanoemulsions. *J. Agric. Food Chem.* 67 (42): 11728–11740.

20 Morris, C., Glennie, S.J., Lam, H.S. et al. (2019). A modular vaccine platform combining self-assembled peptide cages and immunogenic peptides. *Adv. Funct. Mater.* 29 (8): 1807357.

21 Sun, B.B., Chang, R., Cao, S.P. et al. (2020). Acid-activatable transmorphic peptide-based nanomaterials for photodynamic therapy. *Angew. Chem. Int. Ed.* 59 (46): 20582–20588.

22 Mora-Solano, C., Wen, Y., Han, H. et al. (2017). Active immunotherapy for TNF-mediated inflammation using self-assembled peptide nanofibers. *Biomaterials* 149: 1–11.

23 Demircan, M.B., Tohumeken, S., Gunduz, N. et al. (2020). Biotin functionalized self-assembled peptide nanofiber as an adjuvant for immunomodulatory response. *Biotechnol. J.* 15 (12): 2000100.

24 Tang, Y., Wu, Z., Zhang, C.H. et al. (2016). Enzymatic activatable self-assembled peptide nanowire for targeted therapy and fluorescence imaging of tumors. *Chem. Commun.* 52 (18): 3631–3634.

25 Khanra, S., Abdullah-Al Mamun, M., Ferreira, F.F. et al. (2018). Functionalized self-assembled peptide nanotubes with cobalt ferrite nanoparticles for applications in organic electronics. *ACS Appl. Nano Mater.* 1 (3): 1175–1187.

26 Lin, Y.Y., Penna, M., Thomas, M.R. et al. (2019). Residue-specific solvation-directed thermodynamic and kinetic control over peptide self-assembly with 1D/2D structure selection. *ACS Nano* 13 (2): 1900–1909.

27 Dai, B., Li, D., Xi, W.H. et al. (2015). Tunable assembly of amyloid-forming peptides into nanosheets as a retrovirus carrier. *Proc. Natl. Acad. Sci. U. S. A.* 112 (10): 2996–3001.

28 Lee, J., Choe, I.R., Kim, Y.-O. et al. (2017). Proton conduction in a tyrosine-rich peptide/manganese oxide hybrid nanofilm. *Adv. Funct. Mater.* 27 (35): 1702185.

29 Chen, J.J., Zhu, E.B., Liu, J. et al. (2018). Building two-dimensional materials one row at a time: avoiding the nucleation barrier. *Science* 362 (6419): 1135–1139.

30 Smith, D.J., Brat, G.A., Medina, S.H. et al. (2016). A multiphase transitioning peptide hydrogel for suturing ultrasmall vessels. *Nat. Nanotechnol.* 11 (1): 95–102.

31 Jin, H.L., Wan, C., Zou, Z.W. et al. (2018). Tumor ablation and therapeutic immunity induction by an injectable peptide hydrogel. *ACS Nano* 12 (4): 3295–3310.

32 Gao, J., Tang, C., Elsawy, M.A. et al. (2017). Controlling self-assembling peptide hydrogel properties through network topology. *Biomacromolecules* 18 (3): 826–834.

33 Balfourier, A., Kolosnjaj-Tabi, J., Luciani, N. et al. (2020). Gold-based therapy: from past to present. *Proc. Natl. Acad. Sci. U. S. A.* 117 (37): 22639–22648.

34 Lin, Y., Thomas, M.R., Gelmi, A. et al. (2017). Self-assembled 2D free-standing Janus nanosheets with single-layer thickness. *J. Am. Chem. Soc.* 139 (39): 13592–13595.

35 Garifullin, R., Eren, H., Ulusoy, T.G. et al. (2016). Self-assembled peptide nanofiber templated ALD growth of TiO_2 and ZnO semiconductor nanonetworks. *Phys. Status Solidi A* 213 (12): 3238–3244.

36 Tian, Y., Zhang, H.V., Kiick, K.L. et al. (2018). Fabrication of one- and two-dimensional gold nanoparticle arrays on computationally designed self-assembled peptide templates. *Chem. Mater.* 30 (23): 8510–8520.

37 Sun, L.H., Li, P.Y., Seki, T. et al. (2021). Chiral recognition of self-assembled peptides on MoS_2 via lattice matching. *Langmuir* 37 (29): 8696–8704.

38 Khanra, S., Cipriano, T., Lam, T. et al. (2015). Self-assembled peptide–polyfluorene nanocomposites for biodegradable organic electronics. *Adv. Mater. Interfaces* 2 (14): 1500265.

39 Luo, J., Cheng, Y., Gong, Z.W. et al. (2020). Self-assembled peptide functionalized gold nanopolyhedrons with excellent chiral optical properties. *Langmuir* 36 (2): 600–608.

40 Hou, X.L., Dai, X., Yang, J. et al. (2020). Injectable polypeptide-engineered hydrogel depot for amplifying the anti-tumor immune effect induced by chemo-photothermal therapy. *J. Mater. Chem. B* 8 (37): 8623–8633.

41 Martin, C., Kostarelos, K., Prato, M., and Bianco, A. (2019). Biocompatibility and biodegradability of 2D materials: graphene and beyond. *Chem. Commun.* 55 (39): 5540–5546.

42 Kostarelos, K. (2016). Translating graphene and 2D materials into medicine. *Nat. Rev. Mater.* 1 (11): 16084.

43 Molaei, M.J. (2021). Two-dimensional (2D) materials beyond graphene in cancer drug delivery, photothermal and photodynamic therapy, recent advances and challenges ahead: a review. *J. Drug Deliv. Sci. Technol.* 61: 101830.

44 Wu, Y.J., Wang, F., Lu, K. et al. (2017). Self-assembled dipeptide-graphene nanostructures onto an electrode surface for highly sensitive amperometric hydrogen peroxide biosensors. *Sens. Actuat. B Chem.* 244: 1022–1030.

45 Ko, J.W., Choi, W.S., Kim, J. et al. (2017). Self-assembled peptide-carbon nitride hydrogel as a light-responsive scaffold material. *Biomacromolecules* 18 (11): 3551–3556.

46 Wang, S.G., Zeng, P., Zhu, X.H. et al. (2020). Chimeric peptides self-assembling on titanium carbide MXenes as biosensing interfaces for activity assay of post-translational modification enzymes. *Anal. Chem.* 92 (13): 8819–8826.

47 Li, H.N., Sun, J.Y., Zhu, H.Y. et al. (2021). Recent advances in development of dendritic polymer-based nanomedicines for cancer diagnosis. *WIREs Nanomed. Nanobiotechnol.* 13 (2): e1670.

48 Zhang, R.X., Ahmed, T., Li, L.Y. et al. (2017). Design of nanocarriers for nanoscale drug delivery to enhance cancer treatment using hybrid polymer and lipid building blocks. *Nanoscale* 9 (4): 1334–1355.

49 Lian, M.L., Chen, X., Liu, X.J. et al. (2017). A self-assembled peptide nanotube–chitosan composite as a novel platform for electrochemical cytosensing. *Sens. Actuat. B Chem.* 251: 86–92.

50 Liberato, M.S., Kogikoski, S., da Silva, E.R. et al. (2016). Polycaprolactone fibers with self-assembled peptide micro/nanotubes: a practical route towards enhanced mechanical strength and drug delivery applications. *J. Mater. Chem. B* 4 (8): 1405–1413.

51 Cui, M., Wang, Y., Wang, H.P. et al. (2017). A label-free electrochemical DNA biosensor for breast cancer marker BRCA1 based on self-assembled antifouling peptide monolayer. *Sens. Actuat. B Chem.* 244: 742–749.

52 Wang, Y., Cui, M., Jiao, M.X., and Luo, X.L. (2018). Antifouling and ultrasensitive biosensing interface based on self-assembled peptide and aptamer on macroporous gold for electrochemical detection of immunoglobulin E in serum. *Anal. Bioanal. Chem.* 410 (23): 5871–5878.

53 Qian, H.S., Huang, Y., Duan, X.L. et al. (2019). Fiber optic surface plasmon resonance biosensor for detection of PDGF-BB in serum based on self-assembled aptamer and antifouling peptide monolayer. *Biosens Bioelectron.* 140: 111350.

54 Lian, M.L., Chen, X., Lu, Y.L., and Yang, W.S. (2016). Self-assembled peptide hydrogel as a smart biointerface for enzyme-based electrochemical biosensing and cell monitoring. *ACS Appl. Mater. Interfaces* 8 (38): 25036–25042.

55 Qi, G.B., Gao, Y.J., Wang, L., and Wang, H. (2018). Self-assembled peptide-based nanomaterials for biomedical imaging and therapy. *Adv. Mater.* 30 (22): 1703444.

56 Zhao, X.X., Li, L.L., Zhao, Y. et al. (2019). In situ self-assembled nanofibers precisely target cancer-associated fibroblasts for improved tumor imaging. *Angew. Chem. Int. Ed.* 58 (43): 15287–15294.

57 Liu, N., Wu, S.J., Tian, X., and Li, X.M. (2022). Fabrication of injectable hydrogels from an anticancer peptide for local therapeutic delivery and synergistic photothermal–chemotherapy. *J. Mater. Chem. B* 10 (27): 5165–5173.

58 Yan, J., He, W.X., Yan, S. et al. (2018). Self-assembled peptide–lanthanide nanoclusters for safe tumor therapy: overcoming and utilizing biological barriers to peptide drug delivery. *ACS Nano* 12 (2): 2017–2026.

59 Feng, T.Q., Wu, H.Y., Ma, W.D. et al. (2022). An injectable thermosensitive hydrogel with a self-assembled peptide coupled with an antimicrobial peptide for enhanced wound healing. *J. Mater. Chem. B* 10 (32): 6143–6157.

60 Abbas, M., Zou, Q.L., Li, S.K., and Yan, X.H. (2017). Self-assembled peptide- and protein-based nanomaterials for antitumor photodynamic and photothermal therapy. *Adv. Mater.* 29 (12): 1605021.

61 Pigliacelli, C., Sanchez-Fernandez, R., Garcia, M.D. et al. (2020). Self-assembled peptide-inorganic nanoparticle superstructures: from component design to applications. *Chem. Commun.* 56 (58): 8000–8014.

62 Ren, C.H., Wang, Z.Y., Wang, Q. et al. (2020). Self-assembled peptide-based nanoprobes for disease theranostics and disease-related molecular imaging. *Small Methods.* 4 (4): 1900403.

63 Chen, S., Liu, Y.Z., Liang, R. et al. (2021). Self-assembly of amphiphilic peptides to construct activatable nanophotosensitizers for theranostic photodynamic therapy. *Chin. Chem. Lett.* 32 (12): 3903–3906.

64 Chen, P.L., Huang, P.Y., Chen, J.Y. et al. (2022). A self-delivery chimeric peptide for high efficient cell membrane-targeting low-temperature photothermal/photodynamic combinational therapy and metastasis suppression of tumor. *Biomaterials* 286: 121593.

65 Habibi, N., Kamaly, N., Memic, A., and Shafiee, H. (2016). Self-assembled peptide-based nanostructures: smart nanomaterials toward targeted drug delivery. *Nano Today* 11 (1): 41–60.

66 Raza, F., Zhu, Y., Chen, L. et al. (2019). Paclitaxel-loaded pH responsive hydrogel based on self-assembled peptides for tumor targeting. *Biomater. Sci.* 7 (5): 2023–2036.

67 Fu, D.J., Liu, D.C., Zhang, L.B., and Sun, L.M. (2020). Self-assembled fluorescent tripeptide nanoparticles for bioimaging and drug delivery applications. *Chin. Chem. Lett.* 31 (12): 3195–3199.

68 Fan, R.R., Mei, L., Gao, X. et al. (2017). Self-assembled bifunctional peptide as effective drug delivery vector with powerful antitumor activity. *Adv. Sci.* 4 (4): 1600285.

69 Shafiee, A. and Atala, A. (2017). Tissue engineering: toward a new era of medicine. *Annu. Rev. Med.* 68: 29–40.

70 Ribeiro, S., Radvar, E., Shi, Y. et al. (2017). Nanostructured interfacial self-assembled peptide–polymer membranes for enhanced mineralization and cell adhesion. *Nanoscale.* 9 (36): 13670–13682.

71 Li, K.H., Zhang, Z.F., Li, D.P. et al. (2018). Biomimetic ultralight, highly porous, shape-adjustable, and biocompatible 3D graphene minerals via incorporation of self-assembled peptide nanosheets. *Adv. Funct. Mater.* 28 (29): 1801056.

72 Deidda, G., Jonnalagadda, S.V.R., Spies, J.W. et al. (2017). Self-assembled amyloid peptides with Arg-Gly-Asp (RGD) motifs as scaffolds for tissue engineering. *ACS Biomater. Sci. Eng.* 3 (7): 1404–1416.

73 Tran, K.A., Partyka, P.P., Jin, Y. et al. (2020). Vascularization of self-assembled peptide scaffolds for spinal cord injury repair. *Acta Biomater.* 104: 76–84.

74 Yan, Y.H., Li, Y.Z., Zhang, Z.W. et al. (2021). Advances of peptides for antibacterial applications. *Colloids Surf. B Biointerfaces* 202: 111682.

75 Malhotra, K., Shankar, S., Rai, R., and Singh, Y. (2018). Broad-spectrum antibacterial activity of proteolytically stable self-assembled αγ-hybrid peptide gels. *Biomacromolecules* 19 (3): 782–792.

76 Chen, W.K., Yang, S., Li, S.X. et al. (2019). Self-assembled peptide nanofibers display natural antimicrobial peptides to selectively kill bacteria without compromising cytocompatibility. *ACS Appl. Mater. Interfaces* 11 (32): 28681–28689.

77 Sha, X.Y., Li, P., Feng, Y.H. et al. (2020). Self-assembled peptide nanofibrils designed to release membrane-lysing antimicrobial peptides. *ACS Appl. Bio Mater.* 3 (6): 3648–3655.

78 Shi, H.Y., Li, M.L., Shi, J.L. et al. (2021). Self-assembled peptide nanofibers with voltage-regulated inverse photoconductance. *ACS Appl. Mater. Interfaces* 13 (1): 1057–1064.

79 Yuan, H., Han, P.P., Tao, Z. et al. (2022). Peptide coassembly to enhance piezoelectricity for energy harvesting. *ACS Appl. Mater. Interfaces* 14 (5): 6538–6546.

80 Feng, L., Wang, A.H., Ren, P. et al. (2018). Self-assembled peptide hydrogel with porphyrin as a dopant for enhanced photocurrent generation. *Colloid Interface Sci. Commun.* 23: 29–33.

81 Petroff, C.A., Cassone, G., Šponer, J., and Hutchison, G.R. (2021). Intrinsically polar piezoelectric self-assembled oligopeptide monolayers. *Adv. Mater.* 33 (17): 2007486.

82 Brar, S.K., Wangoo, N., and Sharma, R.K. (2020). Enhanced and selective adsorption of cationic dyes using novel biocompatible self-assembled peptide fibrils. *J. Environ. Manage.* 255: 109804.

83 Chen, Y., Yang, G.Z., Liu, B. et al. (2022). Biomineralization of ZrO2 nanoparticles on graphene oxide-supported peptide/cellulose binary nanofibrous membranes for high-performance removal of fluoride ions. *Chem. Eng. J.* 430: 132721.

84 Yang, G.Z., He, P., Zhu, D.Z. et al. (2022). Functional regulation of polymer aerogels by graphene doping and peptide nanofiber-induced biomineralization as sustainable adsorbents of contaminants. *Environ. Sci.: Nano* 9 (12): 4497–4507.

85 Zhang, L.P., Li, Y., Mu, G.N. et al. (2022). Structure of self-assembled peptide determines the activity of aggregation-induced emission luminogen-peptide conjugate for detecting alkaline phosphatase. *Anal. Chem.* 94 (4): 2236–2243.

86 Yang, X., Xie, Y.Y., Wang, Y.F. et al. (2018). Self-assembled microporous peptide-polysaccharide aerogels for oil–water separation. *Langmuir* 34 (36): 10732–10738.

87 Tong, L., Wang, Z., Xia, C.X. et al. (2017). Self-assembly of peptide-polyoxometalate hybrid sub-micrometer spheres for photocatalytic degradation of methylene blue. *J. Phys. Chem. B* 121 (46): 10566–10573.

88 Li, X., Li, J.P., Hao, S.J. et al. (2020). Enzyme mimics based on self-assembled peptides for di(2-ethylhexyl)phthalate degradation. *J. Mater. Chem. B* 8 (41): 9601–9609.

89 Yang, Y.Y., Hao, S.J., Lei, X.M. et al. (2022). Design of metalloenzyme mimics based on self-assembled peptides for organophosphorus pesticides detection. *J. Hazard. Mater.* 428: 128262.

90 Bolat, G., Abaci, S., Vural, T. et al. (2018). Sensitive electrochemical detection of fenitrothion pesticide based on self-assembled peptide-nanotubes modified disposable pencil graphite electrode. *J. Electroanal. Chem.* 809: 88–95.

91 Shi, Y.Q., Zhu, D.Z., Wang, D.J. et al. (2022). Recent advances of smart AIEgens for photoacoustic imaging and phototherapy. *Coord. Chem. Rev.* 471: 214725.

92 Yan, D.Y., Qin, Y., Yan, S.S. et al. (2023). Near-infrared emissive AIE nanoparticles for biomedical applications: from the perspective of different nanocarriers. *Particuology* 74: 103–118.

16

Piezoelectric Self-assembling Peptides for Engineering Applications

Haoran Wu[1,2], *Sarah Guerin*[3], *Syed A. M. Tofail*[3], *Rusen Yang*[4], *Ehud Gazit*[2,5], *Damien Thompson*[3], *and Kai Tao*[1,2]

[1] *State Key Laboratory of Fluid Power and Mechatronic Systems, Key Laboratory of Advanced Manufacturing Technology of Zhejiang Province, Department of Mechanical Engineering, Zhejiang University, Hangzhou, China*
[2] *Zhejiang-Israel Joint Laboratory of Self-Assembling Functional Materials, Department of Future Science Research, ZJU-Hangzhou Global Scientific & Technological Innovation Center, Zhejiang University, Hangzhou, China*
[3] *Department of Physics, Bernal Institute, University of Limerick, V94 T9PX, Ireland*
[4] *School of Advanced Materials and Nanotechnology, Xidian University, Xi'an, China*
[5] *Department of Biomedicine and Cancer Research, George S. Wise Faculty of Life Sciences, Tel Aviv University, Tel Aviv 6997801, Israel*

16.1 Introduction

Since the discovery of electricity-induced mechanical responses in muscle tissue in the late eighteenth century, the coupling between electrical and mechanical phenomena has been found to be a general feature in biological systems. This observation spurred generations of scientists to study the effects of electrical stimuli on the mechanical functioning of biological tissues, which has led to the foundation of the disciplines of electrophysiology and bioelectrochemistry. Electromechanical response of biological, bioderived, and bioinspired materials is now exploited for diverse applications in sustainability and health, but fundamental questions remain regarding its origin and engineerability for microdevices.

16.1.1 What Is Piezoelectricity?

Piezoelectricity is a typical electromechanical coupling phenomenon. The intrinsic electromechanical processes include piezoelectricity, electrostriction, and flexoelectricity, which are coupling responses related to the crystal symmetry and molecular structures of the materials. By contrast, the extrinsic electromechanical processes, such as electrochemical migrations of charges or ions, and elastic deformations under external or produced electrostatic forces, originate from external factors. Piezoelectricity, electrostriction, and flexoelectricity couple mechanical forces (strain

Peptide Self-Assembly and Engineering: Fundamentals, Structures, and Applications, First Edition. Edited by Xuehai Yan.

and stress) with electrical effects (polarization, electric fields, dielectric displacement, and flux) in different ways [1, 2]. Piezoelectricity is the linear coupling between strains and electric fields, whereas electrostriction is the quadratic coupling between them. Furthermore, the direct piezoelectric effect defines the separation of positive and negative charges on the opposite surfaces to accumulate the electric potentials when a mechanical force is applied to the material. The converse piezoelectric effect describes the mechanical deformation of the substance when an electrical bias is applied (Figure 16.1) [3, 4].

Piezoelectric materials require a noncentrosymmetric arrangement of polar molecules to produce net supramolecular dipole moment. In nonpiezoelectric materials, the components are symmetrically distributed around a central point. Therefore, when applying a force along a particular direction, the molecular dipoles cancel each other, thus leading to no excess separation of positive and negative charges. In noncentrosymmetric materials, the dipolar moments cannot quench each other, and this creates a charge imbalance, thus leading to the charges accumulating on opposite sides of the material to produce electric potentials. In some materials, individual dipole components can form a region or domain of local alignments. When the direction of dipoles across the domains is random, the material has no or weak overall polarization because the polarity of each domain is averaged out by its neighbors. In this case, the net piezoelectricity can be negligible, even though each microscopic domain has a nonzero dipole. The piezoelectric response of a material will be maximum when all domains in the material are aligned in the same direction (Figure 16.1), which is important for device engineering.

The discovery of piezoelectricity can be traced back to 1880 [5–8] (Figure 16.2), when the Curie brothers, aged 21 and 24, demonstrated that when pressure is applied to certain crystals, they generate electrical voltage. They showed that the piezoelectric effect was closely correlated to the crystal structures. Voigt's crystallographic studies in 1910 suggested that 20 noncentrosymmetric crystal classes exhibited direct piezoelectric effects [12], leading eventually to the development of the perovskite barium titanate (BTO) and the lead zirconate titanate (PZT) families of high piezoelectric performances [13–17]. Notably, although the PZT family achieves

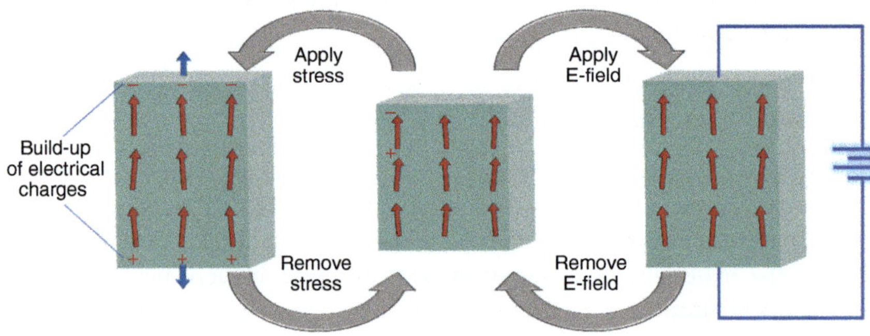

Figure 16.1 Schematic illustration of direct (left) and converse (right) piezoelectric effects. The red and blue arrows represent electric dipoles and the applied mechanical stresses, respectively.

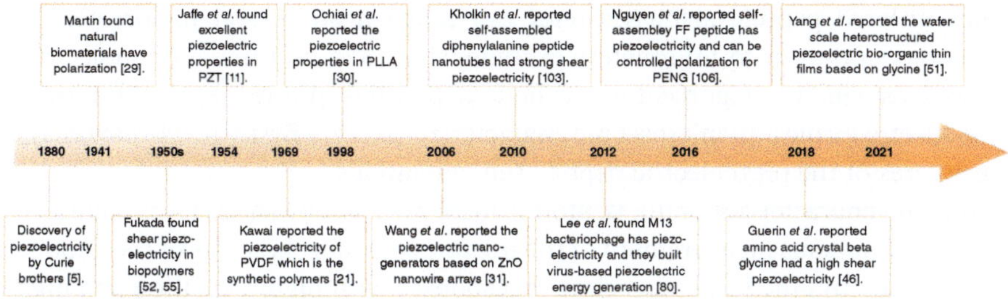

Figure 16.2 A brief roadmap marking the development of piezoelectricity, labeling some of the major milestones including the discovery of piezoelectricity, inorganic piezoelectricity, polymer piezoelectricity, and bioorganic piezoelectricity. Source: Adapted from Refs. [9–11].

outstanding piezoelectricity and dominates the applications of piezoceramics [18], the issue of lead leaching severely limits its widespread utilization, especially in the biological fields [19–21]. On the other hand, the lead-free piezoelectric ceramics suffer small piezoelectric response, inefficient recycling, and low flexibility [22, 23]. By contrast, the discovery of polyvinylidene fluoride (PVDF) was a landmark in the evolution of piezoelectric materials, showing high piezoelectricity, structural flexibility, and more biocompatibility as a supplement to the state-of-the-art inorganic piezoelectrics [24–27]. Extensive studies demonstrated that the piezoelectric PVDF-based polymers and derivatives have promising applications in biomedical fields such as promoting bone growth, cell differentiation, and biological tissue regeneration [28–30]. An unresolved impediment to application is the generation of highly toxic hydrogen fluoride (HF) during PVDF degradation, which hampers utilization in biomedical and biomachine interfaces [31].

Therefore, inspired by the natural piezoelectricity of biological materials, peptides have been attracting increasing interest due to their intrinsic polarity derived from the highly ordered vectored noncovalent assemblies stabilized by hydrogen bonding and aromatic interactions. Peptide materials are inexpensive and have natural biocompatibility and biodegradability and adjustable supramolecular morphologies along with physiochemical properties, mechanical flexibility, and piezoelectricity. They are being explored for wide applications in diverse emerging fields for biomedical and biomechanical interfaces, such as wearable or implantable piezoelectric sensors, flexible actuators, and energy harvesters. Accordingly, studies of piezoelectric peptide self-assemblies have been increasingly reported. Here, we provide a summary of the progress in this field, highlighting converging viewpoints, potential applications, and remaining obstacles to widespread deployment as sustainable, eco-friendly device materials.

16.2 Research Tools for Piezoelectric Self-assembling Peptides

Optimal device fabrication strategies to maximize the piezoelectric properties are directed by the materials morphologies and underlying molecular structures.

Notably, ordered peptide self-assemblies can range from several nanometers to micrometers and even to millimeters in dimension [32], and the supramolecular organizations can be categorized into α-helices, β-sheets, β-turns, etc. [33]. Hence, diverse spectroscopic and microscopic characterizations are firstly needed to obtain the structures of the piezoelectric peptide self-assemblies.

Among the characterization tools, atomic force microscopy (AFM) is unique as it enables simultaneous measurement of the microscopic morphologies of the peptide self-assemblies and the local piezoelectric responses with high resolution and high fidelity. This AFM measurement mode is commonly termed piezoelectric response force microscopy (PFM). PFM can detect the deformation in the subnanometer scale and map the piezoelectric domains with lateral resolution of a few nanometers. Specifically, the PFM operates in contact mode where the cantilever beam is continuously in contact with the peptide supramolecules with a constant force. To apply an electric field, the peptide sample is mounted on a conductive substrate, and the conductive cantilever beam is used as a second electrode (Figure 16.3, bottom panel). The piezoelectric response of the peptide self-assemblies can be recorded, and the corresponding piezoelectric coefficients can be obtained [34, 35].

Once the piezoelectric coefficients are measured, using density functional theory (DFT) calculations and multiphysics finite element models as appropriate to support (see below), one can predict and measure the energy harvesting properties

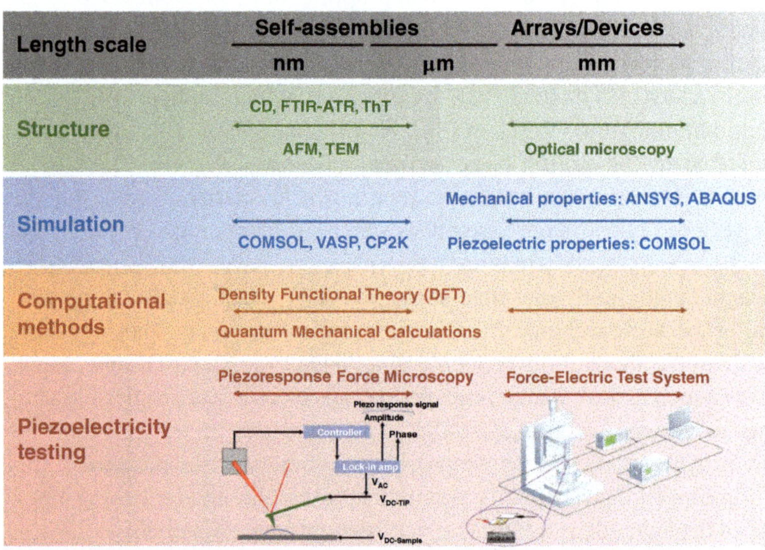

Figure 16.3 Tools for studying piezoelectric self-assembling peptides. The peptides organization process proceeds via self-assembly and oligomerization through to microfabrication steps. Different experimental and computational characterization methodologies are utilized to study the material at various steps. Specifically, for the piezoelectricity study, the theoretical calculations and PFM are used for piezoelectric coefficient investigations of individual peptide self-assemblies, while the force-electric test system is used to measure the piezoelectric properties of the integrated self-assembly arrays.

of the peptide self-assemblies. For example, the open-circuit voltage (V_{oc}) of 0.6 V was measured for a flexible piezoelectric nanogenerator based on FF microrod arrays [36], consistent with the predicted value, thus illustrating the benefit of combined experimental and computational models to explore and optimize the device properties of piezoelectric peptide self-assembles.

It is well known that integration into arrays can help enable the practical applications and industrialization of the peptide self-assemblies [37, 38]. In this regard, the experimental tool for testing the piezoelectric properties of the peptide self-assembled film arrays is the force–electric test system, which uses a linear motor to apply a known load force and characterizes the piezoelectric properties by detecting the generated pulse signal through an electrostatic meter.

The force–electric test system mainly comprises a test module and a signal acquisition module (Figure 16.3, bottom panel). The test module exerts the periodic loading forces on the tested peptide self-assembly arraying films, and the signal acquisition module collects and analyzes the piezoelectric signals (output currents and output voltages). Therefore, with the help of the *quasi*-static method, the piezoelectric coefficient of the peptide arraying films can be accurately measured.

16.3 Piezoelectricity of Peptide Self-assembling Architectures

16.3.1 Amino Acids

Due to the specific molecular structures containing polar amino, carboxyl groups and, in most cases, side-chain moieties connected to α-carbon atoms, amino acids generally self-assemble and crystallize to form supramolecular β-sheets structures, which have intrinsic polarity owing to the vectored hydrogen-bonding interactions. A pioneering study evaluating the piezoelectric responses under high-frequency (~10 MHz) electrical pulses demonstrated that 16 out of the 20 naturally encoded amino acids were found to form piezoelectric crystals at room temperature [39, 40], among which the isoleucine (**I**) crystals showed d_{34} coefficient of 25 pC N^{-1}. In addition, the methionine (**M**) self-assemblies could still show moderate piezoelectricity (15 pC N^{-1}) even at low temperature of 210 K [41]. These findings motivated extensive follow-on studies of amino-acid piezoelectricity.

Furthermore, diverse modulation strategies can be developed to tune the piezoelectric properties of the amino acid-based supramolecules. For example, alanine (**A**), the simplest chiral naturally occurring amino acid [42], self-assembles into plate-like crystals (Figure 16.4a), presenting weak piezoelectricity with the measured d_{25} coefficient of around −3.7 pC N^{-1}. By contrast, when co-assembling the *L*- and *D*-type **A** [43], racemic needle-like orthorhombic crystals were formed, which created a nonzero longitudinal d_{33} coefficient (4.0 pC N^{-1}) together with two transverse ($d_{31} \approx 0.91$ pm V^{-1} and $d_{32} \approx 1.09$ pm V^{-1}) and two shear coefficients ($d_{24} \approx 17.75$ pm V^{-1} and $d_{15} \approx 7.95$ pm V^{-1}), thus showing the promising potentials for piezoelectric applications in diverse emerging devices such as biosensors and actuators.

DFT computations demonstrated that the *DL*-**A** racemic crystals had a strong net dipole in a unit cell due to the parallel arrangement of *L* and *D* isomers (Figure 16.4b),

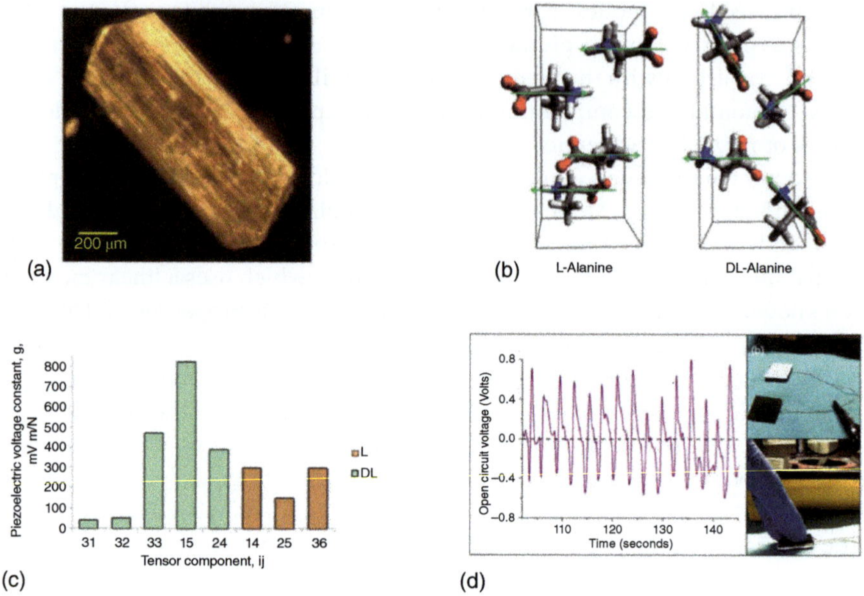

Figure 16.4 Piezoelectricity comparison of *L*-alanine (*L*-**A**) self-assemblies and racemic *DL*-**A** co-assemblies: (a) morphological characterizations of (upper panel) *L*-**A** monoclinic plate-like crystal and (lower panel) needle-like racemic *DL*-**A** cocrystals; (b) molecular dipoles in *L*-**A** single crystals and *DL*-**A** racemic crystals; (c) calculated piezoelectric coefficients for *L*-**A** single crystals and *DL*-**A** racemic crystals; and (d) piezoelectric outputs harvested from *DL*-**A** racemic crystalline films in a power generator operated by simple finger compressions.

compared to the mutually compensating dipoles arising from the antiparallel packing of the monomers in the single-enantiomer self-assemblies [44]. Specifically, the piezoelectric coefficients of the *DL*-**A** racemic crystals were calculated to be −1.09 to 17.75 pm V^{-1}, with the longitudinal (d_{33}) coefficient of 10.34 pm V^{-1} (Figure 16.4c), consistent with the experimental result of 9.1 pC N^{-1}. Therefore, upon compacting the racemic crystals, a bioorganic piezoelectric film could be fabricated, showing an average d_{33} constant of 4.0 pC N^{-1} with the maximal response and output of 4.8 pC N^{-1} and 0.8 V (Figure 16.4d).

The piezoelectric properties of bioorganic amino-acid crystals are generally modest and rarely >10 pC N^{-1}, with the notable exception of β-glycine described below, and the growth mechanism must be controlled to achieve efficient electromechanical coupling. To maximize the piezoelectric response, ordered amino-acid array structures are grown by physical vapor deposition (PVD) based on the Stranski–Krastanov (S-K) growth model. By varying the substrate temperature, chamber pressure, and source–substrate distance, the growth of vertical sheet arrays of valine (**V**), leucine (**L**), and **I** can be tuned to a uniform, controlled "layer-plus-sheet" morphology [45]. The vertically grown sheet array structure can substantially enhance the piezoelectric properties, and the maximum effective piezoelectric constant of the **V** sheet is 11.4 pm V^{-1}, which is close to the predicted maximum value. Crucially, the output voltage of the valine array nanogenerator is about 4.6 times higher than that of the **V** powder nanogenerator. Therefore, the strategy of using PVD-integrated arrays can amplify the piezoelectric properties of bioorganic materials such as amino acids, effectively improving the electromechanical coupling efficiency and enhancing their usefulness in bioorganic piezoelectric devices.

Notably, in addition to the naturally encoded (α-type) amino acids, other isomers may also self-assemble into superstructures with much larger polarity. For example, glycine (**G**), the minimalist amino acid, can self-assemble into three polymorphic forms, namely α-, β-, and γ-type crystals. These different structural organizations present diverse and dramatically different piezoelectric features (Figure 16.5a), due to the distinct polarization ability arising from the vectored noncovalent interactions. As expected, the most common α-phase shows no piezoelectricity due to its

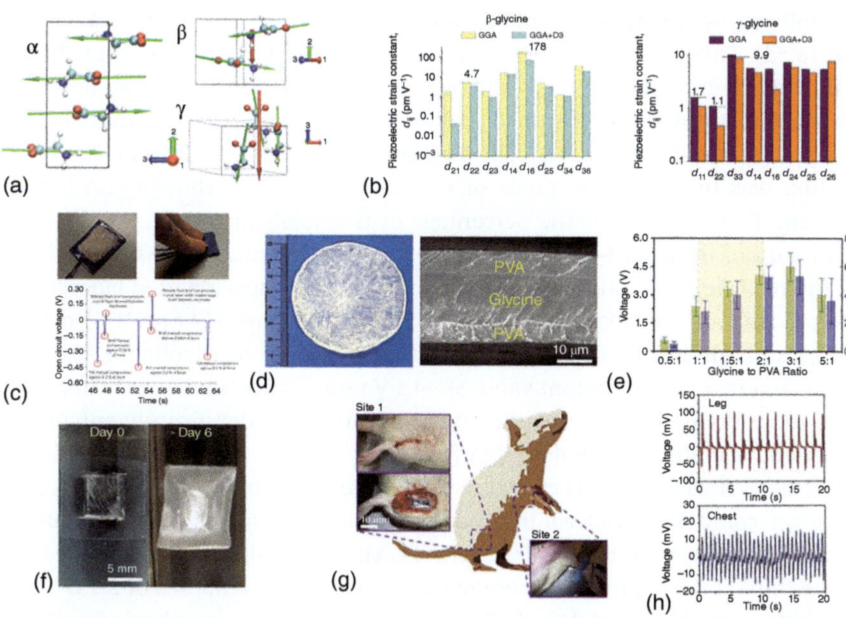

Figure 16.5 Characterization and application of **G** piezoelectricity. (a) Computed molecular dipoles of **G** molecules in different self-assembling polymorphs (α, β, and γ). (b) Calculated piezoelectric coefficients for β- and γ-phase **G** crystals. Note that the β-phase **G** crystals show the highest piezoelectric coefficient (d_{16}) of up to around 180 pm V^{-1}. (c) Photographs of the γ-phase **G** crystals deposited on two square copper electrodes to fabricate a piezoelectric power generator, which can output signals upon manual compressions. (d) Photographic image of the wafer-scale heterostructured piezoelectric bioorganic thin film composed of the γ-phase **G** crystals and PVA. The inset represents the cross-sectional SEM image of the sandwich-structured film. (e) Piezoelectric outputs and the measured d_{33} coefficients of the films prepared at different ratios of γ-phase **G** crystals and PVA. (f) Photographs showing that infiltration of the PBS solution leads to the dissolution of the **G**-PVA film. (g) Schematic image of the implantations of the packaged **G**-PVA films in the thigh and chest areas of an SD rat. (h) Piezoelectric signals of **G**-PVA films implanted in (g). Upper panel, piezoelectric voltage outputs of the **G**-PVA film implanted in the quadriceps muscle of the thigh during gentle stretching. Lower panel, piezoelectric voltage outputs of the **G**-PVA film implanted in the pectoralis major muscle driven by respiration.

centrosymmetric crystal structure. The β- (space group $P2_1$) and γ- (space group $P3_1$) phases show net polarization along the vertical axes, which contribute to the d_{22} and d_{33} piezoelectric coefficients, respectively. Especially, the computational and experimental characterizations demonstrated that the β-phase crystals have an ultrahigh d_{16} coefficient of up to around 178 pm V^{-1} (Figure 16.5b) [46], similar in magnitude to the d_{33} =185 pC N^{-1} measured very recently in an organic–inorganic perovskite crystal [47]. For practical device applications, the β-phase must be stabilized to prevent spontaneous transformation into the other two phases [48–50]. The stable γ-phase **G** crystals were adopted as the active layer in a piezoelectric power generator on 18 mm × 18 mm square copper electrode, showing a maximal output of ~0.45 V under a force of approximately 0.172 N (Figure 16.5c).

Thereafter, upon mixing γ-phase **G** crystals and polyvinyl alcohol (PVA) at 60 °C, wafer-scale sandwiched piezoelectric bioorganic thin films were created in which the crystallized amino-acid assemblies are entrapped between two PVA layers (Figure 16.5d). This heterostructured architecture significantly enhanced the flexibility and tensile properties of the laminated film (~4 GPa), with nearly an order of magnitude enhancement in the mechanical flexibility compared to that of the native γ-phase **G** crystals (~30 GPa). The piezoelectric response coefficient d_{33} of the hybrid film was related to the ratios of **G** crystals and PVA, showing an initial increase and then decrease as the percentage of **G** crystals increased. Specifically, the highest d_{33} of the film, 5–6 pC N^{-1}, was obtained at the ratio of 3:1 (**G** crystals to PVA) (Figure 16.5e). This value is higher than those of the most reported bioorganic piezoelectric membranes composed of silk (1.5 pC N^{-1}), collagen (2.6 pC N^{-1}), chitin (4 pC N^{-1}), and cellulose (1.3 pC N^{-1}). Especially, the peak-to-peak voltage (V_{pp}) output of the film retained a constant value of ~4.1 V under subjection of 30 N impulse force for more than 10,000 cycles, thus demonstrating the significantly enhanced durability and stability conferred by PVA [51].

Furthermore, since both the **G** crystals and PVA are water soluble, the piezoelectric hybrid films could be dissolved into aqueous solutions in less than 5 minutes. Therefore, when packed with polylactic acid (PLA), the V_{pp} significantly dropped by about one-third of the original value of the piezoelectric film composed of 2:1 **G**-PVA after working properly for five days. Followingly, the device was completely dissolved within 10 weeks (Figure 16.5f), demonstrating the beneficial degradability of the device. In addition, the human fibroblast cells (HFC) could survive without significant apoptosis over a period of 3 days when contacting the film, thus indicating the high biocompatibility. Given all these advantages, the **G**-PVA hybrid piezoelectric films could enable the development of biodegradable electromechanical devices for *in vivo* piezoelectric sensing.

In *in vivo* tests, when implanting two PLA-packaged **G**-PVA films of 5 mm × 10 mm under the skins of the thigh and chest of a Sprague–Dawley rat, respectively (Figure 16.5g), the embedded device attached to the quadriceps muscle produced a stable V_{pp} of >150 mV when the rat leg was gently stretched at ~1 Hz, while the one fixed to the top of the thoracic pectoralis major muscle produced a stable V_{pp} of >20 mV in response to rat respiration (Figure 16.5h). These voltage outputs were comparable to those of the previously reported flexible nanogenerators composed of high-performance piezoelectric materials, thus suggesting the promising potential of **G** self-assemblies as bioorganic alternatives for piezoelectric applications in biomedical and biomachine interfaces.

In fact, as mentioned above, the introduction of biocompatible polymers can improve the device potential of individual amino-acid self-assemblies, by creating patterns of bioorganic supramolecular structures with required mechanical properties such as strength and ductility enhancement for realization of macroscopic piezoelectric films and devices that remain biocompatible and biodegradable. For example, in addition to the **G**-PVA case, when incorporating tyrosine (**Y**) crystals, the well-known ultrarigid amino-acid assemblies with Young's modulus of 177 ± 54 GPa, in polydimethylsiloxane (PDMS) tape, the mechanical strength of the hybrid tape was significantly enhanced [25]. It is clear from these examples that co-assembly can endow amino-acid crystals with shear piezoelectric behaviors and improve their mechanical properties for development of smart bioorganic piezoelectric devices.

16.3.2 Proteins

In addition to small-molecule self-assemblies, diverse large-molecular-weight natural biopiezoelectric materials have also been reported, such as wood [52, 53], bone [54–61], tendon [59–62], baleen [63], fish swim bladder [64], fish skin [65], fish scale [66], onion skin [67], crab shell [68], spider silk [69–72], eggshell membrane [73], pomelo fruit membrane [74], chicken feather fiber [75], and tomato peel [76]. Therefore, besides the monopeptides (amino acids) piezoelectric self-assemblies, polypeptides/proteins provide a second type of natural piezoelectric peptides-based supramolecular materials, which are attracting increasing interest. Especially, due to their intrinsic polar nature, the piezoelectric properties of fibrous proteins, such as keratin, elastin, silk, myosin, lysozyme, and actin, have been extensively studied [3, 77–80].

To date, it has been found that the piezoelectric proteins generally have coefficients ranging from 1 to 20 pC N^{-1} (Figure 16.6). Intriguingly, viruses, as the simplest form of life and housed in proteinic protective layers, are piezoelectric. For example, the M13 phage, covered by 2,700 copies of the major capsid protein (pVIII) and five copies of the minor capsid proteins (pIII and pIX) located at either end of its rod-shaped structure, shows high piezoelectricity due to the noncentrosymmetric proteinic shell structure [82]. PFM characterizations of the M13 phages revealed strong piezoelectric responses both in lateral and axial directions, demonstrating the existence of longitudinal and shear piezoelectricity of the virus. The M13 phages self-assembling film showed piezoelectric properties proportional to thickness, with maximal piezoelectric coefficients up to 7.8 pm V^{-1} at thickness of 100 nm. A piezoelectric power generator with M13 phage active layer showed short-circuit current (I_{sc}) of up to 6 nA and V_{oc} of 400 mV under continuous cyclic pressure of 34 N.

Notably, the secondary-assembly strategy enables fabrication of large-scale peptide supramolecular chips for diverse smart device applications. Therefore, by vertically aligning the M13 phage self-assembling nanofibers with porous templates, centimeter-sized bioorganic supramolecular arraying films with enhanced piezoelectricity could be manufactured. The vertically aligned phage nanopillars were found to produce not only a high-voltage electrical response (d_{33} of about 10.4 ± 0.5 pm V^{-1}) but also an

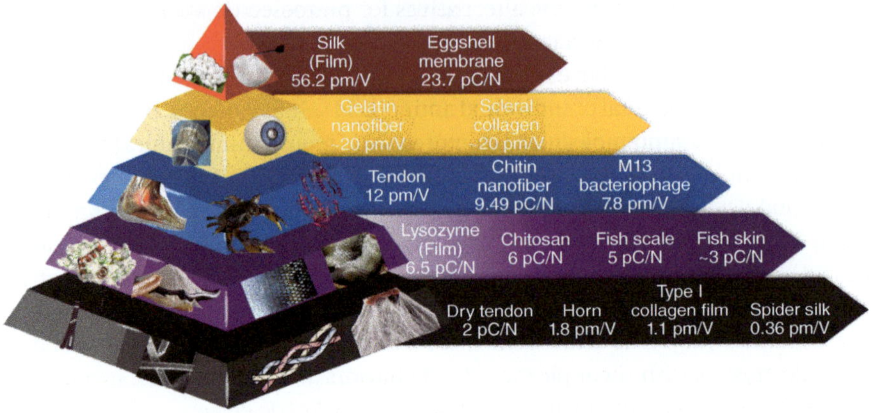

Figure 16.6 Pyramid diagram of the piezoelectric proteins. The items are categorized according to their piezoelectric coefficients. Bottom to top, the items include silk [81], eggshell, gelatin, scleral collagen, tendon, chitin, M13 bacteriophage, lysozyme, chitosan, fish scale, fish skin, dry tendon, horn, type I collagen film, and spider silk.

average output voltage and current of 232 mV and 11.1 nA, respectively, under loading forces [83].

Furthermore, the structural flexibility allowed the capsid protein to be easily modified, thus significantly enhancing the piezoelectric features of the phages. Specifically, when chemically conjugating negatively charged glutamate (**E**) residues to the N-terminal of the capsid protein, the improved polarization dramatically improve the piezoelectricity of the phages, showing larger piezoelectric coefficient than that of the native phages with d_{33} value of $11.2 \pm 0.7\,\text{pm}\,\text{V}^{-1}$.

Nevertheless, despite the inspiring piezoelectric response of virus assemblies, it should be noted that the piezoelectricity of phage films is not yet clearly clarified at the molecular level. Ordered phage structures with centrosymmetric D_6 or C_6 symmetry cannot explain their experimentally observed piezoelectric behaviors. Deeper experimental and computational studies of the underlying mechanism are required to fully unravel the piezoelectricity of phages and to lay the foundation for their further rational reengineering for future applications.

Plausibly, in addition to viruses, the proteins from higher life forms should also be piezoelectric. For example, collagen, a well-known fibrous protein in organs and tissues of mammals, plays a major role in the electromechanical coupling of bones and has been found to show a high piezoelectric coefficient of about $12\,\text{pC}\,\text{N}^{-1}$ [84]. Implants of co-assembled collagen and poly(L-lactic acid) (PLLA, a well-known proteinic macromolecule that can self-assemble into piezoelectric nanofibers [10, 85]) stimulated tissue regeneration in cartilage-damaged rabbits, with potential applications also in implantable/wearable devices and medical electronics [86].

In fact, the extensive distribution of the piezoelectric proteins, along with the discovery of the tactile receptors (Piezo1 and Piezo2) [87–90], suggests that piezoelectricity may play some subtle roles in metabolic activities, and the biological hierarchy of piezoelectric proteins is illustrated in Figure 16.6.

In addition to the protein themselves, the tissues composed of proteinic macromolecules can also show intrinsic piezoelectricity. For instance, the chicken eggshell membranes, primarily composed of keratin and usually discarded as worthless food waste, presented piezoelectric response as high as 23.7 pC N^{-1} [73]. This unexpected piezoelectricity was rationalized by the intertwined nature of the proteinic nanofibers endowing ultrahigh mechanical flexibility and rigidity of the eggshell membranes. Similar material designs, inspired by nature, may be exploited for manufacture of bioinspired smart devices for biomedical fields and biomachine interfaces. Accordingly, sandwich-structured piezoelectric generators composed of eggshell membranes generated a V_{oc} of 26.4 V and I_{sc} of 1.45 μA under a mechanical stress of 81.6 kPa. These high outputs indicate suitability in lighting and wearable sensor applications, for example to detect wrist pulses and throat vibrations in health monitoring and speech enablement, from materials previously considered waste.

Another well-established class of piezoelectric protein is spider silk fibers, the famous natural proteinic materials with astonishing per-weight mechanical rigidity and elasticity, with the vertical piezoelectric coefficient reaching 0.36 pm V^{-1} [69]. Spider silk-based piezoelectric power generators showed a V_{oc} of 21.3 V and I_{sc} of 0.68 μA under a stress of 82.2 kPa. Meanwhile, bioorganic spider silk-based materials prepared as sensor devices can be attached to the surface of human skin for functional signal acquisition and to the throat for acoustic signature acquisition.

It is well known that polarization can improve the ordering and enhance the piezoelectric properties of the organic materials. Therefore, upon repolarization under a high electric field of $3 \times 10^6\,V\,m^{-1}$, the β-sheet secondary structures inside the spider silk were patterned more orderly and formed more semicrystallized regions, which finally resulted in enhanced piezoelectric properties with outputs up to 40.7 mV, three times higher than that of the unpolarized counterparts (13.4 mV) under the same conditions, demonstrating how materials design and device engineering go hand in hand in realization of organic piezoelectrics [70].

16.3.3 Peptides

Peptides offer a wide range of advantages, including a diverse range of raw materials, high design flexibility, simple preparation, and inherent biocompatibility. Their availability and inexpensive nature make them a strong candidate for sustainable materials for all. Short peptides can self-assemble into polar one-dimensional nanosuperstructures, such as nanofibers, nanoribbons, and nanotubes, driven by noncovalent bonding. Most of the resulting self-assembled nanostructures have a noncentrosymmetric crystal structure and so exhibit piezoelectricity. Moreover, peptide self-assembly allows further integration of the properties of individual self-assembled nanostructures and fabrication of large-scale hierarchical structures, thus deploying biologically inspired supramolecular forms into a broad variety of technology applications [91]. Thus, piezoelectric peptide self-assemblies have attracted widespread interest in the past decades and play an important role in the fabrication of piezoelectric generators, ultrasensitive sensors, medical delivery systems, cell culture, metal–organic frameworks, and energy storage devices.

16.3.3.1 Peptide Crystals

The minimal sequence diphenylalanine (**FF**) nanotubes of amyloid-beta protein (Alzheimer's disease protein), which have been extensively studied in recent years, are a unique category of self-assembled functional biomaterials with a wide range of practical properties, including nanostructural variability, mechanical rigidity, and chemical stability [92–94]. During the self-assembly process, the water content in the hydrophilic channels influences the morphological diversity of **FF**-based polypeptides, enabling programmable creation of a variety of nanostructures, including fibers, nanowires, nano/microtubules, hollow tubes, quantum dots, and hydrogels [95–97]. **FF** supramolecules self-assemble into noncentrosymmetric hexagonal ($P6_1$) structures in low-temperature solutions, and thus many hexagonal **FF** nanostructures exhibit useful piezoelectric properties [98–105]. PFM experiments on single **FF** nanotubes have shown that their polarization is along the tube axis and yielded an effective piezoelectric coefficient (shear response for tubes of ~200 nm in diameter) of at least 60 pm V^{-1} (Figure 16.7a, b) [104]. The strong piezoelectric activity of bioinspired peptide nanotubes PNTs makes them candidates for future generations of green devices.

Since the discovery of the strong and stable shear piezoelectric response in **FF** nanotubes, there has been an increasing interest in exploring peptide self-assembly piezoelectricity similar to **FF**. Kholkin et al. reported that the piezoelectric constant d_{15} of **FF** reached 80 ± 15 pm V^{-1}, which is higher than the other piezoelectric constants d_{31} (4 ± 1 pm V^{-1}), d_{33} (18 ± 5 pm V^{-1}), and d_{14} (-10 ± 1 pm V^{-1}) [106]. Multiphysics finite element analysis of the piezoelectricity of **FF** predicted that a

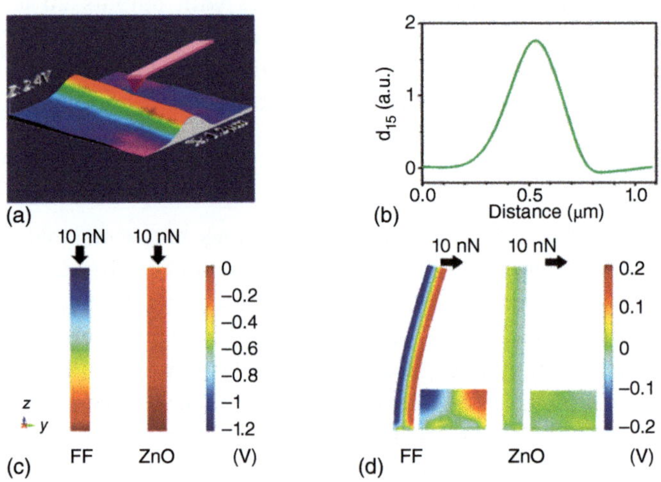

Figure 16.7 (a) In-plane piezoresponse images of single **FF**-PNTs for large *R*/*r* ratios. (b) Cross sections of (a) V_{ac} = 2.5 V, f = 5 kHz. (c) Piezoelectric potential in a *y*–*z* plane slice for **FF** peptide (left) and ZnO (right) nanowires under 10 nN of compressive force. (d) Piezoelectric potential in a *y*–*z* plane slice for **FF** peptide (left) and ZnO (right) nanowires under 10 nN transverse force. Insets show regions of potential reversal at the nanowire roots. Growth of vertical **FF** peptide microrod arrays with polarization controlled by the positive EF (electric field).

single **FF** nanowire can produce an output voltage of −1.3 V at a compressive loading of 10 nN, which is five times higher than that of ZnO nanowires. The lateral loading voltage of **FF** peptide nanowires was more than six times higher than that of ZnO nanowires (Figure 16.7c, d). After further fabrication of a flexible piezoelectric nanogenerator based on a vertical array of **FF** peptide microrods, it was measured to produce an open-circuit voltage of up to 0.6 V [36]. The good agreement with the predicted values verified the accuracy of the model and demonstrated the importance of finite element models in the development of piezoelectric devices based on peptides. Therefore, it provides an effective tool for research in the field of peptide self-assembly piezoelectricity.

Because the generated **FF** peptides usually exhibit random polarization directions, the piezoelectric constants of **FF** peptides d_{33} range between 5 and 30 pm V^{-1} in most studies [107–110]. In order to fix the polarization direction of **FF** at the macroscopic level, numerous researchers have proposed many interesting schemes, for example using electric field-assisted alignment, meniscus-driven alignment, and 3D printing for alignment. To realize the vertical alignment of **FF** nanotubes, weak electric fields can be used to regulate the polarization direction during the self-assembly process. (Figure 16.8a) [107].

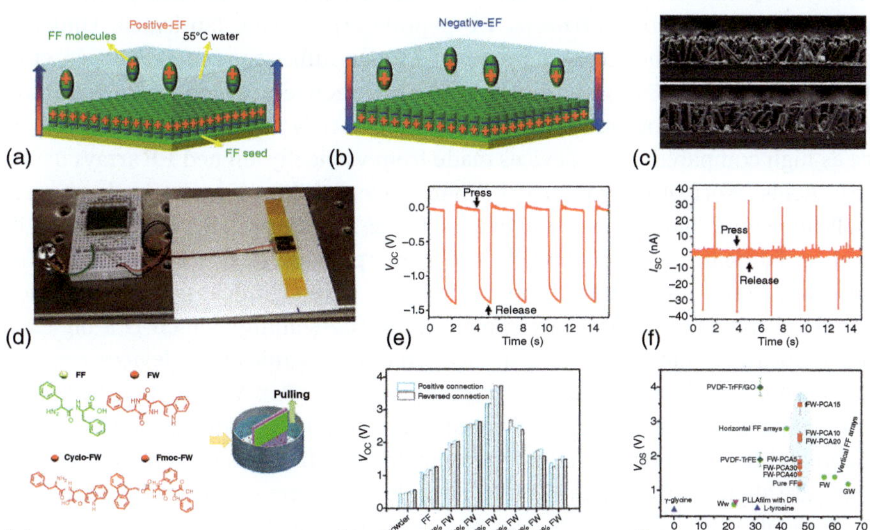

Figure 16.8 Piezoelectric properties of diphenylalanine nanostructures in horizontal and vertical alignments. (a, b) Schematic of the positive-EF (electric field) growth and the negative-EF growth. The large arrows are the directions of the applied electric fields, and the plus and minus signs indicate the polarizations of the **FF** molecules and **FF** microrods. (c) Cross-section views of arrays from the positive- and the negative-EF growth. Scale bars are 100 mm. (d) Photograph of the generator as a direct power source for an LCD. (e, f) Open-circuit voltage and short-circuit current from a generator using microrods from positive-EF growth. (g) Schematic process of the self-assembly of **FF** and the assembly of **FF** with **FW**, **cyclo-FW**, and **Fmoc-FF**. (h) Statistic diagram of the output voltage from three nanogenerators based on **FF** powders, pure **FF** fibers, and **FW/FF** fibers under a force of 48 N. (i) Comparison of V_{oc} from nanogenerators or force sensors.

When making the positive and negative reversals of the electric field, the **FF** microrods can obtain a uniform polarization in the opposite direction (Figure 16.8b). Using this method, vertical **FF** peptide microrods with controlled intrinsic polarization and enhanced piezoelectric strength were obtained, and their macroscopic piezoelectric properties were enhanced with an effective piezoelectric coefficient of 17.9 pm V^{-1} compared to unpolarized **FF** microrods (Figure 16.8c). Furthermore, nanogenerators based on uniformly polarized **FF** microrod arrays were fabricated (Figure 16.8d). In device tests, a stable open-circuit voltage (1.4V) and short-circuit current (39.2 nA) were obtained by applying a pressure of 60 N, and the power density reached 3.3 nW cm^{-2} (Figure 16.8e, f). The nanopiezoelectric generator based on the **FF** microrod array demonstrated good durability and stable output voltage with a cycle count of up to 5000 times. The output was increased by stacking the generators to power LCD panels, showing potential application as a power supply for small electronic products.

The orientation of the arrays formed by different methods of aligning **FF** peptides varies. The self-assembly process using meniscus-driven self-assembly can align **FF** nanotubes horizontally on a large scale, forming horizontal and unidirectionally polarized nanotube arrays [110]. By controlling the **FF** concentration, solvent type, and pulling speed, the morphology of **FF** peptide nanostructures can be controlled to produce architectures from vesicles to elongated aligned nanotubes. Meanwhile, nanogenerators based on horizontal **FF** peptide arrays were fabricated. Under a loading force of 42 N, the nanogenerators of **FF** nanotubes generated voltages, currents, and powers of 2.8 V, 37.4 nA, and 8.2 nW, respectively, which can power multiple LCD panels. The output voltage of the horizontally aligned meniscus drive is twice as high compared to the devices made from vertically aligned **FF** arrays using electric fields. Horizontally aligned **FF** nanotubes exhibit asymmetrically shaped unipolarity. This enables conversion of axial forces into shear deformation, which is critical for fabricating practical piezoelectric energy harvesters. In conclusion, the devices based on arrays of **FF** nanotubes not only have significantly improved piezoelectric properties but also have greatly improved stability, which is a big step forward toward the fabrication and application of bioorganic green devices.

Furthermore, additive manufacturing methods are often used when there is a need to prepare an array of films or devices with a certain level of resistance to compression and impact. For example, liquid materials with viscosity sufficient for 3D printing are aligned through an extrusion nozzle and thermally cured to form a thin film. Through this principle, the use of meniscus-guided 3D printing combined with molecular self-assembly enables the preparation of freeform crystalline **FF** peptide structures [111]. Subsequently, the precise temperature control of the printing platform is leveraged to drive the self-assembly of the printed **FF**. After in-depth characterization, they demonstrated layer-by-layer 3D printing of crystals with a lateral resolution of 2 μm and a longitudinal resolution of 200 nm. 3D-printed **FF** showed piezoelectricity arising from crystal properties, showing potential to become a key component of bioelectronic devices.

Further, the meniscus-driven arrangement was employed to make horizontally arrayed peptide films on which the co-assembly of **FF** peptides was investigated (Figure 16.8g) [112, 113]. The size and area density of the **cyclo-FW/FF** fiber arrays,

FW/FF fiber arrays, and **Fmoc-FF/FF** fiber arrays were controlled by adjusting the temperature, pH, and molar fraction of the constituent peptides. It was shown that the fibers maintained the hexagonal crystal structure of the self-assembled **FF** crystals by mixing **cyclo-FW** and **FF** peptide crystals with different ratio concentrations. When the mole fraction of the **cyclo-FW** is increased to 30%, sparse fibers appear on the substrate. Ordered growth was achieved from the assembly process of **FF** with **Fmoc-FF**. Different morphologies were observed after mixing with different proportional molar fractions, indicating the formation of co-assembled structures. The evolution of the crystal structure and the physical properties of **FW** and **FF** co-assembled with different molar fractions were tracked experimentally. After the introduction of **FW**, the lattice constant changes slightly, and the noncentrosymmetric property of the crystal structure increases. The **FW** with a molar fraction of 20% had the highest effective piezoelectric coefficient of 35.5 $pm\,V^{-1}$, which was 38% higher than that of the pure **FF** peptide. Piezoelectric nanogenerators were prepared from these peptide fibers, and the 15% **FW**-based piezoelectric nanogenerator produced the highest V_{oc} of all the peptide fibers in this study, at 3.2 V. The peptide co-assembly process provides a viable method for enhancing piezoelectric properties (Figure 16.8h), and the co-assembled peptides performed better than nanogenerators based on many other biomolecular piezoelectric materials (Figure 16.8i).

Numerous studies related to piezoelectricity of **FF** crystals are reported above, which encompass predictive models, experiments, and applications. This is a good indication that peptides (in particular, well-ordered, inexpensive, and stable short peptides) have a huge potential for energy generation and storage. In addition to **FF** peptide crystals, other peptides for making piezoelectric generators have been reported. The simplest tryptophan-based peptide cyclic glycine-tryptophan (**cyclo-GW**) forms monoclinic crystals with mechanical robustness (elastic modulus up to 24.0 GPa) and thermal stability up to 370 °C (Figure 16.9a, b). The **cyclo-GW** peptide was prepared as a nanogenerator, and under a force of 65 N, the crystal produced a high and sustained open-circuit voltage (1.2 V) due to a high voltage electric coefficient of 14.1 $pC\,N^{-1}$ [114], which is similar to the performance of nanogenerators prepared using **FF** crystals. Correspondingly, the I_{sc} reached 1.75 nA, which is an order of magnitude higher than the current generated by zinc oxide nanogenerators. The output voltage varies positively with the loading force with a slope of 18.8 $mV\,N^{-1}$ (Figure 16.9c).

W-based aromatic dipeptides, such as the **cyclo-FW** peptide with an orthogonal crystal structure, have high micromechanical toughness and thermal stability, broad-spectrum visible photoluminescence, remarkable optical waveguide behavior, and thermal and light-modulated conductivity (Figure 16.9d, e). In particular, the **cyclo-FW** peptide crystals show significant piezoelectric effects and have also been used to construct energy harvesting devices that generate open-circuit voltages up to 1.4 V and short-circuit currents up to 1.75 nA under continuous compression under periodic pressure pulses of 56 N [115]. The voltage output value of the piezoelectric generator is positively correlated with the external force of the load with a slope of 28 $mV\,N^{-1}$ (Figure 16.9f). Furthermore, the crystal structures can be easily tuned through modulation of the molecular sequences, thereby adjusting their

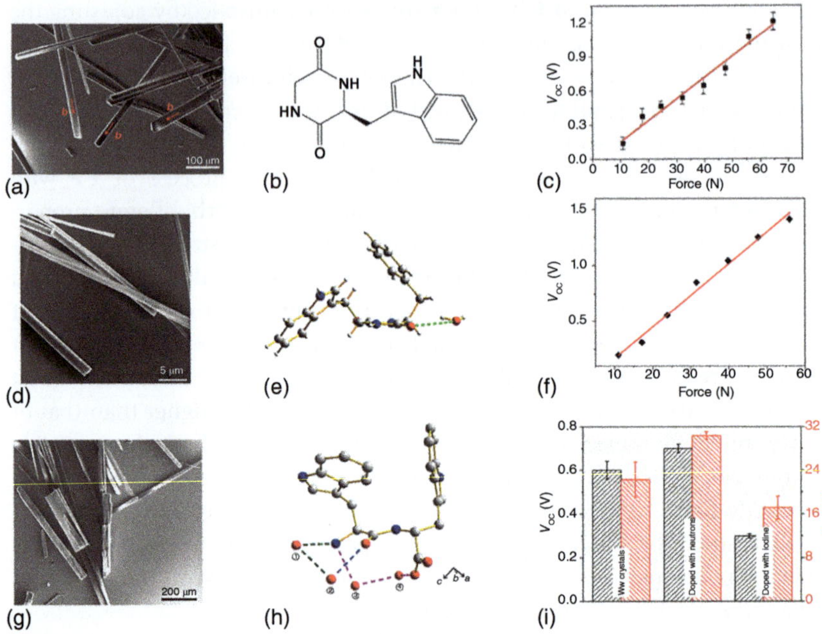

Figure 16.9 (a) SEM image of the **cyclo-GW** needles. The red arrows mark the growth direction along the crystallographic *b*-axis. (b) Molecular structure of **cyclo-GW**. (c) Linear dependence of the open-circuit voltage on the applied force, with the standard deviation estimated from three replicates as the error bars. (d) Molecular structures and the corresponding crystal morphologies of **cyclo-FW**. (e) Monomeric crystal structure of **cyclo-FW**. (f) Linear dependence of the open-circuit voltage on the applied forces. (g) Scanning electron microscopy image of **Ww** crystals. (h) Monomeric structure of the crystal, showing one dipeptide building block incorporating four water molecules by hydrogen bonding. (i) Comparison of the output signals (V_{oc} and I_{sc}) from the generators utilized as a direct power source using undoped or doped **Ww** crystals as the active components.

physiochemical features and functionalities. Given their intrinsic advantages of eco-friendliness, inherent bioavailability, morphological and functional flexibility, and ease of fabrication, these peptide self-assemblies may serve as bioorganic, supramolecular semiconductors to fabricate biocompatible microelectronics for power generation (such as biomechanical energy harvesting) or sensing (such as heartbeat detection), with tailored optoelectronic properties and improved mechanical stability.

The simple aromatic dipeptide L-tryptophan-D-tryptophan (**Ww**) also demonstrates useful piezoelectric properties [116]. **Ww** is a monoclinic symmetric needle-like crystal that crystallizes into a sandwich-like crystal structure composed of alternating water and peptide molecules (Figure 16.9g, h). Its extensive and oriented hydrogen bonding creates large supramolecular dipoles, resulting in a broad range of fluorescence emission and piezoelectric coefficients [117, 118]. These include the most easily accessible and exploitable piezoelectric coefficient d_{33}, measured by PFM as high as $47.4 \pm 12.8\,\mathrm{pC\,N^{-1}}$, which is significantly higher than the aforementioned peptide piezoelectric crystals and competitive with commonly used nonpeptide organic materials.

In addition, this work introduces two doping techniques, namely iodine adsorption and neutron doping (isotope substitution). Both doping strategies promote the motion of hydrogen-bonded water molecules, thus attenuating the red edge excitation shift (REES) effect and promoting charge hopping. Theoretically, the resulting charge transfer enhancement can significantly improve the performance of piezoelectric microdevices. However, the d_{33} value decreases to $17.2 \pm 5.5\,\mathrm{pC\,N^{-1}}$ after doping iodine in **Ww** crystals. The reason for this may be due to the force dispersion of the adsorbed iodine layer under pressure. In contrast, the doping of neutrons in **Ww** crystals increased the average d_{33} value to $61.9 \pm 9.5\,\mathrm{pC\,N^{-1}}$, which represents a very strongly piezoelectric bioorganic material. In agreement with the trend of d_{33}, the performance of output voltage and current decreased after doping iodine in **Ww** crystals in nanogenerator devices, while the performance improved after doping neutrons. For the original **Ww** crystal-based device, an open-circuit voltage of $0.6 \pm 0.04\,\mathrm{V}$ and a short-circuit current of $22.3 \pm 3.2\,\mathrm{nA}$ were generated under an axial force of 38 N with an equivalent resistance of 26.9 MΩ. Compared with the original **Ww**-based device, the neutron-doped assembly showed a 17% higher V_{oc} ($0.7 \pm 0.02\,\mathrm{V}$) and 36% enhancement of I_{sc} ($30.4 \pm 0.7\,\mathrm{nA}$) compared to the original **Ww**-based device. However, the equivalent resistance is almost the same, which confirms that neutron doping enhances the electron transfer of the peptide assemblies. In contrast, the iodine-doped crystal performs relatively poorly, with V_{oc} and I_{sc} peaks reaching $0.3 \pm 0.01\,\mathrm{V}$ and 17.2 ± 2.1 nA, respectively (Figure 16.9i). The lower output signal is consistent with a lower d_{33} piezoelectric response. Nevertheless, the device output signal is reduced to a lesser extent than the piezoelectric coefficient reduction, and the calculated equivalent resistance is 17.4 MΩ, which is 35% smaller than the original resistance of w-based device, thus demonstrating the enhanced electron transfer after iodine doping. Overall, both undoped and doped **Ww** crystals exhibit high conductivity and piezoelectric current. Isotope substitution as a doping method can enhance the charge transfer in bioexcited supramolecular structures, which can significantly improve the performance of piezoelectric microdevices.

The piezoelectricity of biomaterials is not yet fully understood at the molecular level. In particular, the classical piezoelectric model does not include dynamic noncovalent interactions such as host–guest binding, which limits the rational design of environmentally friendly piezoelectric supramolecular materials. Inspired by the conformation-dependent mechanical response of piezoelectric channel proteins, Chen et al. found that guest–host interactions can amplify the electromechanical response of conformationally mobile peptide metal–organic backbones (MOFs) based on endogenous myostatin dipeptides, leading to the development of a novel adaptive piezoelectric supramolecular material. They show that the guest molecule MeCN selectively alters the crystal morphology and acts as a structure-directing agent to lower the symmetry of the unit cell [119]. As a result, unlike the four other guests they tested, the Car_Zn·(MeCN) MOF crystallized into the lowest symmetric system (space group P1) with unconstrained polarization, which created a significant piezoresponse as substantiated by DFT calculations and microscopy. Reminiscent of transmembrane proteins and diphenylalanine peptide nanotubes, the extensive directionally aligned guest molecules in the narrow channel form a macroscopic dipole that can couple with shear force to generate the piezoelectric response [80]. As a proof of concept, they demonstrate the utilization of a stable, robust peptide-MOF with useful 1 V output in a prototype sustainable, eco-friendly power generator. Their findings illustrate the rational modulation of peptide-MOFs to embed tailored functionalities and pave the way for supramolecular engineering of piezoelectric biomaterials for nanotechnology applications through further manipulation and design of internal host–guest interactions that dynamically reconfigure materials morphology and improve device performance.

16.3.3.2 Peptide Nanofibers

In fact, even though peptide piezoelectric materials offer numerous advantages, such crystalline materials still suffer from the problem of degradation. As peptides self-assemble not only into crystals but also into short-range ordered structures such as **Fmoc-FF** and amyloid-like proteins, Ryan et al. measured the in-plane piezoelectric properties of a fibrillar peptide network composed of self-assembled **Fmoc-FF** nanofibers using lateral PFM (LPFM) and showed that it has shear piezoelectric properties [120]. Structural analysis of **Fmoc-FF** nanofibers suggests that the observed piezoelectric response may be caused by the noncentrosymmetric nature of the underlying β-sheet topology. Since peptide hydrogels are biomimetic materials with mechanical properties comparable to those of biogels, the additional functionality resulting from their piezoelectricity could enable the application of these hydrogels as novel piezoelectric scaffolds for tissue engineering.

More studies are required to resolve the nature and functionality of short-range ordered peptide nanofibers. They could potentially provide an ideal bridge to design and develop bioorganic piezoelectric soft devices for biological systems and human–machine interfacing.

16.4 Conclusion and Respective

Inspired by the natural biocompatibility, degradability, and piezoelectric properties of biomaterials, many exciting demonstrations, such as efficient and degradable energy harvesters and sensors with high mechanical stimulation sensitivity, are opening up interesting applications in the field of biomedical devices as well as in bioengineering. Their electromechanical properties are controlled by their chemical composition, crystal structure, and growth processes. The performance can be enhanced at the macroscopic level by tuning the polarity, doping, and array integration. Despite their enormous potential and ease of modulation, peptide-based self-assembled piezoelectric materials are still at an early stage of exploration, and the potential mechanisms underlying the piezoelectric response of biopiezoelectric materials need to be further investigated. Moreover, research on piezoelectric applications of natural materials, proteins, and peptides still faces many challenges. The remaining challenges can be briefly summarized under five aspects of integration, stability, practicality, optimization, and standardization.

1) *Properties integration.* The ideal high-voltage electrical properties of biomaterials usually imply high crystallinity, and materials with high crystallinity have a Young's modulus much higher than that of body tissues and organs and therefore often conflict with flexibility and softness. Future applications in, for example, self-powered implantable medical devices and wearable electronic devices require bionic properties coupled with high-voltage electrical properties, that is soft materials with strong piezoelectricity. In addition, device eco-friendliness in terms of natural degradability limits the durability of the device for long-term implants or environmental sensors.
2) *Stability.* There are many polycrystals with strong piezoelectric properties that are not thermodynamically stable, such as β-glycine, and cannot be used as single components. Moreover, biomaterials have natural larger variability under a large number of cycles compared to inorganic materials. Therefore, in order to put biomaterial-based application devices into practical applications, they need to be investigated for thermochemical stability and extensive variable cycle life experiments. In addition, most biomaterials cannot work properly in relatively harsh environments such as high temperatures, which poses a considerable challenge for field applications in hot climates.
3) *Practicality.* From the application point of view, considering that normal surface external stress is the most common mechanical stimulus, natural and synthetic organic piezoelectric materials still need to be further improved in terms of practicality. This is because most natural and synthetic organic piezoelectric materials have a strong shear component but weak transverse and longitudinal response.
4) *Optimization.* Biomaterials can show improved piezoelectric properties after doping, polarization, or ordered arrangement. However, it is still difficult to achieve well-designed piezoelectric biomaterials with desired characteristics due to the scale and capability limitations of the technology. Most of the arrays are partially ordered arrays, and not only that, the polar groups may also exhibit antiparallel conformation. In order to obtain higher piezoelectric response, more efficient methods are needed to fully align the dipole in biomaterials. The development of large-scale ordered biomaterial arrays with uniform polarization and strong piezoelectricity can potentially maximize the device potential.
5) *Standardization.* More reliable measurement schemes for piezoelectric response of biomaterials need to be established in order to exclude the interference of other factors. The reported piezoelectric coefficients of the same materials can vary over several orders of magnitude, such as fibrin and collagen [30, 84]. Other electromechanical coupling effects may have a large impact on the results due to the abundant crystalline forms contained in these materials and the different measurement methods at different length scales, for example macroscopic PFM and microscopic manometer. In order to establish a reliable relationship between a material and its piezoelectric properties, intrinsic electrostriction and flexoelectricity contributions must be avoided or filtered out, similarly the extrinsic electrochemical ion migration and electrostatic effects. More fundamentally, different preparation methods, different material concentrations, pH, and other variables can cause differences in devices based on the same class of piezoelectric materials.

In conclusion, there is no doubt that the advantages of peptide self-assemblies, such as eco-friendliness, innate biocompatibility, morphological and functional flexibility, and ease of fabrication, make them appealing candidates to link chemistry, materials science, biology, nanotechnology, optoelectronics, energy science, and engineering. As described here, the first fundamental steps toward the rational design and modulation of the bioinspired assemblies potentially pave the way for the realization of a new generation of biointegrated microdevices for diverse optical, electronic, mechanical, medical, and energy applications.

Acknowledgments

This work was supported by National Key R&D Program of China within the China-Israel Cooperative Scientific Research (2022YFE0100800) (Israeli No. 3-18130), the National Natural Science Foundation of China (52175551), Leading Innovative and Entrepreneur Team Introduction Program of Zhejiang Province (2022R01001), Zhejiang University Global Partnership Fund, and Open Foundation of the State Key Laboratory of Fluid Power and Mechatronic Systems. SG and DT acknowledge funding by Science Foundation Ireland under the Grant 12/RC/2275_P2 (SSPC). The authors thank the members of all the laboratories for helpful discussions.

References

1 Seol, D., Kim, B., Kim, Y. et al. (2017). Non-piezoelectric effects in piezoresponse force microscopy. *Curr. Appl. Phys.* 17 (5): 661–674.

2 Kim, S., Seol, D., Lu, X. et al. (2017). Electrostatic-free piezoresponse force microscopy. *Sci. Rep.* 7: 41657.

3 Chae, I., Jeong, C.K., Ounaies, Z. et al. (2018). Review on electromechanical coupling properties of biomaterials. *ACS Appl. Bio Mater.* 1 (4): 936–953.

4 Lines, M.E., Glass, A.M., Burns, G. et al. (1978). Principles and applications of ferroelectrics and related materials. *Phys. Today* 31 (9): 56–58.

5 Curie, J. and Curie, P. (1880). Développement par compression de l'électricité polaire dans les cristaux hémièdres à faces inclinées. *Bull. Soc. Minér. France* 3 (4): 90–93.

6 Eckes, K.M., Baek, K., Suggs, L.J. et al. (2018). Design and evaluation of short self-assembling depsipeptides as bioactive and biodegradable hydrogels. *ACS Omega* 3 (2): 1635–1644.

7 Mason, W.P. (1981). Piezoelectricity, its history and applications. *J. Acoust. Soc. Am.* 70 (6): 1561–1566.

8 Schulz, M.J., Sundaresan, M.J., Mcmichael, J. et al. (2003). Piezoelectric materials at elevated temperature. *J. Intell. Mater. Syst. Struct.* 14: 693–705.

9 Martin, A. (1941). Tribo-electricity in wool and hair. *Proc. Phys. Soc.* 53: 186–189.

10 Ochial, T. and Fukada, E. (1998). Electromechanical properties of poly-L-lactic acid. *Japan. J. Appl. Phys.* 37: 3374–3376.

11 Wang, Z.L. and Song, J. (2006). Piezoelectric nanogenerators based on zinc oxide nanowire arrays. *Science* 312 (5771): 242–246.

12 Voigt, W. (1910). *Lehrbuch der Kristallphysik (mit Ausschluss der Kristalloptik).* Springer-Verlag.

13 Von Hippel, A., Breckenridge, R.G., Chesley, F.G. et al. (1946). High dielectric constant ceramics. *Ind. Eng. Chem.* 38: 1097–1109.

14 Jaffe, B., Roth, R.S., Marzullo, S. et al. (1954). Piezoelectric properties of lead zirconate-lead titanate solid-solution ceramics. *J. Appl. Phys.* 25 (6): 809–810.

15 Haertling, G.H. (1999). Ferroelectric ceramics: history and technology. *J. Am. Ceram. Soc.* 82 (4): 797–818.

16 Acosta, M., Novak, N., Rojas, V. et al. (2017). $BaTiO_3$-based piezoelectrics: fundamentals, current status, and perspectives. *Appl. Phys. Rev.* 4 (4): 041305.

17 Jaffe, H. (1958). Piezoelectric ceramics. *J. Am. Ceram. Soc.* 41: 494–498.

18 Nuffer, J., and Bein, T. (2006). Application of piezoelectric materials in transportation industry. Global symposium on innovative solutions for the Advancement of the Transport Industry

19 Rödel, J., Webber, K.G., Dittmer, R. et al. (2015). Transferring lead-free piezoelectric ceramics into application. *J. Eur. Ceram. Soc.* 35 (6): 1659–1681.

20 Hong, C.-H., Kim, H.-P., Choi, B.-Y. et al. (2016). Lead-free piezoceramics—where to move on? *J. Mater.* 2 (1): 1–24.

21 Bell, A.J. and Deubzer, O. (2018). Lead-free piezoelectrics—the environmental and regulatory issues. *MRS Bull.* 43 (8): 581–587.

22 Okada, K., Yanagisawa, T., Kameshima, Y. et al. (2007). Properties of TiO2 prepared by acid treatment of BaTiO3. *Mater. Res. Bull.* 42 (11): 1921–1929.

23 Kikuta, K., Shimizu, Y., Moriya, M. et al. (2006). Low temperature recycling process for barium titanate based waste. *J. Ceram. Soc. Jpn* 114 (5): 392–394.

24 Kawai, H. (1969). The piezoelectricity of poly (vinylidene fluoride). *Japan. J. Appl. Phys.* 8: 975–976.

25 Ji, W., Xue, B., Arnon, Z.A. et al. (2019). Rigid tightly packed amino acid crystals as functional supramolecular materials. *ACS Nano* 13 (12): 14477–14485.

26 Ding, R., Zhang, X., Chen, G. et al. (2017). High-performance piezoelectric nanogenerators composed of formamidinium lead halide perovskite nanoparticles and poly(vinylidene fluoride). *Nano Energy* 37: 126–135.

27 Huang, T., Wang, C., Yu, H. et al. (2015). Human walking-driven wearable all-fiber triboelectric nanogenerator containing electrospun polyvinylidene fluoride piezoelectric nanofibers. *Nano Energy* 14: 226–235.

28 Laroche, G., Marois, Y., Guidoin, R. et al. (1995). Polyvinylidene fluoride (PVDF) as a biomaterial from polymeric raw material to monofilament vascular suture. *J. Biomed. Mater. Res.* 29: 1525–1536.

29 Persano, L., Dagdeviren, C., Su, Y. et al. (2013). High performance piezoelectric devices based on aligned arrays of nanofibers of poly(vinylidenefluoride-co-trifluoroethylene). *Nat. Commun.* 4: 1633.

30 Ribeiro, C., Sencadas, V., Correia, D.M. et al. (2015). *Colloids Surf B Biointerf.* 136: 46–55.

31 Liu, F., Hashim, N.A., Liu, Y. et al. (2011). Progress in the production and modification of PVDF membranes. *J. Membr. Sci.* 375 (1–2): 1–27.

32 Mendes, A.C., Baran, E.T., Reis, R.L. et al. (2013). Self-assembly in nature: using the principles of nature to create complex nanobiomaterials. *Wiley Interdiscip. Rev. Nanomed. Nanobiotechnol.* 5 (6): 582–612.

33 Hol, W.G.J., Halie, L.M., and Sander, C. (1981). Dipoles of the α-helix and β-sheet: their role in protein folding. *Nature* 294: 532–536.

34 O'Donnell, J., Guerin, S., Makam, P. et al. (2020). Atomistic-benchmarking towards a protocol development for rapid quantitative metrology of piezoelectric biomolecular materials. *Appl. Mater. Today* 21: 100818.

35 O'Donnell, J., Haq, E.U., Silien, C. et al. (2021). A practical approach for standardization of converse piezoelectric constants obtained from piezoresponse force microscopy. *J. Appl. Phys.* 129: 185104.

36 Jenkins, K., Kelly, S., Nguyen, V. et al. (2018). Piezoelectric diphenylalanine peptide for greatly improved flexible nanogenerators. *Nano Energy* 51: 317–323.

37 Adler-Abramovich, L., Aronov, D., Beker, P. et al. (2009). Self-assembled arrays of peptide nanotubes by vapour deposition. *Nat. Nanotechnol.* 4 (12): 849–854.

38 Okosun, F., Guerin, S., Celikin, M. et al. (2021). Flexible amino acid-based energy harvesting for structural health monitoring of water pipes. *Cell Rep. Phys. Sci.* 2 (5): 100434.

39 Lemanov, V.V. (2000). Piezoelectric and pyroelectric properties of protein amino acids as basic materials of Soft State Physics. *Ferroelectrics* 238 (1): 211–218.

40 Lemanov, V.V., Popov, S.N., and Pankova, G.A. (2002). Piezoelectric properties of crystals of some protein aminoacids and their related compounds. *Phys. Solid State* 44: 1929–1935.

41 Lemanov, V.V., Popov, S.N., and Pankova, G.A. (2011). Piezoelectricity in protein amino acids. *Phys. Solid State* 53 (6): 1191–1193.

42 Guerin, S., Tofail, S.A.M., and Thompson, D. (2018). Deconstructing collagen piezoelectricity using alanine-hydroxyproline-glycine building blocks. *Nanoscale* 10 (20): 9653–9663.

43 Tylczynski, Z., Sterczynska, A., and Wiesner, M. (2011). Temperature dependences of piezoelectric, elastic and dielectric constants of L-alanine crystal. *J. Phys. Condens. Matter.* 23 (35): 355901.

44 Guerin, S., O'Donnell, J., Haq, E.U. et al. (2019). Racemic amino acid piezoelectric transducer. *Phys. Rev. Lett.* 122 (4): 047701.

45 Yuan, H., Chen, Y., Lin, R. et al. (2022). Modified Stranski-Krastanov growth of amino acid arrays toward piezoelectric energy harvesting. *ACS Appl. Mater. Interfaces* 14 (41): 46304–46312.

46 Guerin, S., Stapleton, A., Chovan, D. et al. (2018). Control of piezoelectricity in amino acids by supramolecular packing. *Nat. Mater.* 17 (2): 180–186.

47 You, Y.-M., Liao, W.-Q., Zhao, D. et al. (2017). An organic-inorganic perovskite ferroelectric with large piezoelectric response. *Science* 357: 306–309.

48 Ferrari, E.S., Davey, R.J., Cross, W.I. et al. (2003). Crystallization in polymorphic systems: the solution-mediated transformation of β to α glycine. *Cryst. Growth Des.* 3: 53–60.

49 Weissbuch, I., Torbeev, V.Y., Leiserowitz, L. et al. (2005). Solvent effect on crystal polymorphism: why addition of methanol or ethanol to aqueous solutions induces the precipitation of the least stable β form of glycine. *Angew. Chem.* 117 (21): 3290–3293.

50 Isakov, D., Petukhova, D., Vasilev, S. et al. (2014). In situ observation of the humidity controlled polymorphic phase transformation in glycine microcrystals. *Cryst. Growth Des.* 14 (8): 4138–4142.

51 Fan, Y., Jun, L., Yin, L. et al. (2021). Wafer-scale heterostructured piezoelectric bio-organic thin films. *Science* 373: 337–342.

52 Fukada, E. (1955). Piezoelectricity of wood. *J. Phys. Soc. Japan* 10: 149–154.

53 Fukada, E., Date, M., and Hirai, N. (1968). Effect of temperature on piezoelectricity in wood. *J. Polym. Sci. C* 23 (2): 509–517.

54 Marino, A., Becker, R., and Soderholm, S. (1971). Origin of the piezoelectric effect in bone. *Calcified Tissue Res.* 8: 177–180.

55 Fukada, E. and Yasuda, I. (1957). On the piezoelectric effect of bone. *J. Phys. Soc. Japan* 12: 1158–1162.

56 Shanos, M.H., Lavine, L.S., and Shamos, M.I. (1963). Piezoelectric effect in bone. *Nature* 4862: 81.

57 Starkebaum, W., Pollack, S.R., and Korostoff, E. (1979). Midroelectrode studies of stress-generated potentials in four-point bending of bone. *J. Biomed. Mater. Res.* 13 (5): 730–751.

58 Halperin, C., Mutchnik, S., Agronin, A. et al. (2004). Piezoelectric effect in human bones studied in nanometer scale. *Nano Lett.* 4 (7): 1253–1256.

59 Fukada, E. and Yasuda, I. (1964). Piezoelectric effects in collagen. *Japan. J. Appl. Phys.* 3 (2): 117–121.

60 Lang, S.B. (1966). Pyroelectric effect in bone and tendon. *Nature* 212: 704–705.

61 Marino, A.A. and Becker, R.O. (1975). Piezoelectricity in hydrated frozen bone and tendon. *Nature* 253: 627–628.

62 Williams, W.S. and Breger, L. (1975). Piezoelectricity in tendon and bone. *J. Biomech.* 8 (6): 407–413.

63 Fukada, E. (2011). Piezoelectricity of natural biomaterials. *Ferroelectrics* 60 (1): 285–296.

64 Ghosh, S.K. and Mandal, D. (2016). Efficient natural piezoelectric nanogenerator: electricity generation from fish swim bladder. *Nano Energy* 28: 356–365.

65 Ghosh, S.K. and Mandal, D. (2017). Sustainable energy generation from piezoelectric biomaterial for noninvasive physiological signal monitoring. *ACS Sust. Chem. Eng.* 5 (10): 8836–8843.

66 Ghosh, S.K. and Mandal, D. (2016). High-performance bio-piezoelectric nanogenerator made with fish scale. *Appl. Phys. Lett.* 109 (10): 103701.

67 Maiti, S., Kumar Karan, S., Lee, J. et al. (2017). Bio-waste onion skin as an innovative nature-driven piezoelectric material with high energy conversion efficiency. *Nano Energy* 42: 282–293.

68 Hoque, N.A., Thakur, P., Biswas, P. et al. (2018). Biowaste crab shell-extracted chitin nanofiber-based superior piezoelectric nanogenerator. *J. Mater Chem. A* 6 (28): 13848–13858.

69 Karan, S.K., Maiti, S., Kwon, O. et al. (2018). Nature driven spider silk as high energy conversion efficient bio-piezoelectric nanogenerator. *Nano Energy* 49: 655–666.

70 Pan, C.-T., Yen, C.-K., Hsieh, M.-C. et al. (2018). Energy harvesters incorporating silk from the Taiwan-native spider Nephila pilipes. *ACS Appl. Energy Mater.* 1 (10): 5627–5635.

71 Shehata, N., Kandas, I., Hassounah, I. et al. (2018). Piezoresponse, mechanical, and electrical characteristics of synthetic spider silk nanofibers. *Nanomaterials (Basel)* 8 (8): 585.

72 Huang, T., Zhang, Y., He, P. et al. (2020). "Self-matched" tribo/piezoelectric nanogenerators using vapor-induced phase-separated poly(vinylidene fluoride) and recombinant spider silk. *Adv. Mater.* 32 (10): e1907336.

73 Karan, S.K., Maiti, S., Paria, S. et al. (2018). A new insight towards eggshell membrane as high energy conversion efficient bio-piezoelectric energy harvester. *Mater. Today Energy* 9: 114–125.

74 Bairagi, S., Ghosh, S., and Ali, S.W. (2020). A fully sustainable, self-poled, bio-waste based piezoelectric nanogenerator: electricity generation from pomelo fruit membrane. *Sci. Rep.* 10 (1): 12121.

75 Kar, E., Barman, M., Das, S. et al. (2021). Chicken feather fiber-based bio-piezoelectric energy harvester: an efficient green energy source for flexible electronics. *Sust. Energy Fuels* 5 (6): 1857–1866.

76 Saqib, Q.M., Khan, M.U., Song, H. et al. (2021). Natural hierarchically structured highly porous tomato peel based tribo- and piezo-electric nanogenerator for efficient energy harvesting. *Adv. Sust. Syst.* 5 (7): 2100066.

77 Maiti, S., Karan, S.K., Kim, J.K. et al. (2019). Nature driven bio-piezoelectric/triboelectric nanogenerator as next-generation green energy harvester for smart and pollution free society. *Adv. Energy Mater.* 9 (9): 1803027.

78 Fukada, E., Zimmerman, R.L., and Mascarenhas, S. (1975). Denaturation of horn keratin observed by piezoelectric measurements. *Biochem. Biophys. Res. Commun.* 62 (2): 415–418.

79 Liu, Y., Wang, Y., Chow, M.J. et al. (2013). Glucose suppresses biological ferroelectricity in aortic elastin. *Phys. Rev. Lett.* 110 (16): 168101.

80 O'Donnell, J., Cazade, P.A., Guerin, S. et al. (2021). Piezoelectricity of the transmembrane protein ba_3 cytochrome c oxidase. *Adv. Funct. Mater.* 31 (28): 2100884.

81 Joseph, J., Singh, S.G., and Vanjari, S.R.K. (2018). Piezoelectric micromachined ultrasonic transducer using silk piezoelectric thin film. *IEEE Electron Device Lett.* 39 (5): 749–752.

82 Lee, B.Y., Zhang, J., Zueger, C. et al. (2012). Virus-based piezoelectric energy generation. *Nat. Nanotechnol.* 7 (6): 351–356.

83 Shin, D.M., Han, H.J., Kim, W.G. et al. (2015). Bioinspired piezoelectric nanogenerators based on vertically aligned phage nanopillars. *Energy Environ. Sci.* 8 (11): 3198–3203.

84 Denning, D., Kilpatrick, J.I., Fukada, E. et al. (2017). Piezoelectric tensor of collagen fibrils determined at the nanoscale. *ACS Biomater. Sci. Eng.* 3 (6): 929–935.

85 Lee, S.J., Arun, A.P., and Kim, K.J. (2015). Piezoelectric properties of electrospun poly(l-lactic acid) nanofiber web. *Mater. Lett.* 148: 58–62.

86 Liu, Y., Dzidotor, G., Le, T.T. et al. (2022). Exercise-induced piezoelectric stimulation for cartilage regeneration in rabbits. *Sci. Transl. Med.* 14 (627): eabi7282.

87 Coste, B., Mathur, J., Schmidt, M. et al. (2010). Piezo1 and Piezo2 are essential components of distinct mechanically activated cation channels. *Science* 330 (6000): 55–60.

88 Ranade, S.S., Woo, S.H., Dubin, A.E. et al. (2014). Piezo2 is the major transducer of mechanical forces for touch sensation in mice. *Nature* 516 (7529): 121–125.

89 Ge, J., Li, W., Zhao, Q. et al. (2015). Architecture of the mammalian mechanosensitive Piezo1 channel. *Nature* 527 (7576): 64–69.

90 Wang, L., Zhou, H., Zhang, M. et al. (2019). Structure and mechanogating of the mammalian tactile channel PIEZO2. *Nature* 573 (7773): 225–229.

91 Zhang, J., Wang, Y., Rodriguez, B.J. et al. (2022). Microfabrication of peptide self-assemblies: inspired by nature towards applications. *Chem. Soc. Rev.* 51 (16): 6936–6947.

92 Kim, J., Han, T.H., Kim, Y.I. et al. (2010). Role of water in directing diphenylalanine assembly into nanotubes and nanowires. *Adv. Mater.* 22 (5): 583–587.

93 Gorbitz, C.H. (2001). Nanotube formation by hydrophobic dipeptides. *Chem. Eur. J.* 7 (23): 5153–5159.

94 Silva, R.F., Araujo, D.R., Silva, E.R. et al. (2013). L-diphenylalanine microtubes as a potential drug-delivery system: characterization, release kinetics, and cytotoxicity. *Langmuir* 29 (32): 10205–10212.

95 Souza, M.I., Silva, E.R., Jaques, Y.M. et al. (2014). The role of water and structure on the generation of reactive oxygen species in peptide/hypericin complexes. *J. Pept. Sci.* 20 (7): 554–562.

96 Kumaraswamy, P., Lakshmanan, R., Sethuraman, S. et al. (2011). Self-assembly of peptides: influence of substrate, pH and medium on the formation of supramolecular assemblies. *Soft Matter.* 7 (6): 2744–2754.

97 Wang, M., Du, L., Wu, X. et al. (2011). Charged diphenylalanine nanotubes and controlled hierarchical self-assembly. *ACS Nano* 5 (6): 4448–4454.

98 Li, Q., Jia, Y., Dai, L. et al. (2015). Controlled rod nanostructured assembly of diphenylalanine and their optical waveguide properties. *ACS Nano* 9 (3): 2689–2695.

99 Yan, X., Cui, Y., He, Q. et al. (2008). Organogels based on self-assembly of diphenylalanine peptide and their application to immobilize quantum dots. *Chem. Mater.* 20: 1522–1526.

100 Adler-Abramovich, L., Reches, M., Sedman, V.L. et al. (2006). Thermal and chemical stability of diphenylalanine peptide nanotubes implications for nanotechnological applications. *Langmuir* 22: 1313–1320.

101 Reches, M. and Gazit, E. (2004). Formation of closed-cage nanostructures by self-assembly of aromatic dipeptides. *Nano Lett.* 4 (4): 581–585.

102 Adler-Abramovich, L., Kol, N., Yanai, I. et al. (2010). Self-assembled organic nanostructures with metallic-like stiffness. *Angew. Chem. Int. Ed. Engl.* 49 (51): 9939–9942.

103 Amdursky, N., Molotskii, M., Gazit, E. et al. (2009). Self-assembled bioinspired quantum dots: Optical properties. *Appl. Phys. Lett.* 94 (26): 261907.

104 Kholkin, A., Amdursky, N., Bdikin, I. et al. (2010). Strong piezoelectricity in bioinspired peptide nanotubes. *ACS Nano* 4 (2): 610–614.

105 Nguyen, V., Jenkins, K., and Yang, R. (2015). Epitaxial growth of vertically aligned piezoelectric diphenylalanine peptide microrods with uniform polarization. *Nano Energy* 17: 323–329.

106 Vasilev, S., Zelenovskiy, P., Vasileva, D. et al. (2016). Piezoelectric properties of diphenylalanine microtubes prepared from the solution. *J. Phys. Chem. Solids* 93: 68–72.

107 Nguyen, V., Zhu, R., Jenkins, K. et al. (2016). Self-assembly of diphenylalanine peptide with controlled polarization for power generation. *Nat. Commun.* 7: 13566.

108 Heredia, A., Bdikin, I., Kopyl, S. et al. (2010). Temperature-driven phase transformation in self-assembled diphenylalanine peptide nanotubes. *J. Phys. D* 43 (46): 462001.

109 Bdikin, I., Bystrov, V., Delgadillo, I. et al. (2012). Polarization switching and patterning in self-assembled peptide tubular structures. *J. Appl. Phys.* 111 (7): 074104.

110 Lee, J.H., Heo, K., Schulz-Schonhagen, K. et al. (2018). Diphenylalanine peptide nanotube energy harvesters. *ACS Nano* 12 (8): 8138–8144.

111 Yang, J., Chen, M., Lee, H. et al. (2021). Three-dimensional printing of self-assembled dipeptides. *ACS Appl. Mater. Interfaces* 13: 20573–20580.

112 Yuan, H., Han, P., Tao, Z. et al. (2022). Peptide coassembly to enhance piezoelectricity for energy harvesting. *ACS Appl. Mater. Interfaces* 14 (5): 6538–6546.

113 Chung, W.J., Oh, J.W., Kwak, K. et al. (2011). Biomimetic self-templating supramolecular structures. *Nature* 478 (7369): 364–368.

114 Tao, K., Hu, W., Xue, B. et al. (2019). Bioinspired stable and photoluminescent assemblies for power generation. *Adv. Mater.* 31 (12): e1807481.

115 Tao, K., Xue, B., Li, Q. et al. (2019). Stable and optoelectronic dipeptide assemblies for power harvesting. *Mater. Today (Kidlington)* 30: 10–16.

116 Tao, K., Donnell, J.O., Yuan, H. et al. (2020). Accelerated charge transfer in water-layered peptide assemblies. *Energy Environ. Sci.* 13 (1): 96–101.

117 Knowles, T.P. and Buehler, M.J. (2011). Nanomechanics of functional and pathological amyloid materials. *Nat. Nanotechnol.* 6 (8): 469–479.

118 Knowles, T.P., Fitzpatrick, A.W., Meehan, S. et al. (2007). Role of intermolecular forces in defining material properties of protein nanofibrils. *Science* 318 (5858): 1900–1903.

119 Chen, Y., Guerin, S., Yuan, H. et al. (2022). Guest molecule-mediated energy harvesting in a conformationally sensitive peptide-metal organic framework. *J. Am. Chem. Soc.* 144 (8): 3468–3476.

120 Ryan, K., Beirne, J., Redmond, G. et al. (2015). Nanoscale piezoelectric properties of self-assembled Fmoc-FF peptide fibrous networks. *ACS Appl. Mater. Interfaces* 7 (23): 12702–12707.

17

Peptide-based Hydrogels for Soft Electronic Devices and Wearable Biosensors

Sen Liang, Yajie Tian*, and Shuo Bai*

State Key Laboratory of Biochemical Engineering and Key Laboratory of Biopharmaceutical Preparation and Delivery, Institute of Process Engineering, Chinese Academy of Sciences, Beijing 100190, P.R. China

These authors contributed equally to this work.

17.1 Introduction

Current bioelectronics are transitioning from old, nonrecyclable materials to green, biocompatible materials that are degradable [1–3]. Using a minimalistic approach, self-assembled peptide-based supramolecular hydrogels can provide potentially revolutionary advances in the design and fabrication of novel bioelectronic materials owing to their inherent biocompatibility and highly engineerable properties. As natural soft materials, the biological diversity of peptide-based supramolecular hydrogels allows for highly optimized enzyme immobilization [4] and cellular interfacing [5, 6]. These materials elicit a minimal immune response, can be safely degraded or absorbed by the body after use, and have controllable degradation kinetics [7]. In addition, the chemical diversity of peptide molecules allows common electroactive subunits to chemically modify or co-assemble, thus endowing peptide-based supramolecular hydrogels with excellent electrical properties [8]. More importantly, bottom-up processing allows the physicochemical properties of peptide-based supramolecular hydrogels to be easily regulated by manipulating environmental parameters (such as pH, temperature, and ion concentration) to realize customized development of electrical and mechanical properties [9, 10]. In particular, some peptide hydrogels exhibit typical semiconductor characteristics without external electroactive subunits [11]. Therefore, electroactive peptide-based supramolecular hydrogels are among the best candidates for developing new green bioelectronic materials.

In this chapter, we describe the recent examples of electroactive peptide-based hydrogels used in flexible electronic devices and sensors. We first introduce the fabrication and regulation of electroactive peptide-based supramolecular hydrogels to

Peptide Self-Assembly and Engineering: Fundamentals, Structures, and Applications, First Edition.
Edited by Xuehai Yan.

understand the formation mechanism at the molecular level and then demonstrate the process engineering of peptide hydrogels into 3D devices. Furthermore, the applications of electroactive peptide hydrogels in biomedicine, energy storage, and electronic devices are discussed. Finally, challenges in their practical application are analyzed, together with potential research directions that can facilitate further development.

17.2 Assembly of Electroactive Peptide-based Supramolecular Hydrogels

Peptides are composed of a short chain of amino acids. Due to the advantages of being green, safe, flexible, and adjustable, peptides have received high attention in the field of supramolecular self-assembly. And it can perform specific biological and physicochemical functions owing to their highly ordered assembly structures [12–15]. Self-assembly of peptide-based supramolecular materials can be initiated by aromatic stacking, hydrogen bonding, electrostatic interaction, and van der Waals forces [16–18]. By controlling these interactions, the nanostructures of assemblies can range from nanospheres, nanowires, and nanotubes to hydrogels [19–23]. Nevertheless, in this chapter, we mainly focus on self-assembled electroactive peptide-based supramolecular hydrogels. Electroactive peptide-based supramolecular hydrogels can be synthesized from two types of building blocks: peptide–peptide and peptide–π systems. Next, we discuss how these building blocks can be assembled to produce electroactive peptide-based supramolecular hydrogels from a bottom-up approach.

17.2.1 Peptide–Peptide Interactions

Gazit et al. pioneered the concept of peptide self-assembling semiconductors (Figure 17.1) [24]. They showed that the filling of aromatic groups and extensive hydrogen bonding caused the peptide molecules to form quantum-confined structures, significantly reducing the bandgap of the assembly [25] and giving the assemblies typical semiconductor characteristics, including quantum-confined photoluminescence [26, 27], piezoelectric properties [28], ferroelectric properties [29], and conductive properties [30]. Hence, self-assembled semiconductors based on natural aromatic peptides have been studied extensively. The most widely studied aromatic peptides include diphenylalanine (FF), di-tryptophan (WW), and phenylalanine–tryptophan (FW) [31]. However, the semiconductor characteristics of these self-assembled peptides mainly manifest in rigid nanostructures with highly ordered molecular arrangements. Nguyen et al. demonstrated the strong piezoelectric properties of FF peptide microrods. By applying an electric field, vertical FF peptide microrods with controlled polarization have been successfully used to fabricate power generator [32]. Currently, few theoretical reports on semiconductive peptide supramolecular hydrogels can be found in the literature.

Density functional theory (DFT) simulations provide the feasibility of theoretical probing of the mechanisms leading to bandgap formation. It shows the tunability of the semiconductor properties of peptide components and provides a reference for the

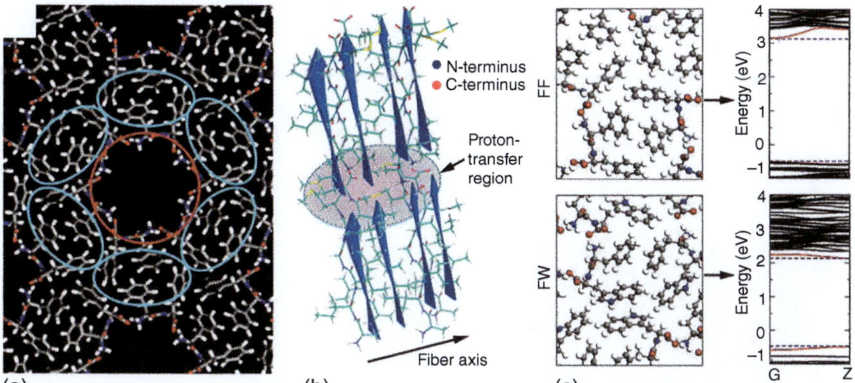

Figure 17.1 The molecular mechanism of peptide self-assembly semiconductor. (a) Display of the model of the construction of FF nanotubes. The structure of quantum restrictions contains a backbone-based tube (red circle). There are six zipper units around them, and each zipper consists of two diphenyl units (cyan circles). (b) Diagram of the cross section of the two adjacent β-sheets in the peptide self-assembly. The shadow oval shape is the quantum-confined region where proton transfers occur. (c) FW dipeptide showed a smaller bandgap than FF dipeptide. Source: Ref. [24] Reproduced with permission of Amer Assoc Advancement Science.

design of building blocks for the subsequent preparation of peptide components with required electronic properties. Through simulation calculations, Amdursky et al. demonstrated that the FW dipeptide network exhibits superior conductivity compared to the FF dipeptide network [33]. Akdim et al. evaluated electronics and photonics properties of FF, dityrosine (YY), and FW self-assembled peptide nanotubes [34]. Theoretical calculation showed that the bandgap of FW dipeptide nanotubes is smaller than that of FF dipeptide nanotubes, which is consistent with the experimental results. And the predicted bandgap for the YY nanotubular structure was found between FF and FW, suggesting that the conductance of YY was between FF and FW. These results enhance our understanding of the electronic properties of self-assembled peptide supramolecular systems and pave the way for their application.

Chemical conjugation can be an effective approach for the preparation and modulation of electroactive peptide-based supramolecular hydrogels. Tert-butyloxycarbonyl (Boc) and N-fluorenyl-9-methoxycarbonyl (Fmoc) are often used for N-terminal modification. The introduction of these aromatic moieties can provide additional driving forces for the peptide self-assembly system, including π–π stacking, hydrophobicity, and spatial optimization [35]. These additional interactions can cause peptide molecules to form assemblies with rapid kinetic and thermodynamic properties. Moreover, directional interactions can be provided to arrange peptide molecules in parallel, antiparallel, or interlocking antiparallel order during the assembly process. Amdursky et al. used Fmoc-FF to prepare dipeptide hydrogels with a final diameter of 7–15 nm (Figure 17.2) [36]. When the external environment is not suitable for self-assembly, Fmoc-FF molecules can form the nongel aggregates. Compared with these aggregates, a remarkable step-like behavior of the absorption curves was observed in UV region of

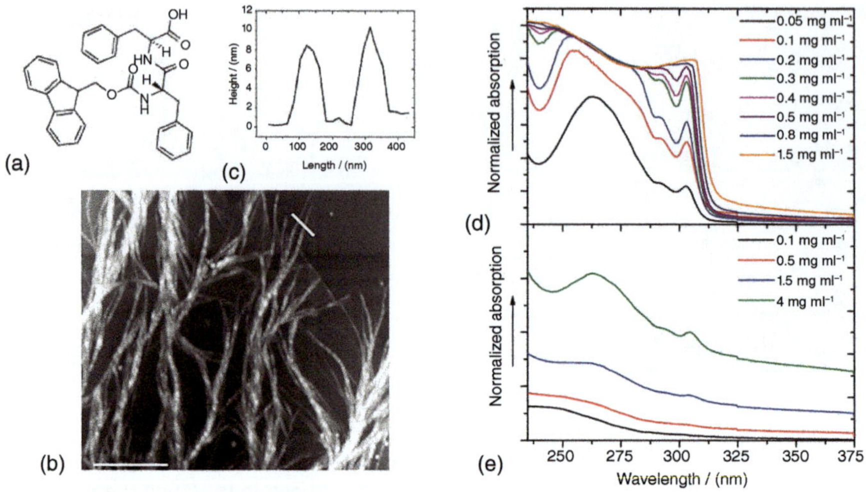

Figure 17.2 (a) Molecular structure of Fmoc-FF. (b) AFM image of the Fmoc-FF hydrogels (the Z scale is 53 nm). (c) A cross section along the white line in (b). (d) Absorption spectra of Fmoc-FF hydrogels at different concentrations (at high concentrations, Fmoc-FF hydrogels show obvious step-like absorption). (e) Absorption spectra of Fmoc-FF aggregates at different concentrations. Source: Ref. [36] Reproduced with permission of John Wiley & Sons.

hydrogel samples, characterized by peptide nanotube network formation. This optical property indicates the formation of a quantum-confined structure within the hydrogel nanotubes. In other words, Fmoc-FF is a self-assembled supramolecular hydrogel with semiconducting characteristics.

In conclusion, strong electronic properties are evident in rigid assemblies (such as crystals) of aromatic peptides and are theoretically possible in peptide supramolecular hydrogels. One major shortcoming of electroactive peptide-based supramolecular hydrogels constructed using pure peptide molecules as building blocks is the lack of desirable electronic properties for practical applications [37, 38].

17.2.2 Peptide–π Interactions

Co-assembly and covalently linked strategies present a promising future for the design of peptide-based supramolecular hydrogels with excellent electrical properties. A variety of organic π-electron subunits with conjugated structures have been used to fabricate electroactive peptide-based supramolecular hydrogels, such as porphyrin, benzothiophene, tetrathiafulvalene, perylene diimide, and naphthalene diimide [14, 35, 39].

The combination of peptides and porphyrins was inspired by natural photosynthesis. In natural photosynthetic systems, the combination of functional pigments and structural proteins can form complexes with high water content to achieve efficient light energy conversion. Proteins in the complex can bind to pigments at specific locations to ensure optimal energy conversion and avoid energy loss due to aggregation quenching [41]. Porphyrins have a core ring structure similar to that of pigment molecules, and their absorption features (400–450 nm for S bands and 500–700 nm for Q bands) can guarantee the efficient use of the solar spectrum. Based on this excellent photoelectric property, porphyrins have become common model molecules for constructing electroactive peptide-based supramolecular hydrogels. For instance, Feng et al. used 5,10,15,20-tetraphenyl-21H,23H-porphine zinc (TPP-Zn) and tripeptide Fmoc-L_3 to co-assemble peptide-based hydrogel capable of effective photoelectric conversion (Figure 17.3) [40]. This peptide-based hydrogel consists of nanofilaments about 50 nm in diameter and hundreds of nanometers in length. Spectral analysis demonstrated that Fmoc-L_3 had regular β-sheet structures in the hydrogel nanofibers. The inherent hydrophobicity of the Fomc group can promote π–π stacking interactions between the fluorenyl and aromatic rings in the porphyrin molecules and guide the porphyrin molecules to arrange the chiral in the form of J-aggregation to form a long-range ordered photoelectron transfer matrix. Similar examples include the co-assembled electroactive supramolecular hydrogel based on acetyl-(isoleucine)$_4$-(lysine)$_2$-NH_2 (Ac-I_4K_2-NH_2) and tetrakis(4-sulfonatophenyl) porphyrin (TPPS) reported by Wang et al. [42] They selected TPPS as a model light-harvesting molecule and self-assembled peptide

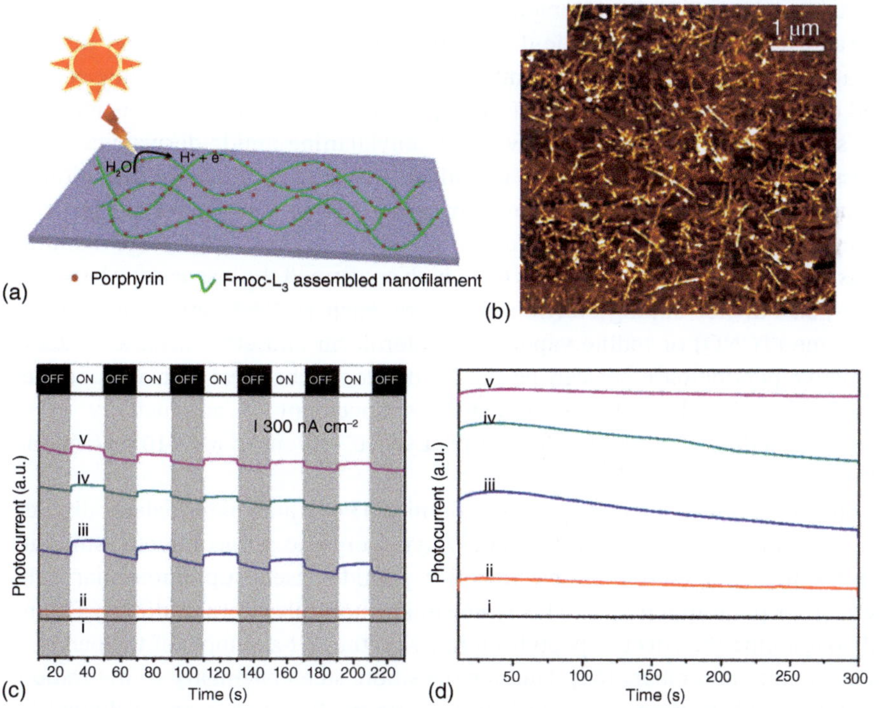

Figure 17.3 (a) Hydrogel made of peptide/porphyrin nanofilament for enhanced photocurrent. (b) Morphology characterization of the hydrogel. (c, d) Photocurrent responses of peptide hydrogels with different TPP-Zn concentrations: (i) ITO substrate; (ii) pure peptide hydrogels; (iii) hydrogels with 0.1 wt% TPP-Zn; (iv) hydrogels with 1 wt% TPP-Zn; and (v) hydrogels with 5 wt% TPP-Zn. Source: Ref. [40] Reproduced with permission of Elsevier.

structures as templates to construct peptide–porphyrin coaggregates. The effects of the concentration of peptides and porphyrins and the pH value of solution on the molecular aggregation behavior and photoelectric properties of the assemblies were systematically studied. The results showed that in the presence of I_4K_2 nanostructures, TPPS J-aggregates are obtained and can be easily regulated by the pH or mole ratio of peptides and porphyrins. The J-aggregates of TPPS exhibited a higher photocurrent response than the other aggregation states in the photoelectric experiment.

Benzothiophene and tetrathiafulvalene are π-electron-rich (p-type) organic semiconductor subunits that have attracted growing interest in recent years owing to their unique redox properties, relatively high conductivities, good solubilities, and excellent processabilities. The [1]benzothieno[3,2-b][1]-benzothiophene (BTBT) molecule has high mobility, which is the common group for the design of electroactive peptide-based supramolecular hydrogels. Fortunato et al. reported BTBT derivatives modified alternately by glutamic acid residues and alanine residues [43]. These molecules can self-assemble in water to produce electroactive peptide-based hydrogels in response to pH changes or variations in salt concentrations. Highly uniform nanofibers of up to 10 μm in length were observed in the hydrogels. The spectral results showed that the formation of hydrogen bond-extended β-sheet structures and π–π stacking interactions between the appended chromophores are at the core of the formation of one-dimensional (1D) assemblies. Nalluri et al. demonstrated the nonaqueous self-assembly of a low-molecular-mass organic gelator based on the tetrathiafulvalene (TTF)-dipeptide ($TTF\text{-}FF\text{-}NH_2$) bioconjugate [44]. They showed that TTF combined with diphenylalanine amide derivatives could self-assemble into one-dimensional nanofibers, which triggered the formation of self-supporting organogels in chloroform and ethyl acetate solutions. The frequency sweep measurements of chloroform gel showed that the storage modulus G' was higher than the loss modulus G", which confirmed the viscoelastic behavior of the gel. Further doping electron acceptors, such as 7,8,8 tetracyanoquinone dimethane (TCNQ) or iodine vapor with chloroform and ethyl acetate, a stable conductive peptide-base gel can be obtained. Electrochemical test of nanofiber xerogel networks showed a remarkable enhancement in conductivity when doped with iodine vapor and TCNQ, from 1.9×10^{-10} S/cm to 6.4×10^{-7} S/cm and 3.6×10^{-4} S/cm, respectively.

Aromatic diimines such as perylene diimide (PDI) and naphthalene diimide (NDI) are common π-electron-deficient (*n*-type) organic semiconductor subunits used for the construction of electroactive peptide-based supramolecular gels. A series of peptide-functionalized perylene imide molecules were studied by Eakins et al. to examine the effect of peptide chirality on the self-assembly of the perylene imide core into nanofibers [45]. The stereoposition, stereochemistry configuration, amphiphilic substitution, and perylene nuclear modification were evaluated by spectroscopy from the perspective of chiral assembly. For dipeptides, the stereocenters of the peptide residues near the perylene nucleus (1–5 units) were found to confer helical chirality on the perylene nucleus, while the stereocenters of the more distant residues exerted no chiral influence. Hence, diastereoisomers involved in stereocentric inversion within proximal residues presented spectroscopically as pseudoenantiomers. The increased demand for side-chain space at the proximal position produced a similar chiral effect but expressed a decrease in the strength of the cotton effect, with additional longer wavelength characteristic to interchain excimers. The substitution of one of the two peptide substituents by an alkyl chain produced a strong amphiphilic perylene bisimide which disrupted the chiral self-assembly. In addition, the amphiphilic structure achieved by partially modifying the nucleus of perylene imide with a bisector moiety facilitated strong exciton coupling and solvoresponsive self-assembly into long chiral nanofilaments. These results emphasize not only the importance of stereogenic positions but also the nature of the amphiphilic structure design of a self-assembled peptide-substituted perylene imide. An example of NDI dipeptide co-assembly gel under catalyzed enzymatic with NDI tyrosine (NDI-Y) and phenylalanine-NH_2 (F-NH_2) was reported by Nalluri et al. (Figure 17.4) [46]. Thermodynamic drive coupled biocatalytic condensation and assembly method, which produced nanostructures with optimized supramolecular interactions, as evidenced by the significant β-sheet-like hydrogen bond network of the peptide and the M-pattern chiral orientation of the NDI chromophore. Furthermore, charge transfer complexes are produced in the presence of dialkoxy or dihydroxy naphthalene (DAN/DHN) donors. This method has broad prospects for the development of functional nanomaterials with enhanced remote charge transfer properties and fewer defects. Kumar et al. used *in situ* modification of NDI with D-tyrosine methyl ester and L-tyrosine methyl ester to control molecular amphiphilism and subsequent assembly patterns [47]. The kinetic competition between amidation and ester hydrolysis allows supramolecular change assembly pathways in the presence of α-chymotrypsin and specific amino acids. On this basis, the semiconducting NDI molecules can be used to form electron wires with temporally regulated electroconductivity.

17.3 Three-dimensional Processing of Electroactive Peptide-based Hydrogels

Electronic devices typically contain intricate and sophisticated structures with multiple levels. The manufacturing of these structures has traditionally relied on conventional techniques such as inkjet printing (Figure 17.5) [48], screen printing [49], aerosol printing [50], electrochemical patterning [51], and lithography [52], which have their limitations and challenges. For instance, these techniques are restricted to low-resolution (>100 μm), two-dimensional patterns with low aspect ratios and/or complex, expensive procedures that involve multiple steps in a cleanroom, including alignments, masks, etchings, and postassemblies [53]. On the other hand, three-dimensional (3D) printing offers a programmable, flexible, and easy-to-use method for fabricating microscale structures in 3D space [54–56], which is not possible with conventional approaches. Furthermore, recent advances in 3D printable materials, such as metals, liquid metals, cell-laden bioinks, glass, liquid crystal polymers, and ferromagnetic elastomers have significantly expanded the range of materials available for 3D printing [57–59]. For example, Yuk et al. have developed a highly efficient 3D printable conducting polymer ink based on poly(3,4-ethylenedioxythiophene): polystyrene sulfonate (PEDOT:PSS) for the fabrication of conducting polymers using

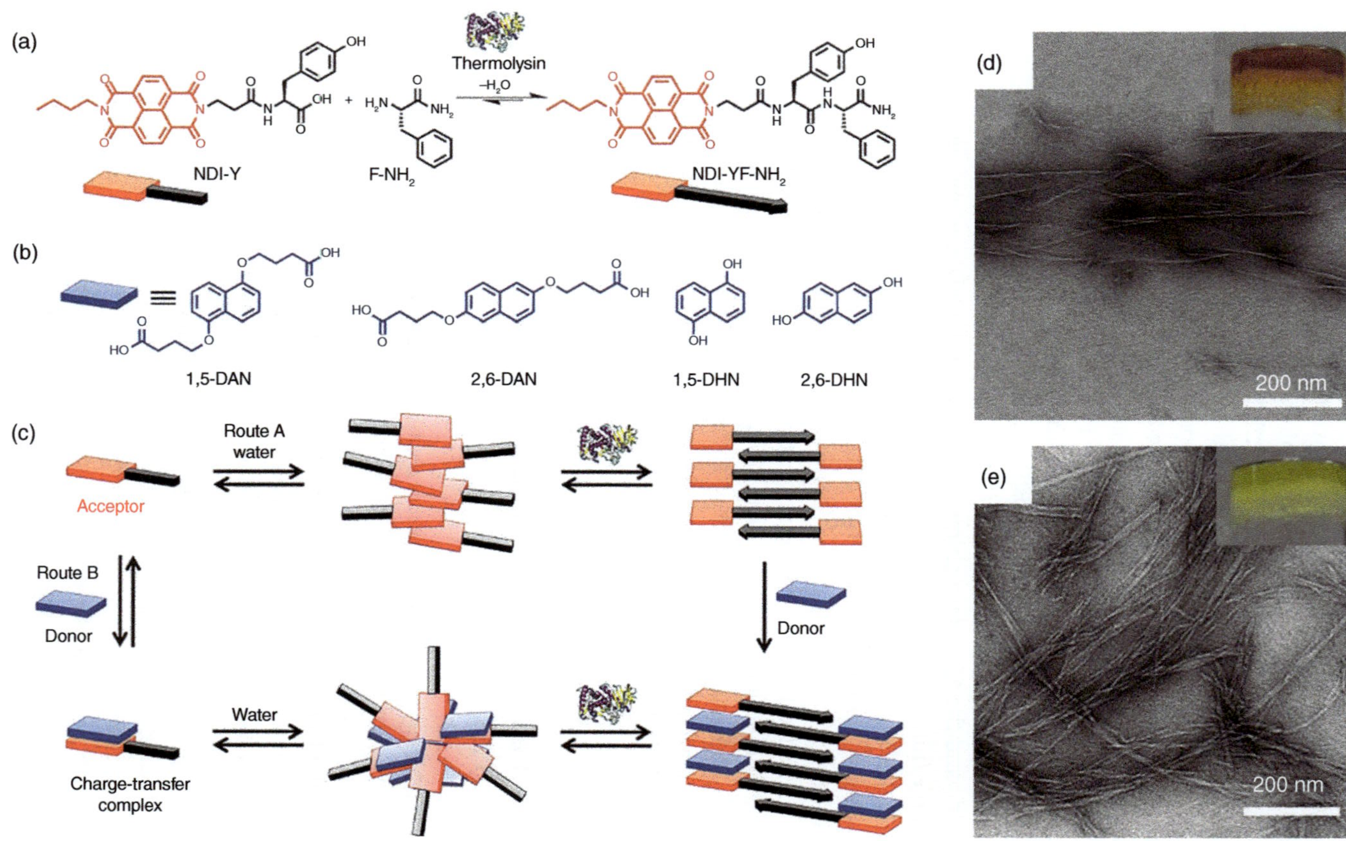

Figure 17.4 (a) Thermolysin-catalyzed condensation into naphthalene diimide dipeptide conjugate receptor (NDI-YF-NH_2). (b) Molecular structure of various dioxy/hydroxynaphthalene (DAN/DHN) donors. (c) Schematic diagram of the differential supramolecular organization of the NDI-Y/NDI-YF-NH_2 receptor in the presence and absence of different DAN/DHN donors. The combination of enzyme catalysis and noncovalent interactions is conducive to form highly ordered chiral 1D supramolecular nanostructures. TEM images of before d and after e adding of thermolysin protease in hydrogel; the illustration corresponds to the corresponding gel sample. Source: Ref. [46] Reproduced with permission of John Wiley & Sons.

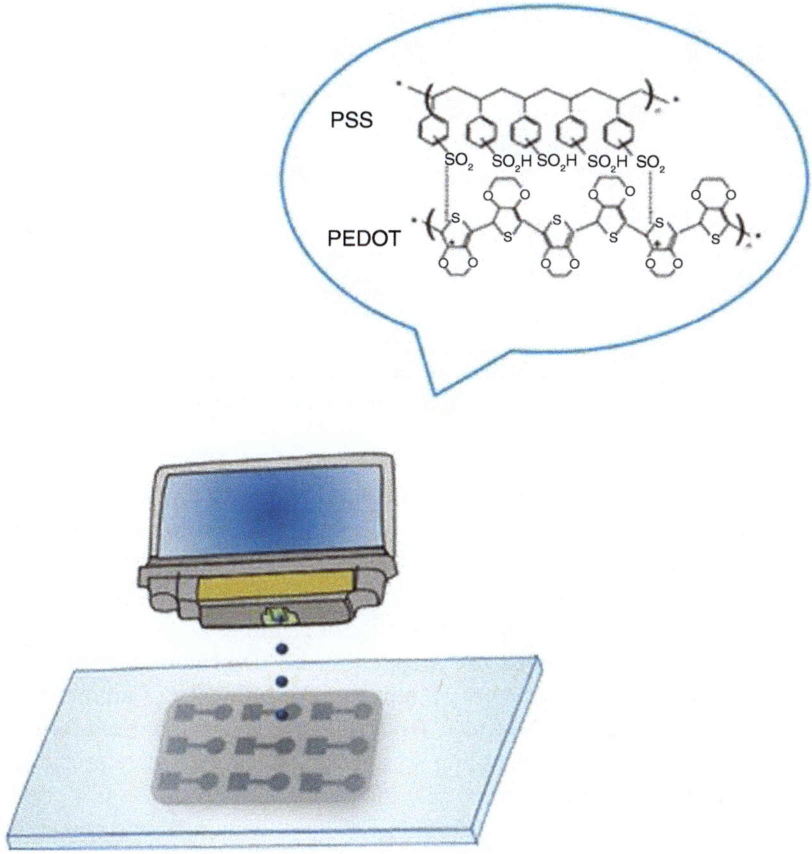

Figure 17.5 Schematic representation of Inkjet-printed PEDOT:PSS electrodes. Source: Adapted from Ref. [48].

3D printing [60]. This ink enables the creation of high-resolution, high-aspect-ratio microstructures that can be easily integrated with other materials, such as insulating elastomers, using multimaterial 3D printing. 3D-printed conducting polymers can also be transformed into soft and highly conductive hydrogel microstructures.

Naturally, complex peptide hydrogel structures are also suitable for manufacturing via 3D printing [59]. Peptides are considered promising 3D printable materials due to their flexible and adjustable physicochemical properties. To improve the weak mechanical strength and poor printability of peptides, Jian et al. designed and synthesized two 9-fluorenylmethoxycarbonyl (Fmoc) dipeptides, Fmoc-tyrosine-aspartic acid (Fmoc-YD) and Fmoc-tyrosine-lysine (Fmoc-YK), with opposite charges on their terminal residues, to construct hydrogel scaffolds (9 mm × 9 mm × 1.5 mm) using a droplet-based 3D printer (Figure 17.6) [61]. Through the electrostatic interaction between Fmoc-YK and Fmoc-YD, the *in situ* gel of two peptides was realized in 3D printing. The fidelity and resolution of the fabricated hydrogel scaffolds can be easily improved by decreasing the droplet distance and volume. More importantly, the mechanical properties of the hydrogel scaffold could be tuned by changing the concentration and composition of the peptides. The rheological results showed that when

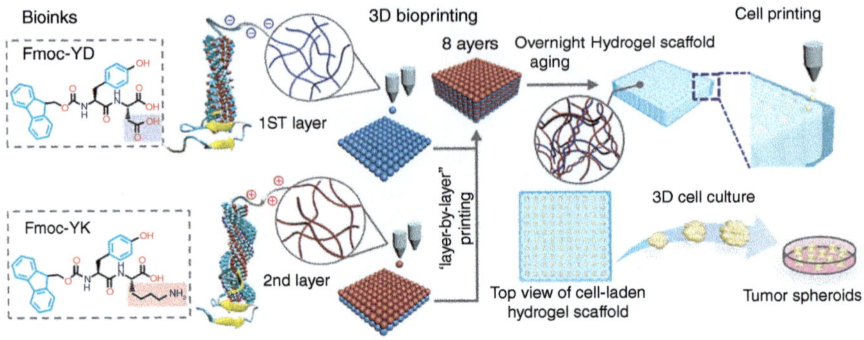

Figure 17.6 Schematic of the Fmoc-dipeptide molecular design, 3D printing, and application of cell culture. Source: Ref. [61] Reproduced with permission of American Chemical Society.

the two dipeptides were mixed in a ratio of 1 : 1, the mechanical strength of the hydrogel was more than five times higher than that of single dipeptide hydrogel. Compared to polymer hydrogel scaffolds, this peptide hydrogel scaffold can completely degrade in a few weeks. The degradation rate can be controlled by changing the concentration of dipeptide solution or the size of droplet at the time of printing.

Similar studies have also included the preparation of 3D-printed peptide gels based on the Hofmeister sequence. Li et al. reported the influence of anions and cations on the gelation of model dipeptides, Fmoc-YK [59]. Based on the characteristics of the rapid gelation of dipeptides and ions, hydrogel scaffolds were prepared by layer-by-layer 3D printing and *in situ* gelation. Sulfate was selected as a good candidate for ion gelation. In addition to rapid gelation, the main characteristic of anion-dipeptide hydrogel scaffold is that the mechanical properties of hydrogels can be enhanced by immersion in cell culture medium. This work did not add any chemical cross-linking agent or introduce any unfriendly external factors such as UV irradiation to construct the peptide hydrogel scaffold, which fully guaranteed the biosafety of the peptide hydrogel scaffold.

17.4 Application of Electroactive Peptide-based Hydrogels

Electroactive peptide-based supramolecular hydrogels are of great interest for the generation of new flexible electronic devices, owing to their electrical properties and potential tissue compatibility. The use of electroactive peptide-based supramolecular hydrogels in fields such as electronic devices and wearable biosensors could be achieved by developing biocompatible supramolecular peptide-based hydrogels with different performance [62].

17.4.1 Soft Electronic Devices

In vivo experiments have preliminarily shown that electroactive peptide-based supramolecular hydrogels of peptide or peptide–π systems have good electrical conductivity and therapeutic potential and could be used in a variety of biomedical applications. The electrical conductivity of peptide-based supramolecular hydrogels is essential for the use of the sensing, stimulating and recording in bioelectrical signals [63]. Therefore, electroactive peptide-based hydrogels were applied in nerve regeneration, electrogenic drug release, tissue engineering, etc. An electroactive system made of peptide nanofibers containing tetraphenylamine (TA) was created by Arioz et al., and it was used for neural regeneration [64]. Electrically active self-assembled peptide nanofibers formed a 3D nanofiber network that mimics the extracellular matrix of neuronal cells. On electroactive TA nanofiber hydrogels, the growth of neutrospheres was improved. On electroactive peptide nanofiber hydrogels, neurodifferentiation of pheochromocytoma cells (PC-12) was more advanced. These electroactive peptide-based supramolecular hydrogels show promise for further therapeutic neural regeneration applications. Hardy et al. introduced electroactive peptide-based supramolecular films based on oligoalanine–oligoaniline–oligoalanine conjugates [65]. These membranes promoted fibroblast adhesion and enabled the triggered release of dexamethasone phosphate, a clinically relevant anti-inflammatory drug under electrical stimulation.

Chakraborty et al. designed a di-Fmoc-based hydrogelator containing a cell-adhesive Arg-Gly-Asp (RGD) fragment and polyaniline (PA), which formed an electroactive peptide-based hydrogel for tissue engineering (Figure 17.7). Molecular dynamics simulations revealed the existence of RGD fragments on the fibers' surface, and further nanoengineering was carried out on the 3D network of the hydrogel by introducing PA. The electroactive peptide-based supramolecular hydrogel combines most of the properties required for genetic tissue engineering, including cell adhesion,

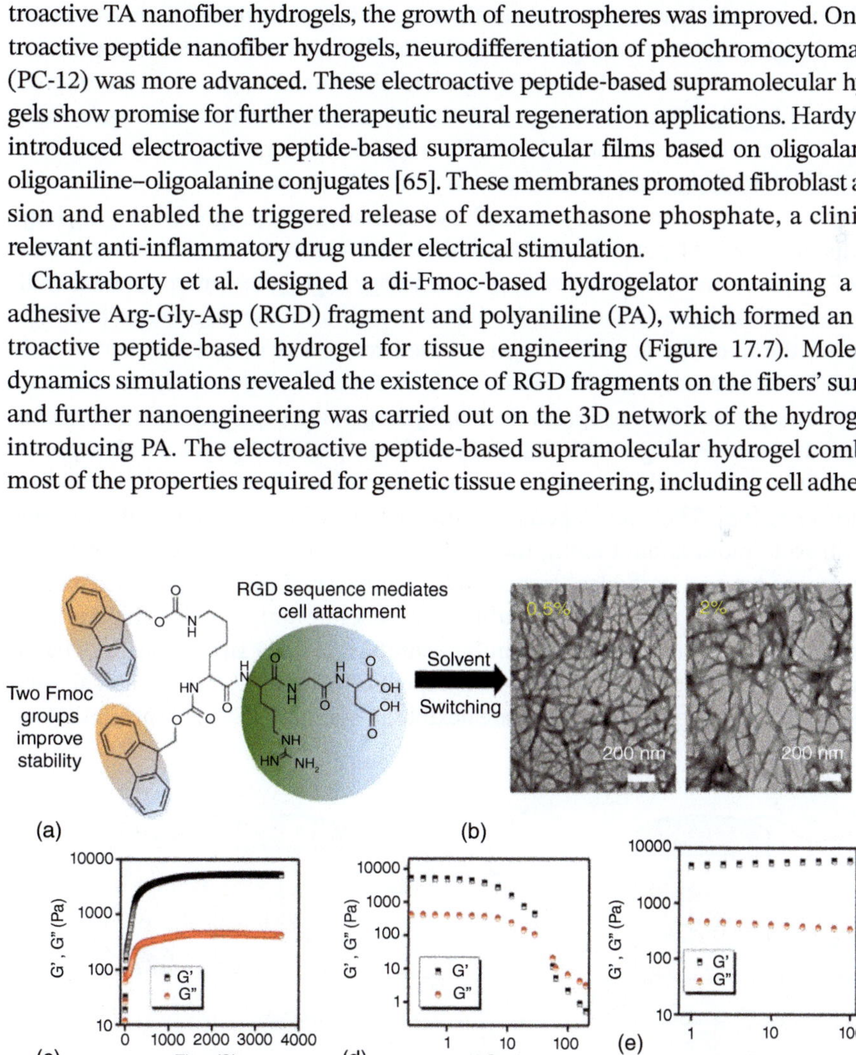

Figure 17.7 Schematic diagram of self-assembly of Fmoc-K(Fmoc)-RGD hydrogel and characterization of its physicochemical properties. (a) Molecular structure. (b) TEM photos of the hydrogel. (c) Time sweep analysis. (d) Strain sweep analysis. (e) Frequency-dependent oscillatory rheology of a 0.5% (w/v) hydrogel. Source: Ref. [66] Reproduced with permission of John Wiley & Sons.

cytocompatibility, conductivity, and antimicrobial property, and can be used to assemble single cardiomyocytes into synchronous contraction cells. These abilities demonstrate their potential use as supramolecular biomaterials for cardiac cell scaffolding in *in vitro* applications, such as drug screening. The application of carbon nanotubes (CNT)-embedded hydrogel sheets in bioactuators and engineered cardiac structures has also been reported [66]. Cardiac patches were fabricated by seeding neonatal rat cardiomyocytes on gelatin methacrylate gels embedded with CNT (CNT-GelMA). This construct displayed sophisticated electrophysiological and mechanical integrity. Cardiac tissue which was cultured on CNT-GelMA (50 μm thick) demonstrated a threefold higher spontaneous synchronized pulsation rate and an 85% lower threshold of excitation in comparison with myocardial tissue that grew on the original GelMA hydrogel. Electroactive peptide-based supramolecular hydrogels have attracted considerable interest for biomedical applications, although they are laboriously difficult to design and the research on them is immature.

Nowadays, lithium-ion battery technology has made great progress, bringing huge benefits to the use of portable devices and electric vehicles as well as energy storage [67]. However, the rapid growth of technology highlights environmental challenges as well as issues related to the safe use and harmless disposal of batteries. However, the material supply of organic-based redox active materials is currently severely limited because so few lithium-ion batteries are being recycled. In this case, electroactive peptide-based supramolecular hydrogels are expected to be one of candidates, due to their degradable and recyclable properties. Nguyen et al. reported peptide films as a classic example of a new generation of energy-storage batteries (Figure 17.8) [68]. They developed a peptide battery without metal, and viologens and nitroxide radicals bind along the peptide backbone as redox active groups to serve as anodes and cathodes, respectively. Moreover, these polypeptides can be degraded on demand under acidic conditions to generate amino acids, other building blocks, and degradation products. Similar examples include supercapacitors based on the Fmoc-glutamic-phenylalanine-NH_2 dipeptide (Fmoc-EF-NH_2). Hu et al. used peptides as electrode materials to prepare flexible all-solid-state SCs on a poly(ethylene

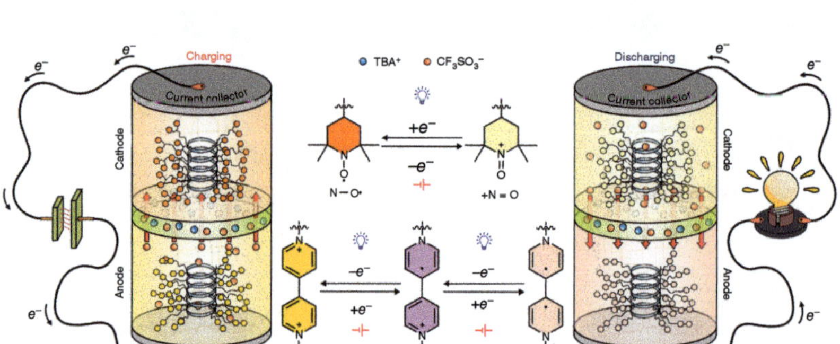

Figure 17.8 Schematic diagram showing the processes that take place when peptide-based organic radical batteries are charged and discharged. Source: Ref. [68] Reproduced with permission of Springer Nature Limited.

terephthalate) substrate [69]. At a current density of $0.1\,A\,g^{-1}$ and a surface capacitance of $8.6\,mF\,cm^{-2}$, the constructed peptide electrode produced an exceptional mass ratio capacitance of $125\,F\,g^{-1}$. In addition, the capacitors exhibit excellent stability, maintaining 95% capacitance after 5000 cycles. These examples could be the first step toward electroactive peptide-based supramolecular hydrogels as a new generation of energy storage devices, especially portable and flexible ones.

17.4.2 Wearable Biosensors

17.4.2.1 Mechanical Sensing

Piezoelectricity is a process that combines mechanical and electrical energy. It is a typical phenomenon that could be observed in many biological systems. Piezoelectric biomaterials such as silk [70], collagen [71], amino acids [72], cellulose [73], and virions [74] can naturally offer many potentially beneficial properties, and peptides are no exception. The custom piezoelectric measurement setup for the silk film is shown in Figure 17.9. However, the strong piezoelectric properties of electroactive peptide-based supramolecular assemblies are usually observed in rigid crystals rather than in flexible hydrogels. Hence, peptide-based flexible piezoelectric sensors are usually manufactured by aligning peptide crystals on flexible substrates on a large scale. Yang et al. prepared a flexible piezoelectric thin-film sensor for monitoring respiration and muscle contraction in rats based on the co-assembly of γ-glycine (G) and polyvinyl alcohol (PVA) [75]. A crystalline glycine layer self-assembled and naturally aligned between two PVA thin films in the sandwich-like structure of the thin film. The piezoelectric coefficients of this heterostructured G-PVA film were $5.3\,pC\,N^{-1}$ or $157.5\times10^{-3}\,V\,m\,N^{-1}$, which are comparable to those of the

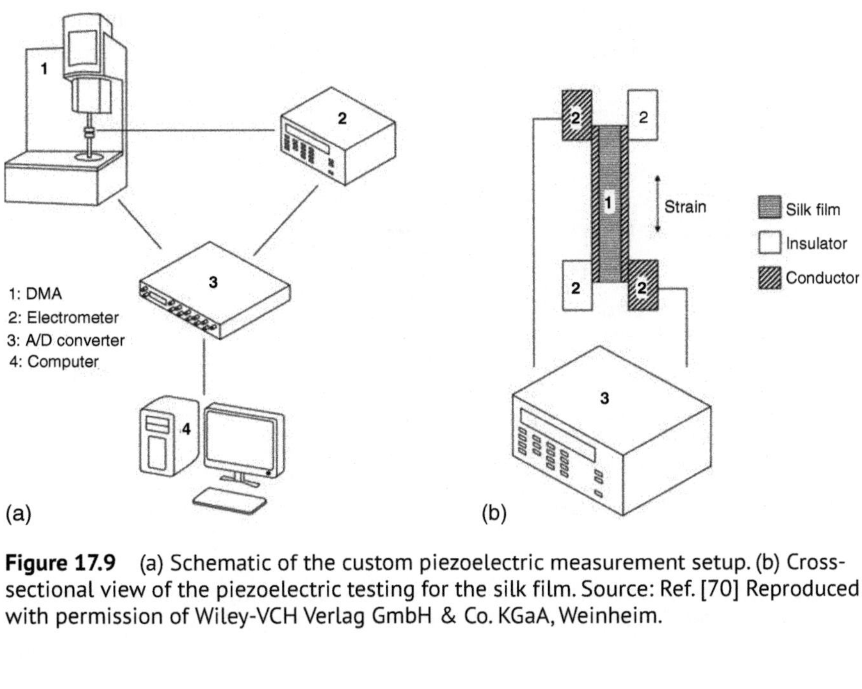

Figure 17.9 (a) Schematic of the custom piezoelectric measurement setup. (b) Cross-sectional view of the piezoelectric testing for the silk film. Source: Ref. [70] Reproduced with permission of Wiley-VCH Verlag GmbH & Co. KGaA, Weinheim.

commercially available soft piezoelectric materials such as polyvinylidene fluoride (PVDF). Animal experiments showed that the piezoelectric film disappeared completely 1 day after implantation. At the same time, the existence and degradation of the film did not cause any anemia or inflammatory reactions, indicating the excellent biocompatibility of the film. In this study, a scalable and straightforward method for fabricating high-efficiency, flexible piezoelectric sensors was presented.

To construct wearable biosensors, Bai et al. developed dipeptide hydrogels with excellent conductivity and transparency based on the enzyme-catalyzed self-assembly of peptides [39]. Thermolysin was employed as a catalyst to promote the forming of dipeptide hydrogels with adjustable physical and chemical properties. In order to create conductive nanofibrils, hydrophilic PPy@PDA nanofillers with good conductivity were included in the hydrogel network (Figure 17.10). This technique gives dipeptide hydrogels excellent conductivity and transparency and offers great application potential for accurately recording tiny human movements using biosensors. Gazit et al. designed a composite hydrogel using Fmoc-FF and polyaniline (PAni) with excellent conductivity [76]. PAni was chosen because of its simple synthesis, stable environment, good electrical conductivity, and good biological safety. Fmoc-FF-PAni composite hydrogels have mechanical strength, electrical conductivity, and self-healing properties. In addition, the hydrogels display conductivity that changes with pressure, as evidenced by the manufacture of sensor devices for pressure. Finally, the devices have been shown to be noncytotoxic and could encourage the development of cardiac cells that respond to electrical stimulation. This study identified Fmoc-FF-PAni hydrogels as a useful mixture having several advantageous qualities that can be used in a variety of applications.

Liu et al. developed a polymer dipeptide dual-network hydrogel with excellent tensile, responsive, and stable properties [77]. The polyacrylic acid (PAA) hydrogels maintain their mechanical and flexible properties through cross-linking and noncovalent interactions to form Fmoc-FF network that contributes to energy dissipation.

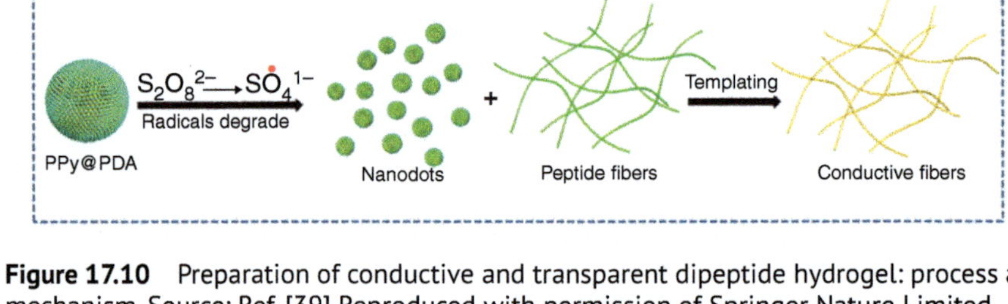

Figure 17.10 Preparation of conductive and transparent dipeptide hydrogel: process and mechanism. Source: Ref. [39] Reproduced with permission of Springer Nature Limited.

PAA/Fmoc-FF hydrogels showed high mechanical strength and rapid recovery with the increase of tensile or compressive strain. In addition, due to the presence of KCl, the electron conductivity was improved, and the mixed hydrogel exhibited cyclic strain–stress properties, which was the basis of strain sensors. Therefore, by observing the motion of human joints such as the forelimbs, wrists, elbows, and knees, its use as a motion sensor was demonstrated. The hybrid polymer peptide hydrogels may therefore be one of the best options for upcoming wearable sensors. Cao et al. engineered dielectric peptide (GAGAGY)-coated graphene (PCG) as a uniformly dispersed electric double layer in hydrogels [78]. The capacitance was strongly affected by any mechanical movement that modifies the microscopic distribution of PCG in the hydrogels. They produced strong and dynamic interfacial contacts between the hydrogel network and graphene via peptide self-assembly. The hydrogel could be stretched 77 times its initial length and restored to the initial form in a matter of minutes.

17.4.2.2 pH Sensing

Liang et al. reported a novel pH-responsive luminescent peptide hydrogel with reversible emission [79]. This smart luminescent hydrogel can be employed as a pH sensor. It was fabricated from pH-sensitive peptides terminated with tetraphenylethylene (TPE). The pH-responsive hydrogel's design structure, known as TPE-MAX, comprised a fluorescent core made of TPE and a responsive nanoformulation made of the pH-sensitive peptide MAX (NH_2-KRKRGSVKVKVKVKVKVKVKVKVKVKVKVKVV-Am). Additionally, they were able to create a variety of TPE-coupled peptide derivatives that had various responses to pH levels by changing polar residues in the peptide sequence, such as changing lysine to histidine or glutamic acid. As a result, a probe library can be generated for detecting a range of pH values.

An alkaline-responsive polydiacetylene-peptide hydrogel for pH monitoring and on-demand antimicrobial release was described by Dong et al. [80]. The polydiacetylene-peptide (PDA-Pep) that served as the basis for the hydrogels had pH-dependent packing and molecular architectures. When pH increased, the PDA domain underwent conformational changes that caused a colorimetric shift from blue to violet. The peptide domain was deprotonated as a result. Deprotonation also caused the fibrous network produced in the PDA-Pep hydrogel to change from a gel to a sol macrophase, which caused the antimicrobial contained in the gel to be released selectively to the site of infection to kill bacteria. On inoculated pig skins, PDA-Pep hydrogels' potential for pH monitoring and on-demand, alkaline-triggered antibiotic administration was established.

17.4.2.3 Temperature Sensing

Shirshin et al. developed a parameter-adjustable sensor based on the self-assembly of Fmoc-FF peptides [81]. Using the turbidity of self-assembled peptide hydrogels, a sensitive defrost sensor with adjustable operating temperature range and alarm time was constructed for continuous monitoring of cold chain logistics in the pharmaceutical industry.

Based on the supramolecular self-assembly of atomically precise silver nanoclusters (Ag9-NCs) with the chiral peptide DD-5, Xin et al. created a temperature and arginine sensor (Figure 17.11) [82]. The Ag_9-NCs/DD-5 luminescent hydrogel was realized through argentophilic interactions [Ag(I)–Ag(I)] and noncovalent forces (H-bonding and π–π stacking). The phosphorescent emission was obtained through aggregation-induced luminescence. The Ag9-NCs/DD-5 xerogels are more suited for temperature sensing, and arginine could be detected using hydrogels' orange-red emission. This research offered a fresh illustration of how metal NC peptide complexes can be built from noncovalent bonds for the purposes of temperature sensing. In the context of temperature fluorescence sensing and biological detection, this work presents a novel illustration of the synthesis of metal NC peptide complexes by noncovalent bonding.

17.4.2.4 Sensing of Biological or Chemical Molecules

The enzyme matrix metalloproteinase-9 (MMP-9) is crucial for several physiological activities. In multiple sclerosis (MS), it is a peripheral biomarker of neuroinflammation. Krause et al. developed a sensor for rapid and direct detection of MMP-9 [83]. This sensor was prepared by coating the electrode with oxidized dextran and subsequently cross-linking with a peptide containing an MMP-9-specific cleavage site. Exposure of the sensor to enzymes caused its degradation and was monitored by impedance measurements. Within 5 minutes of injecting MMP-9, the sensor reacted swiftly, and a large impedance change was typically noticed. The sensor barely reacted to the protease matrix metalloproteinase-2 (MMP-2), which can obstruct the detection of MMP-9. To create a calibration curve, they chose the peptide sequence Leu-Gly-Arg-Met-Gly-Leu-Pro-Gly-Lys, which had the maximum sensitivity and selectivity. MMP-9 was effectively identified in the 50–400 ng mL^{-1} concentration

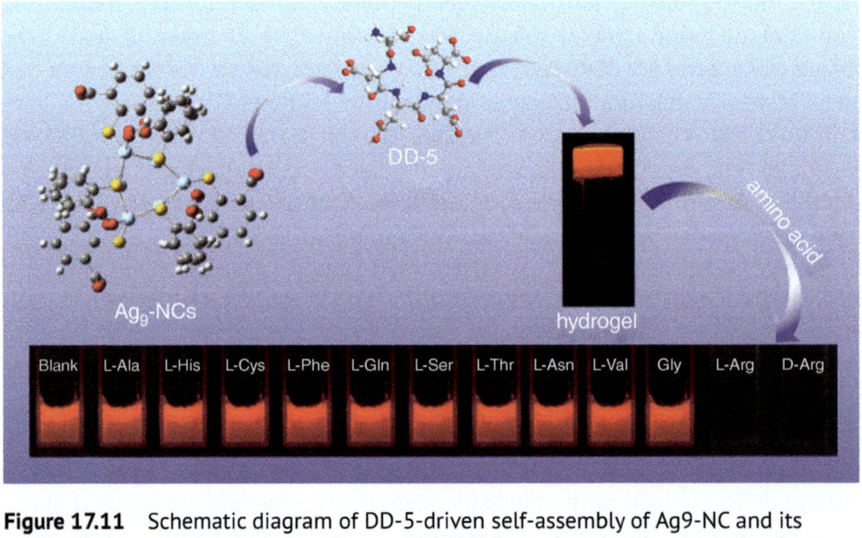

Figure 17.11 Schematic diagram of DD-5-driven self-assembly of Ag9-NC and its application in arginine detection. Source: Ref. [82] Reproduced with permission from MDPI/CC BY 4.0.

range, which was clinically significant. On electrode surfaces with various levels of roughness, two distinct hydrogel degradation processes were seen, both of which seemed appropriate for tracking MMP-9 activity. Gori et al. reported a hydrogel based on a self-assembled peptide (Q3 peptide) with cryogel agarose, which demonstrated simple and robust applications in the fabrication of droplet arrays, overcoming the common limitations of 3D hydrogel analysis (Figure 17.12) [84]. They demonstrated the feasibility of this system in the analysis of serum IgG immunoresponse profiling in COVID-19 patients, which indicated a significant improvement in signal-to-noise ratio standard analysis in 2D format with extremely high specificity. The new two-component hydrogels broadened the application prospects of hydrogel-based arrays and represented an important step forward in their routine application in analytical practice.

For the determination of human cardiac myoglobin, Malhotra et al. reported a microfluidic sensor using cysteine-graphene hydrogels [85]. This study employed surface plasmon resonance (SPR) and differential pulsed voltammetry (DPV) measurements on L-cysteine-graphene hydrogels as bimodal sensing electrodes. With a low lower detection limit (LOD) of 4 pg mL^{-1}, the microfluidic chip demonstrated high sensitivity in the concentration from 0.004 to 1000 ng/mL^{-1}. The LOD for SPR technology, in comparison, was about 2.5 times higher than the above results and ranged from 0.01 to 1000 ng/mL^{-1}. The graphene hydrogels exhibited great

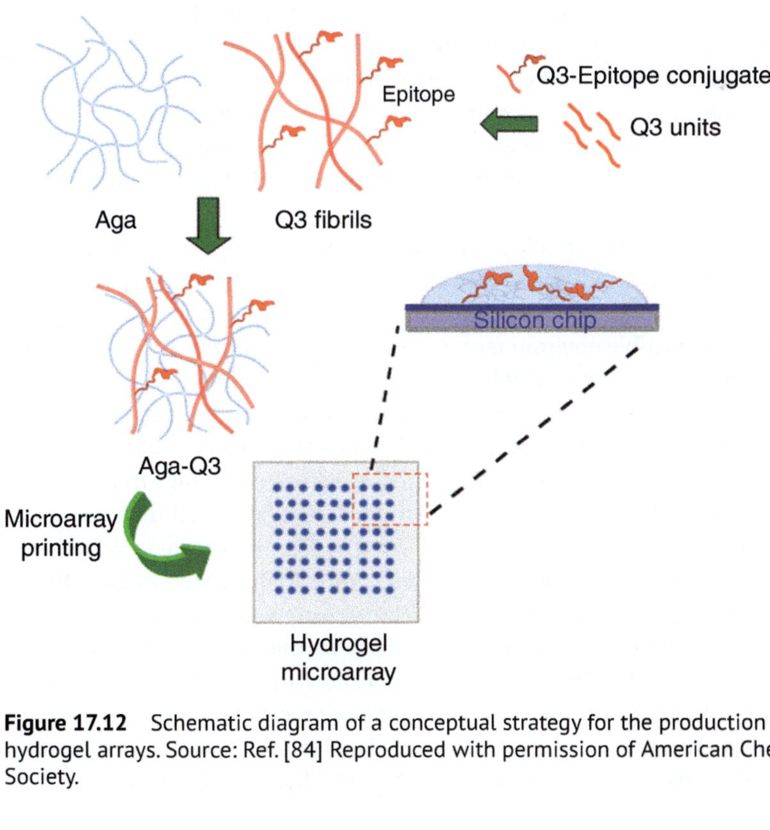

Figure 17.12 Schematic diagram of a conceptual strategy for the production of 3D hydrogel arrays. Source: Ref. [84] Reproduced with permission of American Chemical Society.

performance in detecting human cardiac myoglobin in serum samples due to their high surface reactivity and favorable reaction kinetics.

Park et al. developed a biosensing platform based on a self-assembled peptide hydrogel consisting of Fmoc-FF encapsulated by enzymatic bioreceptors and fluorescent reporters such as quantum dots [86]. By simply combining an aqueous solution containing enzymes and quantum dots with a monomeric peptide (Fmoc-FF) solution, enzymes and quantum dots were physically bound *in situ* in the hydrogel matrix. By photoluminescence quenching of hybrid quantum dots, peptide hydrogels have been successfully applied to the detection of analytes such as glucose and toxic phenolic compounds. For glucose oxidase (GOx) and horseradish peroxidase (HPP), the Michaelis–Menten constant (K_M) of photoluminescent peptide hydrogels was determined to be 3.12 and 0.82 mM, respectively. Compared to conventional hydrogel materials, these findings were significantly lower. According to these findings, peptide hydrogels are a potential replacement for optical biosensing platforms. They have the benefits of being easy to make by self-assembly, effective at diffusing target analytes, and highly effective at encapsulating fluorescent reporters and bioreceptors. Utilizing micromolar quantities of self-assembling peptide, Gori et al. developed a hydrogel matrix which has regulated permeability qualities for the simple confinement of biomolecular probes in arrayed 3D microenvironments [87]. Using this strategy, they obtained stable but highly permeable nanoscaffolds to perform fluorescence immunoassays under solution-like conditions within ultrashort time periods (< 10 min) and picomolar detection limits. Supramolecular hydrogels formed quickly and spontaneously, could be printed using a piezoelectric microarray spotter, and self-adhered to polymethyl methacrylate slides, so hydrogel formation and surface attachment did not require post-spot cross-linking or polymerization, greatly simplifying the manufacturing process. The platform is cost-effective, robust, user-friendly, and features a unique combination of favorable features in hydrogel 3D multiplex bioassays.

Ulijn et al. developed an enzymatic active optical sensor based on a self-assembled Fmoc peptide (Fmoc-TL-OMe) hydrogel interface with a liquid crystal (LC) display [88]. The hydrogel held the LC display in place by providing a semirigid, highly hydrated, and biocompatible environment. It also responded sensitively to enzymes. A two-layer architecture was created, with a lower layer free of phospholipids separating the LC display from the upper hydrogel layer loaded with phospholipids. Subtilis protease (0.15 mM) digested the two layers, which after a few hours produced a gel-to-sol transition, releasing phospholipids and producing an optical change from light to dark in the LC display. Yang et al. developed an intelligent biological interface for a peptide nanofiber hydrogel created using Fmoc-FF [89]. This biological interface was used for enzyme-based electrochemical biosensing. Fmoc-FF hydrogels had two functions. The first one was used as a matrix for HRP in an embedded enzyme model in the course of the assembling of Fmoc-FF peptides. Another one served as a stable surface on which cells might adhere. With a low detection limit of 18 nM, good repeatability, and high selectivity, the resultant third-generation electrochemical biosensor of H_2O_2 displayed excellent sensing performance. The HeLa cells were subsequently attached to the electrode modified by the HRP/Fmoc-FF hydrogel for sensitive *in situ*

H_2O_2 sensing. This Fmoc-FF hydrogel-based biological interface was easy to prepare, environmentally friendly, and can be used to integrate other cells and recognized molecules to monitor various cellular biomolecules.

Luo et al. developed a unique dopamine electrochemical sensor that used a peptide-based hydrogel loaded with ciprofloxacin and gold nanoparticles [90]. Peptide hydrogels were prepared based on the self-assembly of designed Phe-Glu-Lys-Phe short peptide sequences with N-terminal modifications of Fmoc groups. The peptide hydrogels had a nanofiber network structure, exhibiting good shear thinning behavior and good biocompatibility. In addition, it could be easily doped with gold nanoparticles and the antibiotic ciprofloxacin. The loaded antimicrobial provided significant antimicrobial activity to the hydrogel, while the loaded gold nanoparticles provided the hydrogel excellent electrochemical catalytic ability in detecting the typical neurotransmitter dopamine. The antimicrobial properties and electrochemical catalytic capabilities of peptide hydrogels ensured the development of sensitive and antimicrobial electrochemical sensors, a strategy that was expected to facilitate the construction of wearable biosensors without the possibility of infection. Similarly, Wang et al. prepared a biosensor by self-assembly of ferrocene-phenylalanine@graphene oxide hybrid hydrogels for the detection of dopamine (Figure 17.13) [91]. Dopamine concentration in solution was detected with high accuracy by loading a hybrid hydrogel onto the electrode surface. The R^2 value of the linear fitting equation reached 0.9915 in the range of 10–200 μmol/L, indicating its potential as a biosensing electrode material.

Bhattacharya et al. developed a selective visual sensor for Ca^{2+} ions based on hydrogels of a novel prenylated-VPGKG peptide [92]. Other metal ions (such Na^+ and Pb^{2+}) were added, and the resultant suspension either precipitated or underwent no visible changes. Yang et al. synthesized a diacetylene-grafted peptide that could polymerize after triggering by Zn^{2+} [93]. The molecules dissolved well in aqueous solution before adding zinc ions and could not be polymerized by ultraviolet irradiation. After adding Zn^{2+}, the peptide immediately coordinated with them and self-assembled into a supramolecular hydrogel. By passing a UV laser over the molecules for less than 2 minutes, they could quickly polymerize because of their

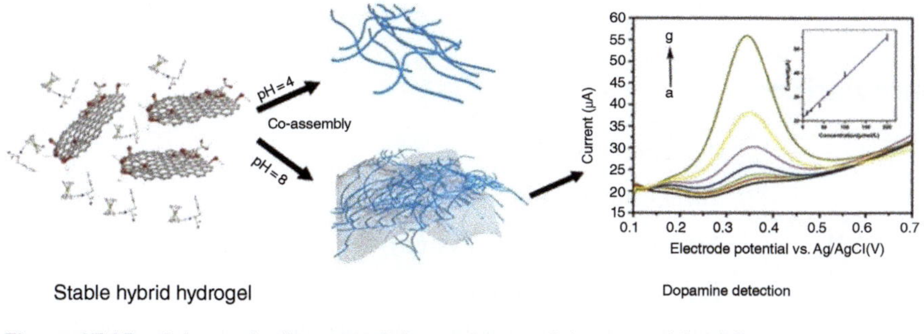

Figure 17.13 Schematic diagram of the structure of the assembly of ferrocene-L-phenylalanine (Fc–F) and graphene oxide (GO) at two different pH values and the responsiveness of the assembly to dopamine. Source: Ref. [91] Reproduced with permission of Wiley-VCH Verlag GmbH & Co. KGaA, Weinheim.

neat arrangement. The system displayed a swift and abrupt change in color from white to dark blue, which enabled observational measurement of self-assembly.

17.5 Conclusions and Perspectives

Self-assembled electroactive peptide-based hydrogels exhibit excellent biological and electronic properties, which allow the development of bioinspired entities into a new generation of bioelectronic materials with biocompatibility and green degradability. Although the rigid nanostructures of aromatic peptide assemblies exhibit strong semiconductor properties, the electronic properties of pure peptide hydrogels with three-dimensional structures are very weak. The ability to conjugate external organic π-electron subunits links supramolecular peptides with conventional organic semiconductors to produce hybrid or extrinsic semiconductor hydrogels with strong electronic properties. As bioelectronic materials, self-assembled electroactive peptide-based supramolecular hydrogels are processed bottom-up in a way that allows their electrical and mechanical properties to be easily modulated by noncovalent forces, enabling the customizable development of their functions for successful applications in biomedicine, energy storage, and sensors. However, this field is remarkably interdisciplinary and is still in its infancy. For self-assembled electroactive peptide-based supramolecular hydrogels that are reliable and widely used as electroactive materials, several challenges must still be addressed, including improving mechanical and electrical stability, evaluating toxicity *in vivo*, identifying the specific assembly mechanisms, and the evolution from scientific progress to industrial engineering.

In the long term, owing to the biocompatibility of peptides, self-assembled electroactive peptide-based hydrogels can be used to develop autonomous biomachines that operate *in vivo* within biological systems. This may allow, for example, direct, label-free, and real-time monitoring and sensing of a wide variety of metabolic activities as well as the analysis of and interference with biological systems. Such technologies have enormous scientific, social, and economic implications.

Abbreviations

1D	One-dimensional
3D	Three-dimensional
$Ac\text{-}I_4K_2\text{-}NH_2$	Acetyl-(Isoleucine)$_4$-(Lysine)$_2$-NH_2
Boc	Tert-butyloxycarbonyl
BTBT	[1]benzothieno[3,2-b][1]-benzothiophene
CD	Carbon dot
cMb	Cardiac myoglobin

DAN	Dialkoxy
DHN	Dihydroxy naphthalene
FF	Diphenylalanine
Fmoc	N-fluorenyl-9-methoxycarbonyl
Fmoc	9-fluorenylmethoxycarbonyl
Fmoc-EF-NH_2	Fmoc-glutamic-phenylalanine-NH_2
Fmoc-L	Fmoc-leucine
Fmoc-LL	Fmoc-dileucine
Fmoc-S	Fmoc-serine
Fmoc-T	Fmoc-threonine
Fmoc-Y	Fmoc-tyrosine
Fmoc-YD	Fmoc-tyrosine-aspartic acid
Fmoc-YK	Fmoc-tyrosine-lysine
F-NH_2	Phenylalanine-NH_2
FW	Phenylalaninetryptophan
G	Glycine
GelMA	Gelatin methacrylate
LC	Liquid crystal
L-NH_2	Leucine-NH_2
LOD	Limit of detection
MAX	NH_2-KRKRGSVKVKVKVKVDPPTVKVKVKVK-Am
MMP-2	Matrix metalloproteinase-2
MS	Multiple sclerosis
NDI	Naphthalene diimide
NDI-Y	NDI-tyrosine
PA	Polyaniline
PAA	Poly(acrylic acid)
PAni	Polyaniline
PC-12	Pheochromocytoma cells
PCG	Peptide-coated graphene
PDA-Pep	Polydiacetylene-peptide
PDI	Perylene diimide
PEDOT:PSS	Poly(3,4-ethylenedioxythiophene):polystyrene sulfonate
PVA	Polyvinyl alcohol

PVDF	Polyvinylidene fluoride
QDs	Quantum dots
RGD	Arg–Gly–Asp
SPR	Surface plasmon resonance
TA	Tetraaniline
TCNQ	7,8,8-Tetracyanoquinodimethane
TPE	Tetraphenylethylene
TPPS	Tetrakis(4-sulfonatophenyl)porphine
TPP-Zn	5,10,15,20-Tetraphenyl-21H,23H-porphine zinc
TTF	Tetrathiafulvalene
WW	Ditryptophan
YY	Dityrosine

References

1 Irimia-Vladu, M., Głowacki, E.D., Voss, G. et al. (2012). Green and biodegradable electronics. *Mater. Today* 15 (7–8): 340–346.

2 Someya, T., Bao, Z., and Malliaras, G.G. (2016). The rise of plastic bioelectronics. *Nature* 540 (7633): 379–385.

3 Han, Q., Wang, A., Song, W. et al. (2021). Fabrication of conductive, adhesive, and stretchable agarose-based hydrogels for a wearable biosensor. *ACS Appl. Bio Mater.* 4 (8): 6148–6156.

4 Fu, J., Reinhold, J., and Woodbury, N.W. (2011). Peptide-modified surfaces for enzyme immobilization. *PLoS One* 6 (4): e18692.

5 Wei, G.J., Yao, M., Wang, Y.S. et al. (2013). Promotion of peripheral nerve regeneration of a peptide compound hydrogel scaffold. *Int. J. Nanomed.* 8: 3217–3225.

6 Wang, X.-M., Qiao, L., and Horii, A. (2011). Screening of functionalized self-assembling peptide nanofiber scaffolds with angiogenic activity for endothelial cell growth. *Prog. Nat. Sci.* 21 (2): 111–116.

7 Jian, H., Wang, M., Wang, S. et al. (2018). 3D bioprinting for cell culture and tissue fabrication. *Bio-Design Manuf.* 1 (1): 45–61.

8 Garifullin, R. and Guler, M.O. (2021). Electroactive peptide-based supramolecular polymers. *Mater. Today Bio.* 10: 100099.

9 Li, J., Xing, R., Bai, S., and Yan, X. (2019). Recent advances of self-assembling peptide-based hydrogels for biomedical applications. *Soft Matter.* 15 (8): 1704–1715.

10 Li, T., Lu, X.-M., Zhang, M.-R. et al. (2022). Peptide-based nanomaterials: self-assembly, properties and applications. *Bioactive Mater.* 11: 268–282.

11 Panda, S.S., Katz, H.E., and Tovar, J.D. (2018). Solid-state electrical applications of protein and peptide based nanomaterials. *Chem. Soc. Rev.* 47 (10): 3640–3658.

12 Tao, K., Levin, A., Adler-Abramovich, L., and Gazit, E. (2016). Fmoc-modified amino acids and short peptides: simple bio-inspired building blocks for the fabrication of functional materials. *Chem. Soc. Rev.* 45 (14): 3935–3953.

13 Hao, L., Wang, A., Fu, J. et al. (2023). Biomineralized dipeptide self-assembled hydrogel with ultrahigh mechanical strength and osteoinductivity for bone regeneration. *Colloids Surf. A* 657: 130622.

14 Tian, Y., Li, J., Wang, A. et al. (2022). Long-range ordered amino acid assemblies exhibit effective optical-to-electrical transduction and stable photoluminescence. *Acta Biomater.* 154: 135–144.

15 Zhang, J., Guerin, S., Wu, H. et al. (2022). Modulating vectored non-covalent interactions for layered assembly with engineerable properties. *Bio-Design Manuf.* 5 (3): 529–539.

16 Ma, Y., Wang, A., Li, J. et al. (2023). Surface self-assembly of dipeptides on porous CaCO3 particles promoting cell internalization. *ACS Appl. Mater. Interfaces* 15 (1): 2486–2497.

17 Li, X., Zhang, Q., Jian, H., and Bai, S. (2023). Chiral implications on Fmoc-dipeptide self-assembly and catalytic kinetics of thermolysin. *Colloids Surf. A* 660: 130863.

18 Hao, L., Liang, S., Han, Q. et al. (2023). Ultralong hydroxyapatite nanowires-incorporated dipeptide hydrogel with enhanced mechanical strength and superior in vivo osteogenesis activity. *Colloids Surf. A* 664: 131153.

19 Yuan, C., Ji, W., Xing, R. et al. (2019). Hierarchically oriented organization in supramolecular peptide crystals. *Nat. Rev. Chem.* 3 (10): 567–588.

20 Yan, X., Zhu, P., and Li, J. (2010). Self-assembly and application of diphenylalanine-based nanostructures. *Chem. Soc. Rev.* 39 (6): 1877–1890.

21 Fleming, S. and Ulijn, R.V. (2014). Design of nanostructures based on aromatic peptide amphiphiles. *Chem. Soc. Rev.* 43 (23): 8150–8177.

22 Wang, J., Liu, K., Xing, R., and Yan, X. (2016). Peptide self-assembly: thermodynamics and kinetics. *Chem. Soc. Rev.* 45 (20): 5589–5604.

23 Wang, M., Zhang, Q., Jian, H. et al. (2020). Role of thermolysin in catalytic-controlled self-assembly of Fmoc-dipeptides. *CCS Chem.* 2 (4): 317–328.

24 Tao, K., Makam, P., Aizen, R., and Gazit, E. (2017). Self-assembling peptide semiconductors. *Science* 358: 6365.

25 Tao, K., Hu, W., Xue, B. et al. (2019). Bioinspired stable and photoluminescent assemblies for power generation. *Adv. Mater.* 31 (12): e1807481.

26 Amdursky, N., Molotskii, M., Aronov, D. et al. (2009). Blue luminescence based on quantum confinement at peptide nanotubes. *Nano Lett.* 9 (9): 3111–3115.

27 Tao, K., Fan, Z., Sun, L. et al. (2018). Quantum confined peptide assemblies with tunable visible to near-infrared spectral range. *Nat. Commun.* 9 (1): 3217.

28 Basavalingappa, V., Bera, S., Xue, B. et al. (2020). Diphenylalanine-derivative peptide assemblies with increased aromaticity exhibit metal-like rigidity and high piezoelectricity. *ACS Nano* 14 (6): 7025–7037.

29 Gan, Z., Wu, X., Zhu, X., and Shen, J. (2013). Light-induced ferroelectricity in bioinspired self-assembled diphenylalanine nanotubes/microtubes. *Angew. Chem. Int. Ed. Engl.* 52 (7): 2055–2059.

30 Lee, J.S., Yoon, I., Kim, J. et al. (2011). Self-assembly of semiconducting photoluminescent peptide nanowires in the vapor phase. *Angew. Chem. Int. Ed. Engl.* 50 (5): 1164–1167.

31 Li, Q., Jia, Y., Dai, L. et al. (2015). Controlled rod nanostructured assembly of diphenylalanine and their optical waveguide properties. *ACS Nano* 9 (3): 2689–2695.

32 Nguyen, V., Zhu, R., Jenkins, K., and Yang, R. (2016). Self-assembly of diphenylalanine peptide with controlled polarization for power generation. *Nat. Commun.* 7: 13566.

33 Amdursky, N. (2013). Enhanced solid-state electron transport via tryptophan containing peptide networks. *Phys. Chem. Chem. Phys.* 15 (32): 13479–13482.

34 Akdim, B., Pachter, R., and Naik, R.R. (2015). Self-assembled peptide nanotubes as electronic materials: An evaluation from first-principles calculations. *Appl. Phys. Lett.* 106 (18): 183707.

35 Ren, P., Li, J., Zhao, L. et al. (2020). Dipeptide self-assembled hydrogels with shear-thinning and instantaneous self-healing properties determined by peptide sequences. *ACS Appl. Mater. Interfaces* 12 (19): 21433–21440.

36 Amdursky, N., Gazit, E., and Rosenman, G. (2010). Quantum confinement in self-assembled bioinspired peptide hydrogels. *Adv. Mater.* 22 (21): 2311–2315.

37 Wang, S., Wang, A., Ma, Y. et al. (2021). In situ synthesis of superorganism-like au NPs within microgels with ultra-wide absorption in visible and near-infrared regions for combined cancer therapy. *Biomater. Sci.* 9 (3): 774–779.

38 Li, J., Xue, Y., Wang, A. et al. (2022). Polyaniline functionalized peptide self-assembled conductive hydrogel for 3D cell culture. *Gels* 8 (6): 372.

39 Jing, Y., Wang, A., Li, J. et al. (2022). Preparation of conductive and transparent dipeptide hydrogels for wearable biosensor. *Bio-Design Manufact.* 5 (1): 153–162.

40 Feng, L., Wang, A., Ren, P. et al. (2018). Self-assembled peptide hydrogel with porphyrin as a dopant for enhanced photocurrent generation. *Colloid Interf. Sci. Commun.* 23: 29–33.

41 Pascal, A.A., Liu, Z., Broess, K. et al. (2005). Molecular basis of photoprotection and control of photosynthetic light-harvesting. *Nature* 436 (7047): 134–137.

42 Wang, S., Zhang, D., Zhang, X. et al. (2019). Short peptide-regulated aggregation of porphyrins for photoelectric conversion. *Sustain. Energy Fuels* 3 (2): 529–538.

43 Fortunato, A., Sanzone, A., Mattiello, S. et al. (2021). The pH- and salt-controlled self-assembly of [1]benzothieno[3,2-b][1]-benzothiophene–peptide conjugates in supramolecular hydrogels. *New J. Chem.* 45 (30): 13389–13398.

44 Nalluri, S.K., Shivarova, N., Kanibolotsky, A.L. et al. (2014). Conducting nanofibers and organogels derived from the self-assembly of tetrathiafulvalene-appended dipeptides. *Langmuir* 30 (41): 12429–12437.

45 Eakins, G.L., Wojciechowski, J.P., Martin, A.D. et al. (2015). Chiral effects in peptide-substituted perylene imide nanofibres. *Supramol. Chem.* 27 (11–12): 746–756.

46 Nalluri, S.K., Berdugo, C., Javid, N. et al. (2014). Biocatalytic self-assembly of supramolecular charge-transfer nanostructures based on n-type semiconductor-appended peptides. *Angew. Chem. Int. Ed. Engl.* 53 (23): 5882–5887.

47 Kumar, M., Ing, N.L., Narang, V. et al. (2018). Amino-acid-encoded biocatalytic self-assembly enables the formation of transient conducting nanostructures. *Nat. Chem.* 10 (7): 696–703.

48 Bihar, E., Roberts, T., Saadaoui, M. et al. (2017). Inkjet-printed PEDOT:PSS electrodes on paper for electrocardiography. *Adv. Healthc. Mater.* 6 (6): 1601167.

49 Zhu, C., Chortos, A., Wang, Y. et al. (2018). Stretchable temperature-sensing circuits with strain suppression based on carbon nanotube transistors. *Nat. Electron.* 1 (3): 183–190.

50 Hong, K., Kim, S.H., Mahajan, A., and Frisbie, C.D. (2014). Aerosol jet printed p- and n-type electrolyte-gated transistors with a variety of electrode materials: exploring practical routes to printed electronics. *ACS Appl. Mater. Interfaces* 6 (21): 18704–18711.

51 Feig, V.R., Tran, H., Lee, M. et al. (2019). An electrochemical gelation method for patterning conductive PEDOT:PSS hydrogels. *Adv. Mater.* 31 (39): e1902869.

52 Wang, S., Xu, J., Wang, W. et al. (2018). Skin electronics from scalable fabrication of an intrinsically stretchable transistor array. *Nature* 555 (7694): 83–88.

53 Cho, Y., Park, S., Lee, J., and Yu, K.J. (2021). Emerging materials and technologies with applications in flexible neural implants: a comprehensive review of current issues with neural devices. *Adv. Mater.* 33 (47): e2005786.

54 Wang, Q., Ma, Z., Wang, Y. et al. (2021). Fabrication and characterization of 3D printed biocomposite scaffolds based on PCL and zirconia nanoparticles. *Bio-Design Manufact.* 4 (1): 60–71.

55 Oladapo, B.I., Zahedi, S.A., Ismail, S.O. et al. (2021). 3D printing of PEEK–cHAp scaffold for medical bone implant. *Bio-Design Manufact.* 4 (1): 44–59.

56 Xie, M., Zheng, Y., Gao, Q., and He, Y. (2021). Facile 3D cell culture protocol based on photocurable hydrogels. *Bio-Design Manufact.* 4 (1): 149–153.

57 Ma, S., Jiang, Z., Wang, M. et al. (2021). 4D printing of PLA/PCL shape memory composites with controllable sequential deformation. *Bio-Design Manufact.* 4 (4): 867–878.

58 Willemen, N.G.A., Morsink, M.A.J., Veerman, D. et al. (2022). From oral formulations to drug-eluting implants: using 3D and 4D printing to develop drug delivery systems and personalized medicine. *Bio-Design Manufact.* 5 (1): 85–106.

59 Li, X., Jian, H., Han, Q. et al. (2023). Three-dimensional (3D) bioprinting of medium toughened dipeptide hydrogel scaffolds with Hofmeister effect. *J. Colloid Interface Sci.* 639: 1–6.

60 Yuk, H., Lu, B., Lin, S. et al. (2020). 3D printing of conducting polymers. *Nat. Commun.* 11 (1): 1604.

61 Jian, H., Wang, M., Dong, Q. et al. (2019). Dipeptide self-assembled hydrogels with tunable mechanical properties and degradability for 3D bioprinting. *ACS Appl. Mater. Interfaces* 11 (50): 46419–46426.

62 Li, Q., Xuan, M., Wang, A. et al. (2022). Biogenic sensors based on dipeptide assemblies. *Matter* 5 (11): 3643–3658.

63 Han, Q., Zhang, C., Guo, T. et al. (2023). Hydrogel nanoarchitectonics of a flexible and self-adhesive electrode for long-term wireless electroencephalogram recording and high-accuracy sustained attention evaluation. *Adv. Mater.* 2209606.

64 Arioz, I., Erol, O., Bakan, G. et al. (2018). Biocompatible electroactive tetra(aniline)-conjugated peptide nanofibers for neural differentiation. *ACS Appl. Mater. Interfaces* 10 (1): 308–317.

65 Hardy, J.G., Amend, M.N., Geissler, S. et al. (2015). Peptide-directed assembly of functional supramolecular polymers for biomedical applications: electroactive molecular tongue-twisters (oligoalanine-oligoaniline-oligoalanine) for electrochemically enhanced drug delivery. *J. Mater. Chem. B* 3 (25): 5005–5009.

66 Shin, S.R., Jung, S.M., Zalabany, M. et al. (2013). Carbon-nanotube-embedded hydrogel sheets for engineering cardiac constructs and bioactuators. *ACS Nano* 7 (3): 2369–2380.

67 Schipper, F. and Aurbach, D. (2016). A brief review: past, present and future of lithium ion batteries. *Russ. J. Electrochem.* 52 (12): 1095–1121.

68 Nguyen, T.P., Easley, A.D., Kang, N. et al. (2021). Polypeptide organic radical batteries. *Nature* 593 (7857): 61–66.

69 Hu, K., Zheng, C., An, M. et al. (2018). A peptide-based supercapacitor and its performance improvement via TiO2 coating. *J. Mater. Chem. A* 6 (17): 8047–8052.

70 Yucel, T., Cebe, P., and Kaplan, D.L. (2011). Structural origins of silk piezoelectricity. *Adv. Funct. Mater.* 21 (4): 779–785.

71 Denning, D., Kilpatrick, J.I., Fukada, E. et al. (2017). Piezoelectric tensor of collagen fibrils determined at the nanoscale. *ACS Biomater. Sci. Eng.* 3 (6): 929–935.

72 Guerin, S., Stapleton, A., Chovan, D. et al. (2018). Control of piezoelectricity in amino acids by supramolecular packing. *Nat. Mater.* 17 (2): 180–186.

73 Garcia, Y., Ruiz-Blanco, Y.B., Marrero-Ponce, Y., and Sotomayor-Torres, C.M. (2016). Orthotropic piezoelectricity in 2D nanocellulose. *Sci. Rep.* 6: 34616.

74 Lee, B.Y., Zhang, J., Zueger, C. et al. (2012). Virus-based piezoelectric energy generation. *Nat. Nanotechnol.* 7 (6): 351–356.

75 Yang, F., Li, J., Long, Y. et al. (2021). Wafer-scale heterostructured piezoelectric bio-organic thin films. *Science* 373: 337–342.

76 Chakraborty, P., Guterman, T., Adadi, N. et al. (2019). A self-healing, all-organic, conducting, composite peptide hydrogel as pressure sensor and electrogenic cell soft substrate. *ACS Nano* 13 (1): 163–175.

77 Luo, X., Ding, B., and Liu, X. (2022). Poly(acrylic acid)/dipeptide double-network hydrogel to achieve a highly stretchable strain sensor. *Chemosensors* 10 (9): 360.

78 Xue, B., Sheng, H., Li, Y. et al. (2022). Stretchable and self-healable hydrogel artificial skin. *National Sci. Rev.* 9 (7): nwab147.

79 Zhang, C.Q., Li, Y.W., Xue, X.D. et al. (2015). A smart pH-switchable luminescent hydrogel. *Chem. Commun.* 51 (20): 4168–4171.

80 Chen, W., Hazoor, S., Madigan, R. et al. (2022). Alkaline-responsive polydiacetylene-peptide hydrogel for pH-sensing and on-demand antimicrobial release. *Mater. Today Adv.* 16: 100288.

81 Tikhonova, T.N., Cohen-Gerassi, D., Arnon, Z.A. et al. (2022). Tunable self-assembled peptide hydrogel sensor for pharma cold supply chain. *ACS Appl. Mater. Interfaces* 14 (50): 55392–55401.

82 Wang, W., Wang, Z., Sun, D. et al. (2022). Supramolecular self-assembly of atomically precise silver nanoclusters with chiral peptide for temperature sensing and detection of arginine. *Nanomaterials* 12 (3): 424.

83 Biela, A., Watkinson, M., Meier, U.C. et al. (2015). Disposable MMP-9 sensor based on the degradation of peptide cross-linked hydrogel films using electrochemical impedance spectroscopy. *Biosens. Bioelectron.* 68: 660–667.

84 Bergamaschi, G., Musico, A., Frigerio, R. et al. (2022). Composite peptide-agarose hydrogels for robust and high-sensitivity 3D immunoassays. *ACS Appl. Mater. Interfaces* 14 (4): 4811–4822.

85 Singh, N., Ali, A., Rai, P. et al. (2020). Dual-modality microfluidic biosensor based on nanoengineered mesoporous graphene hydrogels. *Lab on a Chip* 20 (4): 760–777.

86 Kim, J.H., Lim, S.Y., Nam, D.H. et al. (2011). Self-assembled, photoluminescent peptide hydrogel as a versatile platform for enzyme-based optical biosensors. *Biosens. Bioelectron.* 26 (5): 1860–1865.

87 Gagni, P., Romanato, A., Bergamaschi, G. et al. (2019). A self-assembling peptide hydrogel for ultrarapid 3D bioassays. *Nanoscale Adv.* 1 (2): 490–497.

88 Lin, I.H., Birchall, L.S., Hodson, N. et al. (2013). Interfacing biodegradable molecular hydrogels with liquid crystals. *Soft Matter* 9 (4): 1188–1193.

89 Lian, M., Chen, X., Lu, Y., and Yang, W. (2016). Self-assembled peptide hydrogel as a smart biointerface for enzyme-based electrochemical biosensing and cell monitoring. *ACS Appl. Mater. Interfaces* 8 (38): 25036–25042.

90 Wang, W., Han, R., Tang, K. et al. (2021). Biocompatible peptide hydrogels with excellent antibacterial and catalytic properties for electrochemical sensing application. *Anal. Chim. Acta* 1154: 338295.

91 Zhang, G., Wang, J., Wang, Y. et al. (2020). Self-assembly of ferrocene-phenylalanine@graphene oxide hybrid hydrogels for dopamine detection. *Chempluschem* 85 (10): 2341–2348.

92 Maiti, B., Bhattacharjee, S., and Bhattacharya, S. (2019). Perfluoroarene induces a pentapeptidic hydrotrope into a pH-tolerant hydrogel allowing naked eye sensing of Ca^{2+} ions. *Nanoscale* 11 (5): 2223–2230.

93 Zhang, Y., Pan, Y.-C., Wang, Y. et al. (2018). Fast naked-eye detection of zinc ions by molecular assembly-assisted polymerization of diacetylene. *Nanoscale* 10 (39): 18829–18834.

18

Self-assembled Peptide-based Biocatalyst

Jingjing Han[1], *Xuehai Yan*[2,3,4], *and Juyoung Yoon*[1]

[1] *Department of Chemistry and Nanoscience, Ewha Womans University, Seoul 03760, Republic of Korea*
[2] *State Key Laboratory of Biochemical Engineering, Institute of Process Engineering, Chinese Academy of Sciences, 100190 Beijing, China*
[3] *Center for Mesoscience, Institute of Process Engineering, Chinese Academy of Sciences, 100190 Beijing, China*
[4] *School of Chemical Engineering, University of Chinese Academy of Sciences, 100049 Beijing, China*

18.1 Introduction

Naturally produced catalysts exhibit a variety of catalytic behaviors due to their adaptable three-dimensional architectures. However, three-dimensional enzymes' intrinsic fragility also restricts their application in the eco-friendly sector. Since peroxidase-like Fe_3O_4 nanoparticles (NPs) and the Zn(II)-containing Au nanoparticles show outstanding exquisite properties, they have attracted the attention of researchers [1]. These sophisticated qualities of inorganic catalysts have much in common with those of biocatalysts in terms of kinetics of a chemical transformation. However, they are more stable, less expensive, and simpler than biocatalysts to make. Enzyme mimics have emerged as a crucial substitute for enzymes and have gained prominence in the scientific community [2]. However, few three-dimensional enzyme imitators are available. In addition, they could not meet the demand for selectivity, catalytic activity, or biocompatibility.

Substrate identification and enzymatic catalytic reactions are possible by fine management of conformational changes, which are themselves inherited from supramolecular interactions. Noncovalent interactions are also required for the development of hydrophobic micropores in a flexible protein structure. For example, the supramolecular building blocks shares natural enzyme architecture's amphiphilic properties [3, 4]. In light of these facts, supramolecular assembly, forming the basis of natural enzyme systems, demonstrates special traits of biomimetics, customizability, predictability, and adaptability [4, 5]. It also plays an undeniably important role in generating well-organized arrays of biomolecules or basic elements in artificial enzyme [6–10]. Due to their superior ordered organization, selectivity, and excellent catalytic

Peptide Self-Assembly and Engineering: Fundamentals, Structures, and Applications, First Edition.
Edited by Xuehai Yan.

efficiency, supramolecular nanozymes have emerged as successful alternatives to biocatalysts in a variety of applications [11–16].

Peptides and their analogues, which display spectacular cytocompatibility and graceful features in the construction of supramolecular enzymes, are really simple but crucial basic components of life as opposed to metal complexes and inorganic materials [17–23]. The biological system has enough molecular area for 22 kinds of amino acids to assemble into an orderly architecture [24–28]. The geometric simplicity and diversity of amino-acid functional groups and their importance for assembling processes and behaviors are all characteristics of these groups [29–31].

With the aid of multiple noncovalent interactions and regulations of structural modification, thermodynamics and kinetics are also essential to the growth of nanomaterials [32]. Furthermore, these key parts might potentially lengthen the wavelength at which peptide-based nanoassemblies absorb light [33]. By controlling peptide-based nanostructures, oxygen levels can also affect their highly specific oxidation [34]. The successive assembly mechanism of peptides offers additional flexibility for constructing optimal functional, hierarchically directed architecture of biomimetic systems [35–37]. Herein, this chapter focuses on the assembled peptide-based catalysts through how to select constructed peptide modules, control their functions, and apply catalytic reactions under different catalytic mechanisms, which could be divided into catalytic peptides/amyloids/polypeptides, photosensitive artificial enzymes, and hybrid photo-enzyme-coupled systems (Scheme 18.1). Inspiring readers to create new, highly selective, peptide-based catalysts for improving enzyme-engineering industry and for general bioapplication is main objective of this chapter [38].

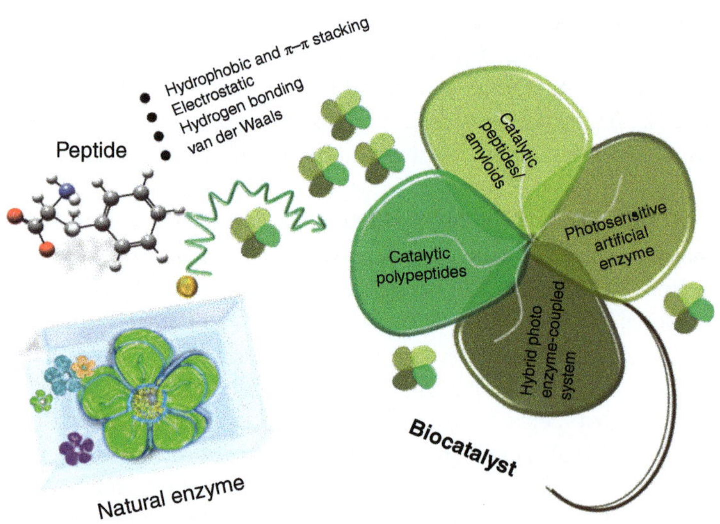

Scheme 18.1 Self-assembled peptide-based biocatalyst. Source: Adapted with permission from Ref. [38]; ©2021 Elsevier.

18.2 Assembled Catalytic Peptides, Amyloids, and Polypeptides

To demonstrate catalytic activity, partially amino acids such as histidine and proline can serve as active sites of an enzymatic biosystem. It is known that positions of active moieties can also influence sorts of catalytic systems and catalytic efficiency of enzyme mimics [21, 39, 40].

18.2.1 Histidine-based Hydrolysis

Histidine features an imidazole motif that may function as a catalyst for common base reactions and a nucleophile to start hydrolysis events. That is frequently seen in a variety of hydrolytic catalysts [41]. Histidine-containing active sites may group together, speeding up the reaction process [42]. Histidine's catalytic activity in solution is significantly lower in its disorganized forms than it is in its supramolecular nanofibers that are properly organized (constructed by peptide amphiphiles). As a result, self-assembled peptide amphiphiles (PAs) with histidine functionality are created. These units eventually come together to form a nanofiber with a significant aspect ratio as well as an internal imidazolyl organization [43].

The synthesized Fmoc-phenylalanine-based selenide is a very smart glutathione peroxide (GPx) mimic. It could self-assemble into nanospheres. It could also transfer into nanotubes along with glutathione and hydroperoxide responsibility. This mimic has been initiated. After active sites are exposed, it displays catalytic activity [44]. Additionally, histidine- or cysteine-containing cyclic dipeptides have enzymatic activities like an esterase that can produce very persistent aggregates. This primary artificial enzyme relies heavily on C—H interactions between phenylalanine and leucine or valine side chains as well as intermolecular cooperation between histidine and cysteine [45].

In addition, catalytic peptides depend on the environment around them. Under physiological circumstances, a histidine-containing unprotected tripeptide (LHis–DPhe–DPhe) can form a thermoreversible hydrogel. Additionally, this thermoreversible hydrogel displays behavior similar to ester hydrolysis [46]. A short peptide motif is built on gold monolayer-protected clusters (Au MPCs) in another supramolecular catalytic system [47]. The multivalent surface of Au MPCs allows the substrate and catalyst to get close to one another. The resulting proximity speeds up the rate of reaction in this chemical environment. Even at two orders of magnitude, this system improves when *p*-nitrophenyl ester of *N*-carboxybenzylphenylalanine is transesterified.

Due to external stimuli (temperature, pH, additives, and light), there are numerous ways for controlling catalytic activities of enzyme mimics [46, 48]. By adding a photoresponsive azobenzene group to the histidine-containing peptide chain, it is possible to create a photoswitchable artificial hydrolase [48]. Histidine and tyrosine residues are the only hydrogel components in a reported amyloid-like fibrillar structure that are organized with ionic strength-dependent hydrolase–oxidase activity in a dual model. In contrast to deconstructed random coils, this works in an assembled fibril [49].

First, common and simple functional esterase-mimicking elements (serine, aspartate, and histidine, Ser-His-Asp) are investigated due to the intricacy of multiple active structures among diverse amino-acid residues. Ser, His, and Asp are crucial residues of ester hydrolysis (e.g. acetylcholine and pNPA). They are created as part of an artificial catalytic triad model by Guler et al. [50]. Three self-assembled peptide motifs (Lauryl-VVAG-) each having a different active terminal residue can come together in this system to form β-sheet configurations with inherent hydrophobic domains, leading to enhanced catalytic performance.

In a typical hydrolase case, for example, the Fmoc-FFH-$CONH_2$ tripeptide is self-assembled to produce nanotubes (PepNTs). It is made by a process of repeatedly changing the solvent [51] (Figure 18.1). Given the hydrophobic microenvironment provided by Fmoc-FF segments and histidine (H) catalytic centers placed at the periphery, the nanotubes' well-ordered active sites demonstrated remarkable hydrolysis of p-nitrophenyl acetate. Following substitution of histidine with arginine as well as adjustment of the molar ratio of active sites and binding sites, the resulting PepNTs-His-Arg_{max} is even further productive than PepNTs-His which has already been obtained previously. The catalytic activity of hydrolase mimics is increased by combined effects of stabilizing the catalytic center, binding site, and transition state. This model of the co-assembled peptide nanotube hydrolase also suggests a catalytic

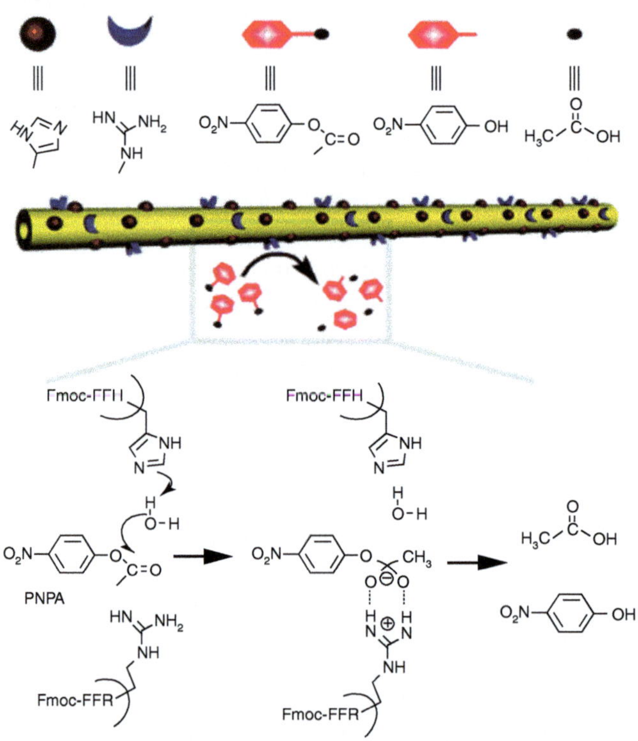

Figure 18.1 A catalytic peptide nanotube consisting of tripeptides. Source: Reproduced with permission from Ref. [51]; ©2014 Royal Society of Chemistry.

mechanism. The histidine residue serves as a catalyst by grabbing protons in solvent molecules. The hydrophobic nucleus of PepNTs-His-Arg_{max} is firstly bound by the benzene ring of the aromatic substrate. With the aid of the nucleophilic moiety and hydroxide ion, it attacks the carbonyl of *p*-nitrophenyl acetate (pNPA) and produces a tetrahedral transition state. The guanidyl on these nanotubes can stabilize the transition state shortly after that. The C—O bond is then broken to produce a subsequent catalytic cycle. Another product (NH_2-HSGQQKFQFQFEQQ-Am) made by Liu et al. is a Q11H self-assembling peptide, which contains histidine. This product is composed of a flexible linker (SG) to catalyze hydrolysis and a portion of self-assembled scaffold (QQKFQFQFEQQ) to overcome unstable features [52]. Activation of the histidine residue's imidazolyl group results in formation of a hydroxide ion from water (H_2O). Following this, the catalytic process enters a tetrahedral transition state when the arginine residue stabilizes the carbonyl moiety of p-nitrophenyl acetate as it has a reaction with the imidazolyl group. The guanidyl group of arginine assists in the breakdown of the C—O linkage to yield the resultant p-nitrophenol.

18.2.2 Proline-based C—C Bond-forming Reactions

Additional stereoselective and powerful organ catalysts such as prolines have the potential to catalyze C—C bond-forming processes (e.g. the aldol reaction and Michael addition). To attack the electrophilic reactant and produce an intermediate called enamine, they function similar to natural aldolase [53–55]. However, because prolines are notorious for being poorly soluble in water, they cannot catalyze an asymmetric aldol reaction [56]. The structural behavior of L-Pro-L-Val organocatalytic gels has been studied since their invention [57]. L-Proline, L-arginine, L-tryptophan, and a hydrocarbon chain are all present in the lipopeptide PRW-C16, which has been shown to exhibit an assembly behavior in water [58]. Additionally, the specificity of the aldol reaction is influenced by where the water and catalytic groups are located. Lipopeptides at the lipopeptide/water interface exhibit high diastereoselectivity (85%) and enantioselectivity (99%) yield under right conditions (ds up to 92 : 8). The aldol reaction is instead boosted by infusing PRW-NH-C16, a lipopeptide with proline functionality, into cubosome, which has a substantial surface [59]. Using an assembly of proline-lysine dipeptide β-tidene, Parquette et al. have produced hydrophobic extracellular matrix in the form of nanotubes in a liquid phase [60]. After dipeptide's packing in the nanotube is changed during the aldol reaction, the enantiomeric excess of this nanotube can increase the selectivity from 85.3% to 93.5%. Under moderately anaerobic environment in water, several proline-based nanocatalysts have been developed. They can be used in a variety of substrates [61]. Highly enantioselective transfer hydrogenation could be observed in DPL-C16. This compound has a lot of potential for use in industry.

18.2.3 Expanded Special Reactions

In addition to previously mentioned amino acids, selenocysteine (Sec), an uncommon amino-acid residue, is also crucial to the catalyzed process, particularly in such a mimicking allosteric enzyme with free radical scavenging qualities [62]. Reactive oxygen species-mediated Ca(II) ions, which are primarily retained in the mitochondrion's aerobic cellular respiration, are produced in this allosteric antioxidant selenoenzyme. Additionally, an opening in the protein scaffold model that binds a substrate is effectively modified to include a catalytic moiety (recoverin). Sec and Arg are employed for catalysis and recognition, respectively. Through an alteration in conformation to an allosteric state, this enzyme mimic controls catalytic activity. A short peptide containing tyrosine has also been shown to have the ability to catalyze cleavage and creation of C—C bonds [63]. According to characteristics of its shape, tyrosine is a hydrogen-bond contributor that makes it easier for a binding region to form, thus boosting an aldose mimic's activity. Increased initial energy conversion is brought on by high substrate selectivity and adduct formation.

18.2.4 Catalytic Amyloids

Lynn et al. have developed asymmetric peptide bilayer membranes, which are constructed by joining positively and negatively charged units together [64]. These nanotubes composed of peptides can serve as the best illustration currently available of such considerable charge segregation in membrane formation. To mimic symptoms of peptides Ac-1KLVF5FAL-NH_2 (K1) and AcRLVFFAL-NH_2 (K1R), which contain a nucleating core (LVFF) of Amyloid-(A) peptide from Alzheimer's disease, homogeneous nanotubes have been produced [65]. In that study, the fluid contains 50% of lysine residues from the K1 nanotube, which could interact with 2,4-pentanedione. Additionally, N-terminal residues on the nanostructure exterior contribute to the substrate's oligomerization. Contrary to first expectations, catalytic repertoires of the cross-assembled grooves might be significantly broader. Lysine, leucine, and imidazoleacetic acid are included in the sequence of Im-KLVFFAL-NH_2 (Im-KL), resulting in an effective covalent catalysis [66]. Its contact with the substrate is improved by exposing the lysine linked within the solvent. Creation of the imine bond triggered by lysine residues is made easier by imidazole group's capacity for hydrolysis. Semirationally designed catalytic amyloids made of several peptides and hemin have been created by Korendovych et al. [67]. The strongest enantioselectivity of cyclopropanation is demonstrated by Ac-LILHLFL-NH_2. Its conversion efficiency is even on par with those of modified hemin proteins. Highly developed amyloidogenic sequences found in modern proteomes come from more ancient species. Additionally, conformers of the β-sheet amyloid have an inherently repetitive structure. They are extraordinarily stable. They also exhibit new multifunctionality (e.g. self-replication in complex mixtures, catalytic activities, and information transfer). These facts provide evidence for the amyloid-first theory on how the current biochemical machinery was created [68–70]. Therefore, we believe that this catalytic amyloid not only widens the scope of its initial peroxidase-like performance to include enantioselective cyclopropanation but also backs the "amyloids-first" theory of how life initially appeared.

Multiple enzymes that are spatially localized inside this cellular environment can combine complex cascade reactions in a tiny system. To add sarcosine oxidase (SOX), Das et al. have used cross-amyloid (Im-KLVFFAL, Im-KL) as a binding and

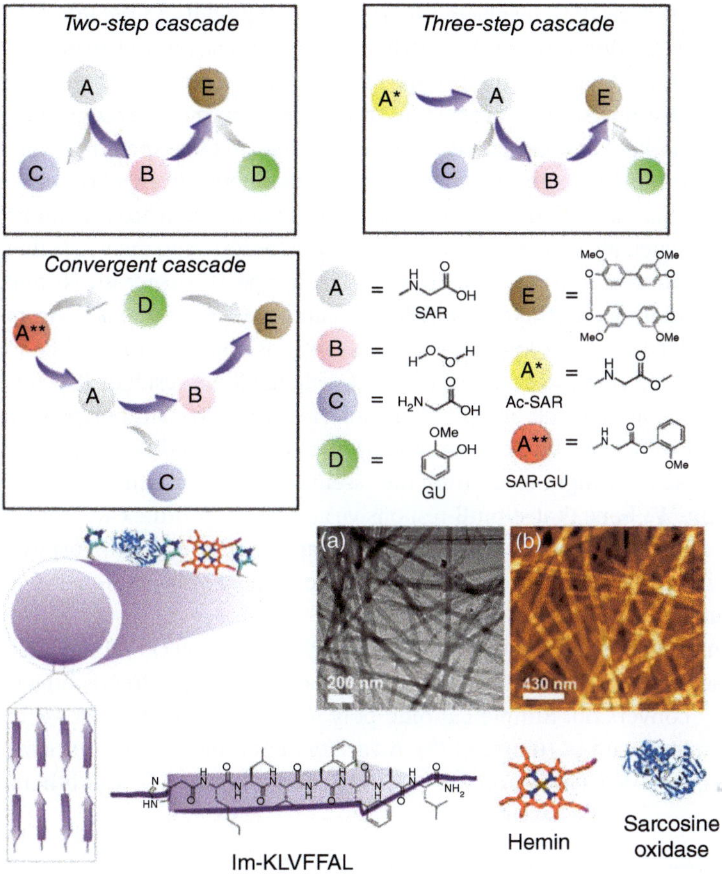

Figure 18.2 Cascade reaction happens on the surface of catalytic peptide. Source: Reproduced with permission from Ref. [71]; ©2021 John Wiley & Sons.

catalytic scaffold [71] (Figure 18.2). They also employed a prosthetic group hemin to carry out various types of cascade reactions. Colocalized sarcosine oxidase (SOX) and hemin are considered artificial peroxidases. Meanwhile, ordered arrangements of imidazole found in amyloid nanotubes are thought to be a hydrolase mimic. This method easily achieves complexity of a single enzyme-based nanohybrid with multigate logic networks, opening the prospect of tightly controlling complicated catalysis in artificial photosynthesis.

18.2.5 Polypeptides

Polymers are composed of amino acids and peptide bonds. These structures of the active sites in natural enzymes are dependent on polypeptide. Inorganic nanoparticle surfaces have polypeptides built on them that can control the separation between a substrate and a catalyst. In catalysis, separation of the catalyst and substrate is also crucial. Arginine residues found in polypeptides can significantly speed up oligoadenylic acid hydrolysis [72]. By placing short peptide fragments on the interface of charged self-assembled thin films on nanostructured materials, a multivalent scaffold of AuNPs is formed, which can enhance the catalysis even more [47]. One of the unique qualities that distinguish natural enzymes from other "smart" materials is their ability to reversibly regulate catalytic activity. Thermo-, redox-, pH-, temperature-, and photoresponsive environmental stimuli, among others, can kinetically affect the polypeptide's structural dynamics. Ulijn et al. disclosed a pH-switchable hydrolase mimic in 2017, which was created by including a catalytic histidine residue into the VK_2H that was responsive to hydrogen ion [73]. This peptide has a type II′ turn with N- and C-terminal-strands. Additionally, this clever hydrolase can simulate the transition from random coil aggregates to β-sheet long nanofibers as well as changes from acidic to alkaline conditions. Long fibrils contain exposed catalytic histidine residues that display esterase-like function in a well-organized fashion (Figure 18.3). This polypeptide has excellent catalytic efficiency without needing a cofactor to maintain its shape stable. Some magical reactions might result from the essential natural enzyme's cofactor. It is forward-looking. We hope that stimuli-responsive acts as a substitute can provide fresh vistas for artificial photosynthesis as well as bioapplication using bioinspired catalysts by combining the nanozyme system's catalytic activity with its underlying nanomaterial nature.

A thylakoid transmembrane protein complex called Photosystem I (PS-I) is related to the initial phase of photosynthesis [74]. The degree of its stability greatly affects subsequent energy conversion. Simple cationic poly amino acids can boost PS-I's photochemical activity by up to 10 times [75]. A variety of peptide surfactants, such as ac-I_6K_2-$CONH_2$, ac-A_6K-$CONH_2$, ac-V_6K_2-$CONH_2$, ac-V_6R_2-$CONH_2$, and others,

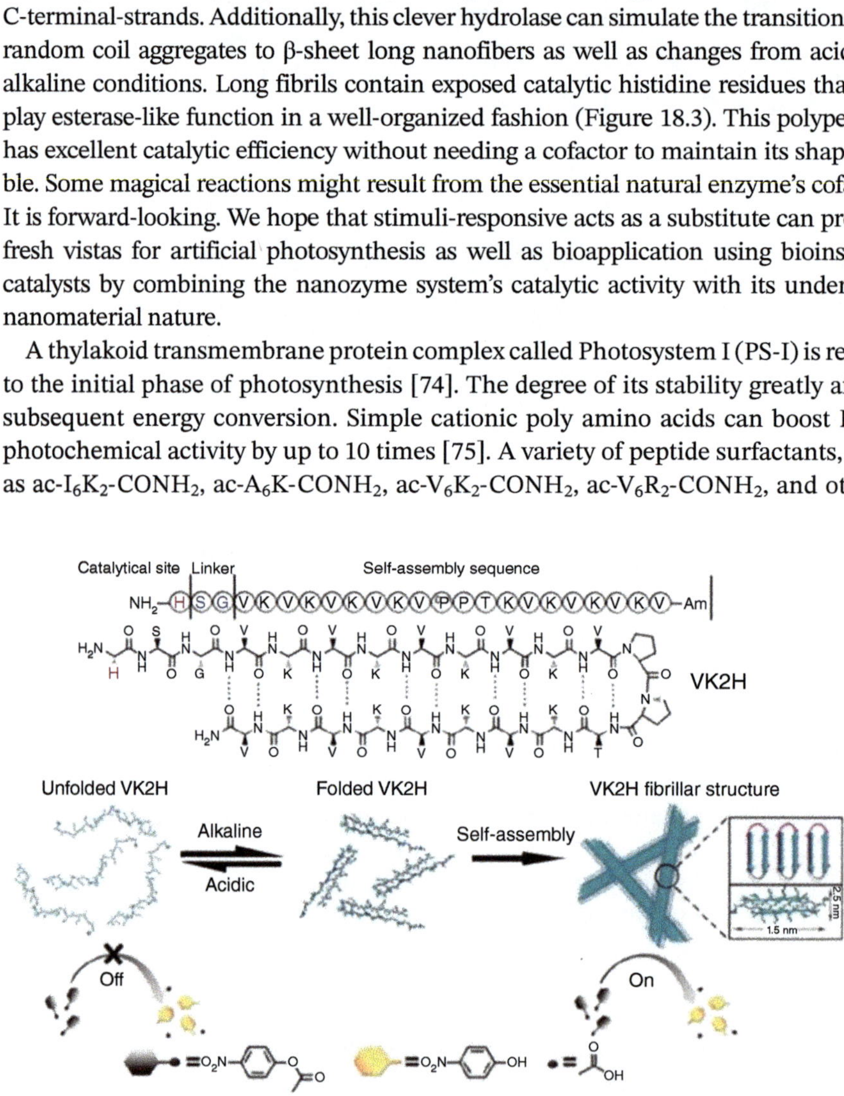

Figure 18.3 A peptide-based catalytic nanofibril constructed through catalytical sites, linker, and self-assembly sequence. Source: Reproduced with permission from Ref. [73]; ©2017 John Wiley & Sons.

were created by Zhang et al. [76] in 2009 to stabilize PS-I and increase its solubility in water. The activity of PS-I was significantly increased by ac-I_6K_2-NH_2 (8.3 times), ac-A_6K-NH_2 (8.9 times), ac-V_6K_2-NH_2 (9.8 times), and ac-V_6R_2-NH_2 (11.6 times). One of them, 0.47 mM ac-A_6K-NH_2, boosted PS-I activity by up to 8.9 times. PS-I can continue to function at a high level even after 2 months with the addition of this compound. Upon doing their research, they discovered that PS-I catalytic activity was governed by amino-acid compositions that determined the placement of charges on the peptide; The low solubility of the side groups has less effect on PS-I activity than they had anticipated. Positive charges on the C-terminal are also important for regulating PS-I activity. They also suggested that PS-I transmembrane protein complex might be molecularly encircled by peptide surfactants. Peptide surfactants can build a macroscopically large three-dimensional network to shield it from the environment. It can be explained by the unique interplay between peptide surfactants and protein complexes, which is brought on by amino-acid sequences, N-terminal acetylation, and C-terminal amidation. Their study's findings suggest that an ideal peptide surfactant should have amidated C-terminus, acetylated N-terminus, six consecutive hydrophobic amino acids, one or two polar positively charged C-terminal amino acids, and six consecutive hydrophobic amino acids.

18.2.6 Metallo-nanozyme

Metal ions serve as cofactors in metalloenzymes, which have high catalytic efficiency and structural stability. The metalloenzyme, which is made of amino acids and metal ions, can serve as a model for the development of metal-based nanozymes. The resulting artificial enzymes can easily be directed toward different substrates using supramolecular methods. These structures can further improve their catalytic activities through transition-state stabilization by introducing various metal ions. The nanostructure can even be given a brand-new function.

18.2.6.1 Single-valence Metal-based Catalyst

Zinc(II) ion, one of the necessary metal elements, is a promising candidate for creating enzyme mimics with excellent biocompatibility and reactivity. Furthermore, the zinc(II) ion can help maintain enzymatic configuration. It typically uses mechanisms resembling hydrolases and increases hydrolysis without altering its valence during the catalyzed process. In addition, it has intrinsic catalytic properties (such as being a Lewis acid and an electron transfer center). In other words, Zn's single-valent state restricts the amount of charge transfer it can undergo during a typical catalytic reaction such as an oxidation–reduction reaction.

A combination of seven-residue peptides and Zn(II) ions was used to construct a Zn(II)-dependent esterase mimic (a stable and folded fibril), where the zinc ion that could help sustain and catalyze in the procedure was repeated. This work was inspired by carbonic anhydrase enzyme. It is worth noting that prion-like fibrils can influence esterase activity as well as its structural evolution. The arrangement of seven-residue peptides in the desired peptide sequence is driven by apolar Leu residues at positions 1, 3, 5, and 7. Its high catalytic efficacy is a result of a tiny size of the catalytic site and good coordination of metal ions. It may serve as a starting point for research into the evolutionary history of contemporary enzymes [77].

Zinc finger hydrolase is one minimum hydrolase that has been modeled. One metallo-nanozyme inspired by zinc finger hydrolase is built on metal ions (zinc ions) and short peptide (*N*-[benzyloxycarbonyl]-L-histidinohydrazide, Z-His-$NHNH_2$) [78] (Figure 18.4). This mimic of lipase has an outstanding enzymatic output that is comparable to those of lipases found in nature. Similar to the activation mechanism of lipase, this metallo-nanozyme can stimulate and improve the mimicking enzyme's reactivity. A powerful enzymatic building item with supramolecular amyloid-like ordered architecture was created by Gazit's group to produce considerably simpler peptide-based biocatalysts. Additionally, this supramolecular amyloid-like structure made of phenylalanine was thought to be a type of nonproteinaceous hydrolase with capacity to catalyze hydration of CO_2 [79]. By combining zinc ions with phenylalanine (F) molecules, this structure is created. Results showed a reduced molecular mass with an enhanced reactivity, offering a suggested layout for a basic enzyme mimic. Coordination of Zn(II) ions with either phenylalanine or histidine molecules is possible.

18.2.6.2 Multivalence Metal-based Catalyst

Multivalent metals could enhance the hydrolysis in which zinc ions are primarily involved. The novel bioinspired catalysis that occurs together with valent alterations in Mn, Cu, and Fe stands out particularly. Examples include ATPase- and catalase-like reactivity and Diels–Alder cycloaddition. Diaz-Espinoza et al. have produced a catalytic amyloid that contains the sequence of SDIDVFI, which is the catalytic center of a DNA polymerase [80]. Additionally, this functional amyloid exhibits ATPase-like behavior that is dependent on Mn(II).

Cu(II) might catalyze substrates in catalytic systems as well as serve as a stabilizer for nanostructure. The chiral catalytic process is also carried out at the nanoscale, mediated by divalent copper ions. In the presence of Cu ions, this type of nanomaterial

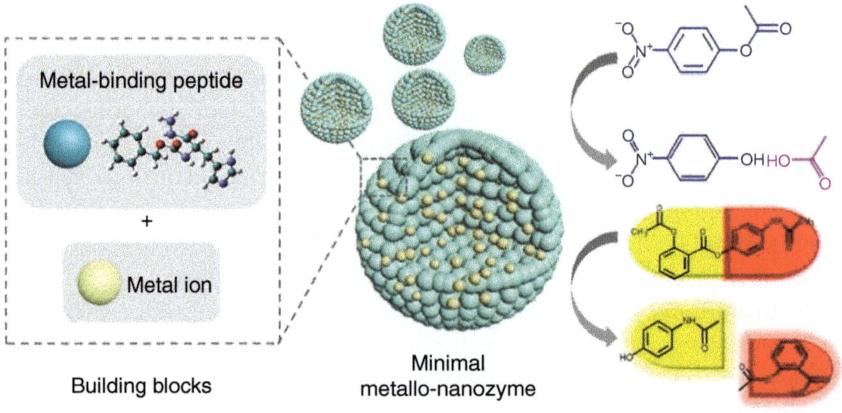

Figure 18.4 A minimal metallo-nanozyme constructed through metal ions and amino acids. Source: Reproduced with permission from Ref. [78]; ©2020 Elsevier.

could function as an asymmetric catalyst to cycloadd cyclopentadiene and azachalcone [81]. It has been discovered that Cu(II) can cause a glutamic acid bolaamphiphile, *N*,*N*′-hexadecanedioyl-di-L-glutamic acid (L-HDGA), monolayer nanotube to transform into an intricate nanotube. Due to the anchoring action of substrates on the outer surface of the nanotube, this mimic can increase its enantiomeric selectivity. Laccase, a biocatalyst that contains copper in nature, can oxidize organic molecules by accepting oxygen as an electron acceptor. A nanostructure resembling diphenylalanine nanochains was constructed by Li et al. [82] (Figure 18.5). The cationic diphenylalanine (H-PhePhe-NH_2HCl) and glutaraldehyde can undergo an imine condensation process, which results in a bola-like building block CDPGA. These dipeptide-based hierarchical nanochains are produced because of systemic interactions among hydrophobic bonds, stacking interactions, and Cu-coordination-driven assembly. These Cu-mediated nanostructures can enable facile transformation of nanoparticles into nanochain-like nanozymes that rely on divalent copper ions and hydrogen ions. They might also improve catalytic properties of this artificial enzyme.

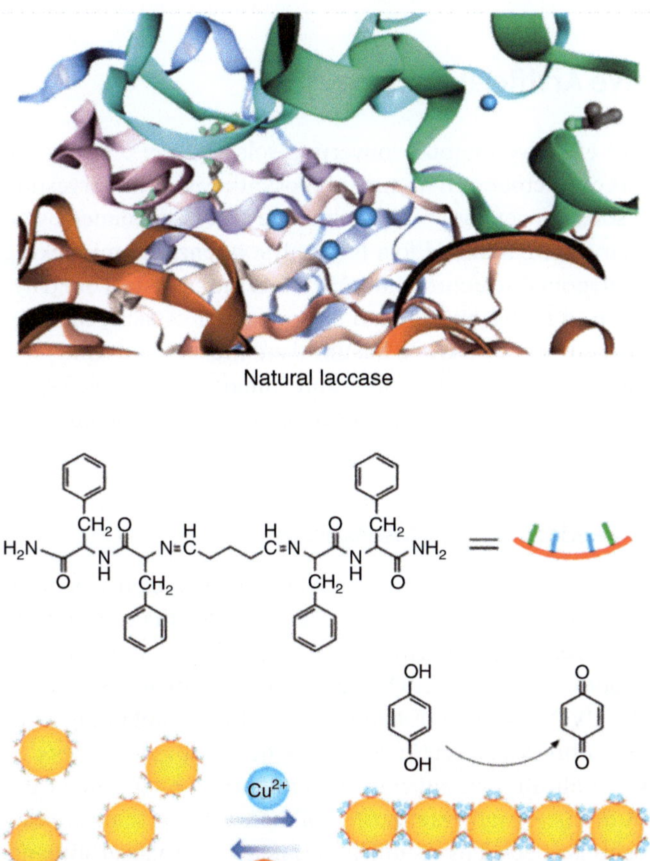

Figure 18.5 A minimal metallo-nanozyme constructed through metal ions and amino acid. Source: Reproduced with permission from Ref. [82]; ©Willey.

N-Histidyl *N′*-myristry ethyl amine (AM1), a histidine-based amphiphile, has the ability to produce hydrogels in the presence of ferric ions or mercury ions [83]. A histidine residue has the capacity to bind metal ions, while an acyl chain and amide group of *N*-histidyl *N′*-myristry ethyl amine can boost hydrophobic molecular and intermolecular hydrogen bonding. By varying the ratio of AM1 with metallic ions, this metallohydrogel might also be accurately controlled and exhibit hydrolysis of p-nitrophenyl esters. These studies mentioned before have mostly focused on structure creation, although unique Fe catalytic characteristics show promise. A ferric iron-driven photosensitizing artificial enzyme toward light therapy has been created since this coordinated enzyme mimic [84]. Ferric ions can considerably facilitate coordination with Fmoc-cysteine as well as generation of nanovesicles. The dispatch of ferric ions from this enzyme mimic can aid in an efficient intracellular delivery of oxygen via catalase-like activity. We can boost a peptide-based catalyst in low oxygen tension due to the catalase-like nanozyme's ability to provide oxygen on its own.

18.3 Photosensitive Artificial Enzyme

Photosynthesis is the most effective method converting solar energy on a microscopic scale of green plants or microbes. In natural photosynthesis, light harvesting plays a substantial role in solar conversion in addition to the process mediated by an enzyme. Typically, light harvesting is added to a biocatalyst or enzyme-mimicking system. Additionally, the integrated structure that surrounds the catalytic core plays a crucial role in the creation of nanozymes. It can improve their capacity for light absorption. Its energy-harvesting processes and beautiful architecture are what photosynthesis mostly depends on [85–87]. Utilizing and imitating these biological functions of the photosystem may encourage the development of unique qualities in structures [88, 89].

18.3.1 Co-assembly of Peptides and Photosensitizers

Active sites and peptidic microenvironment are two essential characteristics of an enzyme mimic. Supramolecular hydrogels may act as skeletons for the catalytic site (such as hemin, a photosensitizer) to function during catalysis. They may also make it easier to take the catalyst out of the mixture when an enzyme-mediated reaction is complete. According to the UV/Vis spectra of hemin in a hydrogel containing histidine, an amplification of 387.1 times and a 60% nascent reaction conditions under this system have been observed, indicating its superior performance in bioinspired catalysts [90]. Additionally, the ultimate catalytic efficiency of these enzyme mimics based on supramolecular hydrogels is affected by modifications made to distal substituents in several heme model compounds [91]. The creation of enzyme mimics lacks the ability to select host molecules and incorporate them into useful, three-dimensional architectures. However, spinach chloroplasts have a photooxidase enzyme (e.g.

cytochrome c) that can facilitate photooxidating electron donors. The chlorophyll lipoprotein complex is the active component of photooxidase [92]. An amphiphilic amino acid, *N*-alpha-(9-fluorenylmethoxycarbonyl)-L-histidine (Fmoc-His-OH), and phthalocyanine are co-assembled to form a photooxidative-imitating nanovesicle [93] (Figure 18.6). By assembling photosensitizers and amphiphilic amino acids into membrane-like nanovesicles and limiting their significant self-agglomeration due to numerous supramolecular interactions between them, the organization of phthalocyanine and Fmoc-His-OH can be carefully tuned using nanovesicles as a scaffold. In this work, this nanovesicles combines increased stability with hypersensitive oxidation's high rate of efficiency when mediated by reactive oxygen species (Figure 18.6). After illuminating a 680-nm laser in this photooxidase-mimicking nanovesicle, the energy first stimulates the photosensitive sensitizer. It then crosses the intersystem barrier to the triplet state. When energy is transferred from a photosensitizer in the triplet state to molecular oxygen, singlet oxygen is also produced. Finally, the conversion of sunlight into chemical energy is completed by the photomediated catalytic process.

Catalytic centers of natural peroxidases are imitated using a molecularly imprinted technique with co-assembly of hemin and Fmoc-Phe-Phe-His-COOH (Fmoc-FFH) to create a peroxidase-like mimic with excellent enzymatic performance and substrates selectivity. This method overcomes the low substrate specificity and catalytic activity of a peptide-based enzyme mimic [94]. Peroxidase-like mimics have better selectivity for 2,2′-azinobis-(3-ethylbenzthiazoline-6-sulfonate) than 3,3′,5,5′-tetramethylbenzidine due to their electrostatic activity and spatial uniqueness. Their peroxidase-like activity is the focus of this research, not its photosensitivity.

Even in natural photosynthesis, a catalytic reaction has the advantage of efficiently isolating the substrate and products. By combining diphenylalanine (L-Phe-L-Phe) and sulfonated porphyrin (tetrakis(4-sulfonatophenyl)porphine, [H_2TPPS]), this

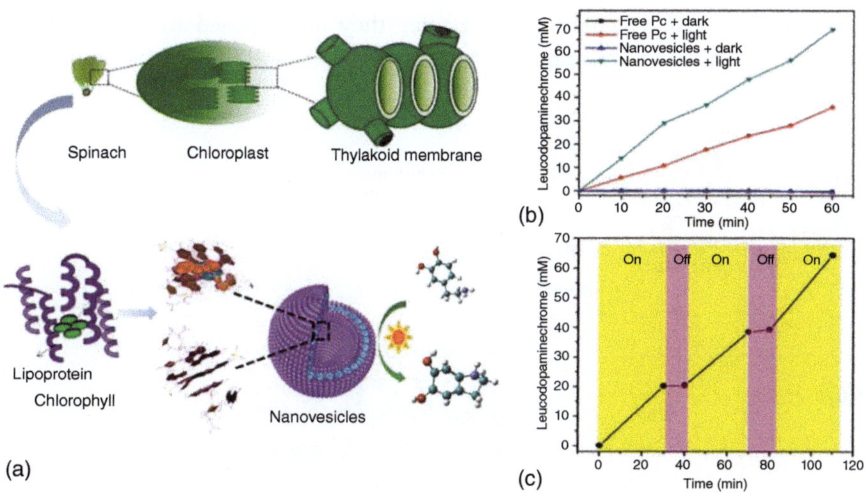

Figure 18.6 A peptide-based catalytic nanovesicle with photooxidase-like activity. Source: Reproduced with permission from Ref. [93]; ©2019 Willey.

multifunctional hierarchical porous microsphere mimics many chambers that make up early abiotic cellularity and its source of energy [95]. Four sulfonic acid groups in H_2TPPS undergo deprotonation when the pH falls below 2, while nitrogen atoms in pyrrole undergo protonation. The sulfonated porphyrin could form J-aggregates. Electrostatic interaction that occurs after the FF leads to assembly of photosensitizers' surfaces, ultimately leading to the creation of a biomolecular-based microsphere. Another minimal example might be the bioinspired system that we have recently developed, which is reliant on combining amino acids and hemin [96]. Fmoc-His-OH is co-assembled with hemin, creating a bioinspired biocatalyst with adaptable morphologies and nanostructures that depend on the molar ratio to mimic the coordination interaction in natural horseradish peroxidase between the imidazolyl group of heme and the iron of heme. This bioinspired biocatalyst has demonstrated the amazing peroxidase-mimicking catalytic activity and high resilience in three catalytic cycles of a simple nanozyme. The increased catalytic reaction sparked by this nanozyme, once it has been incorporated into the sensing system, is advantageous for highly effective glucose sensing. This research reveals another potential use for biosensors for nanozymes made of peptides. The co-assemblies' photosensitivity of hemin could be used to create photosensitive nanozyme biosensors based on artificial enzymes.

One new assembled method is different from the assembly process to establish a self-ordering setup route that depends on peptide-induced long-range structural order and alignment over a range of scales [97] (Figure 18.7). First, depending on hydrogen bonding and electrostatic attraction, a simple positively charged dipeptide (L-Lys-L-Lys, KK) induces an oppositely charged porphyrin molecule (tetrakis (4-sulfonatophenyl) porphine, H_2TPPS) to organize into nanorods. The H_2TPPS is organized into J-aggregates in microscale nanotubes around with KK. In addition to continuing these nanorods, given their self-orienting growth, another notable Stokes shift that can be seen in fiber bundles is anisotropically aligned and exaggerated chirality. Oriented Pt nanowires are introduced. These assemblies containing Pt nanowires exhibit good photocatalytic performance after they are exposed to visible light. They offer a potential design approach for creating bioinspired, multifaceted, and

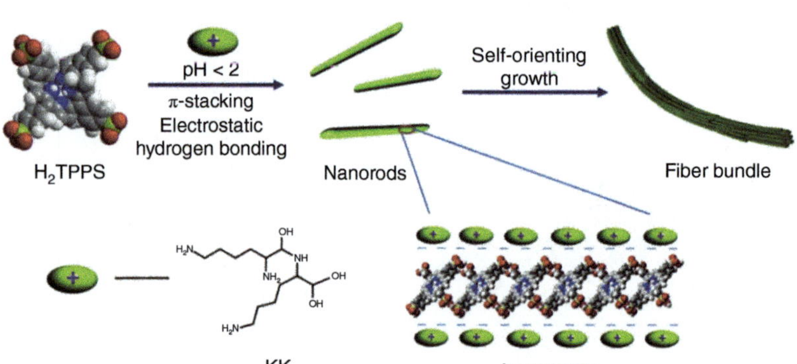

Figure 18.7 Peptide-based hierarchical nanoassemblies with self-orienting growth and photocatalytic activity. Source: Reproduced with permission from Ref. [97]; ©2015 Willey.

sophisticated artificial photosynthesis systems. Amino acids and photosensitizers such as those produced by primordial photobacteria and photobacteria that mimic the evolution of oxygen can build a more complicated system that is full of numerous original enzymes [98, 99].

Acid environments that resemble prebiotics include hot, mineral-rich water that is 70 °C. To accomplish bioinspired energy conversion in a prebiotic-like environment, a co-assembling fiber system made of simple peptide and porphyrin (tetrakis(4-sulfonatophenyl) porphine, TPPS) with a self-mineralized reaction center has been designed to mimic primary photobacteria [98]. The peptide controls assembling tendency of photosynthetic pigment systems, and porphyrins are photosynthetic pigment precursors. TPPS molecules under pH 2 are present in J-aggregates of slid face-to-face fiber structures throughout this prebiotic-like environment. Owing to its hydrophilic effect, surface tension, and electrostatically increased hydrogen bonding, the hydrophilic peptide then grows into fiber bundles from a slim fiber. After illumination, *in situ* mineralization of TiO_2 NPs may also produce hydrogen and separate charges. One model of early photobacteria could be an integrated nanoarchitecture. This model is even comparable to green sulfur bacteria.

Amino acid (9-fluorenylmethoxycarbonyl-L-lysine, Fmoc-L-lys), porphyrin (Sn(IV) tetrakis(4-pyridyl)porphyrin, SnTPyP), 3,4-dihydroxyphenylalanine (DOPA), and Co_3O_4 nanoparticles are basic building blocks of oxygen-evolving photobacteria mimics that could generate oxygen. Chlorophyll and the inorganic PSII core in cyanobacteria are highly comparable to one another [99]. In a peptide framework, Fmoc-L-Lys is initially assembled into a nanofiber in this cyanobacteria model via π-stacking and hydrogen bonding. Fmoc-L-Lys fibers can receive L-DOPA on their surface, thanks to a Schiff base reaction with the ε-amino group. By producing DOPA melanin, this chemical process provides a sticky characteristic. Through a coordination bond and an electrostatic interaction, SnTPyP and Co_3O_4 nanoparticles are combined near each other on the peptide framework, facilitating energy transfer and charge separation. From photoexcited Sn(IV)TPyP*, quinone species can aid in the formation of radical cation Sn(V)TPyP$^+$. In addition, the amino acid-based assembly could help the membrane organize itself into a spontaneous phospholipid vesicle and give inspiration for the origin of life [100].

18.3.2 Conjugates of Peptides and Photosensitizers

As a building block, a conjugate of porphyrin (5-mono[4-carboxyphenyl] 10,15,20-triphenyl porphine) and diphenylalanine is introduced into multiporous nanofiber-based nanospheres. In addition to having a noteworthy electron transfer and a wide excitation redshift, these multiporous nanoparticles also exhibit broad-spectrum light sensitivity when they are illuminated. As a result, broad-spectrum absorption might be used as a light-harvesting antenna for synthetic photosynthesis [101]. It has been further demonstrated that with only Pt nanoparticles and NADH as an accompaniment, this platform composed of photosensitizers and amnio acids may effectively create L-Glu in biocatalytic processes without using outside mediators. Short peptide motif has been extensively studied [102]. Depending on solvent composition, combinations of photosensitive constitutes and peptides can build a variety of nanostructures, such as strong excitonic couplets in fibril antennas that have been quenched. Soon afterward, Coutsolelos et al. have revealed that peptide nucleic acid may create various nanostructures using the "good–bad" solvent after being covalently bonded to two porphyrin molecules and boron-di-pyrromethene chromophores [103]. With the aid of Pt nanoparticles, these peptide nucleic acid conjugates exhibit capabilities for hydrogen production and sunlight collecting, indicating that these nanoassemblies favor photocatalysis. They provide us with guidance on what to do to manage such intriguing peptide–photosensitizer conjugates for photocatalysis.

The photosystem II (PSII) contains an enzyme that uses solar energy to oxidize water. The TyrZ/His190 pair of amino acids serves as a directed electron relay during this process, which is necessary for the oxygen-evolving complex (OEC) to function [104]. To investigate the as-yet-unknown process of light-induced electron transfer, a TyrZ/His190 model of photosystem II with a hydrogen-bonded phenol/imidazole and a porphyrin sensitizer is covalently attached [105]. It has been demonstrated that the water molecule is necessary to cause this P680/TyrZ/His190 bioinspired design to undergo a one-electron, two-proton-coupled transfer. It is possible to stabilize the resulting phenoxyl radical via a hydrogen-bonded imidazole fragment and molecular porphyrin.

18.4 Hybrid Photo-enzyme-coupled Systems

18.4.1 Nanocatalyst with Peptide Scaffold

Encapsulation in noncovalent interactions may prevent organometallic complexes from interacting with residues of amino acids in the ideal system, which may cause a portion of their activity to be lost [106]. To promote functioning of an enzyme's catalytic site and reestablish enzymatic activity or an enzyme imitation, supramolecular hydrogels have been employed as scaffolds. To better understand how supramolecular-hydrogel systems work, hemin chloride has been introduced to this system composed of two kinds of simple amino-acid derivatives [90]. This fiber keeps free hemin stable during the peroxidization procedure and offers catalytic sites in a customizable microenvironment. Additionally, it has been demonstrated that embryonic activity of oxidation reaction has reached roughly 60% of free hemin. The research of supramolecular hydrogels offers a prototype for creating synthetic enzyme skeletons using supramolecular hydrogel.

Tetra(p-hydroxyphenyl) porphyrin (THPP) molecules can be combined with FF-based framework to collect photons for artificial photosynthesis [7, 107]. These porphyrin molecules exhibit light-harvesting behavior. Porphyrin molecules are in the process of aggregation with the aid of a short peptide assembly by supramolecular interaction (Figure 18.8a and b). For each excited state, the FF assembly with platinum nanoparticle coating efficiently separates and transfers. Structure and electrical characteristics of chlorophyll in a natural photosynthetic system have also been imitated by FF/THPP nanotubes. In such systems, units are put together with energy transfer from chromophores to active centers mediated by peptide building blocks. Together with a redox enzyme, this system fulfills a light-driven transformation of NAD^+ to NADH.

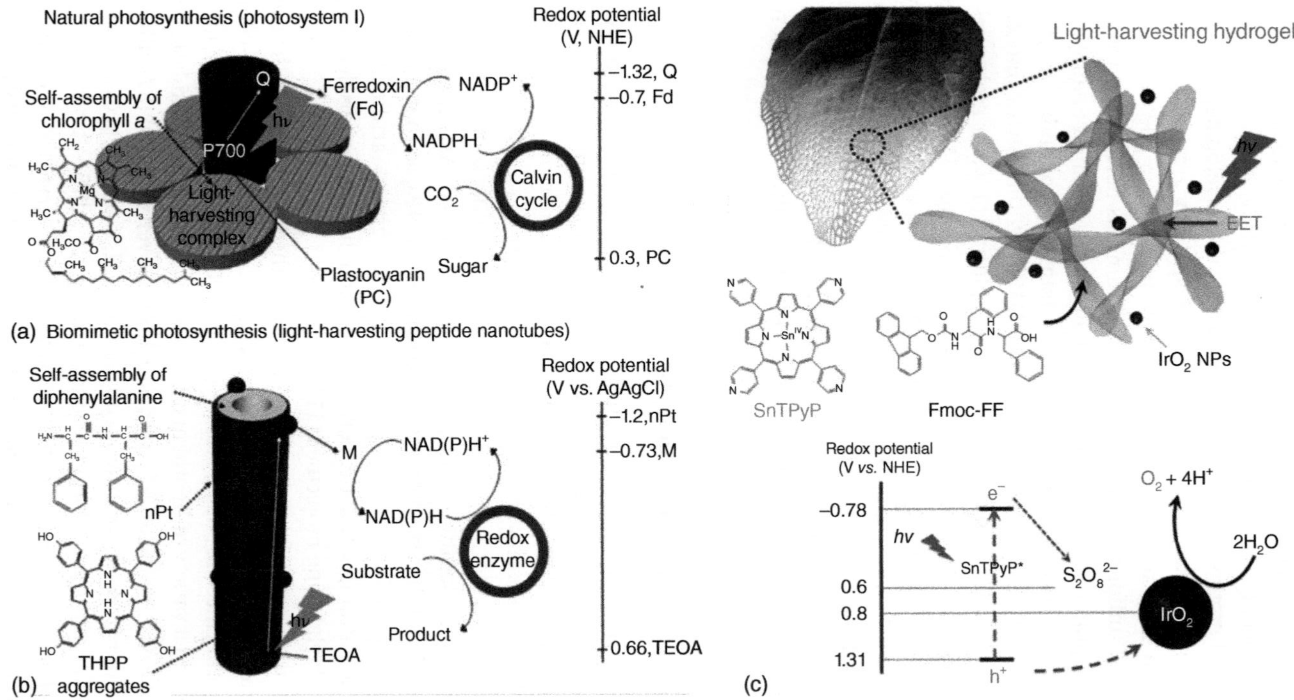

Figure 18.8 (a) and (b) Light-harvesting peptide nanotubes for mimicking photosynthesis. (c) Light-harvesting hydrogel for solar water oxidation. Source: (a) and (b) Reproduced with permission from Ref. [107]; ©2012 Willey; (c) Reproduced with permission from Ref. [108]; ©2014 Willey.

To accomplish water oxidation, metalloporphyrins (meso-tetra(4-pyridyl) porphine, TPyP) are coupled with redox catalysts (iridium oxide nanoparticles) in a diphenylalanine-based hydrogel [108] (Figure 18.8c). In a face-to-tail arrangement like the core of chlorophyll molecules, the Fmoc-FF could cause metalloporphyrins. All those supramolecular interactions between the pyridyl group of TPyP and carboxylic/hydroxyl groups of Fmoc-FF are crucial for the development of a photosensitizer and iridium oxide nanoparticles that are spatially arranged in a clearly defined manner to aid reactivity. To achieve visible-light-driven photocatalysis, an extremely thin and uniform peptide-assembled biofilm has been created via cold-plasma-assisted supramolecular assembly [109]. Eosin Y (EY) and Pt nanoparticles that are supported by this biofilm can effectively transfer photoinduced electrons from the highest occupied molecular orbital (HOMO) to the lowest unoccupied molecular orbital (LUMO), which in turn triggers splitting of water molecules and reduction of carbon dioxide (CO_2). Lipidic cubic mesophases (LCMs) have been recently used as a scaffold by Raffaele Mezzenga et al. [110] to encapsulate enzyme benzaldehyde lyase (BAL). They exhibit good photocatalytic activity in accelerating condensation of achiral benzaldehyde to chiral (R)-benzoin because of the unique nanoconfined environment of LCMs. We hypothesize that the emergence of an unexpected catalytic performance may benefit from integration of a special nanoconfined microenvironment with a peptide-based nanocatalyst.

18.4.2 Photo-enzyme-coupled Nanozymes

One crucial factor in assessing an enzyme's catalytic behavior is selectivity. The medium's pH level primarily controls the chirality of nanoassemblies. Amino-acid sequences can also control the chirality of nanoassemblies. These could be exploited for selective catalysis, specifically asymmetric reactions [111, 112]. Considering these factors, a twisted nanoribbon has been created by carefully controlling peptide-interdigitating amphiphiles that are inspired by lipids (LIPIAs). As a chiral scaffold, this twisted nanoribbon has been employed to support AuNPs, so that the catalytic reaction can be carried out subsequently. This integrated artificial enzyme demonstrates outstanding catalytic performance and high enantioselectivity of 3,4-dihydroxyphenylalanine molecules [113].

Graphene-based photocatalyst systems are currently the foundation for the expansion of systems associated with photosensitive enzyme. In a photo-enzyme-coupled system, artificial enzymes are substitutes for biocatalysts. In artificial photosynthesis, enzyme mimics and a variety of hybrid materials, such as cytochrome oxidase, bacteriorhodopsin, and ATP synthase (ATPase), have been proven essential [87], although peptide-based photoenzymes are infrequently observed. The emergence of extremely similar enzyme imitators to natural enzymes is extremely difficult because of the intricacy of living processes and how they work. We have suggested a supramolecular technique to create chloroplast imitators to replicate chloroplast previously [114]. It is built here on cysteine stone-inspired mineralization of the amino acid cysteine under the control of metal ions. After stacking nanorods in a hierarchical pattern, this assemblage has a porous spherical structure. This nanomaterial can incorporate alcohol dehydrogenase (ADH) and tetrakis(4-sulfonatophenyl) porphine (TPPS) as photosynthesis catalysts, active components in photoenzymatic processes, and sustainable producers of acetaldehyde and hydrogen. The procedure is as follows: platinum nanoparticles photodeposited *in situ* that exhibit charge separation might produce photoexcited TPPS. With the help of NADH as an electron donor, the transferred charge is utilized to lower H^+ and produce hydrogen. The NADH under the assistance of ADH may be restored, and acetaldehyde could convert to ethanol during this process. This system can effectively integrate the photocatalyst and enzyme, favoring the flow of substrate and electrons.

A photoenzyme system needs primordial pigment to absorb photons. A few pigment-forming systems that do not require a photosensitizer have been built from peptides or amino acids. In 2005, cysteine-containing hydrophobic polypeptides engineered a light-harvesting complex using an *Escherichia coli* expression system, similar to a purple photosynthetic bacterium *Rhodobacter sphaeroides*. Furthermore, it has been established that the assembly process is impacted by cysteine's position [115]. Our team has developed several photo-enzyme-coupled systems to address these issues using a more straightforward approach [114, 116]. Under hydrothermal circumstances, amino acid cysteine and metal ion could spontaneously produce a rudimentary color [116] (Figure 18.9a). This functional element can

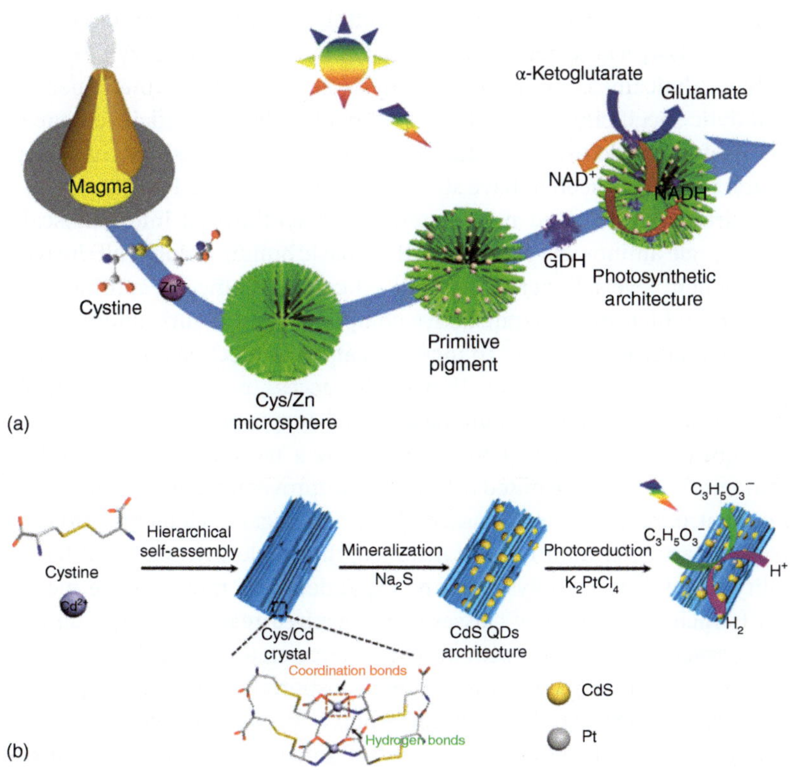

Figure 18.9 (a) Chemical evolution from cystine and zinc ion, primitive pigments to final photosynthetic architecture. (b) A hierarchical amino-acid architecture for hydrogen evolution. Source: (a) Reproduced with permission from Ref. [116]; ©2018 Willey; (b) Reproduced with permission from Ref. [117]; ©2018 American Chemical Society.

act as a sunlight collector to capture solar energy and an aid to photochemical processes. As an effective artificial photosynthetic microreactor, it might have glutamate dehydrogenase (GDH) to help with glutamate photoenzymatic synthesis. Using a chelating agent and a binding agent, they can create a hierarchically ordered biomimetic light-harvesting antenna [117] (Figure 18.9b). Coordination-driven assembly and mineralization inspired by biological processes can work together synergistically to achieve this. This nanostructure produces H_2 by *in situ* mineralization of cadmium sulfide (CdS). In both cases, amino acids coupled with metal ions create complex structures to harvest light. These photocoupled systems also achieve energy storge and give good options in application for self-assembled peptide-based catalyst.

18.5 Summary

In conclusion, the present design approach of creating enzyme mimics for synthetic biomimetic catalysis draws inspiration from nature. The creation of a synthetic enzyme in three dimensions is still ongoing. Advantages of peptide-based materials include high resistance, amphiphilicity, optoelectronic capabilities [118–121], and the unique properties (autocatalysis or as a scaffold) of its ordered supramolecular assemblies [49, 122–124]. These benefits can help supramolecular nanozymes function supremely catalytically as bioinspired catalysis in terms of enzymatic performance and catalytic specificity. Currently created peptide-based artificial enzymes are extremely useful for bioinspired catalysis. Contrary to biocatalysts, however, bioinspired nanozymes still need to have stronger affinity and reactivity.

These bioinspired peptide-based nanomaterials are synthesized into nanoscale structures using single amino-acid residues as their basic building blocks all the way up to multicomponent levels. Superior catalytic efficacy and efficient confinement of multicompetent, which can separate active components from surroundings and products, are advantages of catalysis. To increase catalytic selectivity, it is essential that enzyme mimics have surfaces that allow simple access to reactants by controlling noncovalent interactions and enhancing artificial enzymes' chirality.

A series of highly complex arrangements made by a natural enzyme or other unique constituents have demonstrated astounding improvements in the selectivity and activity of controlled catalysis. Co-assembled or conjugated elements also give artificial enzymes particular abilities. For instance, the single-valence metal-based catalyst's ability to catalyze hydrolysis can be expanded by a multivalence metal-based catalyst to include brand-new classes of bioinspired reactivity. The catalytic performance of several metal ions with varied valence states found in inorganic nanoparticles is greatly influenced by the oxygen transportation, the region providing oxygen, and the chemical activity of oxygen atoms in unique valence states, such as Mn_2O_3 and Mn_3O_4 [125]. However, peptide-based micronanozymes' mechanism is not completely understood yet. Inclusion of photosensitive species makes it possible for spatiotemporal control of photosensitive nanozymes. Enzyme mimics' ability to be increased by light also increases their catalytic performances to a certain extent. It will be easier to emulate relevant natural systems involving creation of peptide-based photo- and metallo-nanocatalyst.

One can expect seeing more peptide-based catalysts: (i) equipping nanozymes with similar catalytic efficiency but stronger robustness than natural enzymes; (ii) obtaining new enzyme functions, such as those of metallo-nanozymes and photosensitive nanozymes, with an unnatural cofactor or without a cofactor of advanced peptide nanoarchitecture, but has therapies' capacity [126]; (iii) creating complex structures for separating nanocatalysts from the environment, substrate identification, highly effective enzymatic transformation, and provider of goods via only a few basic building blocks; (iv) development of supramolecular peptide-based catalytic therapy via peptide-based nanozymes from bioinspired catalysis (*in vitro*) is anticipated (*in vivo*). It is also anticipated that nanozyme-coupled nanosensors will function as sensors for accurate detecting and treating illness. Ideally, expanding the applicability of cascade reactions can be achieved by incorporating complex peptide structures. Greater performance and selectivity of supramolecular nanozymes with better biological properties and safety will provide high potential for the traditional enzyme-engineering industry.

Acknowledgment

This work was supported by the National Research foundation of Korea (NRF) grant funded by the Korea government (MSIT) (No. 2022R1A2C3005420 and RS-2023-00217701).

References

1 Gao, L., Zhuang, J., Nie, L. et al. (2007). Intrinsic peroxidase-like activity of ferromagnetic nanoparticles. *Nat. Nanotechnol.* 2: 577–583.

2 Liang, M. and Yan, X. (2019). Nanozymes: from new concepts, mechanisms, and standards to applications. *Acc. Chem. Res.* 52: 2190–2200.

3 Henzler-Wildman, K. and Kern, D. (2007). Dynamic personalities of proteins. *Nature* 450: 964–972.

4 Dong, Z., Wang, Y., Yin, Y., and Liu, J. (2011). Supramolecular enzyme mimics by self-assembly. *Curr. Opin. Colloid Interface Sci.* 16: 451–458.

5 Siegel, J.S. (1996). Molecular collectives: supramolecular chemistry. *Science* 271: 949.

6 Wang, T., Fan, X., Hou, C., and Liu, J. (2018). Design of artificial enzymes by supramolecular strategies. *Curr. Opin. Struct. Biol.* 51: 19–27.

7 Wasielewski, M.R. (2009). Self-assembly strategies for integrating light harvesting and charge separation in artificial photosynthetic systems. *Acc. Chem. Res.* 42: 1910–1921.

8 Frischmann, P.D., Mahata, K., and Wuerthner, F. (2013). Powering the future of molecular artificial photosynthesis with light-harvesting metallosupramolecular dye assemblies. *Chem. Soc. Rev.* 42: 1847–1870.

9 Kim, J.H., Nam, D.H., and Park, C.B. (2014). Nanobiocatalytic assemblies for artificial photosynthesis. *Curr. Opin. Biotechnol.* 28: 1–9.

10 Raynal, M., Ballester, P., Vidal-Ferran, A., and van Leeuwen, P.W.N.M. (2014). Supramolecular catalysis. Part 2: artificial enzyme mimics. *Chem. Soc. Rev.* 43: 1734–1787.

11 Ma, M., Liu, Z., Gao, N. et al. (2020). Self-protecting biomimetic nanozyme for selective and synergistic clearance of peripheral amyloid-β in an Alzheimer's disease model. *J. Am. Chem. Soc.* 142: 21702–21711.

12 Huang, Y.Y., Liu, Z., Liu, C.Q. et al. (2016). Self-assembly of multi-nanozymes to mimic an intracellular antioxidant defense system. *Angew. Chem. Int. Ed.* 55: 6646–6650.

13 Ma, M., Gao, N., Li, X. et al. (2020). A biocompatible second near-infrared nanozyme for spatiotemporal and non-invasive attenuation of amyloid deposition through scalp and skull. *ACS Nano* 14: 9894–9903.

14 Cao, H., Yang, Y., Liang, M. et al. (2021). Pt@polydopamine nanoparticles as nanozymes for enhanced photodynamic and photothermal therapy. *Chem. Commun.* 57: 255–258.

15 Xu, Y.Q., Fei, J.B., Li, G.L. et al. (2019). Nanozyme-catalyzed cascade reactions for mitochondria-mimicking oxidative phosphorylation. *Angew. Chem. Int. Ed.* 58: 5572–5576.

16 Li, Y., Feng, X.Y., Wang, A.H. et al. (2019). Supramolecularly assembled nanocomposites as biomimetic chloroplasts for enhancement of photophosphorylation. *Angew. Chem. Int. Ed.* 58: 796–800.

17 Lu, Y., Yeung, N., Sieracki, N., and Marshall, N.M. (2009). Design of functional metalloproteins. *Nature* 460: 855–862.

18 Heinisch, T. and Ward, T.R. (2010). Design strategies for the creation of artificial metalloenzymes. *Curr. Opin. Chem. Biol.* 14: 184–199.

19 Meeuwissen, J. and Reek, J.N.H. (2010). Supramolecular catalysis beyond enzyme mimics. *Nat. Chem.* 2: 615–621.

20 Thordarson, P., Bijsterveld, E.J.A., Rowan, A.E., and Nolte, R.J.M. (2003). Epoxidation of polybutadiene by a topologically linked catalyst. *Nature* 424: 915–918.

21 Davies, C.L., Dux, E.L., and Duhme-Klair, A.-K. (2009). Supramolecular interactions between functional metal complexes and proteins. *Dalton Trans.*: 10141–10154.

22 Gao, Y., Zhao, F., Wang, Q. et al. (2010). Small peptide nanofibers as the matrices of molecular hydrogels for mimicking enzymes and enhancing the activity of enzymes. *Chem. Soc. Rev.* 39: 3425–3433.

23 Wiester, M.J., Ulmann, P.A., and Mirkin, C.A. (2011). Enzyme mimics based upon supramolecular coordination chemistry. *Angew. Chem. Int. Ed.* 50: 114–137.

24 Atkins, J.F. and Gesteland, R. (2002). Biochemistry. the 22nd amino acid. *Science* 296: 1409–1410.

25 Scanlon, S. and Aggeli, A. (2008). Self-assembling peptide nanotubes. *Nano Today* 3: 22–30.

26 Toksoz, S. and Guler, M.O. (2009). Self-assembled peptidic nanostructures. *Nano Today* 4: 458–469.

27 Yang, Y.L., Khoe, U., Wang, X.M. et al. (2009). Spectroscopy in sculpted fields. *Nano Today* 4: 193–210.

28 Liu, L., Klausen, L.H., and Dong, M.D. (2018). Two-dimensional peptide based functional nanomaterials. *Nano Today* 23: 40–58.

29 Tao, K., Xue, B., Li, Q. et al. (2019). Stable and optoelectronic dipeptide assemblies for power harvesting. *Mater. Today* 30: 10–16.

30 Yuan, C., Levin, A., Chen, W. et al. (2019). Nucleation and growth of amino acid and peptide supramolecular polymers through liquid-liquid phase separation. *Angew. Chem. Int. Ed.* 58: 18116–18123.

31 Zhang, X. (2020). Liquid-liquid phase separation: the promoter of nucleation and growth of supramolecular polymers. *Acta Phys. Chim. Sin.* 36: 2004004.

32 Wang, J., Liu, K., Xing, R., and Yan, X. (2016). Peptide self-assembly: thermodynamics and kinetics. *Chem. Soc. Rev.* 45: 5589–5604.

33 Zhao, L., Li, S., Liu, Y. et al. (2019). Kinetically controlled self-assembly of phthalocyanine–peptide conjugate nanofibrils enabling superlarge redshifted absorption. *CCS Chem.* 1: 173–180.

34 Ren, X., Zou, Q., Yuan, C. et al. (2019). The dominant role of oxygen in modulating the chemical evolution pathways of tyrosine in peptides: dityrosine or melanin. *Angew. Chem. Int. Ed.* 58: 5872–5876.

35 Yuan, C., Ji, W., Xing, R. et al. (2019). Hierarchically oriented organization in supramolecular peptide crystals. *Nat. Rev. Chem.* 3: 567–588.

36 Zou, Q., Xing, R., and Yan, X. (2020). Peptide-based supramolecular colloids. *Acta Phys. Chim. Sin.* 36: 1909048.

37 Cui, Y., Fei, J., and Li, J. (2011). Molecular assembly and application of biomimetic microcapsules. *Sci. Sin. Chim.* 41: 273–280.

38 Han, J., Gong, H., Ren, X., and Yan, X. (2021). Supramolecular nanozymes based on peptide self-assembly for biomimetic catalysis. *Nano Today* 41: 101295.

39 Bethel, R.D., Singleton, M.L., and Darensbourg, M.Y. (2010). The modular assembly of clusters is the natural synthetic strategy for the active site of [FeFe] hydrogenase. *Angew. Chem. Int. Ed.* 49: 8567–8569.

40 Kano, K. (2008). Porphyrin-cyclodextrin supramolecular complexes as myoglobin model in water. *Colloid Polym. Sci.* 286: 79–84.

41 Massiah, M.A., Viragh, C., Reddy, P.M. et al. (2001). Short, strong hydrogen bonds at the active site of human acetylcholinesterase: proton NMR studies. *Biochemistry* 40: 5682–5690.

42 Pengo, P., Polizzi, S., Pasquato, L., and Scrimin, P. (2005). Carboxylate-imidazole cooperativity in dipeptide-functionalized gold nanoparticles with esterase-like activity. *J. Am. Chem. Soc.* 127: 1616–1617.

43 Guler, M.O. and Stupp, S.I. (2007). A self-assembled nanofiber catalyst for ester hydrolysis. *J. Am. Chem. Soc.* 129: 12082–12083.

44 Huang, Z., Luo, Q., Guan, S. et al. (2014). Redox control of GPx catalytic activity through mediating self-assembly of Fmoc-phenylalanine selenide into switchable supramolecular architectures. *Soft Matter* 10: 9695–9701.

45 Kleinsmann, A.J. and Nachtsheim, B.J. (2020). A minimalistic hydrolase based on co-assembled cyclic dipeptides. *Org. Biomol. Chem.* 18: 102–107.

46 Garcia, A.M., Kurbasic, M., Kralj, S. et al. (2017). A biocatalytic and thermoreversible hydrogel from a histidine-containing tripeptide. *Chem. Commun.* 53: 8110–8113.

47 Zaramella, D., Scrimin, P., and Prins, L.J. (2012). Self-assembly of a catalytic multivalent peptide-nanoparticle complex. *J. Am. Chem. Soc.* 134: 8396–8399.

48 Zhao, Y.A., Lei, B.Q., Wang, M.F. et al. (2018). A supramolecular approach to construct a hydrolase mimic with photo-switchable catalytic activity. *J. Mater. Chem. B* 6: 2444–2449.

49 Díaz-Caballero, M., Navarro, S., Nuez-Martínez, M. et al. (2021). pH-responsive self-assembly of amyloid fibrils for dual hydrolase-oxidase reactions. *ACS Catal.* 11: 595–607.

50 Gulseren, G., Khalily, M.A., Tekinay, A.B., and Guler, M.O. (2016). Catalytic supramolecular self-assembled peptide nanostructures for ester hydrolysis. *J. Mater. Chem. B* 4: 4605–4611.

51 Huang, Z., Guan, S., Wang, Y. et al. (2013). Self-assembly of amphiphilic peptides into bio-functionalized nanotubes: a novel hydrolase model. *J. Mater. Chem. B* 1: 2297–2304.

52 Zhang, C., Xue, X., Luo, Q. et al. (2014). Self-assembled peptide nanofibers designed as biological enzymes for catalyzing ester hydrolysis. *ACS Nano* 8: 11715–11723.

53 Guillena, G., Nájera, C., and Ramón, D.J. (2007). Enantioselective direct aldol reaction: the blossoming of modern organocatalysis. *Tetrahedron Asymmetry* 18: 2249–2293.

54 Escuder, B., Rodríguez-Llansola, F., and Miravet, J.F. (2010). Supramolecular gels as active media for organic reactions and catalysis. *New J. Chem.* 34: 1044–1054.

55 Gröger, H. and Wilken, J. (2001). The application of L-proline as an enzyme mimic and further new asymmetric syntheses using small organic molecules as chiral catalysts. *Angew. Chem. Int. Ed.* 40: 529–532.

56 List, B., Lerner, R.A., and Barbas, C.F. (2000). Proline-catalyzed direct asymmetric aldol reactions. *J. Am. Chem. Soc.* 122: 2395–2396.

57 Rodríguez-Llansola, F., Escuder, B., Hamley, I.W. et al. (2012). Structural and morphological studies of the dipeptide based l-Pro-l-Val organocatalytic gels and their rheological behaviour. *Soft Matter* 8: 8865–8872.

58 Soares, B.M., Aguilar, A.M., Silva, E.R. et al. (2017). Chiral organocatalysts based on lipopeptide micelles for aldol reactions in water. *Phys. Chem. Chem. Phys.* 19: 1181–1189.

59 Castelletto, V., Edwards-Gayle, C.J.C., Hamley, I.W. et al. (2019). Self-assembly of a catalytically active lipopeptide and its incorporation into cubosomes. *ACS Appl. Bio Mater.* 2: 3639–3647.

60 Lee, K.S. and Parquette, J.R. (2015). A self-assembled nanotube for the direct aldol reaction in water. *Chem. Commun.* 51: 15653–15656.

61 Dolan, M.A., Basa, P.N., Zozulia, O. et al. (2019). Catalytic nanoassemblies formed by short peptides promote highly enantioselective transfer hydrogenation. *ACS Nano* 13: 9292–9297.

62 Zhang, C., Pan, T., Salesse, C. et al. (2014). Reversible Ca(II) switch of an engineered allosteric antioxidant selenoenzyme. *Angew. Chem. Int. Ed.* 53: 13536–13539.

63 Reja, A., Afrose, S.P., and Das, D. (2020). Aldolase cascade facilitated by self-assembled nanotubes from short peptide amphiphiles. *Angew. Chem. Int. Ed.* 59: 4329–4334.

64 Li, S., Mehta, A.K., Sidorov, A.N. et al. (2016). Design of asymmetric peptide bilayer membranes. *J. Am. Chem. Soc.* 138: 3579–3586.

65 Omosun, T.O., Hsieh, M.-C., Childers, W.S. et al. (2017). Catalytic diversity in self-propagating peptide assemblies. *Nat. Chem.* 9: 805–809.

66 Sarkhel, B., Chatterjee, A., and Das, D. (2020). Covalent catalysis by cross β amyloid nanotubes. *J. Am. Chem. Soc.* 142: 4098–4103.

67 Zozulia, O. and Korendovych, I.V. (2020). Semi-rationally designed short peptides self-assemble and bind hemin to promote cyclopropanation. *Angew. Chem. Int. Ed.* 59: 8108–8112.

68 Carny, O. and Gazit, E. (2005). A model for the role of short self-assembled peptides in the very early stages of the origin of life. *FASEB J.* 19: 1051–1055.

69 Greenwald, J. and Riek, R. (2012). On the possible amyloid origin of protein folds. *J. Mol. Biol.* 421: 417–426.

70 Maury, C.P.J. (2009). Self-propagating beta-sheet polypeptide structures as prebiotic informational molecular entities: the amyloid world. *Orig. Life Evol. Biosph.* 39: 141–150.

71 Chatterjee, A., Mahato, C., and Das, D. (2021). Complex cascade reaction networks via cross β amyloid nanotubes. *Angew. Chem. Int. Ed.* 60: 202–207.

72 Barbier, B. and Brack, A. (1987). Search for catalytic properties of simple polypeptides. *Orig. Life Evol. Biosph.* 17: 381–390.

73 Zhang, C., Shafi, R., Lampel, A. et al. (2017). Switchable hydrolase based on reversible formation of supramolecular catalytic site using a self-assembling peptide. *Angew. Chem. Int. Ed.* 56: 14511–14515.

74 Ferreira, K.N., Iverson, T.M., Maghlaoui, K. et al. (2004). Architecture of the photosynthetic oxygen-evolving center. *Science* 303: 1831–1838.

75 Matsumoto, K., Zhang, S., and Koutsopoulos, S. (2010). Enhanced electron transfer activity of photosystem I by polycations in aqueous solution. *Biomacromolecules* 11: 3152–3157.

76 Matsumoto, K., Vaughn, M., Bruce, B.D. et al. (2009). Designer peptide surfactants stabilize functional photosystem-I membrane complex in aqueous solution for extended time. *J. Phys. Chem. B* 113: 75–83.

77 Rufo, C.M., Moroz, Y.S., Moroz, O.V. et al. (2014). Short peptides self-assemble to produce catalytic amyloids. *Nat. Chem.* 6: 303–309.

78 Han, J., Zou, Q., Su, W., and Yan, X. (2020). Minimal metallo-nanozymes constructed through amino acid coordinated self-assembly for hydrolase-like catalysis. *Chem. Eng. J.* 394: 124987.

79 Makam, P., Yamijala, S.S.R.K.C., Tao, K. et al. (2019). Non-proteinaceous hydrolase comprised of a phenylalanine metallo-supramolecular amyloid-like structure. *Nat. Catal.* 2: 977–985.

80 Castillo-Caceres, C., Duran-Meza, E., Nova, E. et al. (2021). Functional characterization of the ATPase-like activity displayed by a catalytic amyloid. *Biochim. Biophys. Acta Gen. Subj.* 1865: 129729.

81 Jin, Q., Zhang, L., Cao, H. et al. (2011). Self-assembly of copper (II) ion-mediated nanotube and its supramolecular chiral catalytic behavior. *Langmuir* 27: 13847–13853.

82 Wang, C., Fei, J., Wang, K., and Li, J. (2020). A dipeptide-based hierarchical nanoarchitecture with enhanced catalytic activity. *Angew. Chem. Int. Ed.* 59: 18960–18963.

83 Gayen, K., Basu, K., Bairagi, D. et al. (2018). Amino acid-based metallo-hydrogel that acts like an esterase. *ACS Appl. Bio Mater.* 1: 1717–1724.

84 Li, Y., Sun, P., Zhao, L. et al. (2020). Ferric ion driven assembly of catalase-like supramolecular photosensitizing nanozymes for combating hypoxic tumors. *Angew. Chem. Int. Ed.* 59: 23228–23238.

85 Yoon, H., Lim, J.M., Gee, H.-C. et al. (2014). A porphyrin-based molecular tweezer: guest-induced switching of forward and backward photoinduced energy transfer. *J. Am. Chem. Soc.* 136: 1672–1679.

86 Chen, C., Liu, K., Li, J., and Yan, X. (2015). Functional architectures based on self-assembly of bio-inspired dipeptides: structure modulation and its photoelectronic applications. *Adv. Colloid Interf. Sci.* 225: 177–193.

87 Xuan, M.J., Zhao, J., Shao, J.X. et al. (2017). Green. Perspective of energy transfer from light energy into biological energy. *Energy Environ.* 2: 18–22.

88 Lampel, A. (2020). Biology-inspired supramolecular peptide systems. *Chem* 6: 1222–1236.

89 Yan, X.H. (2017). Bio-inspired photosystem for green energy. Green. *Energy Environ.* 2: 66–66.

90 Wang, Q., Yang, Z., Zhang, X. et al. (2007). A supramolecular-hydrogel-encapsulated hemin as an artificial enzyme to mimic peroxidase. *Angew. Chem. Int. Ed.* 46: 4285–4289.

91 Wang, Q., Yang, Z., Ma, M. et al. (2008). High catalytic activities of artificial peroxidases based on supramolecular hydrogels that contain heme models. *Chem. Eur. J.* 14: 5073–5078.

92 Nieman, R.H. and Vennesland, B. (1957). Cytochrome c photooxidase of spinach chloroplasts. *Science* 125: 353–354.

93 Han, J.J., Liu, K., Chang, R. et al. (2019). Photooxidase-mimicking nanovesicles with superior photocatalytic activity and stability based on amphiphilic amino acid and phthalocyanine co-assembly. *Angew. Chem. Int. Ed.* 58: 2000–2004.

94 Li, J., Zhu, M., Wang, M. et al. (2020). Molecularly imprinted peptide-based enzyme mimics with enhanced activity and specificity. *Soft Matter* 16: 7033–7039.

95 Zou, Q., Zhang, L., Yan, X. et al. (2014). Multifunctional porous microspheres based on peptide-porphyrin hierarchical co-assembly. *Angew. Chem. Int. Ed.* 53: 2366–2370.

96 Geng, R., Chang, R., Zou, Q. et al. (2021). Biomimetic nanozymes based on coassembly of amino acid and hemin for catalytic oxidation and sensing of biomolecules. *Small* 17: 2008114.

97 Liu, K., Xing, R., Chen, C. et al. (2015). Peptide-induced hierarchical long-range order and photocatalytic activity of porphyrin assemblies. *Angew. Chem. Int. Ed.* 54: 500–505.

98 Liu, K., Xing, R., Li, Y. et al. (2016). Mimicking primitive photobacteria: sustainable hydrogen evolution based on peptide-porphyrin co-assemblies with a self-mineralized reaction center. *Angew. Chem. Int. Ed.* 55: 12503–12507.

99 Liu, K., Zhang, H., Xing, R. et al. (2017). Biomimetic oxygen-evolving photobacteria based on amino acid and porphyrin hierarchical self-organization. *ACS Nano* 11: 12840–12848.

100 Fu, M. and Li, J. (2018). Spontaneous membrane generation and extension in a dipeptide single crystal and phospholipid mixed system. *Angew. Chem. Int. Ed.* 57: 11404–11407.

101 Tao, K., Xue, B., Frere, S. et al. (2017). Multiporous supramolecular microspheres for artificial photosynthesis. *Chem. Mater.* 29: 4454–4460.

102 Charalambidis, G., Georgilis, E., Panda, M.K. et al. (2016). A switchable self-assembling and disassembling chiral system based on a porphyrin-substituted phenylalanine-phenylalanine motif. *Nat. Commun.* 7: 12657.

103 Nikoloudakis, E., Karikis, K., Han, J.J. et al. (2019). A self-assembly study of PNA-porphyrin and PNA-BODIPY hybrids in mixed solvent systems. *Nanoscale* 11: 3557–3566.

104 Westermann, B. (2012). Bioenergetic role of mitochondrial fusion and fission. *Biochim. Biophys. Acta* 1817: 1833–1838.

105 Chararalambidis, G., Das, S., Trapali, A. et al. (2018). Water molecules gating a photoinduced one-electron two-protons transfer in a tyrosine/histidine (Tyr/His) model of photosystemII. *Angew. Chem. Int. Ed.* 57: 9013–9017.

106 Wang, Z.J., Clary, K.N., Bergman, R.G. et al. (2013). A supramolecular approach to combining enzymatic and transition metal catalysis. *Nat. Chem.* 5: 100–103.

107 Kim, J.H., Lee, M., Lee, J.S., and Park, C.B. (2012). Self-assembled light-harvesting peptide nanotubes for mimicking natural photosynthesis. *Angew. Chem. Int. Ed.* 51: 517–520.

108 Kim, J.H., Nam, D.H., Lee, Y.W. et al. (2014). Self-assembly of metalloporphyrins into light-harvesting peptide nanofiber hydrogels for solar water oxidation. *Small* 10: 1272–1277.

109 Pan, Y.-X., Cong, H.-P., Men, Y.-L. et al. (2015). Peptide self-assembled biofilm with unique electron transfer flexibility for highly efficient visible-light-driven photocatalysis. *ACS Nano* 9: 11258–11265.

110 Zhou, T., Vallooran, J.J., and Mezzenga, R. (2019). Supramolecular chirality and crystallization from biocatalytic self-assembly in lipidic cubic mesophases. *Nanoscale* 11: 5891–5895.

111 Reetz, M.T. (2011). Laboratory evolution of stereoselective enzymes: a prolific source of catalysts for asymmetric reactions. *Angew. Chem. Int. Ed.* 50: 138–174.

112 Yu, F., Cangelosi, V.M., Zastrow, M.L. et al. (2014). Protein design: toward functional metalloenzymes. *Chem. Rev.* 114: 3495–3578.

113 Song, S., Wang, J., Song, N. et al. (2020). Peptide interdigitation-induced twisted nanoribbons as chiral scaffolds for supramolecular nanozymes. *Nanoscale* 12: 2422–2433.

114 Liu, K., Yuan, C.Q., Zou, Q.L. et al. (2017). Self-assembled zinc/cystine-based chloroplast mimics capable of photoenzymatic reactions for sustainable fuel synthesis. *Angew. Chem. Int. Ed.* 56: 7876–7880.

115 Dewa, T., Yamada, T., Ogawa, M. et al. (2005). Design and expression of cysteine-bearing hydrophobic polypeptides and their self-assembling properties with bacteriochlorophyll a derivatives as a mimic of bacterial photosynthetic antenna complexes. Effect of steric confinement and orientation of the polypeptides on the pigment/polypeptide assembly process. *Biochemistry* 44: 5129–5139.

116 Liu, K., Ren, X., Sun, J. et al. (2018). Primitive photosynthetic architectures based on self-organization and chemical evolution of amino acids and metal ions. *Adv. Sci.* 5: 1701001.

117 Xie, Z., Liu, K., Ren, X. et al. (2018). Amino-acid-mediated biomimetic formation of light-harvesting antenna capable of hydrogen evolution. *ACS Appl. Bio Mater.* 1: 748–755.

118 Yan, X., Zhu, P., and Li, J. (2010). Self-assembly and application of diphenylalanine-based nanostructures. *Chem. Soc. Rev.* 39: 1877–1890.

119 Tao, K., Makam, P., Aizen, R., and Gazit, E. (2017). Self-assembling peptide semiconductors. *Science* 358: eaam9756.

120 Sun, B., Tao, K., Jia, Y. et al. (2019). Photoactive properties of supramolecular assembled short peptides. *Chem. Soc. Rev.* 48: 4387–4400.

121 Zou, Q., Liu, K., Abbas, M., and Yan, X. (2016). Peptide-modulated self-assembly of chromophores toward biomimetic light-harvesting nanoarchitectonics. *Adv. Mater.* 28: 1031–1043.

122 Zozulia, O., Dolan, M.A., and Korendovych, I.V. (2018). Catalytic peptide assemblies. *Chem. Soc. Rev.* 47: 3621–3639.

123 Hauser, C.A.E. and Zhang, S. (2010). Nanotechnology: peptides as biological semiconductors. *Nature* 468: 516–517.

124 de la Rica, R. and Matsui, H. (2010). Applications of peptide and protein-based materials in bionanotechnology. *Chem. Soc. Rev.* 39: 3499–3509.

125 Wang, H., Chen, H., Wang, Y., and Lyu, Y.-K. (2019). Performance and mechanism comparison of manganese oxides at different valence states for catalytic oxidation of NO. *Chem. Eng. J.* 361: 1161–1172.

126 Kim, H., Yang, M., Kwon, N. et al. (2023). Recent progress on photodynamic therapy and photothermal therapy. *Bull. Korean Chem. Soc.* 44: 236–255.

19

Short Peptide Supramolecular Hydrogels for Antimicrobial Applications

Xuzhi Hu[1], Haoning Gong[2], Mingrui Liao[1], and Jian Ren Lu[1]

[1] *University of Manchester, Biological Physics Group, School of Natural Sciences, Department of Physics and Astronomy, Oxford Road, Manchester, M13 9PL, UK*
[2] *State Key Laboratory of Biochemical Engineering, Institute of Process Engineering, Chinese Academy of Sciences, Beijing 100190, China*

19.1 Introduction

Microbial infections have been posing serious health care threats worldwide, causing not only public health emergencies but also heavy financial burdens [1]. Microbial infections can dramatically increase the level of toxins at susceptible interfaces, significantly disturbing wound healing, increasing the risk of sepsis, and threatening patient's life under certain circumstances [2]. This problem has been recently exacerbated by an urgent global crisis due to the ever-increasing antimicrobial resistance (AMR). The overuse and misuse of traditional antibiotics [3] can often lead to the development of multiple drug resistance (MDR) to traditional antibiotics. Over the past decade, MDR incidences are occurring at a pace much faster than our anticipation because of the rapid reproduction and massive population [4, 5]. Thus, it is ever pressing to develop novel antimicrobial agents that can minimize the microbial multidrug resistance while maximizing antimicrobial efficacy.

Extensive efforts have been dedicated to microbial infection controls and treatments that are beyond current antibiotics, marked by the continuous development of alternative antimicrobial materials and clinical trials of new antimicrobial agents including metal ions, self-assembling peptides, quantum dots, and polymers, many of which can overcome multidrug resistance via more effective bactericidal targeting, controlled release, and bacterial membrane permeation and disruption [6]. Among them, peptides are structurally diverse and highly biocompatible with a potent ability for broad spectrum killing, which has been widely reported as the attractive candidate for developing next-generation antimicrobial agents [7]. Most natural antimicrobial peptides (AMPs) are cationic and amphiphilic, making it

Peptide Self-Assembly and Engineering: Fundamentals, Structures, and Applications, First Edition.
Edited by Xuehai Yan.

advantageous in targeting the negatively charged bacterial membrane and co-assembling with the amphiphilic lipid bilayer [8]. However, natural AMPs often have long sequences and complex structures. Long natural sequences are vulnerable to be hydrolyzed by various enzymes. These features make it difficult for their commercial usage due to structural instability and the high production cost at an industrial scale [9]. Thus, short rationally designed peptides bearing similar cationicity and amphiphilicity to natural ones are preferred. These short peptides normally contain less than 20 amino acids and are simple in molecular design, easy for synthesis, and can escape the recognition of proteolytic enzymes [10].

In general, short peptides are easy to self-assemble into various nanostructures. This is also true to many AMPs to form supramolecular hydrogels via multiple non-covalent interactions such as hydrogen bonding, π–π stacking, hydrophobic interaction, and ionic interactions [11, 12]. Hydrogel systems often comprise two coexistent phases: an aqueous phase and a solid fibrous network which encapsulates the liquid and stops the flow [13]. Short peptide-based antimicrobial hydrogels can be formed by either self-assembling antimicrobial peptides or peptide networks encapsulating other antimicrobial agents or gel-promoting chemicals and environments [14]. Compared to polymeric cross-linked hydrogels, short peptide supramolecular hydrogels normally exhibit low cytotoxicity and high biocompatibility [15]. Antimicrobial hydrogels can also provide a moist environment and remain in place under physiological conditions, making them very effective for a vast range of medical applications [16]. The 3D fibrous network closely resembles the extracellular matrix, which supports the growth of most mammalian cells and creates an intrinsic cultivation microenvironment that any 2D material cannot provide. This can make difference at the wound position where bacterial infections always form biofilm and exhibit strong drug resistance. AMP hydrogels could eradicate the biofilm, inhibit the bacterial growth, and support the host cell growth, making them beneficial for wound healing.

This chapter highlights the recent advances of short peptide supramolecular hydrogels devoted to antimicrobial applications, including the molecular design of AMPs via modifying their physical and chemical properties to facilitate the intended antimicrobial capability (Section 19.2), methods for peptide hydrogelation (Section 19.3), rheological physics of peptide hydrogels (Section 19.4), the mode of actions of antimicrobial peptide hydrogels in attacking different pathogens (Section 19.5), key features observed from applications of peptide hydrogels recently reported (Section 19.6), and conclusion and our future perspective in this area (Section 19.7).

19.2 Molecular Design of AMP Supramolecular Structures

19.2.1 Peptide Sequence

Peptides can be constituted from 20 basic amino acids and their derivatives, natural or synthetic. Apart from glycine, all amino acids are chiral with one or two chiral sites. Amino acids vary in size, charge, amphiphilicity, and potency for hydrogen bonding. By *de novo* designing, amino acids possessing different characters are selected, so that the chirality, electronegativity, and polarity of the peptide chain can be tuned [17].

As the main features of an AMP are cationic and amphiphilic, its sequence must contain positively charged lysine, arginine, and histidine and also some hydrophilic and hydrophobic motifs formed by polar and nonpolar amino acids. A good example is a cationic surfactant-like peptide (SLP) consisting of a hydrophobic tail formed by nonpolar amino-acid residues and a cationic hydrophilic head formed by positively charged amino acids [18]. These peptides usually exhibit excellent broad spectrum antibacterial activity due to electrostatic binding with negatively charged bacterial membrane. Although electrostatic interaction is crucial at priming the binding process, the exact antimicrobial activity of these peptides is predominantly determined by their hydrophobicity that can be enhanced by either increase in the number of the nonpolar residues or substitution of hydrophobic amino acids with more hydrophobic ones [19]. In terms of handiness, evidence has shown that amino acids with right handiness can prevent the formation of bacterial biofilm and break down the existing biofilm [20, 21].

19.2.2 Secondary Structure

Due to the hydrogen bonding between the amino hydrogen and carboxyl oxygen atoms in the peptide backbone, the secondary structures are spontaneously formed. The two most common secondary structures are α-helix and β-sheet. Other secondary structures reported include random coil, coiled coil, and α-sheet in spite of arguments on the stability of these structures [22]. Peptide secondary structures can greatly affect their peptide antimicrobial ability and cytotoxicity. A review by Xiong et al. has discussed how peptide secondary structures affect their antimicrobial ability [23]. AMPs folding into α-helix normally have distinguishable amphiphilic motifs. Their amphiphilic nature drives their hydrophobic domains into the bacterial membrane, causing membrane distortion and disruption. Excellent correlation between the extent of α-helicity and antimicrobial ability has been reported for LL-37, melittin, and kiadin peptides. However, similar damage could also be imposed to mammalian cell membrane, causing undesirable cytotoxicity. Modulating the secondary structures can improve the selectivity of AMPs. Some natural AMPs adopt a random coiled conformation with low cytotoxicity under physiological conditions and can readily transform into α-helical structures in response to varied stimuli. For example, Marín-Medina et al. [24] have reported that Magainin adopted a coiled conformation under physiological conditions due to the electrostatic repulsion of positively charged side chains. After inserting into the bacterial membrane, it transformed to the helical structure via the interaction with the lipid membrane, which reduced the charge repulsion in the side chains of the peptide. Due to the secondary-structure-transitioning ability, many Magainin derivatives are used in clinical applications. Apart from the transition of AMPs into α-helix, some AMPs can also transform into β-sheet when embedded into the bacterial membrane. In contrast with the membrane-penetrating α-helical AMPs, the β-sheet AMPs only bind to the negatively charged lipid and induce slow leakage [25]. As a result, β-sheet AMPs do not kill bacteria rapidly but possess less cytotoxicity, and their higher selectivity is generally observed [26].

19.2.3 Self-assembly and Higher Ordered Structures

Not all AMPs can self-assemble, as this process is driven by noncovalent interactions including hydrogen bonding, van der Waals forces, electrostatic interactions, hydrophobic interactions, and π-π stacking [11]. Figure 19.1 illustrated an example of self-assembly of KI_4K and its analogues from monomer to secondary structures to further supramolecular structures [27]. Under most circumstances, an amphiphilic peptide self-assembles prior to its contact with bacterial membrane. Balancing between self-assembly and interaction with bacterial membrane has direct impact on its antimicrobial ability. Two reviews have provided comprehensive discussion and assessment about how peptide self-assembly affects their antimicrobial ability [28, 29]. Generally, charge distribution inside a peptide within a self-assembled structure is different from that in a monomer under much less constraints in a solution environment. For the peptide inside the self-assembly in aqueous solution, the polar residues tend to orientate to the aqueous phase, while the nonpolar motifs prefer to retain in the interior, creating a hydrophobic microenvironment. This structure may stabilize the secondary structure. As both charges and secondary structures of AMP might be altered when self-assembling occurs,

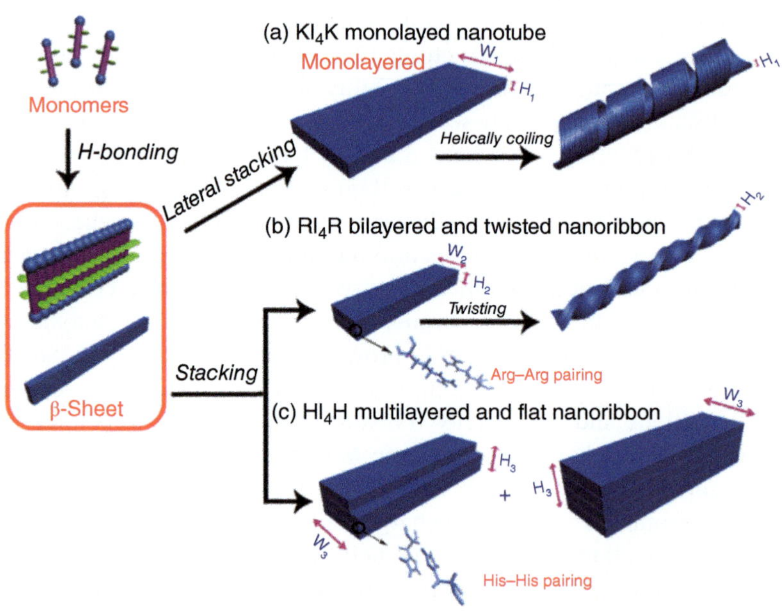

Figure 19.1 Schematic diagram depicting the self-assembly of KI_4K and its analogues (RI_4R and HI_4H) from monomer to secondary structure (β-sheet) to further supramolecular structures of nanotubes and nanoribbons. Source: Reproduced from Ref. [27] with the permission from Wiley.

the interaction between the AMP and bacterial membranes could be affected significantly. It is particularly delicate to balance the self-assembling process of the membrane-lytic peptide and its interaction with the bacterial membrane, as this could create a powerful in-membrane nanostructuring to disrupt the lipid membrane by forming pores [8]. Gazit and his coworkers have demonstrated that the antimicrobial ability of diphenylalanine is enhanced after self-assembling. The diphenylalanine self-assemblies completely inhibit bacterial growth, induce substantial disruption to bacterial morphology, and cause membrane permeation and depolarization [30]. We have recently developed a group of self-assembling lipopeptides C_x-G(IIKK)$_2$I-NH$_2$ (C_xG_2, $x = 4$–12), which self-assemble into nanofibers above their critical aggregation concentrations (CACs) [31]. The most hydrophobic lipopeptide $C_{12}G_2$ can self-assemble nanofibers, which can not only impose broad spectrum bactericidal activity within few minutes but also display lower cytotoxicity than their nonaggregated homologues. The latter impose more aggressive membrane lytic ability. These examples indicated that the peptide–membrane interaction could be significantly affected by the self-assembling tendency of the peptide and its extent of mediation when interacting with the lipid membrane.

Under certain circumstances, peptide self-assembling can even endow the nonantimicrobial peptide with antibacterial activity. For examples, Chu et al. have reported that human α-defensin 6 (HD6), a peptide expressed by secretory Paneth cells of the small intestine, lacks appreciable bactericidal activity as a monomer. After stochastic binding to bacterial membrane, however, it undergoes ordered self-assembly to form fibrils and nanonets that surround and entangle bacteria, protecting the small intestine from invasion by enteric bacterial pathogens [32]. Paulmann et al. reported a dermcidin derivative named DCD-1L, an anionic AMP present in human sweat, whose antibacterial activity is exerted via forming oligomeric complexes stabilized by Zn^{2+} [33]. These factors suggested that the endowed antibacterial activity is generally achieved by different membrane-binding modes by self-assembling peptides compared to monomers.

These examples together suggest that we should combine sequence design, secondary structure, and higher ordered nanostructure to design more intelligent AMP nanomaterials with self-assembling capabilities.

19.2.4 Antimicrobial Drug Delivery Platform

Short AMPs are easy to self-assemble into various nanostructures, which enables AMPs inhibit bacterial growth and deliver other antimicrobial agents/antibiotics simultaneously. In this way, the therapeutic efficiency of the mixed formulations is significantly enhanced. For example, Peng et al. have reported that a gemini surfactant-like peptide Ac-AAAAAAPKKPAAAAAA-NH$_2$ (APK) is capable of inhibiting bacterial growth, and the hydrophobic two tails make the peptide more readily to self-assemble, encapsulating and delivering several hydrophobic drugs including paclitaxel, doxorubicin, etomidate, and propofol concurrently [34]. The drug-encapsulated APK exhibited improved efficacy compared to the clinical formulations due to the synergistic effects.

Moreover, short peptides can self-assemble to form hydrogels, which are capable of delivering different drugs, responding to varied stimuli and controlling the release process. We designed a hydrogel formed by I_3K nanofibers mixed with thermal-responsive polymer PNIPAM [35, 36]. When the temperature increases above the lower critical solution temperature of the PNIPAM, the molecules transit to globular particles, which cross-link different peptide nanofibers and form hydrogel. As this process is physically driven by temperature, the hydrogel is thermal reversible. Antibacterial peptide of G(IIKK)$_3$I-NH$_2$ (G$_3$) is conveniently loaded in the solution phase at low temperature and spontaneously forms hydrogel at high temperature. The hydrogel gives a sustained and controlled linear release of G(IIKK)$_3$I-NH$_2$ over time. As the antimicrobial peptide hydrogels mimic the extracellular matrix, they could be used for multiple medical applications. These examples indicated that peptide hydrogels are quite advantageous in antimicrobial applications with high biocompatibility and exertion of a variety of synergistic antimicrobial effects.

19.3 Methods for Peptide Hydrogel Formation

Hydrogels are quite advantageous in the antimicrobial application. It is thus of great importance to understand how to effectively form peptide-based hydrogels. Several reviews from Gazit's, Yan's, and Wei's groups have summarized the methods for forming peptide hydrogels [13, 37, 38]. In this section, we introduce three major ways for forming antimicrobial peptide hydrogels, which have been widely reported in open literatures.

19.3.1 Spontaneous Peptide Self-assembly

The most direct way to form a peptide hydrogel is simply via peptide's spontaneous self-assembly in aqueous solution. Peptides self-assemble into nanostructures that separate the aqueous solution into solid and liquid phases. Diphenylalanine (FF) peptide is one of the simplest peptides that can self-assemble into nanofiber network hydrogels, with the mechanical stiffness being readily adjusted by peptide concentrations [39]. Normally, FF is terminally capped with chemical groups such as Fmoc to prevent its N- and C-terminus from protonation or deprotonation. The resulting Fmoc-FF can still self-assemble into hydrogels and adopt a typical β-sheet secondary structure [40, 41]. The adopted β-sheet structure can transform to an α-helix upon charge induction as reported by Yan and his coworkers [42]. Many other well-studied self-assembling peptides can also spontaneously form hydrogels for multiple medical applications such as EAK16 (AEAEAKAKAEAEAKAK) and RADA16 (RADARADARADARADA) developed by Zhang and his coworkers [43].

Our studies have demonstrated that surfactant-like peptide I_3K and its analogues can self-assemble into nanofibrils and form hydrogels under physiological conditions [44] as shown in Figure 19.2a and b. The dynamic formation process of long nanofibrils of the I_3K self-assembly is driven by end-to-end connections of short ones, with no monomer exchange after self-assembling, as reflected by mixing of

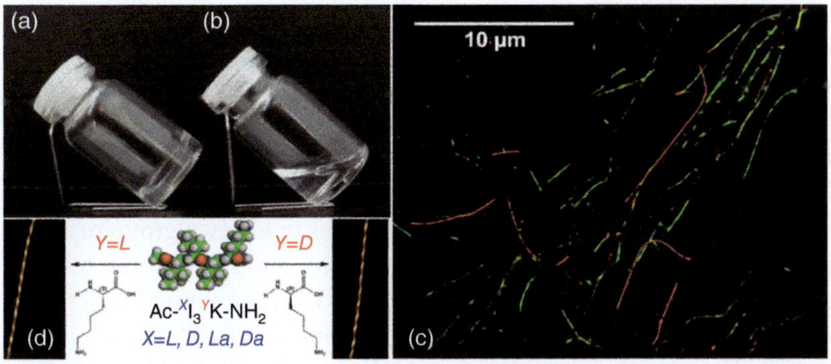

Figure 19.2 Photographs of (a) Ac-I_3CGK-NH_2 (0.5 mM) and (b) Ac-I_3K-NH_2 (0.5 mM) after 40 days of incubation in the air. (c) Representative image of the two-color STORM images collected from I_3K peptide fibrils (8 mM). The red and green channels are from Alexa Fluor 647 and Cy3B dyes, respectively. (d) The handedness of twisted Ac-I_3K-NH_2 nanofibers is determined by the chirality of the C-terminal Lys residue. Source: (a) and (b) Reproduced from Ref. [44] with permission from Springer. Source: (c) and (d) Reproduced from Refs. [45, 46] respectively, with permission from ACS.

two individually labeled I_3K samples revealed by two-color super-resolution fluorescence microscopy, specifically stochastic reconstruction microscopy (STORM) (Figure 19.2c) [45]. Substitution of D-amino acid in I_3K series can twist the nanofibers in which the chirality of lysine determines the twist of the assembly, while the chirality of the isoleucine determines the secondary structure Figure 19.2d [46].

19.3.2 Enzymatically Assisted Hydrogelation

Peptide self-assembling hydrogels triggered by enzyme can offer great advantages in biomedical applications due to high biocompatibility and mild reaction conditions. The hydrogels formed are normally homogeneous and stable. Many enzymatic formations of supramolecular hydrogels are achieved via chemical bond formation. Ulijn and his coworkers have explored the use of proteases to catalyze peptide self-assembly via peptide synthesis and reverse hydrolysis [47]. The proteases trigger Fmoc amino acids to bind with dipeptides, forming tripeptides that self-assemble into higher ordered structures, which lead to hydrogelation. The major advantage of this reverse hydrolysis method is that no by-products except water are formed. This enzymatically controlled hydrogelation is greatly affected by the presence of ions. The salts added affect the nucleation and growth of the self-assembled nanostructures, resulting in differential order and chirality as well as variable mechanical properties of the hydrogels [48]. Under enzymatic catalysis, excellent antimicrobial abilities have been observed for these self-assembling peptide hydrogels [49]. In our recent work, we designed an amphiphilic short peptide with a sequence of I_3QGK [50]. Though I_3QGK self-assembled into long nanoribbons in aqueous solution, the system was a transparent and free-flowing dispersion even at the high concentration up to 16 mM. Upon adding transglutaminase (TGase), the peptide solution at a concentration of lower than 8 mM could undergo a distinct sol–gel transition to form hydrogel. It appeared that the peptide existed in the formation of both assembly and monomers in aqueous solutions. After addition of transglutaminase, the monomers were enzymatically converted to dimers that rapidly self-assembled into nanofibers, leading to the formation of hydrogels.

Peptide-based hydrogels can also be formed by bond breakage. Yang and Xu utilized an alkaline phosphatase to dephosphorylate the PO_4^{3-} of the Fmoc-Y-PO_4^{3-} under basic conditions for hydrogelation [51]. Yang later in his own group reported that the enzyme-assisted self-assembly of the peptide could transform into an α-helix conformation [52]. A peptide with a sequence of chlorambucil-$G^DF^DFp^DY$ (p stands for PO_4^{3-}) could be dephosphorylated to chlorambucil-$G^DF^DF^DY$ by alkaline phosphatase. The resulting peptide formed a hydrogel with an α-helix conformation, exhibiting better tolerance against proteinase K digestion, compared with other peptides with a β-sheet conformation.

19.3.3 Cross-linking Enhanced Hydrogelation

Cross-linking within peptides or with other macromolecules using various chemical linkers can trigger peptides to form hydrogels. Peptide-based hydrogels formed by this method normally bear enhanced stiffness and stability as the fibers are generally connected to form networks. Collier and coworkers modulated self-assembling peptide hydrogels via native chemical ligation, which produced peptide bonds between the termini of fibrous β-sheet peptides. As a result, the stiffness of the hydrogel was enhanced [53]. Tovar and coworkers have designed short peptide–chromophore–peptide sequences displaying different reactive functional groups that can form cross-links with appropriately modified bifunctional polyethylene glycol (PEG)-based small guest molecules [54]. The peptides self-assembled into free-flowing 1D fibrils, and the cross-links induced a secondary network that physically locked the preassembled π-conjugated peptide strands, leading to phase separation within the system and forming hydrogel. Wang et al. reported a photo-cross-linking method for peptide hydrogelation, which is based on the ruthenium-complex-catalyzed ($Ru[bpy]_3^{2+}$) conversion of tyrosine to dityrosine upon light irradiation [55], as shown in Figure 19.3a. Upon catalyzing, the two tyrosine residues on different peptide molecules become close to each other. The cross-linking could be readily completed within 2 min as the reaction became rapid. The mechanical stability was significantly improved due to the formation of a denser entangled peptide fibrous network.

Apart from chemical cross-linkers, supramolecular linking with bio-based materials including enzymes, proteins, and polysaccharides can also be exploited to generate hydrogels. The linkers used in this method are highly biocompatible, plus this biological cross-linking usually requires little chemical modification and mild reaction conditions only. These makes this strategy much advantageous in biological applications. Wang and coworkers have developed a two-step hydrogelation method using dual enzymatic polymerization [56], with the schematic showing the hydrogelation process in Figure 19.3b–e. The dual enzyme system is composed of glucose oxidase (GOx), glucose, horseradish peroxidase (HRP), acetyl acetone

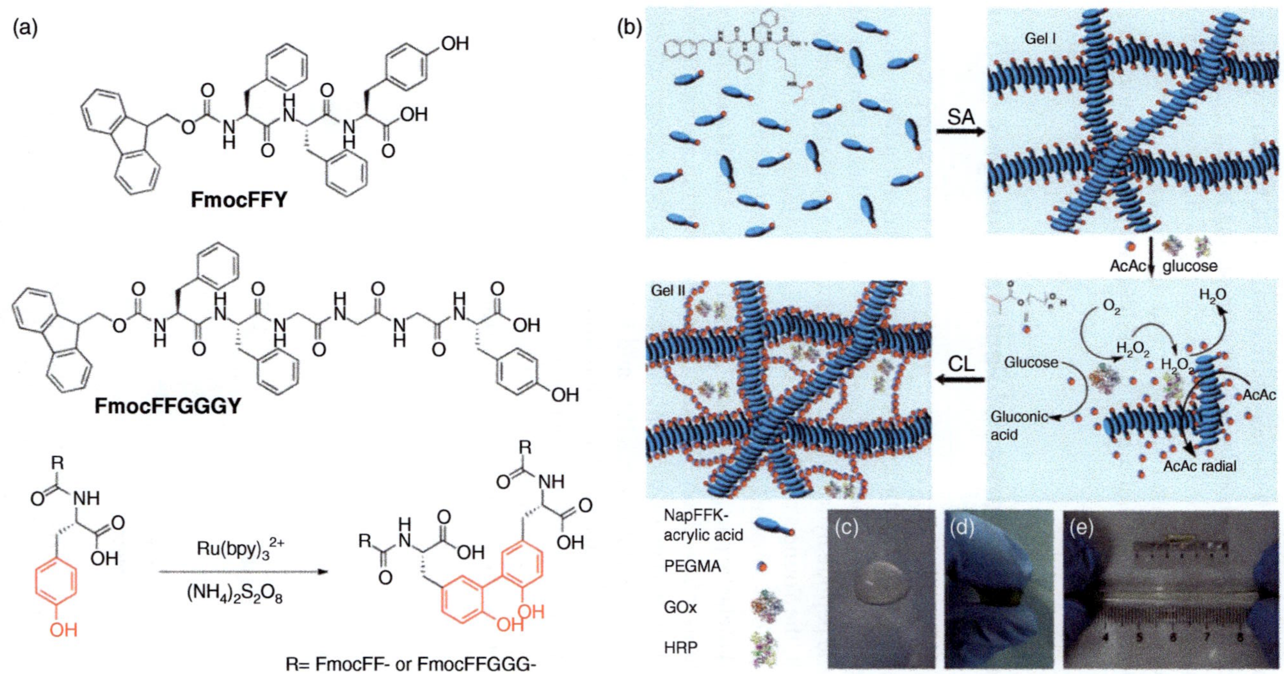

Figure 19.3 (a) Schematic illustration of the structures of FmocFFY and FmocFFGGGY and the $Ru(bpy)_3Cl_2$-catalyzed photo-cross-linking reaction, reprinted from [55], with permission from ACS. (b) Schematic of the preparation of hybrid hydrogel, NapFFK-acrylic acid, PEGMA, GOx, and HRP (SA = self-assembly, CL = cross-linking). (c) Optical image of Gel I. (d) Optical image of Gel II. (e) The tensile state of Gel II. Source: Reproduced from Ref. [56], with permission from RSC / CC BY 3.0.

(AcAc), and poly(ethylene glycol) methacrylate (PEGMA). After self-assembly of a designed peptide NapFFK and acrylic acid, the GOx first oxidizes glucose to gluconic acid. Subsequently, O_2 is reduced to H_2O_2 by flavin adenine dinucleotide (FAD). The H_2O_2 generated is then involved in the generation of AcAc radicals via HRP catalyzation, through which the polymerization of PEGMA with acrylic modified hydrogelators was initiated. This mechanically strong hybrid hydrogel maintained high reusability and thermal stability. Yang group and Adams group showed the methods to form peptide-based hydrogels with enhanced mechanical properties by the incorporation of multicomponent peptides and polysaccharides, respectively [57, 58].

19.4 Rheological Properties of Peptide Hydrogels

Peptide hydrogel is not a uniform elastic material. It contains a solid phase (entangled fibers), which contributes to the elastic element, and a liquid phase, which contributes to the inelastic element. The existence of the inelastic element means that if we distort the peptide hydrogel, it may not return to exactly the same form as it starts. As a result, the Young's modulus of the peptide hydrogel (the ratio between stress and strain) is not a constant, instead it should be a complex value combining the elastic part and inelastic part, denoted as G' and G'', also known as storage modulus and loss modulus, respectively. The storage and loss moduli represent the elastic and rheological properties of the peptide hydrogels, which greatly affect their applications in terms of coating, wettability, and injectability [59].

It is clear that the ratio between G'' and G' reflects how rigid/viscous the material is, as demonstrated in Figure 19.4a. When the phase angle between G'' and G' is 90°, it indicates the pure fluidity of the material. When the phase angle is 0°, it indicates the pure rigidity of the material. Peptide hydrogel should have both G' and G''

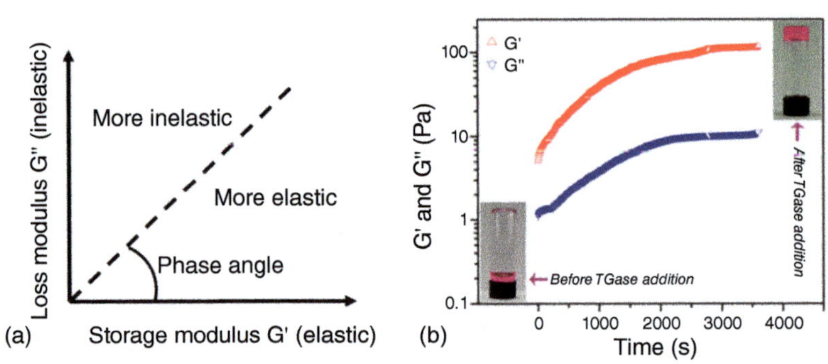

Figure 19.4 (a) Schematic plot showing the relation between storage modulus G' and loss modulus G'' of the peptide hydrogel. (b) Rheological time sweep (G' and G'' change) of 8 mM I_3QGK at 25 °C immediately after addition of TGase. The insets show the photographs of the peptide solution taken before and 60 min after addition of TGase with trace Rhodamine B introduced for better visualization. Source: Reproduced from Ref. [50], with permission from ACS.

moduli, and the ratio of the two values can be used to estimate the elasticity of the hydrogel. A good example shows the storage and loss moduli change for I_3QGK enzymatic assistant hydrogelation as mentioned in Section 19.3.2 (Figure 19.4b) [50]. Upon enzymatic addition of TGase, the time sweep rheology displayed an obvious increase in the storage modulus G′ from about 5 Pa to about 120 Pa after 60 min, indicating the improved rigidity of the hydrogel against tensile strain. The ratio between G′ and the corresponding loss modulus G″ increased from 5 to some 12, indicating that the gelation had occurred and a rigid and solid-like hydrogel with heavily cross-linked network had formed.

19.5 Mode of Action for Antimicrobial Peptide Hydrogel

Figure 19.5 shows the summary of the four modes of actions for AMP hydrogens to effectively kill the bacteria as reported so far in open literatures.

19.5.1 Extracellular Interaction

Some bacteria can form biofilm on wet surfaces in which the bacteria become embedded within a slimy extracellular matrix (ECM). When AMP interacts with these bacteria, they first come into direct contact with the ECM. This makes it a targeting component in the ECM and trapping the entire bacteria becomes an important mode of action in the biofilm network.

The bacterial ECM is mainly composed of peptidoglycan (PGN), which is porous and not a permeability barrier for either particles of approximately 2 nm or globular, hydrophilic, and nonsticky molecules with a size of 50 kDa [60]. As short AMPs are typically less than 6 kDa and PGN carries both teichoic acid and amine groups (its net charges are pH dependent), PGN is an energetically unfavorable binding site for

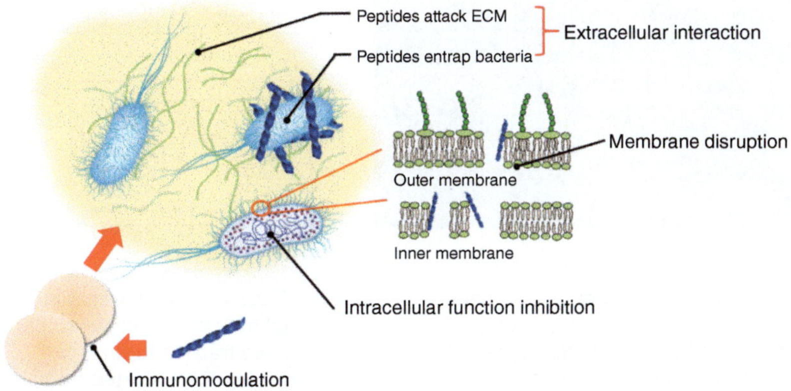

Figure 19.5 Four modes of actions for AMP hydrogen to kill the bacteria. Source: The figure is created by Xuzhi Hu and Jian Ren Lu.

most AMPs compared to heavily negatively charged membranes. Thus, the targeting of AMPs generally does not directly destroy the PGN systems, but some of them may inhibit the biosynthesis of the PGN. For example, the branched tricyclic glycopeptide vancomycin and families of cyclic lipo(glyco)peptides and lipoglycodepsipeptides like the macrocyclic ramoplanin bind to PGN precursors and hinder further enzyme activity [61, 62]. Self-assembling peptide hydrogels have an ECM-like fibrous network structure which can entrap isolated bacteria and prevent bacterial mobility [63]. This mode of action was reported for human HD6 peptides [64, 65] and synthetic multidomain peptides [66].

19.5.2 Membrane Disruption

Membrane disruption is regarded as the primary way of killing bacteria as it is less likely to trigger drug resistance. Therefore, the interaction between AMPs and microbial lipid membrane has been extensively studied both *in vitro* and *in vivo*. In our recent work [67], we have shown that G_3 peptide achieved low minimum inhibition concentrations and effective dynamic kills against antibiotic-resistant and susceptible bacteria due to its rapid membrane disruption ability. As shown by our STROM image (Figure 19.6a), strong green fluorescent signals have been observed for the Cy3B-labeled G_3 peptides on living *Escherichia coli*, indicating the accumulation of G_3 on the natural *E. coli* membrane and the great potency of G_3 against membrane.

However, to gain the exact distributions of peptides across the bacterial membrane at the molecular level, *in vitro* study using model lipid membrane is preferred. Model lipid membrane can be formed either as monolayer at the air/water interface or as bilayer on a supported substrate. The monolayers formed at air/water are

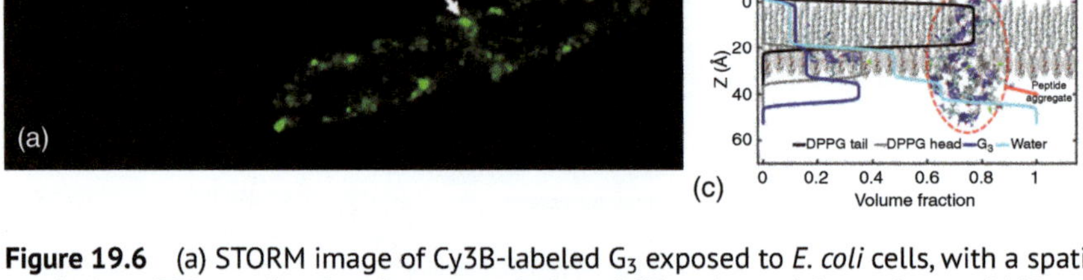

Figure 19.6 (a) STORM image of Cy3B-labeled G_3 exposed to *E. coli* cells, with a spatial resolution of 20 nm, showing the accumulation of G3 on bacterial membrane. (b) Neutron reflection profiles and c fitted scattering length density and volume fraction profiles for DPPG monolayer in the absence and presence of G_3 at air/water interface, collected from four contrasts (d/hDPPG G_3 D_2O/H_2O). The profiles demonstrated that G_3 become adsorbed and embedded into the model lipid membrane. Source: Reproduced from Ref. [67] with permission from ACS.

pressure controlled by a Langmuir trough. Thus, the physical states of the lipid monolayer must be clearly addressed before peptide injection, and the results are typically presented in π-A curves, where π is surface pressure, and A is area per molecule [68]. Typically, the lipid molecules should undergo transition from a liquid-expanded state to a liquid-condensed state over intermediate pressure. Peptides are normally injected from the subliquid phase onto the lipid monolayer at a liquid condensed state and are allowed to freely adsorb onto the monolayer. To further explore how G_3 peptides distribute across the membrane, we formed a model DPPG lipid monolayer (negatively charged) that mimics the bacterial natural membrane [67]. The detailed structural change of the DPPG monolayer was studied by neutron reflection. Neutron reflection is very sensitive to isotope labeling especially hydrogen and deuterium as the two isotopes have distinctly different scattering length densities (SLD) (H_2O SLD: $-0.56\times10^{-6}\,\text{Å}^{-2}$ and D_2O SLD: $6.35\times10^{-6}\,\text{Å}^{-2}$). As lipid monolayer is formed at the air/water interface, it is possible to use a mixture of H_2O and D_2O to make water and air indistinguishable to neutron (Air SLD: 0), so that the adsorbed material could be highlighted. The null reflection water (NRW) can be readily formed by mixing 8 vol% H_2O and 92 vol% D_2O. Thus, four contrasts (d/h-DPPG G_3 D_2O/NRW) were performed in parallel (Figures 19.5b and c). Our NR results indicated that G_3 became inserted into the DPPG monolayer occupying about 20 vol% in the lipid monolayer.

Bilayer lipid membrane model can be alternatively established on an optically flat surface such as silicon oxide, known as supported lipid bilayer (SLB). Despite no pressure being applied onto the membrane and the membrane properties sometimes are affected by the properties of the substrate, SLBs are advantageous in characterizing the detailed peptide–membrane interaction as both inner and outer lipid leaflets are formed in a typical SLB. Furthermore, asymmetric lipid bilayer can be formed in which the inner and outer leaflets have varied compositions. Several pioneering experiments by Clifton et al. have demonstrated the successful fabrication and novel application of the symmetric and asymmetric SLBs in addition to the floating lipid bilayer [69–71]. In a recent collaborative work involving Clifton [72], an asymmetric SLB was formed with the inner layer being composed of DPPG and the outer layer being composed of rough C lipopolysaccharides (RcLPS), which mimics the outer membrane of Gram-negative bacteria. Neutron reflection was used to characterize the distributions of peptides across the model outer membrane, as shown in Figure 19.7. Both G_3 and C_8G_2 peptides could quickly penetrate the asymmetric SLB, causing direct removal of some membrane lipids and creating nanopores through which the cytoplasm was leaked.

Neutron technique can provide statistical information and appropriate resolution on peptide distribution across the model lipid membrane in *Z*-axis. To obtain the morphology of model lipid membrane upon peptide binding at the *XY*-plane, several techniques including Brewster angle microscopy, atomic force microscopy, molecular simulation, and fluorescent analysis can be applied [67, 73, 74]. These studies together help understand how an AMP peptide interacts with a given lipid membrane at the molecular level. By combining all the observations together, we can generate a better description of structural characteries at both *XY*-plane and *Z*-axis.

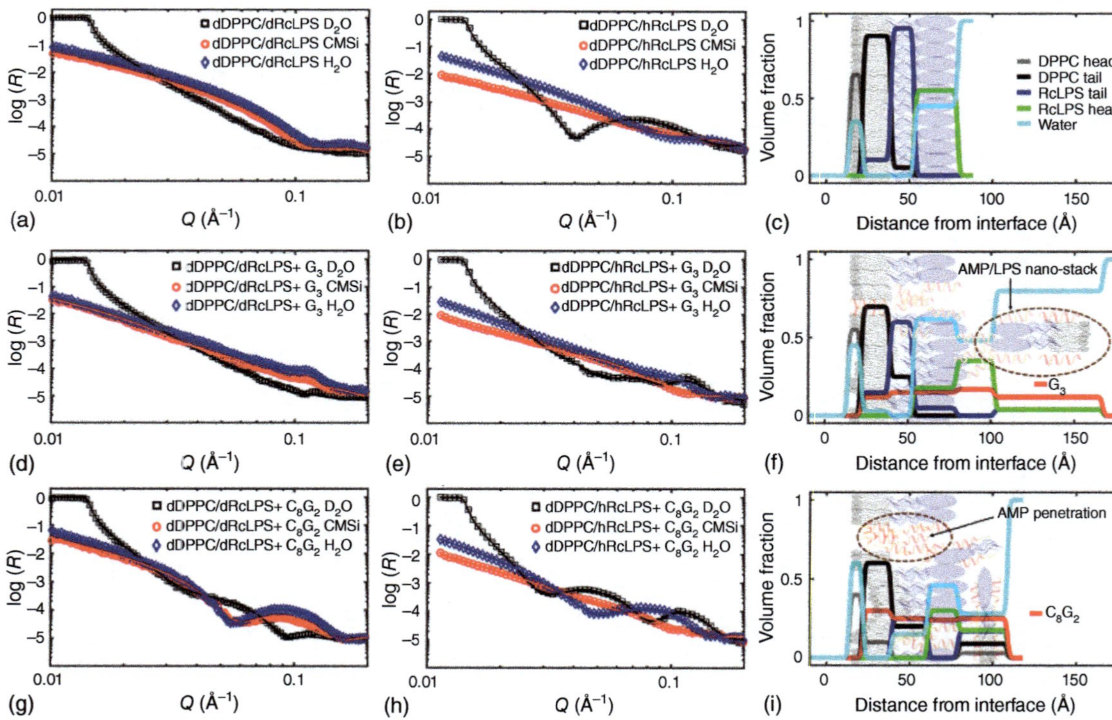

Figure 19.7 NR profiles and analyses from supported asymmetric bilayers. (A–C) RcLPS/DPPC bilayers at the solid/liquid interface, (D–F) upon interaction with G_3, and (G–I) with C_8G_2. Panels (C), (F), and (I) show the SLD profiles and spatial distributions of the different components derived from the model fits to the neutron reflectivity data. Source: Reproduced from Ref. [72] with permissions form ACS.

19.5.3 Intracellular Function Inhibition

In addition to membrane disruptions, some AMPs can penetrate bacterial membranes and kill bacteria intracellularly by inhibiting synthesis or functions of some key enzymes/proteins or nucleic acids, as reviewed by Scocchi et al. [75]. An increasing amount of evidence has accumulated to demonstrate the intracellular functional inhibition by AMPs. For example, the proline-rich AMP Onc112 kills bacteria via inhibiting key protein synthesis. The Onc112 peptide binds within the ribosomal exit tunnel and extends toward the peptidyl transferase center, where it overlaps with the binding site for an aminoacyl-Trna. As a result, the initiation complex is blocked and destabilized [76]. In addition to proline-rich AMP, a proteome microarray study showed that three other AMPs including bactenecin 7, a hybrid of pleurocidin and dermaseptin, and lactoferricin B can hit 47–231 proteins in *E. coli*, while 30 of them are common targets for all four peptides [77]. Besides, the AMP buforin II can penetrate bacterial membrane and accumulate inside *E. coli* even below its MIC. Buforin II inhibits the bacterial function by binding to DNA and RNA, resulting in rapid cell death [78].

19.5.4 Enhanced Host Defense/Immunomodulation

Rather than direct interaction with bacteria, some AMPs can also participate in the immune regulation of the host through which the pathogens are killed indirectly, as discussed by recent reviews [79, 80]. Human immune cells can generate AMPs which are generally divided into three main families: defensins, cathelicidins, and histatins. Defensins play a key important role in local and systemic innate immunity and are widely found in immune cells such as neutrophils, macrophages, lymphocytes, and epithelial cells of skin. For examples, human beta defensins (HBD) can stimulate the expression of interleukin 6 (IL 6), IL 10, and other immunostimulatory cytokines in human keratinocytes, promoting the migration and proliferation of keratinocytes to induce wound healing [81]. Apart from natural AMPs, rationally designed AMPs can also participate in immune regulation. For example, evidence has shown that an artificial AMP with a sequence of tide KLKLLLLLKLK can induce predominantly a T_H2-type immune response to coinjected model antigen ovalbumin as high levels of antigen-specific antibodies are induced [82].

19.6 Key Features and Practical Usages of Antimicrobial Peptide Hydrogels

Evident by rapid killing, low resistance and cytotoxicity, stimuli responsiveness, and smart drug delivery, extensive efforts have been devoted to developing peptide hydrogels for antimicrobial applications. Some remarkable studies have demonstrated the high bacterial inhibitory effects and biocompatibility for some peptide hydrogels, including A_9K_2 [83], FF [30], and I_4K_2 [84]. In the following sections, we have outlined several key features of peptide hydrogels for antimicrobial applications reported in recent open publications.

19.6.1 Antimicrobial Peptide Hydrogels with Multiple Functions

It is preferable to endow AMP hydrogels with as many functions as possible. A latest study reported that the hydrogel formed from a natural AMP peptide jelleine-1 [85] with excellent antimicrobial efficacy, hemostasis, and antiadhesion ability. Our recent work has demonstrated the ease of hydrogelation of our lead AMP G_3 ($G(IIKK)_3I\text{-}NH_2$) and its homologues and their novel antimicrobial features including amphiphilicity, high antimicrobial efficacy, low cytotoxicity, high selectivity, high stability against enzymatic degradation, potency in killing resistant microbial strains, and low immunogenicity. From the Schiffer–Edmundson wheel drawn, we can see that G_3 has a well-defined helical structure with clear charged/uncharged and hydrophobic/hydrophilic faces (separated by the dash-dotted red line). Note that G_3 assumes random coiled structure in aqueous solution and only transforms to the helical structure when interacting with bacterial membrane, resulting in the enhanced potency against negatively charged bacterial membranes (Figure 19.8a).

The MICs for G_3 and its homologues against *E. coli*, drug-resistant *E. coli*, *Bacillus subtilis*, and *Staphylococcus aureus* are as low as 10, 8, 5, and 7.5 μM, respectively [86]. G_3 and its homologues also exhibited relatively lower MICs but much faster dynamical killing against fungi when compared with conventional antifungal drugs amphotericin B and fluconazole [87]. Against *C. albicans*, four other albicans, and *Cryptococcus neoformans*, amphotericin B produced MIC values between 1 and 5 μM, while fluconazole produced MIC values between 3 and 100 μM. Both antifungal drugs required well over 1 h. to show inhibitory effects. In contrast, MICs from G_3 varied between 3 and 50 μM, but the yeasts could be killed within much shorter periods (Figure 19.8b).

G_3 and its homologues were also very effective in killing biofilms formed from bacteria, fungi, and drug-resistant pathogens as the 50% biofilm-eradicating concentration (BEC50) for G_3 against most model biofilms is in the range of 12–60 μM [89]. Compared with some well-known antimicrobial agents, G_3 and its homologues are effective against a wide range of pathogens and impose lower cytotoxicity toward host cells. For example, Ag^+ has high potency, but it is cytotoxic to host cells. Vancomycin and levofloxacin are highly potent with extremely low MICs against planktonic pathogens. However, they can be very ineffective against the resistant wound biofilms. Moreover, we have shown the great potential for G_3 and its homologues in antitumor therapy. G_3 and its homologues are able to kill cancer cells effectively while remaining benign to the host cells at micromolar concentrations (Figure 19.8c) [88]. Apart from high potency against microbial membrane, the peptides can also induce the programmed cell death of cancer cells via both mitochondrial and death receptor pathways, without inducing nonspecific immunogenic responses (Figure 19.8d and e). These studies confirm the broad-spectrum activity of G_3 and its homologues against infections and the great potential for clinical usage.

19.6.2 Enzymatically Assisted Smart Antimicrobial Drug Delivery

The fibrous network of the hydrogels formed by a self-assembling peptide can entrap varied antimicrobial drugs. The rate of drug release is normally determined

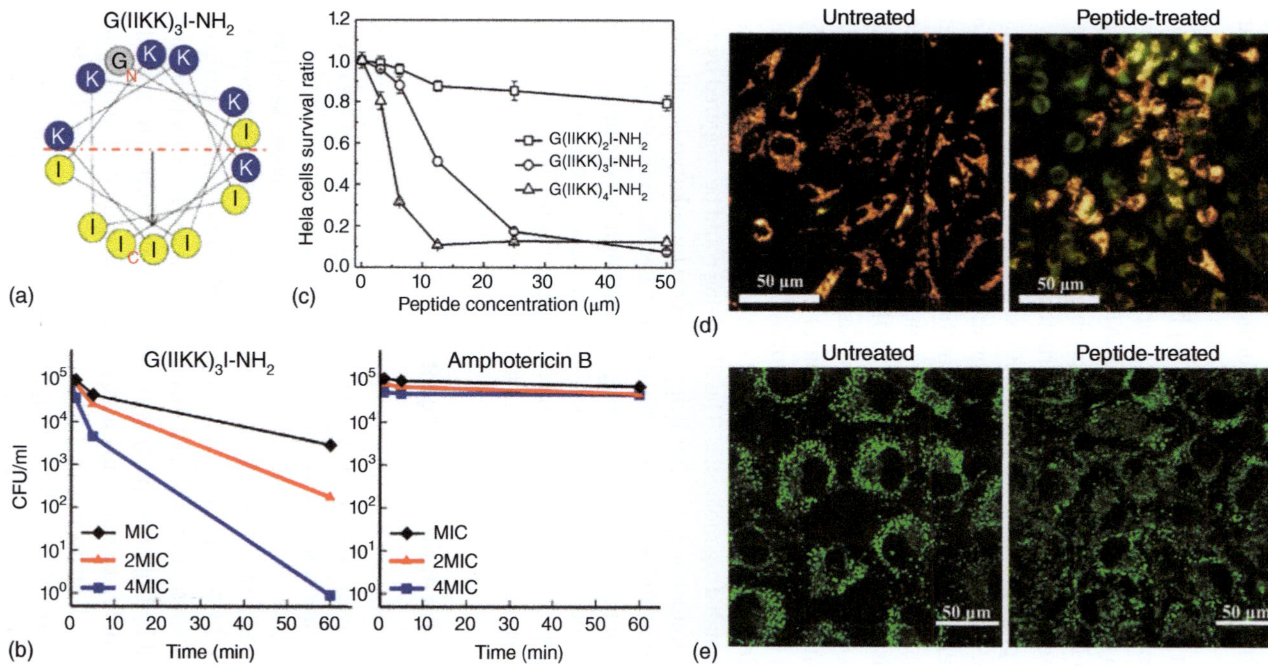

Figure 19.8 (a) Schiffer–Edmundson wheel projection of G(IIKK)$_3$I-NH$_2$, its N-terminal variants (upper, pink arrows), and C-terminal variants (lower, yellow arrows). Yellow circles denote hydrophobic amino acid I, and blue circles represent hydrophilic amino acid K. Gray circles denote G, reprinted from [86], with permission from ACS. (b) Time-dependent killing plots of G_3 and Amphotericin B in the unit of log(CFU/ml) against *Candida albicans* at MIC, 2MIC, and 4MIC. Source: Reproduced from Ref. [87], with permission from Elsevier. (c) Cancer cell survival rate against concentrations for G_3 and its analogues. (d) Fluorescent images of mitochondrial membrane potential staining with tetraethylbenzimidazolcarbocyanine iodide of HeLa cells before and after incubation with 10 μM G_3 for 24 h, indicating the mitochondrial dysfunction. (e) Immunofluorescence staining of Cyt c of HeLa cells before and after incubation with 10 μM G_3 for 24 h. Source: Reproduced from Ref. [88], with permission from Elsevier.

by the diffusion coefficient of the drug through the hydrogel network [90]. Through specific enzymatic cleavage, the drug-loaded peptide hydrogels can rapidly respond to particular biological environment and release the cargos spontaneously at the exact target sites. This smart drug delivery platform has been reported in delivering anticancer drug, and the drug carrier can be further delivered to subcellular organelles.

Two studies by Cao et al. [91] and He et al. [92, 93] have demonstrated the great potential of these enzymatically assisted peptide delivery platforms. In the work by Cao et al., a peptide with a sequence of Nap-FFGPLGLARKRK can self-assemble into long fibrous network to form hydrogels. The hydrophobic cores (Nap-FF-) encapsulate a considerable amount of anticancer drug doxorubicin (DOX). Enzymatic cleavage by the cancer-overexpressed matrix metalloproteinase-7 (MMP7) on the fragment of GPLGLA at the tumor sites resulted in fibrous degradation and sustainable release of DOX, leading to cancer cell death (Figure 19.9a). In the work by He et al., reversed enzyme-assisted hydrogelation was used for drug delivery (Figure 19.9b). The branched peptides consisted of a FLAG-tag (DYKDDDDK), a self-assembling peptide sequence D-1 composed of a 2-acetylnaphthyl group (Nap), a right-handed tripeptide ($^{D}F^{D}F^{D}K$, denoted as ffk), and a nitrobenzoxadiazolyl ethylenediamino moiety (NBD-EA, for enhanced fluorescence upon self-assembly). A glycine (G) was used as a spacer between peptide and Flag-tag. The peptide conjugation self-assembled into micelles that could trap small drug molecules. The FLAG-tag could be triggered by an enterokinase (ENTK) in mitochondria. After being taken up by eukaryotic cells, the micelles were turned into nanofibers through the action of ENTK, thus releasing the cargos from the micelles at mitochondria. Although a small number of studies have reported the enzyme-assisted drug delivery for antibacterial application, these studies have showcased a new approach using enzymatic cleavage to realize controlled drug release at the targeted sites with enhanced selectivity.

19.6.3 Stimuli-responsive Antimicrobial Agents

Biofilm infections can induce chronic inflammation and significantly disrupt the wound-healing process. Given that the pH values at the acidic environments of the infected chronic wounds are mostly around 5.5–5.6, it is of great importance to develop pH-responsive antimicrobial peptide hydrogels. Wang and coworkers have developed a pH-switchable AMP hydrogel formed by a self-assembling octapeptide with a sequence of IKFQFHFD at neutral pH [94]. IKFQFHFD bears an intrinsic nature similar to an AMP under acidic conditions as it can be divided into two parts (positive charge part and hydrophobic part) as shown in Figure 19.10a. As a result, the peptide is biocompatible at neutral pH and possesses activated antimicrobial activity in the pathological environment (pH 5.5). IKFQFHFD can readily self-assemble into entangled nanofibers to form a supramolecular hydrogel via intermolecular interactions of ionic bonding, π–π stacking, and hydrogen bonding, making the AMP a perfect carrier for drug delivery (Figure 19.10b). The bare IKFQFHFD hydrogel can prevent the formation of biofilm but exhibit impaired capability for the removal of integrated biofilm due to the existence of extracellular polymeric

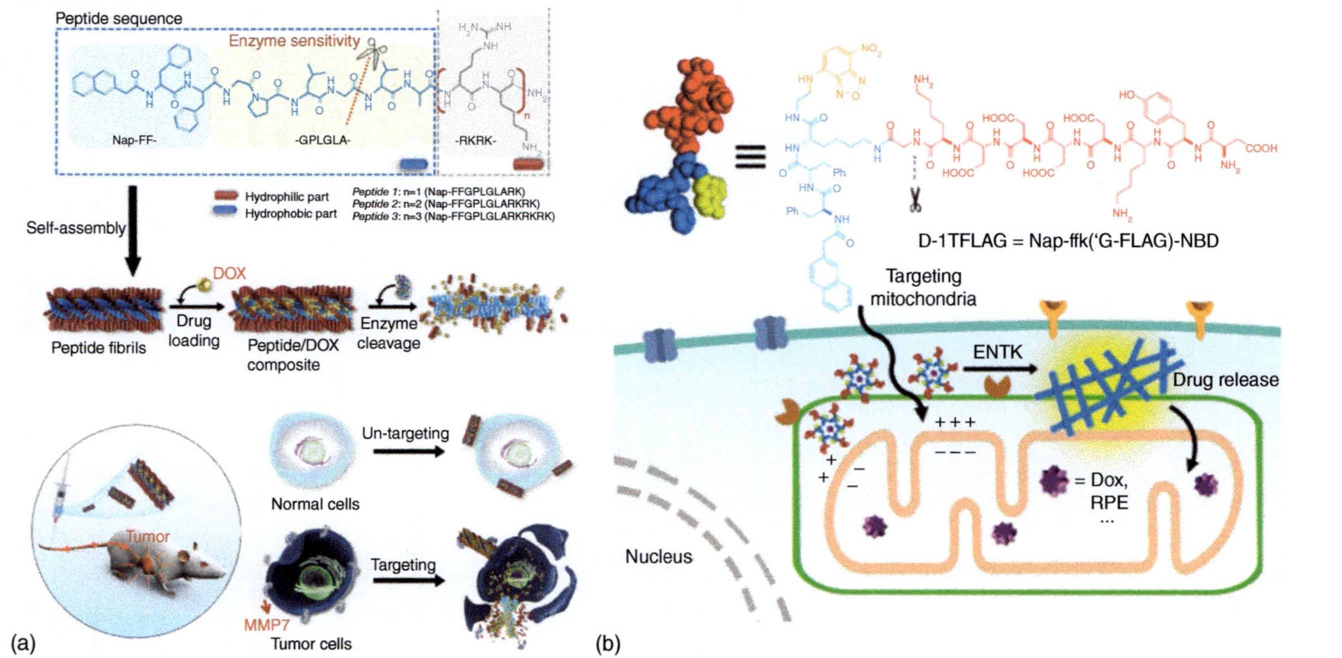

Figure 19.9 (a) Smart drug release by the enzymatic cleavage of Nap-FFGPLGLARKRK. Source: Reproduced from Ref. [91]. (b) Smart drug release by the enzymatic cleavage of Nap-ffk(εG-FLAG)Y. Source: Reproduced from Ref. [92]. The copyright is gained from ACS.

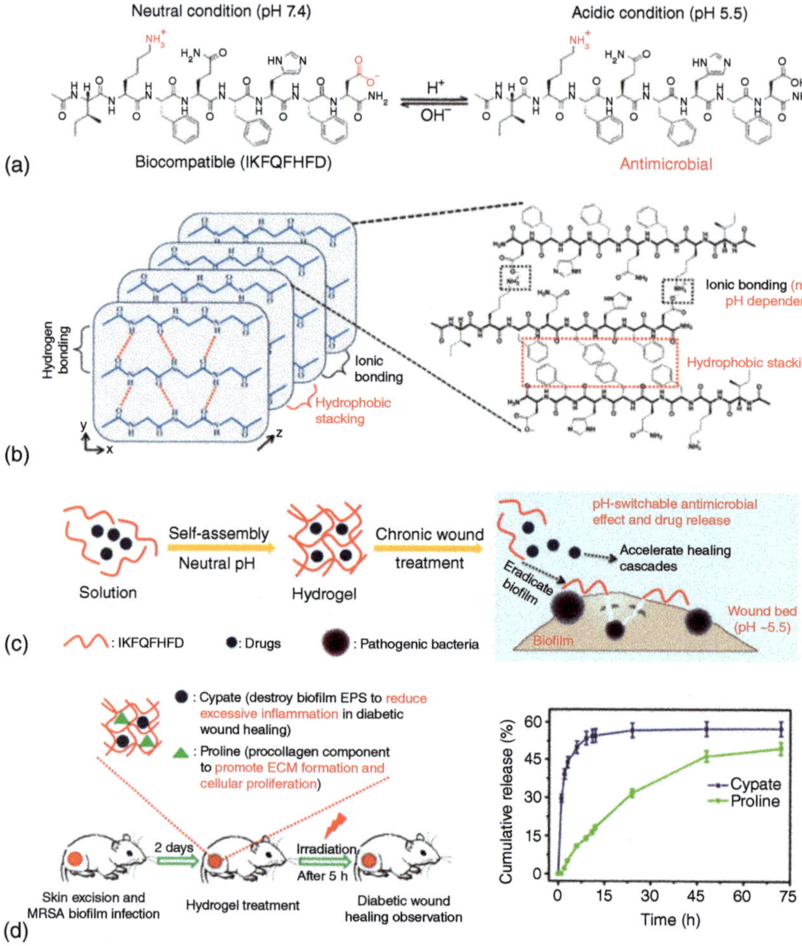

Figure 19.10 (a) Chemical structure of IKFQFHFD at pH 7 and 5.5. (b) The proposed molecular arrangement of IKFQFHFD to form self-assembled supramolecular nanofiber networks of hydrogel at neutral pH. (c) Conceptual illustration of pH-switchable antimicrobial IKFQFHFD-based nanofiber networks for biofilm eradication and rescuing stalled healing in chronic wound. (d) Schematic representation of cypate- and proline-loaded hydrogels for biofilm eradication and wound healing and the sustainable release of the cypate and proline from the hydrogel under pH 5.5. Source: Reproduced from Ref. [94] with permission from ACS.

substances (EPS), which blocks the destruction of the hydrogel on bacteria inside the biofilm. Herein, they subsequently entrapped two drugs, cypate and proline, into the peptide hydrogel. The former could effectively eradicate the biofilm EPS, and the latter could accelerate the wound-healing process. The cypate and proline can be sustainably released from the hydrogel, eradicating the *S. aureus* biofilm and rescuing stalled wound healing in diabetic mice at acidic conditions (Figure 19.10c and d). This work has shown the great potential of AMP hydrogels as dressings for the management of chronic wounds.

19.6.4 Short Peptide Mimicking the Antibacterial Effect of the Immune System

In addition to persistently enhancing AMP's antimicrobial ability, the alternative way is to stimulate the immune systems to combat microbes by immune modulators (pattern recognition receptors, innate defense regulator peptides, or microbial signaling molecules) to boost immunity for prophylactic application. Huang and coworkers used a supramolecular peptide assembly to mimic the natural immune system called neutrophil extracellular traps (NETs) which stick to bacteria to prevent infections [95]. The assembly system was used to imitate the innate immune process of NETs to fight against methicillin-resistant *Staphylococcus epidermidis* (MRSE). They synthesized a quinazolinone derivative capped with a linker of aryl boronate immolative, which is linked with the tetra-peptide of GGFF (denoted as BQA-GGFF). The glucose oxidase (Gox)/glucose could oxidize BQA-GGFF to yield BQH-GGFF and trigger the self-assembly process as shown in Figure 19.11a. The small molecule BQH-GGFF showed the propensity to form fibrous network hydrogels under the oxidative environment of reactive oxygen species (ROS) and spontaneously emitted green fluorescence as shown in Figure 19.11b and c. The fibers entangled the MRSE bacteria and rapidly caused cell death via transcriptome alteration. The subsequent *in vivo* study using a mouse model showcased a significant antibacterial activity with spontaneous consumption of ROS and the formation of antibacterial networks. This study has thus demonstrated a new strategy of applying biomimetic nanomaterials to combat bacterial infections (Figure 19.11d).

19.7 Conclusion, Challenges, and Future Perspectives

We have outlined the recent advances in the development of short peptide-based hydrogels for antimicrobial applications, with emphasis on molecular design of AMPs, methods for peptide-based hydrogelation, mode of actions, and key features of peptide hydrogels. New studies that have been accumulated over the past decade have depicted a promising landscape for peptide supramolecular hydrogels. Short peptide building blocks can be tuned to form hydrogels via self-assembly, enzymatic assistance, and chemical cross-linking. AMPs kill pathogens mostly by disrupting microbial membranes. As a crucial benefit is the rapid killing, it is unlikely for pathogens to generate resistance. Apart from the effective antimicrobial ability, the fibrous network of the peptide hydrogels mimics the extracellular matrix that supports host cell growth. It also provides enough space to entrap antimicrobial drugs for delivery. As the physiochemical properties of the peptide can be modified by sequence variation or stimuli-responsive motif conjugation, through which the peptide can better respond to varied stimuli, peptide-based antimicrobial hydrogels can be made stimuli responsive, better selectivity, and more effective in controlled drug release.

Although peptide-based antimicrobial hydrogels are highly biocompatible from early studies as outlined above, further studies along the development pipeline are

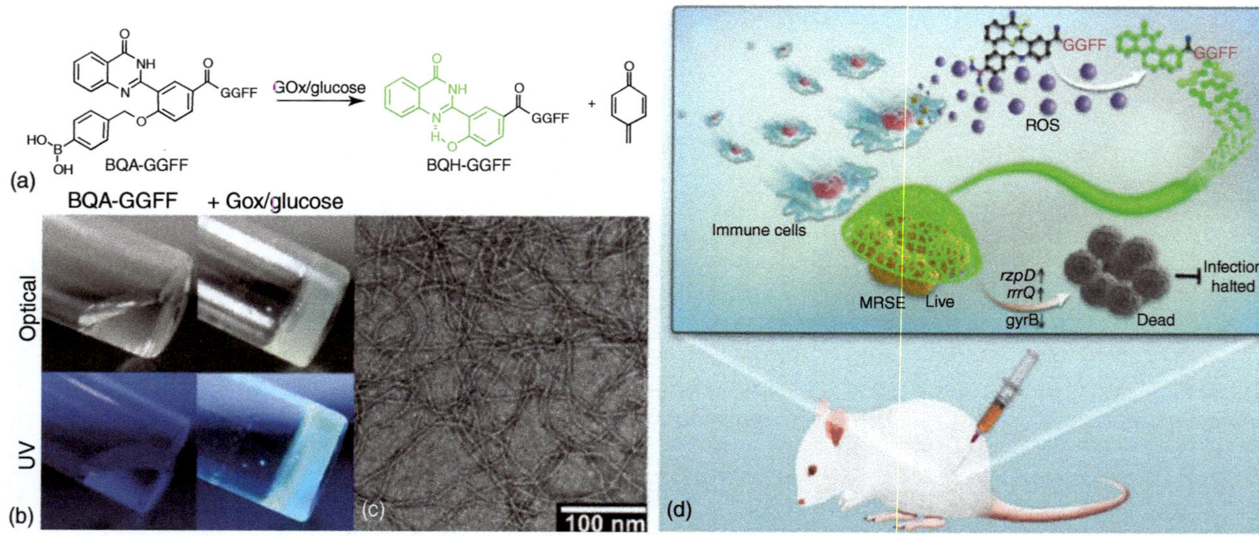

Figure 19.11 (a) Chemical structure of BQA-GGFF. (b) Optical and fluorescent images of the solution of BQA-GGFF and the hydrogel of BQH-GGFF at the concentration of 10 mM. (c) A typical TEM image of the nanofibers in the hydrogel of BQH-GGFF. (d) Schematic diagram of *in vivo* trapping of MRSE bacteria inside the natural immune mimicking process of NETs. Source: Reproduced from Ref. [95] with permission from Elsevier.

essential to verify the cytotoxicity and efficacy and overcome technical sophistications, e.g. enzymatic degradation of AMPs in real wound sites, pharmacodynamics, and possible allergic reactions using different *ex vivo* and *in vivo* models. The stability of the peptide hydrogels during storage and transport may hinder peptide hydrogels from adoption as clinical antimicrobial agents. The biggest challenge for short peptide supramolecular antimicrobial hydrogels lies on the safe passage of the clinical trials. This will require systematic investigations by following a set of preclinical studies to get data for regulatory approvals before the first-in-human trials.

In addition to the issues of stability at different stages of development of peptide hydrogels, the current high costs of the peptides as antimicrobial biomaterials represent another hurdle in the uptake of AMPs. Most AMPs are produced by solid-phase synthesis, but prospects may come from organic syntheses for short and regular peptide sequences and for longer ones, via recombinant approaches.

A fast-expanding field on the horizon is to design and develop short peptides and their hydrogels for DNA/RNA delivery [96], as vaccines or therapeutics. DNA- or RNA-based peptide hydrogels can be easily tuned for their viscoelastic properties and can be made easy to load, easy to inject, and easy to set, thus avoiding some constraints from conventional lipid nanoparticles. Finally, involvement of artificial intelligence (AI) and simulations in combination with experiments to predict the hydrogelation and antimicrobial behavior of the peptide-based materials will help experimental design and data interpretation, making the screening for antimicrobial peptides more efficient [97]. With the fast accumulated knowledge and technical skills, more commercial successes will be witnessed from peptide supramolecular hydrogels in our fight against infections and AMR over the next few years.

Acknowledgments

The authors thank an Industrial Collaboration Fund project from University of Manchester with Syngenta as industrial collaborator (United Kingdom, R126013). HG and ML thank an award from China Scholarship Council. This work benefits from the research funding provided by Syngenta through a studentship (P120479) to XH and a knowledge transfer fellowship through a joint Innovate UK and Syngenta project (KTP 12697). This work also benefited from National Natural Science Foundation of China (Project No. 22102187). The authors thank ISIS Neutron Facility, STFC for awards of neutron beam times.

References

1 Aslam, B., Wang, W., Arshad, M.I. et al. (2018). Antibiotic resistance: a rundown of a global crisis. *Infect. Drug Resist.* 11: 1645.

2 MacGowan, A. and Macnaughton, E. (2017). Antibiotic resistance. *Medicine* 45 (10): 622–628.

3 Carlet, J., Collignon, P., Goldmann, D. et al. (2011). Society's failure to protect a precious resource: antibiotics. *Lancet* 378 (9788): 369–371.
4 Serra-Burriel, M., Keys, M., Campillo-Artero, C. et al. (2020). Impact of multi-drug resistant bacteria on economic and clinical outcomes of healthcare-associated infections in adults: systematic review and meta-analysis. *PLoS ONE* 15 (1): e0227139.
5 Tanwar, J., Das, S., Fatima, Z., and Hameed, S. (2014). Multidrug resistance: an emerging crisis. *Interdiscip. Perspect. Infect. Dis.* 2014: 541340.
6 Sun, D., Babar Shahzad, M., Li, M. et al. (2015). Antimicrobial materials with medical applications. *Mater. Technol.* 30 (sup6): B90–B95.
7 Fjell, C.D., Hiss, J.A., Hancock, R.E., and Schneider, G. (2012). Designing antimicrobial peptides: form follows function. *Nat. Rev. Drug Discov.* 11 (1): 37–51.
8 Ciumac, D., Gong, H., Hu, X., and Lu, J.R. (2019). Membrane targeting cationic antimicrobial peptides. *J. Colloid Interface Sci.* 537: 163–185.
9 Craik, D.J., Fairlie, D.P., Liras, S., and Price, D. (2013). The future of peptide-based drugs. *Chem. Biol. Drug Design* 81 (1): 136–147.
10 Zhao, Y., Yang, W., Chen, C. et al. (2018). Rational design and self-assembly of short amphiphilic peptides and applications. *Curr. Opin. Colloid Interface Sci.* 35: 112–123.
11 Wang, J., Liu, K., Xing, R., and Yan, X. (2016). Peptide self-assembly: thermodynamics and kinetics. *Chem. Soc. Rev.* 45 (20): 5589–5604.
12 Hu, X., Liao, M., Gong, H. et al. (2020). Recent advances in short peptide self-assembly: from rational design to novel applications. *Curr. Opin. Colloid Interface Sci.* 45: 1–13.
13 Fichman, G. and Gazit, E. (2014). Self-assembly of short peptides to form hydrogels: design of building blocks, physical properties and technological applications. *Acta Biomater.* 10 (4): 1671–1682.
14 Zhou, P., Yuan, C., and Yan, X. (2022). Computational approaches for understanding and predicting the self-assembled peptide hydrogels. *Curr. Opin. Colloid Interface Sci.* 62: 101645.
15 Dou, X.Q. and Feng, C.L. (2017). Amino acids and peptide-based supramolecular hydrogels for three-dimensional cell culture. *Adv. Mater.* 29 (16): 1604062.
16 Chakraborty, P., Adler-Abramovich, L., and Gazit, E. (2022). Short peptide hydrogels for biomedical applications. In: *Multifunctional Hydrogels for Biomedical Applications* (ed. R.A. Pires, I. Pashkuleva, and R.L. Reis), 127–147. Wiley.
17 Zhou, P., Wang, J., Wang, M. et al. (2019). Amino acid conformations control the morphological and chiral features of the self-assembled peptide nanostructures: young investigators perspective. *J. Colloid Interface Sci.* 548: 244–254.
18 Li, J., Wang, J., Zhao, Y. et al. (2020). Surfactant-like peptides: from molecular design to controllable self-assembly with applications. *Coord. Chem. Rev.* 421: 213418.
19 Gong, H., Zhang, J., Hu, X. et al. (2019). Hydrophobic control of the bioactivity and cytotoxicity of de novo-designed antimicrobial peptides. *ACS Appl. Mater. Interfaces* 11 (38): 34609–34620.

20 Chen, M., Zhang, S., and He, Z. (2020). Controlled block polypeptide composed of d–type amino acids: a therapeutics delivery platform to inhibit biofilm formation of drug-resistant bacteria. *ACS Appl. Bio Mater.* 3 (9): 6343–6350.

21 Guo, Z., Wang, Y., Tan, T. et al. (2021). Antimicrobial d-peptide hydrogels. *ACS Biomater. Sci. Eng.* 7 (4): 1703–1712.

22 Zhou, P., Hu, X., Li, J. et al. (2022). Peptide self-assemblies from unusual α-sheet conformations based on alternation of d/l amino acids. *J. Am. Chem. Soc.* 144 (47): 21544–21554.

23 Liang, Y., Zhang, X., Yuan, Y. et al. (2020). Role and modulation of the secondary structure of antimicrobial peptides to improve selectivity. *Biomater. Sci.* 8 (24): 6858–6866.

24 Marín-Medina, N., Mescola, A., and Alessandrini, A. (2018). Effects of the peptide magainin H2 on supported lipid bilayers studied by different biophysical techniques. *Biochim. Biophys. Acta (BBA)-Biomembr.* 1860 (12): 2635–2643.

25 Hetru, C., Letellier, L., Oren, Z. et al. (2000). Androctonin, a hydrophilic disulphide-bridged non-haemolytic anti-microbial peptide: a plausible mode of action. *Biochem. J.* 345 (3): 653–664.

26 Blazyk, J., Wiegand, R., Klein, J. et al. (2001). A novel linear amphipathic β-sheet cationic antimicrobial peptide with enhanced selectivity for bacterial lipids. *J. Biol. Chem.* 276 (30): 27899–27906.

27 Zhao, Y., Deng, L., Yang, W. et al. (2016). Tuning one-dimensional nanostructures of bola-like peptide amphiphiles by varying the hydrophilic amino acids. *Chem.—Eur. J.* 22 (32): 11394–11404.

28 Häffner, S.M. and Malmsten, M. (2018). Influence of self-assembly on the performance of antimicrobial peptides. *Curr. Opin. Colloid Interface Sci.* 38: 56–79.

29 Tian, X., Sun, F., Zhou, X.-R. et al. (2015). Role of peptide self-assembly in antimicrobial peptides. *J. Pept. Sci.* 21 (7): 530–539.

30 Schnaider, L., Brahmachari, S., Schmidt, N.W. et al. (2017). Self-assembling dipeptide antibacterial nanostructures with membrane disrupting activity. *Nat. Commun.* 8 (1): 1365.

31 Gong, H., Sani, M.A., Hu, X. et al. (2020). How do self-assembling antimicrobial lipopeptides kill bacteria? *ACS Appl. Mater. Interfaces* 12 (50): 55675–55687.

32 Chu, H., Pazgier, M., Jung, G. et al. (2012). Human α-defensin 6 promotes mucosal innate immunity through self-assembled peptide nanonets. *Science* 337 (6093): 477–481.

33 Paulmann, M., Arnold, T., Linke, D. et al. (2012). Structure-activity analysis of the dermcidin-derived peptide DCD-1L, an anionic antimicrobial peptide present in human sweat. *J. Biol. Chem.* 287 (11): 8434–8443.

34 Peng, F., Chen, Y., Liu, J. et al. (2021). Facile design of gemini surfactant-like peptide for hydrophobic drug delivery and antimicrobial activity. *J. Colloid Interface Sci.* 591: 314–325.

35 Cao, M., Wang, Y., Hu, X. et al. (2019). Reversible thermoresponsive peptide-PNIPAM hydrogels for controlled drug delivery. *Biomacromolecules* 20 (9): 3601–3610.

36 Cox, H., Cao, M., Xu, H. et al. (2019). Active modulation of states of prestress in self-assembled short peptide gels. *Biomacromolecules* 20 (4): 1719–1730.

37 Li, J., Xing, R., Bai, S., and Yan, X. (2019). Recent advances of self-assembling peptide-based hydrogels for biomedical applications. *Soft Matter* 15 (8): 1704–1715.

38 Wang, Y., Zhang, W., Gong, C. et al. (2020). Recent advances in the fabrication, functionalization, and bioapplications of peptide hydrogels. *Soft Matter* 16 (44): 10029–10045.

39 Reches, M. and Gazit, E. (2003). Casting metal nanowires within discrete self-assembled peptide nanotubes. *Science* 300 (5619): 625–627.

40 Mahler, A., Reches, M., Rechter, M. et al. (2006). Rigid, self-assembled hydrogel composed of a modified aromatic dipeptide. *Adv. Mater.* 18 (11): 1365–1370.

41 Smith, A.M., Williams, R.J., Tang, C. et al. (2008). Fmoc-diphenylalanine self assembles to a hydrogel via a novel architecture based on π–π interlocked β-sheets. *Adv. Mater.* 20 (1): 37–41.

42 Xing, R., Yuan, C., Li, S. et al. (2018). Charge-induced secondary structure transformation of amyloid-derived dipeptide assemblies from β-sheet to α-helix. *Angew. Chem. Int. Ed.* 57 (6): 1537–1542.

43 Gelain, F., Luo, Z., and Zhang, S. (2020). Self-assembling peptide EAK16 and RADA16 nanofiber scaffold hydrogel. *Chem. Rev.* 120 (24): 13434–13460.

44 Cao, C., Cao, M., Fan, H. et al. (2012). Redox modulated hydrogelation of a self-assembling short peptide amphiphile. *Chin. Sci. Bull.* 57 (33): 4296–4303.

45 Cox, H., Georgiades, P., Xu, H. et al. (2017). Self-assembly of mesoscopic peptide surfactant fibrils investigated by STORM super-resolution fluorescence microscopy. *Biomacromolecules* 18 (11): 3481–3491.

46 Wang, M., Zhou, P., Wang, J. et al. (2017). Left or right: how does amino acid chirality affect the handedness of nanostructures self-assembled from short amphiphilic peptides? *J. Am. Chem. Soc.* 139 (11): 4185–4194.

47 Toledano, S., Williams, R.J., Jayawarna, V., and Ulijn, R.V. (2006). Enzyme-triggered self-assembly of peptide hydrogels via reversed hydrolysis. *J. Am. Chem. Soc.* 128 (4): 1070–1071.

48 Roy, S., Javid, N., Sefcik, J. et al. (2012). Salt-induced control of supramolecular order in biocatalytic hydrogelation. *Langmuir* 28 (48): 16664–16670.

49 Hughes, M., Debnath, S., Knapp, C.W., and Ulijn, R.V. (2013). Antimicrobial properties of enzymatically triggered self-assembling aromatic peptide amphiphiles. *Biomater. Sci.* 1 (11): 1138.

50 Chen, C., Zhang, Y., Fei, R. et al. (2016). Hydrogelation of the short self-assembling peptide I_3QGK regulated by transglutaminase and use for rapid hemostasis. *ACS Appl. Mater. Interfaces* 8 (28): 17833–17841.

51 Yang, Z., Gu, H., Fu, D. et al. (2004). Enzymatic formation of supramolecular hydrogels. *Adv. Mater.* 16 (16): 1440–1444.

52 Liang, C., Zheng, D., Shi, F. et al. (2017). Enzyme-assisted peptide folding, assembly and anti-cancer properties. *Nanoscale* 9 (33): 11987–11993.

53 Jung, J.P., Jones, J.L., Cronier, S.A., and Collier, J.H. (2008). Modulating the mechanical properties of self-assembled peptide hydrogels via native chemical ligation. *Biomaterials* 29 (13): 2143–2151.

54 Liyanage, W., Ardoña, H.A.M., Mao, H.-Q., and Tovar, J.D. (2017). Cross-linking approaches to tuning the mechanical properties of peptide π-electron hydrogels. *Bioconjug. Chem.* 28 (3): 751–759.

55 Ding, Y., Li, Y., Qin, M. et al. (2013). Photo-cross-linking approach to engineering small tyrosine-containing peptide hydrogels with enhanced mechanical stability. *Langmuir* 29 (43): 13299–13306.

56 Wei, Q., Xu, M., Liao, C. et al. (2016). Printable hybrid hydrogel by dual enzymatic polymerization with superactivity. *Chem. Sci.* 7 (4): 2748–2752.

57 Wang, J., Wang, Z., Gao, J. et al. (2009). Incorporation of supramolecular hydrogels into agarose hydrogels—a potential drug delivery carrier. *J. Mater. Chem.* 19 (42): 7892.

58 Chen, L., Revel, S., Morris, K. et al. (2010). Low molecular weight gelator–dextran composites. *Chem. Commun.* 46 (36): 6738.

59 Chen, M.H., Wang, L.L., Chung, J.J. et al. (2017). Methods to assess shear-thinning hydrogels for application as injectable biomaterials. *ACS Biomater. Sci. Eng.* 3 (12): 3146–3160.

60 Malanovic, N. and Lohner, K. (2016). Antimicrobial peptides targeting gram-positive bacteria. *Pharmaceuticals* 9 (3): 59.

61 Allen, N.E. (2010). From vancomycin to oritavancin: the discovery and development of a novel lipoglycopeptide antibiotic. *Anti-Infect. Agents Med. Chem. (Formerly Curr. Med. Chem.-Anti-Infect. Agents)* 9 (1): 23–47.

62 Bionda, N., Pitteloud, J.-P., and Cudic, P. (2013). Cyclic lipodepsipeptides: a new class of antibacterial agents in the battle against resistant bacteria. *Future Med. Chem.* 5 (11): 1311–1330.

63 Cardoso, P., Glossop, H., Meikle, T.G. et al. (2021). Molecular engineering of antimicrobial peptides: microbial targets, peptide motifs and translation opportunities. *Biophys. Rev.* 13 (1): 35–69.

64 Chairatana, P., Chu, H., Castillo, P.A. et al. (2016). Proteolysis triggers self-assembly and unmasks innate immune function of a human α-defensin peptide. *Chem. Sci.* 7 (3): 1738–1752.

65 Chairatana, P. and Nolan, E.M. (2017). Human α-defensin 6: a small peptide that self-assembles and protects the host by entangling microbes. *Acc. Chem. Res.* 50 (4): 960–967.

66 Jiang, L., Xu, D., Sellati, T.J., and Dong, H. (2015). Self-assembly of cationic multidomain peptide hydrogels: supramolecular nanostructure and rheological properties dictate antimicrobial activity. *Nanoscale* 7 (45): 19160–19169.

67 Gong, H., Liao, M., Hu, X. et al. (2020). Aggregated amphiphilic antimicrobial peptides embedded in bacterial membranes. *ACS Appl. Mater. Interfaces* 12 (40): 44420–44432.

68 Hu, X., Carter, J., Ge, T. et al. (2022). Impacts of chain and head lengths of nonionic alkyl ethoxylate surfactants on cytotoxicity to human corneal and skin cells in agri-spraying processes. *J. Colloid Interface Sci.* 628: 162–173.

69 Paracini, N., Clifton, L.A., Skoda, M.W.A., and Lakey, J.H. (2018). Liquid crystalline bacterial outer membranes are critical for antibiotic susceptibility. *Proc. Natl. Acad. Sci.* 115 (32): E7587–E7594.

70 Clifton, L.A., Holt, S.A., Hughes, A.V. et al. (2015). An accurate in vitro model of the E. coli envelope. *Angew. Chem. Int. Ed.* 54 (41): 11952–11955.

71 Clifton, L.A., Campbell, R.A., Sebastiani, F. et al. (2020). Design and use of model membranes to study biomolecular interactions using complementary surface-sensitive techniques. *Adv. Colloid Interf. Sci.* 277: 102118.

72 Gong, H., Hu, X., Liao, M. et al. (2021). Structural disruptions of the outer membranes of gram-negative bacteria by rationally designed amphiphilic antimicrobial peptides. *ACS Appl. Mater. Interfaces* 13 (14): 16062–16074.

73 Montis, C., Salvatore, A., Valle, F. et al. (2020). Biogenic supported lipid bilayers as a tool to investigate nano-bio interfaces. *J. Colloid Interface Sci.* 570: 340–349.

74 Liao, M., Gong, H., Quan, X. et al. (2023). Intramembrane nanoaggregates of antimicrobial peptides play a vital role in bacterial killing. *Small* 19 (3): 2204428.

75 Scocchi, M., Mardirossian, M., Runti, G., and Benincasa, M. (2016). Non-membrane permeabilizing modes of action of antimicrobial peptides on bacteria. *Curr. Top. Med. Chem.* 16 (1): 76–88.

76 Seefeldt, A.C., Nguyen, F., Antunes, S. et al. (2015). The proline-rich antimicrobial peptide Onc112 inhibits translation by blocking and destabilizing the initiation complex. *Nat. Struct. Mol. Biol.* 22 (6): 470–475.

77 Ho, Y.-H., Shah, P., Chen, Y.-W., and Chen, C.-S. (2016). Systematic analysis of intracellular-targeting antimicrobial peptides, bactenecin 7, hybrid of pleurocidin and dermaseptin, proline–arginine-rich peptide, and lactoferricin B, by using *Escherichia coli* proteome microarrays. *Mol. Cell. Proteom.* 15 (6): 1837–1847.

78 Park, C.B., Kim, H.S., and Kim, S.C. (1998). Mechanism of action of the antimicrobial peptide buforin II: buforin II kills microorganisms by penetrating the cell membrane and inhibiting cellular functions. *Biochem. Biophys. Res. Commun.* 244 (1): 253–257.

79 Wei, D. and Zhang, X. (2022). Biosynthesis, bioactivity, biotoxicity and applications of antimicrobial peptides for human health. *Biosaf. Health* 4 (2): 118–134.

80 Guryanova, S.V. and Ovchinnikova, T.V. (2022). Immunomodulatory and allergenic properties of antimicrobial peptides. *Int. J. Mol. Sci.* 23 (5): 2499.

81 Niyonsaba, F., Ushio, H., Nakano, N. et al. (2007). Antimicrobial peptides human β-defensins stimulate epidermal keratinocyte migration, proliferation and production of proinflammatory cytokines and chemokines. *J. Investig. Dermatol.* 127 (3): 594–604.

82 Fritz, J.H., Brunner, S., Birnstiel, M.L. et al. (2004). The artificial antimicrobial peptide KLKLLLLLKLK induces predominantly a TH2-type immune response to co-injected antigens. *Vaccine* 22 (25–26): 3274–3284.

83 Bai, J., Chen, C., Wang, J. et al. (2016). Enzymatic regulation of self-assembling peptide A_9K_2 nanostructures and hydrogelation with highly selective antibacterial activities. *ACS Appl. Mater. Interfaces* 8 (24): 15093–15102.

84 Bai, J., Gong, Z., Wang, J., and Wang, C. (2017). Enzymatic hydrogelation of self-assembling peptide I4K2 and its antibacterial and drug sustained-release activities. *RSC Adv.* 7 (77): 48631–48638.

85 Zhou, J., Zhang, H., Fareed, M.S. et al. (2022). An injectable peptide hydrogel constructed of natural antimicrobial peptide J-1 and ADP shows anti-infection, hemostasis, and antiadhesion efficacy. *ACS Nano* 16 (5): 7636–7650.

86 Chen, C., Chen, Y., Yang, C. et al. (2015). High selective performance of designed antibacterial and anticancer peptide amphiphiles. *ACS Appl. Mater. Interfaces* 7 (31): 17346–17355.

87 Zhang, J., Gong, H., Liao, M. et al. (2022). How do terminal modifications of short designed IIKK peptide amphiphiles affect their antifungal activity and biocompatibility? *J. Colloid Interface Sci.* 608: 193–206.

88 Chen, C., Hu, J., Zeng, P. et al. (2014). Molecular mechanisms of anticancer action and cell selectivity of short α-helical peptides. *Biomaterials* 35 (5): 1552–1561.

89 Zhang, J., Chen, C., Chen, J. et al. (2020). Dual mode of anti-biofilm action of G3 against *Streptococcus mutans*. *ACS Appl. Mater. Interfaces* 12 (25): 27866–27875.

90 Zhu, J., Han, H., Ye, T.-T. et al. (2018). Biodegradable and pH sensitive peptide based hydrogel as controlled release system for antibacterial wound dressing application. *Molecules* 23 (12): 3383.

91 Cao, M., Lu, S., Wang, N. et al. (2019). Enzyme-triggered morphological transition of peptide nanostructures for tumor-targeted drug delivery and enhanced cancer therapy. *ACS Appl. Mater. Interfaces* 11 (18): 16357–16366.

92 He, H., Wang, J., Wang, H. et al. (2018). Enzymatic cleavage of branched peptides for targeting mitochondria. *J. Am. Chem. Soc.* 140 (4): 1215–1218.

93 He, H., Wang, H., Zhou, N. et al. (2018). Branched peptides for enzymatic supramolecular hydrogelation. *Chem. Commun.* 54 (1): 86–89.

94 Wang, J., Chen, X.-Y., Zhao, Y. et al. (2019). pH-switchable antimicrobial nanofiber networks of hydrogel eradicate biofilm and rescue stalled healing in chronic wounds. *ACS Nano* 13 (10): 11686–11697.

95 Huang, Z., Liu, Y., Wang, L. et al. (2020). Supramolecular assemblies mimicking neutrophil extracellular traps for MRSE infection control. *Biomaterials* 253: 120124.

96 Medina, S.H., Li, S., Howard, O.Z. et al. (2015). Enhanced immunostimulatory effects of DNA-encapsulated peptide hydrogels. *Biomaterials* 53: 545–553.

97 Chen, C.H., Starr, C.G., Troendle, E. et al. (2019). Simulation-guided rational de novo design of a small pore-forming antimicrobial peptide. *J. Am. Chem. Soc.* 141 (12): 4839–4848.

20

Supramolecular Peptide-based Nanomaterials for the Treatment of Fibrosis

Jikang Liu and Qianli Zou

School of Pharmacy, Anhui Medical University, Hefei 230032, China

20.1 Introduction

Fibrosis is an unregulated outcome of the tissue repair process following various types of tissue injury. The pathological manifestation of fibrosis is an extensive accumulation of extracellular matrix (ECM) substances such as collagen and fibronectin, which can remodel and destroy normal tissue architecture [1]. Numerous diseases are associated with fibrosis, including nonalcoholic steatohepatitis (NASH) [2], chronic kidney disease, myocardial infarction (MI) [3], heart failure, and idiopathic pulmonary fibrosis (IPF) [4]. Despite the fact that fibrosis is a serious threat to human health and life [5], there are currently no efficient drugs available to prevent or reverse fibrosis [6]. Therefore, there is an urgent need to develop innovative therapeutic strategies for antifibrotic applications. Nanomedicine has emerged as a result of the application of nanotechnology in medicine and is expected to provide alternative solutions to challenging medical problems [7]. Decades of dedication to the field of nanomedicine have yielded successful clinical applications of a variety of therapeutic nanomaterials, such as liposomes, polymer-based nanoparticles, and protein-based nanoagents [8]. Most clinically approved nanomedicines are for cancer therapy [9]. For antifibrotic treatment, most of the marketed or clinically tested drugs are small molecule drugs [10]. The potential of applying nanotechnology to improve antifibrotic treatment is far from being realized. Recent studies have focused on the application of nanotechnology to enhance the antifibrotic efficacy of small molecule drugs by increasing drug accumulation in fibrotic tissues and achieving cell-specific targeting, leading to positive results in animal models [11–13]. Hence, nanomedicine is expected to be a promising strategy to realize efficient antifibrotic therapy.

Peptide Self-Assembly and Engineering: Fundamentals, Structures, and Applications, First Edition.
Edited by Xuehai Yan.

Inspired by natural functional materials produced by self-assembly, molecular self-assembly has been widely explored as a bottom-up approach to construct functional nanomaterials [14]. Biomolecules are excellent building blocks for creating nanomaterials for biomedical applications because of their exceptional biocompatibility, bioactivity, and unambiguous components. Peptides are the most attractive building blocks among biomolecules because they possess many distinctive properties, including a simple structure, fantastic biodegradability, ease of synthesis, and programmability. Stable nanostructures formed by self-assembling peptides are determined by the synergy of a variety of noncovalent interactions, involving hydrogen bonding, electrical interaction, π–π stacking, hydrophobic force, and van der Waals force [15]. Thus, a variety of peptide-based nanostructures can be obtained by modulating these weak interactions. A typical example is diphenylalanine-based building blocks, which can be transformed into various nanostructures by influencing the noncovalent force by changing their molecular composition, charge state, and assembly environment (e.g. solvent) [16]. In addition, supramolecular peptide-based nanomaterials can be endowed with self-healing and responsive characters due to the reversible and dynamic properties of noncovalent forces. Hence, the creation of supramolecular peptide-based nanomaterials with specific functionality has received much attention. For instance, supramolecular peptide-based nanomaterials with various nanostructures have been widely used in the medical fields, such as bioimaging, cancer therapy, tissue engineering, and antimicrobial therapy [17]. For antifibrotic treatment, peptide-based nanomaterials have also shown great potential.

In this chapter, we summarize the recent progress in peptide-based nanomaterials for antifibrotic treatment. Two approaches for constructing peptide-based nanomaterials with antifibrotic properties are highlighted, including self-assembly of peptide–drug conjugates and self-assembly of bioactive peptides (Figure 20.1). The methods for designing the self-assembling building blocks and the supramolecular interactions involved in self-assembly are emphasized. In addition, we discuss how supramolecular peptide-based nanomaterials enhance the antifibrotic effect within various therapeutic applications, including delivery of peptides and proteins, gene therapy, cell therapy, and extracellular vesicle therapy (Figure 20.2). We believe that the use of peptide self-assembly strategies enables the construction of diverse, safe, and effective nanomaterials for the treatment of fibrosis, thus advancing preclinical studies and accelerating the clinical translation of antifibrotic nanomaterials.

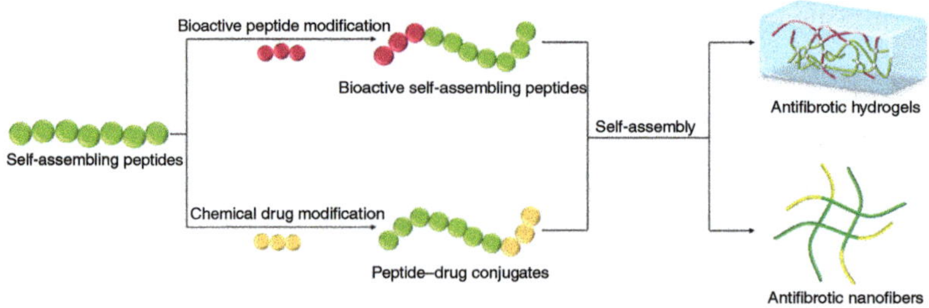

Figure 20.1 Illustration of antifibrotic nanomaterials fabricated from the approaches of self-assembly of peptide–drug conjugates and self-assembly of bioactive peptides.

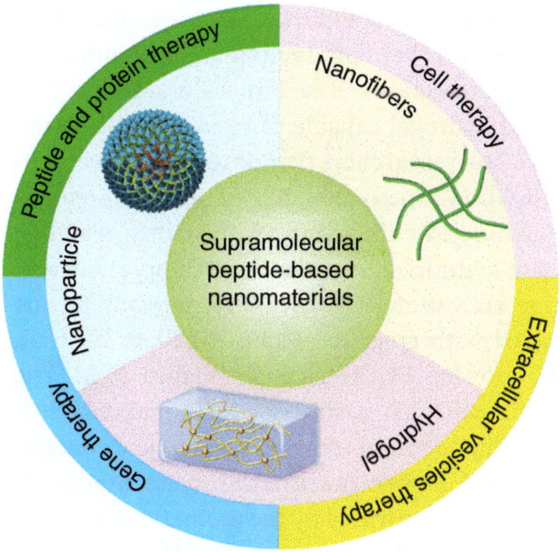

Figure 20.2 Multiple antifibrotic applications of peptide-based nanomaterials to enhance antifibrotic effect.

20.2 Antifibrotic Nanomaterials Based on Self-assembly of Peptide–Drug Conjugates

The side chains and amino and carboxyl groups at both ends of peptides provide active sites for chemical conjugation. Hence, conjugation of peptides with drugs is a universal strategy to design self-assembling building blocks, providing a facile approach for constructing peptide-based nanomaterials with therapeutic properties. For instance, a hydrogelator precursor, Nap-Phe-Phe-Lys(Dex)-Tyr(H_2PO_3)-OH, was designed by conjugating dexamethasone (Dex), an anti-inflammatory drug, and phosphoric acid to the side chain of a self-assembling peptide backbone via ester and phosphate linkages [18]. Considering that alkaline phosphatase (ALP) and esterase are overexpressed in fibrogenic liver, the precursor was expected to be enzyme-responsive building blocks in treating liver fibrosis. When injected intraperitoneally into mice, the hydrogel precursor enters the liver parenchyma through the blood circulation and forms a self-assembling peptide under the action of alkaline phosphatase dephosphorylation, which subsequently self-assembles into nanofibers. The nanofibers are then hydrolyzed by esterase, resulting in the slow release of Dex, which can inhibit the activation and proliferation of hepatic stellate cells that play an important role in fibrogenesis. The enzyme-mediated self-assembly strategy achieves targeted accumulation of antifibrotic nanomaterials in focal tissues, thereby exhibiting a more potent anti-inflammatory effect than free Dex.

The peptide–drug conjugates can be further co-assembled with pharmacologically active compounds to create multifunctional antifibrotic nanomaterials. During myocardial ischemia-reperfusion (I/R) injury, excessive reactive oxygen species (ROS) may initiate and exacerbate inflammatory responses, which in turn may further promote ROS production, ultimately leading to further damage. Therefore, parallel therapeutic strategies to suppress both ROS production and inflammation have been proposed to block malignant interactions. Based on such a design concept, Liao et al. reported a co-assembled hydrogel capable of scavenging ROS and exerting anti-inflammatory effects [19]. The researchers first designed a novel self-assembling peptide rhein-^{D}F^{D}FG-ss-ERGD (Rh-pep), which consisted of three primary components: D-form diphenylalanine to enhance *in vivo* stability, disulfide bond to trigger self-assembly in response to thiols, and anti-inflammatory rhein that suppresses inflammation by inhibiting activation of TLR4/NF-B pathway. In the presence of GSH, Rh-peps co-assembled with epigallocatechin-3-gallate (EGCG), which is capable of scavenging ROS, forming EGCG@Rh-gel (Figure 20.3). The characterization results show that EGCG@Rh-gel is superior to Rh-gel, which is formed by self-assembly from a single component, in terms of mechanical strength and gel-forming capabilities. These superior performances of the co-assemblies are due to the substantial noncovalent interactions provided by the aromatic EGCG and peptides. *In vivo* tests showed that after intracardiac injection, EGCG@Rh-gel significantly improved cardiac function and reduced the severity of myocardial fibrosis through effective removal of ROS and inhibition of inflammation.

Co-assembly of peptide–drug conjugates with distinct chemical structures provides a method to integrate multiple functional peptides and drugs into one kind of nanomaterials. In an example, two types of peptide amphiphile (PA) molecules (Met-PepA and ATRA-PepB) were rationally designed to realize synergistic targeting effect of bioactive peptides and dual-pathway therapeutic functions generated by drug combination (Figure 20.4a) [20]. In the Met-PepA structure, the hydrophilic head is peptide moiety (KSLSRHDHIHHHH)-targeted c-Met receptor expressed in pancreatic cancer cells (PCCs); palmitic acid (C16) is used as a hydrophobic tail; and metformin (Met), which is able to inhibit the activation of pancreatic stellate cells (PSCs) by suppressing the secretion of TGF-β by pancreatic cancer cells (PCCs), is covalently linked to the cysteine residue of the linker peptide moiety (VVVAAAGCG). All-trans-retinoic acid (ATRA), which reverses activated PSCs into quiescent state, is designed as a hydrophobic tail, and the other end of the structure is targeting peptide sequence (HTTIPKV), binding α-SMA-positive PSCs with high affinity, in the ATRA-PepB structure. Due to the strong positive surface

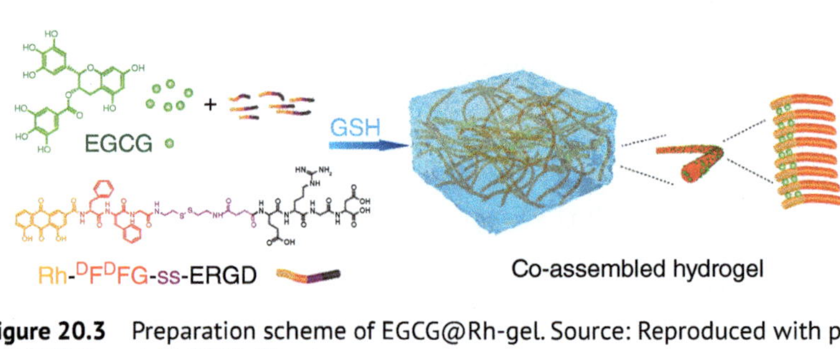

Figure 20.3 Preparation scheme of EGCG@Rh-gel. Source: Reproduced with permission Ref. [19]. Copyright 2022, Elsevier.

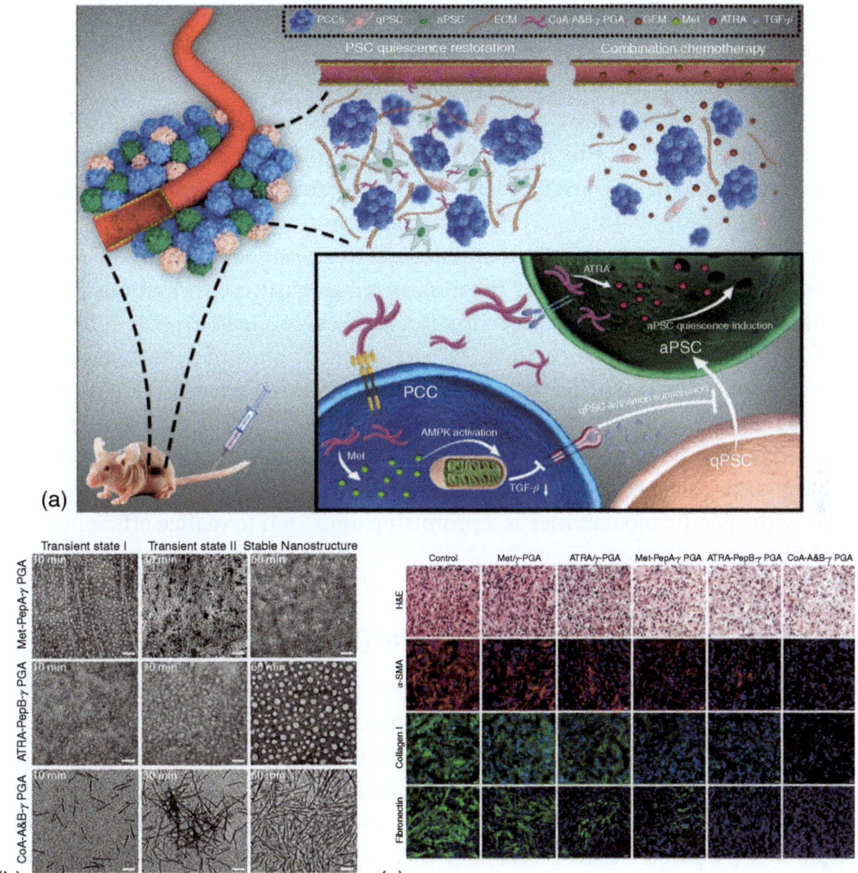

Figure 20.4 (a) Schematic of synergistic targeting effect of bioactive peptides and dual-pathway PSC quiescence restoration function generated by drug combination of CoA-A&B-γPGA codelivering Met and ATRA based on a co-assembly strategy. (b) The morphology of Met-PepA-γPGA, ATRA-PepB-γPGA, and CoA-A&B-γPGA by TEM examination. Scale bars, 50 nm. (c) H&E and IF stainings of α-SMA, collagen I, and fibronectin of subcutaneous AsPC-1/hPSC tumor sections. Scale bars, 20 μm. Source: Reproduced with permission Ref. [20]. © 2022, John Wiley and Sons.

charge generated by the PA molecules dispersed in deionized water, anionic gamma-polyglutamic acid (γPGA) is used to coat the PA to construct more biocompatible Met-PepA-γPGA and ATRA-PepB-γPGA. After undergoing a transformation process in which irregular aggregates exist accompanied by formation and elongation of nanofibers, the co-assembly of Met-PepA-γPGA and ATRA-PepB-γPGA (CoA-A&B-γPGA) finally forms uniform nanofibers with diameters of ≈7 nm (Figure 20.4b). CoA-A&B-γPGA shows enhanced accumulation in fibrous tumor microenvironment and effective inhibitory effect on excessive ECM formation, both in pancreatic cancer mice with abundant desmoplasia (Figure 20.4c) and 3D cell model.

20.3 Antifibrotic Nanomaterials Based on Self-assembly of Bioactive Peptides

Due to their ease of synthesis, the use of bioactive peptides as building blocks provides a convenient way to create functional nanomaterials by self-assembly. Bioactive peptides usually consist of less than 50 residues and exhibit diverse activities, including antimicrobial, antihypertensive, antioxidant, and other activities [21]. In peptide nanomaterials, the biological functions are determined not only by the peptide sequences but also by the nanostructures and conformations [22–24]. In addition, modulation of intermolecular interactions can lead to structural transitions of peptide-based nanostructures [25]. The integration of bioactive peptides and self-assembled peptides in the same sequence can be used to construct self-assembling peptide with therapeutic capabilities. Thus, antifibrotic peptide-based nanomaterials can be prepared by self-assembly of peptides that exhibit both self-assembling and antifibrotic properties. Hence, constructing nanomaterials using peptides with specific bioactivities is a promising approach to realize efficient treatment of fibrosis.

20.3.1 Bioactive Peptides Based on Natural Peptides

In the living body system, bioactive peptides have specialized functions such as antioxidant, antimicrobial, antihypertensive, cytomodulatory, and immunomodulatory effects [26]. Integrating natural peptides exhibiting antifibrotic properties with self-assembling peptides provides a facile method to design self-assembling antifibrotic peptides, which can be further manipulated into nanomaterials. In a research, hydrogel was prepared via self-assembly of a (RADA)4-SDKP peptide, which is composed of a natural tetrapeptide (Ac-SDKP) with anti-inflammatory and antifibrotic properties [27] and the self-assembling RADA16-I (AcN-RADARADARADA-CONH2) (Figure 20.5a) [28]. The peptide hydrogel is prepared by adding Ca^{2+} to a solution containing 0.25% (RADA)4-SDKP (Figure 20.5b). The hydrogel is then used to deliver bone marrow mesenchymal stem cells (BM-MSCs) into the injured myocardium of MI rats. The results of the *in vivo* study showed that both the free hydrogel and the cell-loaded hydrogel significantly improved cardiac function, enhanced vascularization, and reduced fibrosis (Figure 20.5c) and inflammation compared to the negative control or BM-MSCs alone. Importantly, there was no discernible difference between the effects of free or cell-loaded hydrogels on cardiac repair, suggesting that the single use of SDKP-modified self-assembling peptide hydrogel is a simple and effective antifibrotic approach and avoids safety issues associated with combination with cell therapy.

The self-assembling RADA16-II sequence (AcN-RARADADARADADA-CONH2) was also combined with the sequence of substance P(SP), a neuropeptide that promotes the recruitment of autologous stem cells and results in angiogenesis and tissue healing, forming the bioactive self-assembling peptide RADA-SP (AcNRARAD ADARADADAGGRPKPQQFFGLMCONH2) [29]. To prepare the bioactive peptide hydrogel, RADA16-II and RADA-SP were mixed in a 200:1 ratio and then dissolved

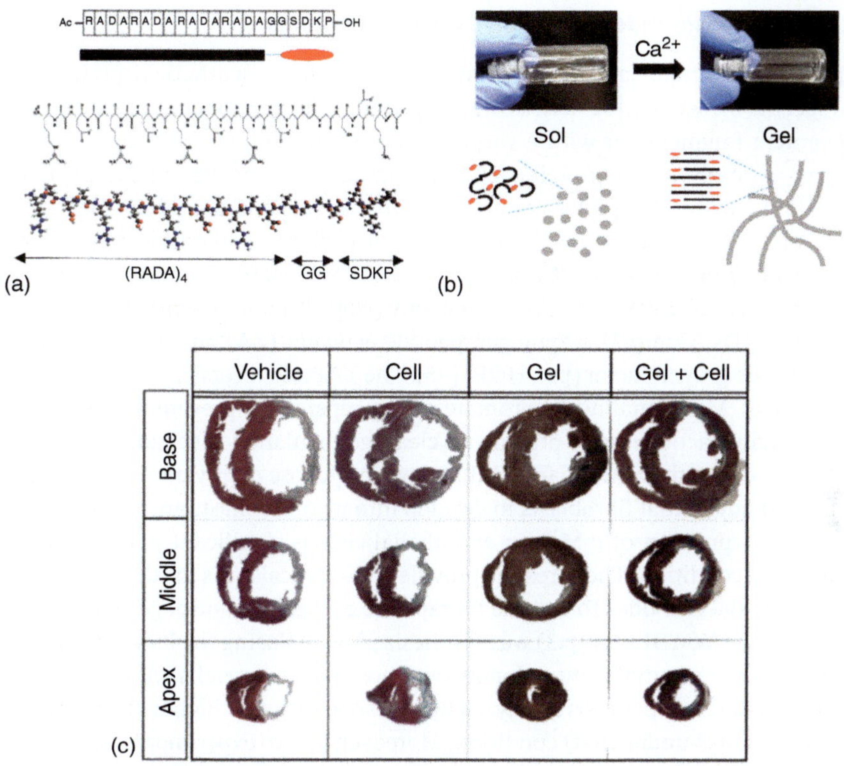

Figure 20.5 (a) Linear, chemical, and three-dimensional structure of the (RADA)4-SDKP as a precursor of the SAP hydrogel. (b) Visual illustration of gel formation by addition of Ca^{2+} to the 0.25% (RADA)4-SDKP solution. (c) Representative images of Masson's trichrome (MT)-stained heart sections at the apex, middle, and base areas for all groups. Source: Reproduced with permission Ref. [27]. © 2020, MDPI.

in 1% (wt/vol) sterile sucrose and subjected to sonication for 30 minutes. Ischemic hind limb models were used to evaluate the SP release characteristics and antifibrotic efficacy of the hydrogels. In mice, the application of the bioactive peptide hydrogel continued to release substance P during 28 days. In addition, the injection of bioactive peptide hydrogel into ischemic regions can reduce the formation of fibrosis more than the injection of SP alone or in combination with RADA16-II.

Co-assembly of bioactive peptides and chemical drugs has also been reported to fabricate nanomaterials. For instance, Wen et al. reported hybrid supramolecular nanofibers formed by co-assembly of a peptide NBD-^{D}F^{D}F^{D}Y^{D}E^{D}EG-DRVYIHP and telmisartan, a clinically used angiotensin II receptor antagonist with high affinity for the AT1R [30]. The peptide is composed of the fluorophore NBD, the bioactive peptide Ang1–7, which exerts cardioprotective effects by binding to the receptor MasR [31], and the strong self-assembling motif FFYEEG composed of D-amino acids. Based on the dual targeting and synergistic therapeutic benefits, the hybrid nanofibers exhibit superior targeting of diseased myocardial tissue and antifibrotic and anti-inflammatory activities in MI rats than the combination of telmisartan and Ang1–7.

20.3.2 Bioactive Peptides Based on Synthetic Peptides

By mimicking the binding and/or functional sites of proteins, synthetic peptides can achieve specific bioactivity [32–34]. Synthetic peptides can be produced as exact replicas of protein fragments or with a variety of chemical modifications, such as the addition of a variety of nonproteinogenic amino acids or changes to the peptide backbone [32]. Synthetic peptides can also be used to create self-assembling peptides with antifibrotic properties. In a research, Guo et al. designed and synthesized a self-assembling functional peptide (Nap-FFEG-IVGGYPWWMDV, Comp.1), which is mainly composed of a self-assembling segment (Nap-FF) and a synthetic peptide (IVGGYPWWMDV, Comp.2), a zymogen peptide activator (ZAPtide) of the precursor of hepatocyte growth factor (pro-HGF) [35]. The ZAPtide reversibly activates pro-HGF-dependent Met signaling to promote tissue repair and prevent fibrosis and avoids irreversible activation by proteolytic cleavage regulation mechanism [36]. It should be noted that the authors found that oxygen/glucose deprivation (OGD) can cause vascular adventitial fibroblasts to develop into myofibroblasts and secrete pro-HGF, and the expression of c-Met on endothelial cells is significantly upregulated under the OGD condition. These results provide a theoretical basis for the treatment of acute MI via the ZAPtide. To test the therapeutic efficacy, a control peptide (Nap-FFEG-YPGGVWVWMDI, Comp.3) was synthesized by replacing the bioactive motif of Comp.1 with a scrambled functional sequence. *In vitro* results indicated that Comp.1 had better antiapoptosis ability, angiogenesis ability, and higher affinity than Comp.2 and Comp.3 under OGD condition. Moreover, *in vivo* experiments suggested that Comp.1, in contrast to Comp.2 and Comp.3, had a greater ability to restore microcirculation (Figure 20.6a), protect cardiomyocytes, and reduce myocardial fibrosis (Figure 20.6b,c) after MI.

Nanomaterials based on bioactive peptides can be a substitute for protein-based therapeutics. For example, Shang et al. reported a nanofiber formed by the self-assembling peptide (Nap-FFGSSSR) comprising the tetrapeptide SSSR from the C region of insulin-like growth factor (IGF-1) [37]. *In vitro* studies showed that the self-assembling peptide significantly reduced dexamethasone-induced myoblast mortality, promoted proliferation, and helped myoblasts successfully differentiate into myotubes. To evaluate the *in vivo* effect of Nap-FFGSSSR nanofiber, sarcopenia mice were constructed by dexamethasone (Dex) induction. Results showed that sarcopenia mice with the treatment of both Nap-FFGSSSR and IGF-1 protein have more increase in muscle mass, lager muscle fibers, and less deposition of collagen than their counterparts treated by the peptide Ac-SSSR. Especially, the nanofiber, which shows similar bioactivity to IGF-1, can activate the insulin signaling pathway to present therapeutic effect based on RNA sequencing results.

Longer peptide mimics are also suitable for modifying self-assembling peptides to produce bioactive nanomaterials. Boopathy et al. designed an RJ peptide consisting of three moieties: the self-assembling sequence RADA16-II (H2N-RARADADARARADADAOH), a synthetic bioactive sequence (H2N-CDDYYYGFGCNKFCRPROH) capable of mimicking the Notch1 ligand Jagged1, and a seven-glycine sequence that served as a linker by connecting the two

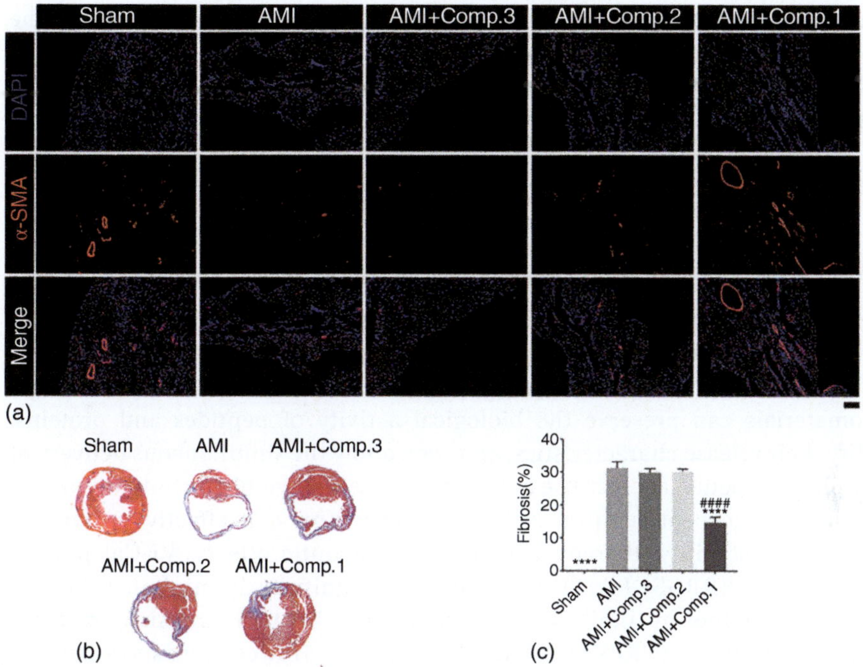

Figure 20.6 (a) Representative fluorescent images of blood vessels (α-SMA-stained) in the marginal area of the MI. Scale bar = 100 μm. (b) Representative images of Masson's trichrome staining of the heart sections. (c) Quantification of the area of fibrosis. (****, $p < 0.0001$ versus AMI; ####, $p < 0.0001$ versus AMI + Comp.2; n = 5.)
Source: Reproduced with permission Ref. [35]. © 2021, American Chemical Society.

aforementioned moieties [38]. In addition, the RS peptide was synthesized as a control by replacing the synthetic bioactive moiety of RJ with a scrambled peptide motif (H2NRCGPDCFDNYGRYKYCF-OH). According to the previous research, varying % concentrations of 1–3% w/v RADA16-II were combined with RJ or RS in a ratio of 10:1 to form a hydrogel [39]. To evaluate the therapeutic benefits of RJ, MI rats were intramyocardially injected with three kinds of peptide hydrogels composed separately of RADA16-II and RJ, RADA16-II and RS, and RADA16-II alone. The results showed that the peptide hydrogel with RJ significantly reduced cardiac fibrosis and promoted the formation of endothelial vessels in the injured areas than the hydrogel with RS and RADA16-II alone.

20.4 Applications of Peptide-based Nanomaterials in Multiple Antifibrotic Treatments

Due to the heterogeneity of different diseases, a single therapy modality is not suitable for the treatment of multiple fibrosis-related diseases. As a result, many unique therapeutic approaches have been included to treat fibrosis within different diseases.

In addition, some methods are the best choice for specific diseases. For example, the most promising treatment for incurable genetic diseases is gene therapy [40]. However, these therapies suffer from shortcomings that prevent them from achieving satisfactory results in the treatment of fibrosis. Here, we discuss how supramolecular peptide-based nanomaterials can overcome such shortcomings and thus improve antifibrotic efficacy in combination with various therapies.

20.4.1 Peptide Therapy and Protein Therapy

Due to their bioactivities, peptides and proteins can be used as drugs directly. However, the therapeutic efficacy of free peptides and proteins is generally limited because they are unstable and easily cleared *in vivo* [41]. Peptide-based nanomaterials can preserve the biological activity of peptides and proteins, modify their release characteristics, and even allow the simultaneous delivery of multiple therapeutic agents. The application of self-assembly techniques to convert therapeutic peptides into stable nanostructures can effectively improve their *in vivo* stability, thereby enhancing therapeutic effects. VI-Cal peptide (YGRKKRRQRRRGSGRAITILDTEKS) could significantly minimize the size of cardiac infarcts by inhibiting the interaction between transient receptor potential vanilloid 1 (TRPV1) and calcineurin [42]. However, its short half-life prevents therapeutic efficacy. Wang et al. reported a V1-Cal/NapFFY hydrogel to enable the slow release of V1-Cal (Figure 20.7b) [43]. The nanofiber hydrogel

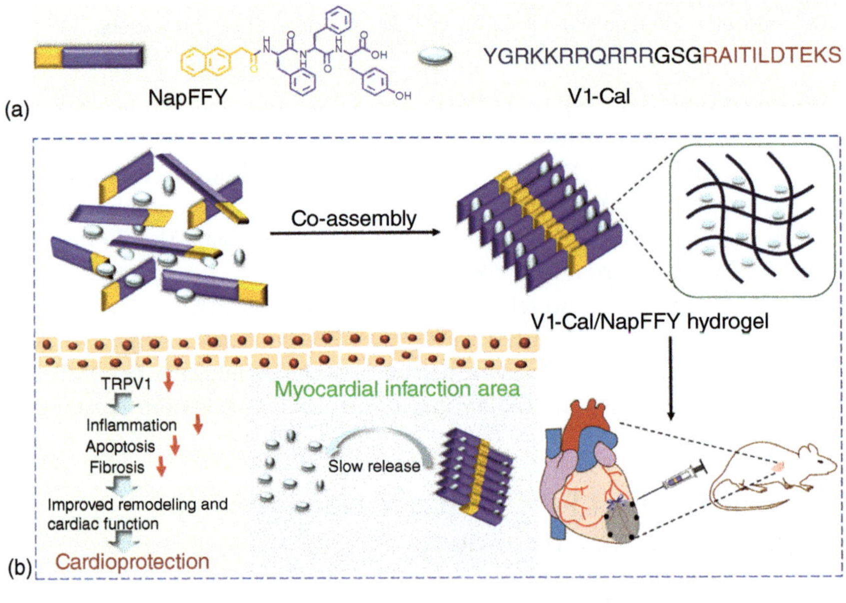

Figure 20.7 (a) Chemical structure of NapFFY hydrogelator and the peptide sequence of V1-Cal. (b) Schematic illustration of a supramolecular hydrogel V1-Cal/NapFFY improving cardiac function of a rat MI model by myocardial injection. Source: Reproduced with permission Ref. [43]. © 2022, Elsevier.

was constructed by co-assembly of VI-Cal and a self-assembling peptide Nap-Phe-Phe-TyrOH (NapFFY) (Figure 20.7a). Circular dichroism (CD) spectra showed that the addition of V1-Cal peptide did not disturb the microstructure of the self-assembling peptide. In other words, the molecular arrangement of the self-assembling peptide is essentially the same in the NapFFY and V1-Cal/NapFFY gels. The mechanical strength of the V1-Cal/NapFFY hydrogels was found to be significantly more robust than that of the NapFFY hydrogels. The result showed that the V1-Cal/NapFFY hydrogel achieved sustained release of V1-Cal. Compared to V1-Cal alone, *in vivo* tests showed that V1-Cal/NapFFY significantly inhibited TRPV1 expression and activation, reduced fibrosis and inflammation, and improved cardiac function in MI rats.

Peptide-based nanomaterials can also be used for delivery of therapeutic proteins. Vascular endothelial growth factor (VEGF) is an important signaling protein that can enhance angiogenesis and blood flow after MI. However, clinical trials have shown that direct intravenous administration of VEGF is not therapeutically effective [44]. The short half-life and instability of VEGF in the blood circulation contributed to the results of the degradation of the protein. In addition, only a small amount of VEGF can reach the target tissue when administered systemically. Dose escalation to stimulate drug accumulation in target tissues is also prohibited because excessive VEGF can cause serious side effects [45]. To address these problems, a novel self-assembling peptide was designed to achieve sustained delivery of VEGF [46]. The peptide is composed of the well-known RADA16-I sequence and a functional sequence LRKKLGKA, which can bind VEGF with heparin-binding property. Under physiological conditions, the peptide can self-assemble into nanofiber scaffolds. According to the results of the analysis of preserved VEGF at the injection site in rat myocardium, the nanofibers achieve sustained VEGF release for 28 days, while VEGF with RADA16-I or without vector administration is rapidly cleared within 7 days. According to *in vivo* studies, the mixture of VEGF and the peptide nanofibers dramatically reduced cardiac fibrosis and infarcted areas at 28 days post-MI compared to VEGF alone or VEGF in combination with RADA16-I. Based on these results, sustained delivery via peptide-based nanomaterials can significantly improve the antifibrotic efficacy of growth factors.

Delivery of multiple drugs can be facilely realized using peptide-based nanomaterials. It has been reported that RADA16-II had the ability to deliver two growth factors simultaneously with slow release: fibroblast growth factor 2 (FGF-2) and platelet-derived growth factor BB (PDGF-BB) [47]. Measurement of myocardial infarct area showed that the infarct size in the treatment group receiving the combination of FGF-2, PDGF-BB, and RADA16-II was the smallest of all treatment groups and was significantly different from the other treatment groups. In addition to codelivery and sustained release of multiple drugs, peptide-based nanomaterials allow for programmable release of multiple drugs. A hydrogel based on a self-assembling peptide and heparin was designed to deliver hepatocyte growth factor (HGF) and anti-TNF-α, an antibody that neutralizes TNF [48]. The hydrogel was formed via electrostatic interaction between the cationic peptide KLD2R (Ac-KLDLKLDLKLDLRR-CONH2) and anionic heparin. Since heparin has a high affinity for HGF, the hydrogel is able to release HGF in a sustained manner. Drug release assays demonstrate that the hydrogel can provide fast anti-TNF-α release along with sustained HGF release. In a renal I/R mouse model, the combinations actually provided better therapeutic efficacy than either anti-TNF-α or HGF alone. A series of *in vivo* analyses showed that after I/R injury, treatment with the hydrogel containing anti-TNF-α/HGF dramatically reduced levels of renal fibrosis and inflammation while promoting tissue repair.

Morphological changes of peptide-based nanomaterials under suitable triggers enable their applications as intelligent drug delivery platforms capable of enhancing drug retention at the target site, just like "transformers." For example, Wang et al. designed a self-assembling peptide K2 (KKPLGLAGFF), which is specifically cleaved by matrix metallopeptidase 9 (MMP-9) (Figure 20.8a), to achieve targeted delivery and slow release of basic fibroblast growth factor (bFGF) in a unique manner [49]. Specifically, K2 self-assembled into core–shell nanostructured micelles *in vitro*, the hydrophobic core of which mediated loading of bFGF (Figure 20.8b).

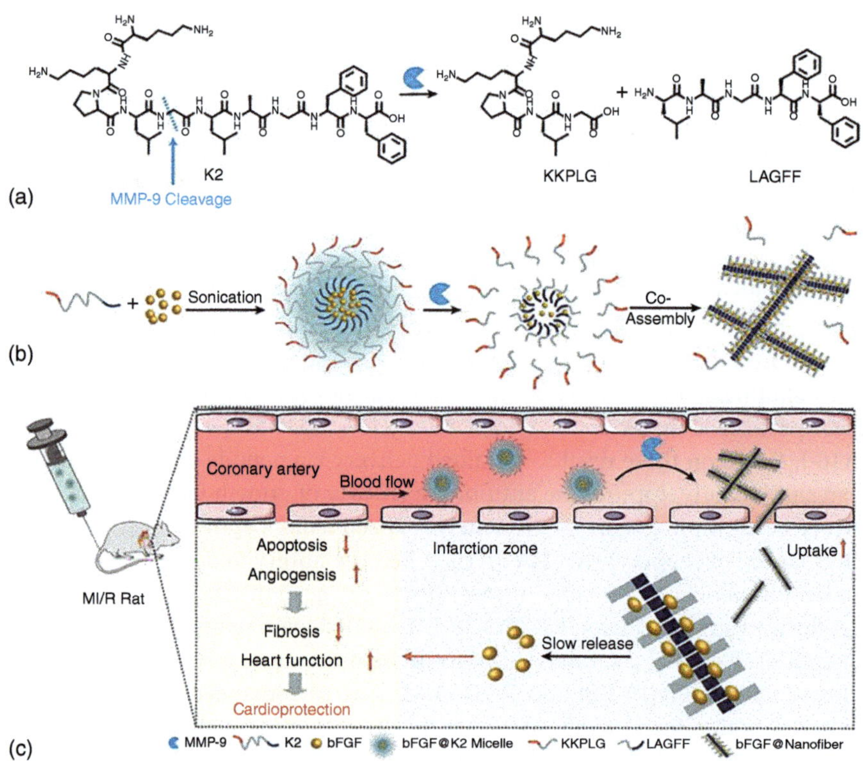

Figure 20.8 (a) Chemical structure of the MMP-9-responsive peptide K2. (b) Schematic illustration of the composition of bFGF@K2 micelle and its transformation to bFGF@ Nanofiber upon MMP-9 cleavage. (c) Schematic illustration of the conversion of bFGF@ K2 micelle to bFGF@Nanofiber in response to high expression of MMP-9 in the ischemic myocardium after intravenous injection. Source: Reproduced with permission Ref. [49]. © 2022, Ivyspring International Publisher.

Due to the increased permeability of the vessels in the infarcted areas [50], bFGF-loaded K2 micelles enter the circulating blood and accumulate in the ischemic myocardium, where they then transformed into nanofibers by the action of MMP-9, which is elevated in the short term after MI (Figure 20.8c). Transformed nanofibers achieve long-term retention and slow release of bFGF in diseased tissue. The combination of bFGF with K2 micelles dramatically reduced myocardial fibrosis and improved cardiac function in MI rats compared to bFGF alone. Taken together, these studies demonstrate that peptide-based nanomaterials have great potential for the delivery of drugs such as peptides and proteins to realized efficient antifibrotic-related therapies.

20.4.2 Cell Therapy

Cell therapy is a therapeutic modality that uses cells as therapeutic agents to alleviate or cure disease [51]. Compared to traditional therapies, cell therapy offers unique therapeutic advantages, primarily due to the fact that therapeutic cells are living entities that can dynamically respond to biological signals while performing complex biological functions [52]. Cell therapy is expected to be used as a novel treatment for incurable diseases [53]. However, poor cell engraftment and retention after transplantation prevent cell-based therapy from being used effectively [54–56]. Peptide hydrogels with excellent biocompatibility are used to provide a suitable microenvironment for exogenous cells, thus improving cell survival and retention. For example, nanofibrous hydrogels formed by the self-assembling peptide RADA16-I or RADA16-II are an excellent substitute for ECM, which is essential for cell growth and function [57]. In the MI models, the efficacy of transplanted cells was further enhanced in the presence of RADA16-I or RADA16-II, exerting better therapeutic performances of reducing infarct size and improving myocardial regeneration compared to that in the absence of self-assembling peptide [58, 59]. More importantly, functional peptide hydrogels can be used as carriers to further enhance the efficacy of cell therapy. The most commonly used stem cells in clinical settings are mesenchymal stem cells (MSCs) because they are free of ethical concerns, abundant sources, low immunogenicity, and no teratoma risks [60]. To improve the therapeutic effect of MSCs, Guo et al. designed a novel self-assembling peptide by modifying RADA16-I with a functional motif RGDSP, which enhances cell attachment to improve the survival rate of transplanted cells [61]. Bone marrow-derived cardiac stem cells (MCSCs) and RGDSP nanofibers formed by the self-assembling peptide were administered together into the infarcted myocardium of MI rats. Meanwhile, MI rats treated separately with MCSCs alone, RGDSP nanofibers alone, or MCSCs in RADA16-I nanofibers were set as control groups. Compared with other groups, the MCSCs and RGDSP nanofibers groups had more transplanted cells that survived and dramatically less myocardial fibrosis. In addition, cardiac function assessment results showed that MCSCs together with RGDSP nanofibers improved ventricular contractile function. Similarly, functional oligopeptide-modified RADA16-I has been successively reported to improve cell therapy for MI. In some researches, RADA-I is functionalized by bioactive peptide motif QHREDGS or

SVVYGLR to enhance the therapeutic efficiency of MSCs for MI [62, 63]. In addition to improving the survival of transplanted cells at infarct lesions, these modified self-assembling peptides promote angiogenesis of cardiac tissue.

In addition to increasing the cell transplantation rate, peptide hydrogels can further improve the therapeutic efficacy by enhancing the therapeutic effects of transplanted cells. Huang et al. fabricated a new self-assembling peptide Nap-GFFYK-Thiol hydrogel to deliver human placenta-derived MSCs (hP-MSCs) for the treatment of limb ischemia [64]. To generate the peptide, the precursor Nap-GFFYK-ss-EE was first synthesized, which was subsequently reduced by glutathione (GSH) and converted to Nap-GFFYK-Thiol. According to the *in vitro* results, both proangiogenic and antiapoptotic effects of hP-MSCs were enhanced by the Nap-GFFYK-Thiol hydrogel. Compared to hP-MSCs or Nap-GFFYK-Thiol hydrogel alone, treatment of hP-MSCs with Nap-GFFYK-Thiol hydrogel dramatically reduced collagen deposition and improved capillary and microvascular density in ischemic limbs of mice with hindlimb ischemia. The peptide hydrogel itself can exert therapeutic effects and synergistically promote the efficacy of cell therapy. Wang et al. designed a novel functional hydrogel to deliver hP-MSCs [65]. The hydrogel building block (Figure 20.9a) is obtained by binding the self-assembling peptide motif (Nap-^{D}F^{D}FG), which introduces D-amino acids to enhance enzyme stability, and a peptide mimicking insulin-like growth factor-1 domain C (IGF-1C), via heating–cooling methods to form a supramolecular hydrogel (Figure 20.9b) with a β-sheet second structure. In mice with acute kidney injury (AKI), co-transplantation of hydrogel and hP-MSCs resulted in less fibrotic tissue (Figure 20.9c) and more blood vessels compared to treatment with hydrogel alone or hP-MSCs alone. In addition, the VEGF/VEGFR2 signaling pathway is activated after injury, and the hydrogel or hP-MSCs could enhance this effect according to the results of *in vivo* bioluminescence imaging assay. These results suggest that the hydrogels not only provide a suitable microenvironment for the transplanted cells but also exert therapeutic effects that synergistically promote cell therapy.

The integration of functional polymers into peptide hydrogels is used to create multifunctional nanomaterials to enhance the efficacy of cell therapy. After MI, the ROS microenvironment in the damaged myocardium and the obstruction of electrical signal conduction caused by continuous fibrotic deposition severely impede cardiac repair, contributing to cardiac dysfunction, and even leading to heart failure. To address the above problems, an injectable ROS-scavenging/conducting hybrid hydrogel (R&C gel) was designed to provide a favorable microenvironment for exogenous cardiomyocytes [66]. Aiming to fabricate the hybrid hydrogel, two self-assembling peptides (P1 and P2) were rationally designed. In the P1 structure, the antioxidant TEMPOL is coupled to the lysine residue, and the RGD peptide motif responsible for cell adhesion is added at the tail. P2 incorporates the T59 sequence to increase its ability to interact with the conductive polypyrrole (PPy). In addition, both P1 and P2 contain the self-assembling Nap-FF motif. The suspension of PPy nanoclusters at a concentration of 2 mg/mL is then added to the hydrogel fabricated from co-assembly of two peptides. The mixture is ultrasonically dispersed and allowed to rest, forming a stable hybrid hydrogel in which PPy nanoparticles are

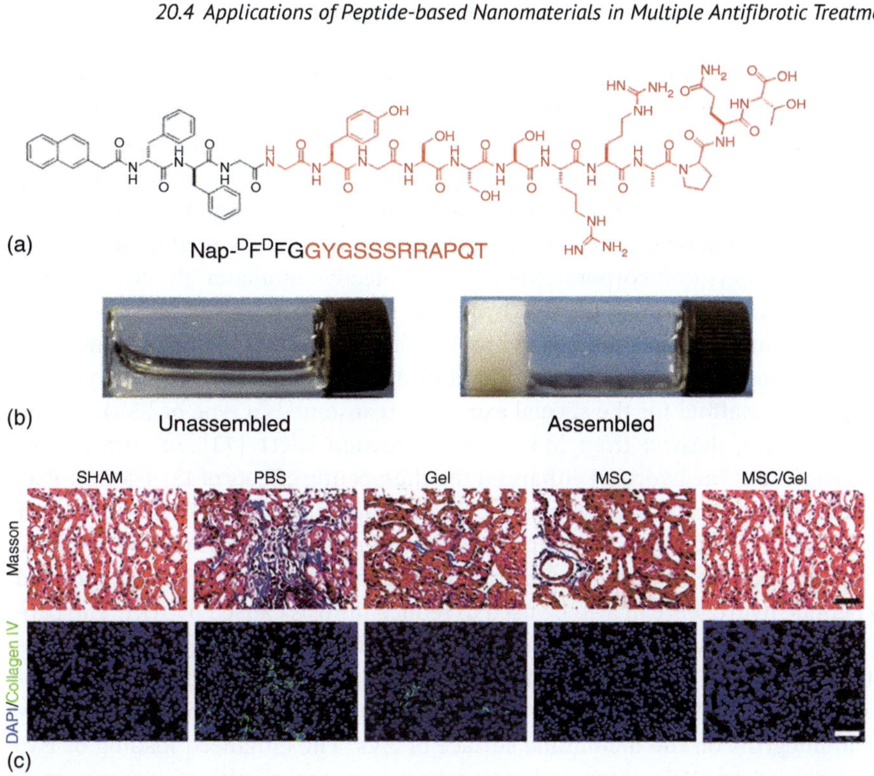

Figure 20.9 (a) Chemical structure of the self-assembling peptide. (b) Optical images of unassembled IGF-1C (solution) versus assembled IGF-1C (hydrogel) in the phosphate-buffered solution (PBS) buffer solvent (pH 7.4) (c) Histological assay revealing the repair process at day 3 post-acute kidney injure (AKI). Scale bar = 50 μm. Source: Reproduced with permission Ref. [65]. © 2020, Dove Medical Press.

uniformly attached to self-assembling elements through binding interactions mediated by the T59 peptide. *In vitro* tests showed that the hydrogel could effectively prevent apoptosis in cardiomyocytes, eliminate ROS from these cells, and improve their electrical and contractile capabilities when exposed to oxygen–glucose deprivation (OGD) conditions. The composite hydrogel encapsulating cardiomyocytes effectively reduced fibrosis and improved conduction dysfunction in infarcted myocardium.

20.4.3 Extracellular Vesicle Therapy

Extracellular vesicles (EVs) are spherical, phospholipid-enclosed vesicles secreted by cells that mediate intermolecular communication via loaded biological molecules [67, 68]. The great therapeutic potential of EVs is highlighted by the fact that they are involved in a variety of psychological and pathological processes [69] and have a wide range of biological functions such as immune regulation, tissue regeneration, and inflammation modulation [70]. In particular, the cellular source is considered as the first concern for the development of EV-based therapies.

Studies on stem cell-derived EVs have mostly focused on MSCs [71]. MSC-derived EVs (MSC-EVs) exert therapeutic effects similar to their source cells [70]. Thus, MSC-EV-based therapy is recognized as an attractive approach to replace MSCs therapy. In addition, EVs have fewer safety concerns and are easier to produce and obtain than cell therapy [72]. However, low retention rates significantly hamper the *in vivo* therapeutic efficacy of EVs in free form [73, 74]. A method to prolong retention of EVs is to incorporate them into protective biomaterials, such as peptide hydrogels. Importantly, peptide hydrogels can be further functionalized with bioactive motifs [75] to meet specific requirements. To improve the treatment of MI with exosome therapy, Hu et al. developed a Nap-GFFYGQHREDGS peptide hydrogel as a scaffold for the special exosomes (exosome is a type of EVs), named ISL1-MSCs-Exo, derived from MSCs overexpressing islet1 [73]. *In vitro* experiments show that the hydrogel enhanced the therapeutic effects of ISL1-MSCs-Exo, including stimulation of angiogenesis and cell proliferation and migration. Further studies showed that the hydrogel improved the retention of ISL1-MSCs-Exo in the infarcted myocardium and enhanced their antifibrotic effects. EVs incorporated into peptide hydrogels can also be used to reduce fibrosis caused by AKI. The peptide hydrogel that can increase the loading of MSC-EVs was reported [76]. The peptide biotin-GFFYGRGD is mainly composed of biocompatible hydrogelator biotin, well-known self-assembling FF motif, and RGD peptide, which can strongly bind to integrins on the membrane surface of EVs. The enhanced loading of EVs was attributed to RGD–integrin binding based on the results of integrin gene knockdown experiments. Bioluminescence imaging results confirmed that the hydrogel enhanced the retention and stability of EVs in the renal region of AKI mice after local injection. Further *in vivo* assays showed that the hydrogel enhanced the nephroprotective and antifibrotic effects of EVs.

Peptide hydrogels can also enhance the efficacy of EVs through altering their release kinetics. Based on the fact that matrix metalloproteinase-2 (MMP-2) presents a stronger activity in tissues after I/R injury, an MMP2-sensitive peptide, KMP2 (Ac-KLDLPVGLIGKLDL-CONH2), was developed by attaching the self-assembling KLDL sequence to each terminus of the PVGLIG motif, which can be degraded by MMP-2 [77]. The formed KMP2 hydrogel is used to encapsulate MSC-EVs to enhance the ability of tissue regeneration. *In vivo* experiments showed that by stimulating endothelial cell proliferation and angiogenesis, KMP2 hydrogel loaded with MSC-EVs dramatically reduced chronic renal fibrosis than EVs alone. Another MMP-2-degradable peptide was designed using a cardioprotective sequence (GHRPS) and an MMP-2 degradable sequence (GTAGLIGQ) [78]. Due to poor gelatinization property, the resulting peptide is co-assembled with Nap-FF to form a hydrogel, which is used for the delivery of exosomes derived from human umbilical cord MSCs. *In vitro*, the hydrogel improved the viability of cardiomyocytes subjected to oxidative stress. In addition, the hydrogel enabled the release of exosomes at a steady and consistent rate. Subsequent *in vivo* tests showed that the exosome/hydrogel mixture had significantly improved efficacy in reducing fibrosis and cellular apoptosis, inhibiting inflammation and promoting angiogenesis in infarcted myocardium compared to exosomes alone.

20.4.4 Gene Therapy

Cystic fibrosis (CF), an autosomal recessive disease, is caused by mutations in the gene encoding the CF transmembrane conductance regulator (CFTR), which is responsible for chloride ion transport across the apical membranes of epithelial cells in respiratory tissues [79]. Gene therapy is a promising option, but the efficacy is significantly influenced by the delivery vectors. The safety issues caused by viral vectors make nonviral vectors more potential for gene therapy [80]. Lipoplexes (cationic lipids complexed with DNA) and polyplexes (cationic polymers complexed with DNA) are the most widely used nonviral vectors for delivery of intracellular DNA in treating CF [81]. However, the therapeutic efficacy of nonviral vectors is typically limited by low transfection in the airways *in vivo*. To address this deficiency, a ternary self-assembling vector system for CF gene therapy was designed by introducing a receptor-targeting/DNA-binding peptide based on common lipoplex vector systems [82]. Specifically, the vector system (LED) is a formulation consisting of lipofectin (L, a cationic liposome), an intercellular adhesion molecule-1 receptor targeting/DNA-binding peptide (E, K_{16}-GACSERSMNFCG), and plasmid DNA (D). By varying the lipid composition, two different formulations, LED-1 and LED-2, were developed. The two new vectors were compared with two other vectors, GL67 (cationic lipid) and polyethyleneimine (PEI), to evaluate the safety and efficacy for CF gene therapy. *In vitro* and *in vivo* assays showed that only LED-1 can effectively and safely transfect airway epithelial cells and can be applied repeatedly. A further study was conducted to investigate the feasibility of delivering LED-1 in the form of nanoparticles with the size of approximately 150 nm by inhalation [83]. The results showed that nebulized LED-1 retained its biophysical properties and transfection efficacy *in vitro* and *in vivo*, which is more favorable for clinical translation. Using a similar strategy, a self-assembling nanoparticle formulation (LPR) was designed to deliver siRNA for CF therapy [84]. The building blocks of LPRs are a cationic liposome (L), a peptide (P) with a targeting sequence and nucleic acid-binding moiety, and siRNA (R) that reduces the activity of the epithelial Na^+ channel (ENaC), whose dysfunction promotes disease exacerbation. In mice, LPRs effectively deliver siRNA to the airway epithelium and silence gene expression related to ENaC.

Different from the above peptide–lipid–nucleic acid formulations, nanoparticles consisting of amphiphilic copolymers (poloxamine 704, T704), synthetic peptides, and nucleic acids have also been investigated for the treatment of CF [85]. Poloxamines are attractive gene delivery vectors due to their excellent biocompatibility, commercial viability, and ability to self-assemble into micelles under aqueous conditions [86]. However, transfection of airway epithelia with T704 alone did not achieve the desired results. To improve transfection efficiency, researchers designed a class of peptides consisting of three different functional moieties: an anchoring moiety that provides interaction with T704, a cationic moiety that condenses nucleic acids and facilitates efficient endosomal escape, and a targeting moiety. In addition, they systemically investigated the subcellular fate of both the peptide-based ternary complex and the T704-based binary complex. The results show that ternary complexes containing peptides are able to effectively overcome a variety of intracellular obstacles, providing advantages over their

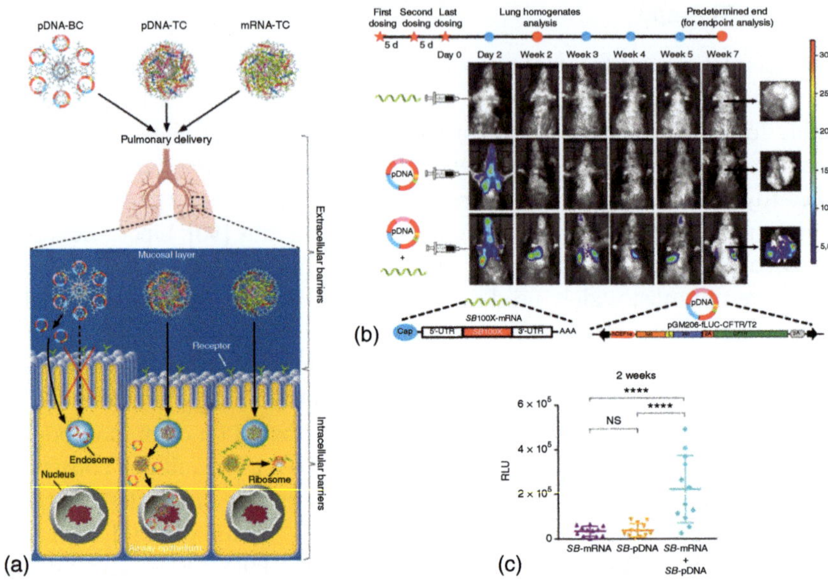

Figure 20.10 (a) A proposed pulmonary delivery process of pDNA-based binary complex (pDNA-BC), pDNA-based binary complex (pDNA-BC), and mRNA-based ternary complex (mRNA-TC). (b) Exemplary bioluminescence images were taken at the indicated time points after dosing. Mice treated with the single formulation of pGM206-fLUC-CFTR/T2 (SB-pDNA) or SB100X-mRNA (SB-mRNA) were applied as controls. (c) Luciferase activity in lung homogenates of mice 2 weeks after dosing. Each symbol represents one animal ($n = 12$ biologically independent animals for 2 weeks. Data are shown as means ± s.d. One-way ANOVA with Tukey's *post hoc* test was used to determine significance (NS, not significant; 2 weeks, $^{****}P < 0.0001$ for the indicated comparisons). Source: Reproduced with permission Ref. [85]. © 2019, Springer Nature.

binary counterparts (Figure 20.10a). Subsequently, they optimized ternary nanocomplexes with different peptides, and the optimal nanocarrier for effectively mediating both mRNA and pDNA transfection was found to contain peptide 9 (KETWWETWWTEWWWKKRRRKKKGACSERSMNFCG). The peptide 9-based nanoparticles are used to deliver the optimized Sleeping Beauty (SB) transposon system consisting of SB transposase encoding SB100X mRNA and pGM206-fLUC-CFTR/T2 transposon (pDNA) to enable long-term restoration of CFTR. Thus, two peptide-9-based ternary complexes containing SB100X mRNA and transposon pGM206-fLUC-CFTR/T2, respectively, were established as a peptide-poloxamine/SB genomic integration system for *in vitro* and *in vivo* studies. Two weeks after peptide-poloxamine/SB-mediated transfection, strong fluorescent signals occur in the lungs of mice, whereas the counterpart is barely perceptible in the mice treated just with pGM206-fLUC-CFTR/T2 (Figure 20.10b). Further luciferase analysis is consistent with the above results (Figure 20.10c). At 18 weeks after peptide-poloxamine/SB treatment, mature CFTR proteins could be successfully expressed by transfected CF epithelial cells, while no signal could be seen in controls. Whole-genome resequencing results show that the peptide-poloxamine/SB system has successfully integrated the CFTR gene into the genome of CF mice. A series of *in vivo* experiments demonstrated the ability of the system to restore CFTR in the lungs of CF mice over the long term. Taken together, these results demonstrate that the self-assembling peptide, which not only initiates and stabilizes the system but also imparts targeting properties to the system, plays a critical role in multicomponent delivery systems for efficient gene therapy.

20.5 Conclusion and Perspective

In summary, we have mainly introduced two methods to fabricate peptide-based nanomaterials for antifibrosis treatment: (1) self-assembly of peptide–drug conjugates and (2) self-assembly of bioactive peptides that integrate a self-assembling sequence with a therapeutic sequence. The resulting peptide-based nanomaterials can enhance the accumulation of drugs in fibrotic tissues via enzyme-triggered reactions or disease-targeting peptides. The nanomaterials of bioactive peptides achieve superior therapeutic effects compared to free peptides by preserving their *in vivo* stability, providing them with sustainable release rates or stabilizing a specific secondary structure. Hence, self-assembled peptide nanomaterials have great potential to be carrier-free nanomedicines for antifibrotic applications. In addition to self-assembly, co-assembly of multiple building blocks and utilizing peptide-based nanomaterials as drug carriers have also been extensively investigated to fabricate therapeutic nanomaterials for the treatment of fibrosis. Especially, peptide-based nanomaterials are readily to be endowed with multiple therapeutic functions through the integrating of multiple bioactive peptides and drugs, enabling the treatment of fibrosis with the combination of many other therapies. The morphological changes of peptide-based nanomaterials facilitate the rational design of environment-responsive nanomaterials toward specific and sustained drug release. Efficient loading and sustained release of therapeutic proteins from peptide-based nanomaterials can be designed based on the strong affinity of therapeutic proteins with the peptide motifs in nanomaterials. Peptide-based nanomaterials are also ideal vehicles for delivery of live cells and EVs for treatment of fibrosis-associated diseases to overcome the lack of low retention. Importantly, the peptide-based nanomaterials can be designed as therapeutic carriers or regulate the release rate of loaded cargo, thus further enhancing the therapeutic effect of cells and EVs. In gene therapy, self-assembling peptides are introduced to fabricate ternary nanocomplexes, medicating more efficient gene transfection over binary delivery vehicles based on lipid or copolymer. Collectively, peptide-based nanomaterials exhibit multiple advantages in the treatment of fibrosis-related diseases: excellent biosafety; universality, especially good applicability to a wide range of therapeutics; can be customized to achieve functionality; and intelligent delivery, such as enzyme-responsive release.

Despite the fact that peptide-based nanomaterials have shown promising therapeutic potential for the treatment of fibrosis and for the enhancement of existing antifibrotic therapies, there are some critical issues that need to be addressed. The self-assembling design approach is too homogeneous and often relies on several widely used self-assembling peptides, such as FF, RADA16-I, and RADA16-II. Most of the reported peptide-based nanomaterials for fibrosis treatments are in the form of hydrogels, which can only be administered by local injection. More suitable formulations that can be administered by more convenient methods need to be further explored. Current researches on the applications of peptide-based nanomaterials in some fibrotic diseases are lacking or even absent, such as liver fibrosis and intestinal fibrosis. More researches are needed in these diseases. Since fibrosis is a highly complex pathological process involving multiple cell types and signaling pathways, multifunctional peptide-based nanomaterials that can act on multiple therapeutic targets should be one of the major research directions. In addition, fibrosis is an important factor in tumor growth that can promote tumor growth through multiple mechanisms and lead to chemotherapy resistance and immune escape [87]. The development of peptide-based nanomaterials for antifibrosis treatment will effectively advance current cancer treatment. A better understanding of the principles underlying peptide self-assembly and the structure–function relationships of peptide-based nanomaterials is expected to advance the clinical treatment of fibrosis and fibrotic diseases in the near future.

References

1 Wynn, T.A. (2008). Cellular and molecular mechanisms of fibrosis. *J. Pathol.* 214 (2): 199–210.

2 Kisseleva, T. and Brenner, D. (2021). Molecular and cellular mechanisms of liver fibrosis and its regression. *Nat. Rev. Gastroenterol. Hepatol.* 18 (3): 151–166.

3 Frangogiannis, N.G. (2021). Cardiac fibrosis. *Cardiovasc. Res.* 117 (6): 1450–1488.

4 Hamanaka, R.B. and Mutlu, G.M. (2021). Metabolic requirements of pulmonary fibrosis: Role of fibroblast metabolism. *FEBS J.* 288 (22): 6331–6352.

5 Henderson, N.C., Rieder, F., and Wynn, T.A. (2020). Fibrosis: from mechanisms to medicines. *Nature* 587 (7835): 555–566.

6 Zhao, X., Kwan, J.Y.Y., Yip, K. et al. (2020). Targeting metabolic dysregulation for fibrosis therapy. *Nat. Rev. Drug Discov.* 19 (1): 57–75.

7 Soares, S., Sousa, J., Pais, A., and Vitorino, C. (2018). Nanomedicine: Principles, properties, and regulatory issues. *Front. Chem.* 6: 360.

8 Zhang, C., Yan, L., Wang, X. et al. (2020). Progress, challenges, and future of nanomedicine. *Nano Today* 35: 101008.

9 de Lazaro, I. and Mooney, D.J. (2021). Obstacles and opportunities in a forward vision for cancer nanomedicine. *Nat. Mater.* 20 (11): 1469–1479.

10 Zhao, M., Wang, L., Wang, M. et al. (2022). Targeting fibrosis, mechanisms and clinical trials. *Signal Transduct. Target. Ther.* 7 (1): 206.

11 Zhou, L., Liang, Q., Li, Y. et al. (2022). Collagenase-I decorated co-delivery micelles potentiate extracellular matrix degradation and hepatic stellate cell targeting for liver fibrosis therapy. *Acta Biomater.* 152: 235–254.

12 Sun, H., Shi, K., Zuo, B. et al. (2022). Kidney-targeted drug delivery system based on metformin-grafted chitosan for renal fibrosis therapy. *Mol. Pharm.* 19 (9): 3075–3084.

13 Fan, Q.Q., Zhang, C.L., Qiao, J.B. et al. (2020). Extracellular matrix-penetrating nanodrill micelles for liver fibrosis therapy. *Biomaterials* 230: 119616.

14 Zhang, S. (2003). Fabrication of novel biomaterials through molecular self-assembly. *Nat. Biotechnol.* 21 (10): 1171–1178.

15 Wang, J., Liu, K., Xing, R., and Yan, X. (2016). Peptide self-assembly: Thermodynamics and kinetics. *Chem. Soc. Rev.* 45 (20): 5589–5604.

16 Yan, X., Zhu, P., and Li, J. (2010). Self-assembly and application of diphenylalanine-based nanostructures. *Chem. Soc. Rev.* 39 (6): 1877–1890.

17 Qi, G.B., Gao, Y.J., Wang, L., and Wang, H. (2018). Self-assembled peptide-based nanomaterials for biomedical imaging and therapy. *Adv. Mater.* 30 (22): 1703444.

18 Tang, W., Zhao, Z., Chong, Y. et al. (2018). Tandem enzymatic self-assembly and slow release of dexamethasone enhances its antihepatic fibrosis effect. *ACS Nano* 12 (10): 9966–9973.

19 Liao, X., Song, X., Li, J. et al. (2022). An injectable co-assembled hydrogel blocks reactive oxygen species and inflammation cycle resisting myocardial ischemia-reperfusion injury. *Acta Biomater.* 149: 82–95.

20 Zhang, W., Zhan, J., Zhao, R. et al. (2022). Parallelism to conquer: Binary supramolecular peptide amphiphiles launch synergistic stromal reprogramming to remove the baffle in pancreatic cancer therapy. *Adv. Funct. Mater.* 32 (38): 2203767.

21 Akbarian, M., Khani, A., Eghbalpour, S., and Uversky, V.N. (2022). Bioactive peptides: synthesis, sources, applications, and proposed mechanisms of action. *Int. J. Mol. Sci.* 23 (3): 1445.

22 Liang, Y., Zhang, X., Yuan, Y. et al. (2020). Role and modulation of the secondary structure of antimicrobial peptides to improve selectivity. *Biomater. Sci.* 8 (24): 6858–6866.

23 Shang, Y., Zhi, D., Feng, G. et al. (2019). Supramolecular nanofibers with superior bioactivity to insulin-like growth factor-I. *Nano Lett.* 19 (3): 1560–1569.

24 Eiriksdottir, E., Konate, K., Langel, U. et al. (2010). Secondary structure of cell-penetrating peptides controls membrane interaction and insertion. *Biochim. Biophys. Acta* 1798 (6): 1119–1128.

25 Xing, R., Yuan, C., Li, S. et al. (2018). Charge-induced secondary structure transformation of amyloid-derived dipeptide assemblies from beta-sheet to alpha-helix. *Angew. Chem. Int. Ed. Engl.* 57 (6): 1537–1542.

26 Sánchez, A. and Vázquez, A. (2017). Bioactive peptides: a review. *Food Qual. Saf.* 1 (1): 29–46.

27 Kumar, N., Nakagawa, P., Janic, B. et al. (2016). The anti-inflammatory peptide AC-SDKP is released from thymosin-beta4 by renal meprin-alpha and prolyl oligopeptidase. *Am. J. Physiol. Renal Physiol.* 310 (10): F1026–F1034.

28 Firoozi, S., Pahlavan, S., Ghanian, M.-H. et al. (2020). A cell-free SDKP-conjugated self-assembling peptide hydrogel sufficient for improvement of myocardial infarction. *Biomolecules* 10 (2): 205.

29 Kim, J.H., Jung, Y., Kim, B.-S., and Kim, S.H. (2013). Stem cell recruitment and angiogenesis of neuropeptide substance P coupled with self-assembling peptide nanofiber in a mouse hind limb ischemia model. *Biomaterials* 34 (6): 1657–1668.

30 Wen, Z., Zhan, J., Li, H. et al. (2021). Dual-ligand supramolecular nanofibers inspired by the renin-angiotensin system for the targeting and synergistic therapy of myocardial infarction. *Theranostics* 11 (8): 3725–3741.

31 Padda, R.S., Shi, Y., Lo, C.S. et al. (2015). Angiotensin-(1–7): a novel peptide to treat hypertension and nephropathy in diabetes? *J. Diabetes Metab.* 6 (10): 1000615.

32 Gross, A., Hashimoto, C., Sticht, H., and Eichler, J. (2015). Synthetic peptides as protein mimics. *Front. Bioeng. Biotechnol.* 3: 211.

33 Hill, T.A., Shepherd, N.E., Diness, F., and Fairlie, D.P. (2014). Constraining cyclic peptides to mimic protein structure motifs. *Angew. Chem. Int. Ed. Engl.* 53 (48): 13020–13041.

34 Sachdeva, S., Joo, H., Tsai, J. et al. (2019). A rational approach for creating peptides mimicking antibody binding. *Sci. Rep.* 9 (1): 997.

35 Guo, W., Feng, W., Huang, J. et al. (2021). Supramolecular self-assembled nanofibers efficiently activate the precursor of hepatocyte growth factor for angiogenesis in myocardial infarction therapy. *ACS Appl. Mater. Interfaces* 13 (19): 22131–22141.

36 Landgraf, K.E., Steffek, M., Quan, C. et al. (2014). An allosteric switch for pro-HGF/Met signaling using zymogen activator peptides. *Nat. Chem. Biol.* 10 (7): 567–573.

37 Shang, Y., Kuang, M., Wang, Z. et al. (2020). An ultrashort peptide-based supramolecular hydrogel mimicking igf-1 to alleviate glucocorticoid-induced sarcopenia. *ACS Appl. Mater. Interfaces* 12 (31): 34678–34688.

38 Boopathy, A.V., Martinez, M.D., Smith, A.W. et al. (2015). Intramyocardial delivery of notch ligand-containing hydrogels improves cardiac function and angiogenesis following infarction. *Tissue Eng. Part A* 21 (17–18): 2315–2322.

39 Boopathy, A.V., Che, P.L., Somasuntharam, I. et al. (2014). The modulation of cardiac progenitor cell function by hydrogel-dependent notch1 activation. *Biomaterials* 35 (28): 8103–8112.

40 Shahryari, A., Saghaeian Jazi, M., Mohammadi, S. et al. (2019). Development and clinical translation of approved gene therapy products for genetic disorders. *Front. Genet.* 10: 868.

41 Wang, L., Wang, N., Zhang, W. et al. (2022). Therapeutic peptides: current applications and future directions. *Signal Transduct. Target. Ther.* 7 (1): 48.

42 Hurt, C.M., Lu, Y., Stary, C.M. et al. (2016). Transient receptor potential vanilloid 1 regulates mitochondrial membrane potential and myocardial reperfusion injury. *J. Am. Heart Assoc.* 5 (9): e003774.

43 Wang, B., Wu, C., He, S. et al. (2022). V1-cal hydrogelation enhances its effects on ventricular remodeling reduction and cardiac function improvement post myocardial infarction. *Chem. Eng. J.* 433: 134450.

44 Simon-Yarza, T., Formiga, F.R., Tamayo, E. et al. (2012). Vascular endothelial growth factor-delivery systems for cardiac repair: An overview. *Theranostics* 2 (6): 541–552.

45 Zisch, A.H., Lutolf, M.P., and Hubbell, J.A. (2003). Biopolymeric delivery matrices for angiogenic growth factors. *Cardiovasc. Pathol.* 12 (6): 295–310.

46 Guo, H.-d., Cui, G.-h., Yang, J.-j. et al. (2012). Sustained delivery of VEGF from designer self-assembling peptides improves cardiac function after myocardial infarction. *Biochem. Biophys. Res. Commun.* 424 (1): 105–111.

47 Kim, J.H., Jung, Y., Kim, S.-H. et al. (2011). The enhancement of mature vessel formation and cardiac function in infarcted hearts using dual growth factor delivery with self-assembling peptides. *Biomaterials* 32 (26): 6080–6088.

48 Liu, S., Zhao, M., Zhou, Y. et al. (2020). A self-assembling peptide hydrogel-based drug co-delivery platform to improve tissue repair after ischemia-reperfusion injury. *Acta Biomater.* 103: 102–114.

49 Wang, Y., Wang, D., Wu, C. et al. (2022). MMP 9-instructed assembly of bFGF nanofibers in ischemic myocardium to promote heart repair. *Theranostics* 12 (17): 7237–7249.

50 Durymanov, M., Kamaletdinova, T., Lehmann, S.E., and Reineke, J. (2017). Exploiting passive nanomedicine accumulation at sites of enhanced vascular permeability for non-cancerous applications. *J. Control. Release* 261: 10–22.

51 Lasiter, L., Campbell, A., Basch, E. et al. (2020). Use of patient-reported outcomes to understand & measure the patient experience of novel cell and gene therapies. *Ther. Innov. Regul. Sci.* 54 (6): 1566–1575.

52 Wang, L.L., Janes, M.E., Kumbhojkar, N. et al. (2021). Cell therapies in the clinic. *Bioeng Transl. Med.* 6 (2): e10214.

53 Golchin, A. and Farahany, T.Z. (2019). Biological products: cellular therapy and FDA approved products. *Stem Cell Rev. Rep.* 15 (2): 166–175.

54 Zhao, M., Fan, C., Ernst, P.J. et al. (2019). Y-27632 preconditioning enhances transplantation of human-induced pluripotent stem cell-derived cardiomyocytes in myocardial infarction mice. *Cardiovasc. Res.* 115 (2): 343–356.

55 He, N., Xu, Y., Du, W. et al. (2015). Extracellular matrix can recover the downregulation of adhesion molecules after cell detachment and enhance endothelial cell engraftment. *Sci. Rep.* 5: 10902.

56 Cheng, K., Malliaras, K., Li, T.S. et al. (2012). Magnetic enhancement of cell retention, engraftment, and functional benefit after intracoronary delivery of cardiac-derived stem cells in a rat model of ischemia/reperfusion. *Cell Transplant.* 21 (6): 1121–1135.

57 Yu, Z., Cai, Z., Chen, Q. et al. (2016). Engineering beta-sheet peptide assemblies for biomedical applications. *Biomater. Sci.* 4 (3): 365–374.

58 Tokunaga, M., Liu, M.L., Nagai, T. et al. (2010). Implantation of cardiac progenitor cells using self-assembling peptide improves cardiac function after myocardial infarction. *J. Mol. Cell. Cardiol.* 49 (6): 972–983.

59 Cui, X.J., Xie, H., Wang, H.J. et al. (2010). Transplantation of mesenchymal stem cells with self-assembling polypeptide scaffolds is conducive to treating myocardial infarction in rats. *Tohoku J. Exp. Med.* 222 (4): 281–289.

60 Wei, X., Yang, X., Han, Z.P. et al. (2013). Mesenchymal stem cells: A new trend for cell therapy. *Acta Pharmacol. Sin.* 34 (6): 747–754.

61 Guo, H.-d., Cui, G.-h., Wang, H.-j., and Tan, Y.-z. (2010). Transplantation of marrow-derived cardiac stem cells carried in designer self-assembling peptide nanofibers improves cardiac function after myocardial infarction. *Biochem. Biophys. Res. Commun.* 399 (1): 42–48.

62 Cai, H., Wu, F.Y., Wang, Q.L. et al. (2019). Self-assembling peptide modified with QHREDGS as a novel delivery system for mesenchymal stem cell transplantation after myocardial infarction. *FASEB J.* 33 (7): 8306–8320.

63 Gao, X.R., Xu, H.J., Wang, L.F. et al. (2017). Mesenchymal stem cell transplantation carried in SVVYGLR modified self-assembling peptide promoted cardiac repair and angiogenesis after myocardial infarction. *Biochem. Biophys. Res. Commun.* 491 (1): 112–118.

64 Huang, A., Liu, D., Qi, X. et al. (2019). Self-assembled GFFYK peptide hydrogel enhances the therapeutic efficacy of mesenchymal stem cells in a mouse hindlimb ischemia model. *Acta Biomater.* 85: 94–105.

65 Wang, H., Shang, Y., Chen, X. et al. (2020). Delivery of MSCs with a hybrid beta-sheet peptide hydrogel consisting IGF-1C domain and D-form peptide for acute kidney injury therapy. *Int. J. Nanomedicine* 15: 4311–4324.

66 Zhan, J., Liao, X., Fan, X. et al. (2022). An injectable and conductive TEMPOL/polypyrrole integrated peptide co-assembly hydrogel promotes functional maturation of cardiomyocytes for myocardial infarction repair. *Compos. Part B Eng.* 236: 109794.

67 El Andaloussi, S., Mager, I., Breakefield, X.O., and Wood, M.J. (2013). Extracellular vesicles: biology and emerging therapeutic opportunities. *Nat. Rev. Drug Discov.* 12 (5): 347–357.

68 van der Pol, E., Boing, A.N., Harrison, P. et al. (2012). Classification, functions, and clinical relevance of extracellular vesicles. *Pharmacol. Rev.* 64 (3): 676–705.

69 Mulcahy, L.A., Pink, R.C., and Carter, D.R. (2014). Routes and mechanisms of extracellular vesicle uptake. *J. Extracell. Vesicles* 3: 24641.

70 Wiklander, O.P.B., Brennan, M.A., Lotvall, J. et al. (2019). Advances in therapeutic applications of extracellular vesicles. *Sci. Transl. Med.* 11 (492): eaav8521.

71 Park, K.S., Bandeira, E., Shelke, G.V. et al. (2019). Enhancement of therapeutic potential of mesenchymal stem cell-derived extracellular vesicles. *Stem Cell Res. Ther.* 10 (1): 1–15.

72 Kou, M., Huang, L., Yang, J. et al. (2022). Mesenchymal stem cell-derived extracellular vesicles for immunomodulation and regeneration: a next generation therapeutic tool? *Cell Death Dis.* 13 (7): 580.

73 Hu, X., Ning, X., Zhao, Q. et al. (2022). Islet-1 mesenchymal stem cells-derived exosome-incorporated angiogenin-1 hydrogel for enhanced acute myocardial infarction therapy. *ACS Appl. Mater. Interfaces* 14 (32): 36289–36303.

74 Zhang, Y., Cai, Z., Shen, Y. et al. (2021). Hydrogel-load exosomes derived from dendritic cells improve cardiac function via treg cells and the polarization of macrophages following myocardial infarction. *J. Nanobiotechnol.* 19 (1): 271.

75 Firoozi, S., Pahlavan, S., Ghanian, M.-H. et al. (2020). Mesenchymal stem cell-derived extracellular vesicles alone or in conjunction with a SDKP-conjugated self-assembling peptide improve a rat model of myocardial infarction. *Biochem. Biophys. Res. Commun.* 524 (4): 903–909.

76 Zhang, C., Shang, Y., Chen, X. et al. (2020). Supramolecular nanofibers containing arginine-glycine-aspartate (RGD) peptides boost therapeutic efficacy of extracellular vesicles in kidney repair. *ACS Nano* 14 (9): 12133–12147.

77 Zhou, Y., Liu, S., Zhao, M. et al. (2019). Injectable extracellular vesicle-released self-assembling peptide nanofiber hydrogel as an enhanced cell-free therapy for tissue regeneration. *J. Control. Release* 316: 93–104.

78 Han, C., Zhou, J., Liang, C. et al. (2019). Human umbilical cord mesenchymal stem cell derived exosomes encapsulated in functional peptide hydrogels promote cardiac repair. *Biomater. Sci.* 7 (7): 2920–2933.

79 Bell, S.C., Mall, M.A., Gutierrez, H. et al. (2020). The future of cystic fibrosis care: A global perspective. *Lancet Respir. Med.* 8 (1): 65–124.

80 Yin, H., Kanasty, R.L., Eltoukhy, A.A. et al. (2014). Non-viral vectors for gene-based therapy. *Nat. Rev. Genet.* 15 (8): 541–555.

81 Gbian, D.L. and Omri, A. (2021). Current and novel therapeutic strategies for the management of cystic fibrosis. *Expert Opin. Drug Deliv.* 18 (5): 535–552.

82 Tagalakis, A.D., McAnulty, R.J., Devaney, J. et al. (2008). A receptor-targeted nanocomplex vector system optimized for respiratory gene transfer. *Mol. Ther.* 16 (5): 907–915.

83 Manunta, M.D.I., McAnulty, R.J., Tagalakis, A.D. et al. (2011). Nebulisation of receptor-targeted nanocomplexes for gene delivery to the airway epithelium. *PloS One* 6 (10): e26768.

84 Manunta, M.D.I., Tagalakis, A.D., Attwood, M. et al. (2017). Delivery of enac sirna to epithelial cells mediated by a targeted nanocomplex: A therapeutic strategy for cystic fibrosis. *Sci. Rep.* 7 (1): 1–12.

85 Guan, S., Munder, A., Hedtfeld, S. et al. (2019). Self-assembled peptide-poloxamine nanoparticles enable in vitro and in vivo genome restoration for cystic fibrosis. *Nat. Nanotechnol.* 14 (3): 287–297.

86 Almeida, M., Magalhães, M., Veiga, F., and Figueiras, A. (2018). Poloxamers, poloxamines and polymeric micelles: Definition, structure and therapeutic applications in cancer. *J. Polym Res.* 25 (1): 1–14.

87 Chandler, C., Liu, T., Buckanovich, R., and Coffman, L.G. (2019). The double edge sword of fibrosis in cancer. *Transl. Res.* 209: 55–67.

21

Self-assembly of Peptides and Chromophores for Design of Theranostic Nanodrugs and Cancer Precision Therapy

Rui Chang[1], *Ruirui Xing*[1,2], *and Xuehai Yan*[1,2,3]

[1] *State Key Laboratory of Biochemical Engineering, Institute of Process Engineering, Chinese Academy of Sciences, Beijing 100190, P. R. China*
[2] *School of Chemical Engineering, University of Chinese Academy of Sciences, Beijing 100049, P. R. China*
[3] *Center for Mesoscience, Institute of Process Engineering, Chinese Academy of Sciences, Beijing 100190, P. R. China*

21.1 Introduction

Self-assembly is crucial in the formation of complex structures and the realization of complex functions of biological systems [1, 2]. It involves the spontaneous formation of ordered structures using basic structural units and weak intermolecular interactions, such as electrostatic interaction, hydrogen bond interaction, hydrophobic interaction, and van der Waals interaction [3, 4]. Inspired by biological systems, self-assembly strategies have been used to construct biomedical materials, especially for cancer therapy [5, 6]. Because of the heterogeneity of tumors and the characteristics of easy recurrence and metastasis, precise cancer therapy is needed to achieve the best treatment effect [7, 8]. As a means of tumor treatment, phototherapy uses phototherapeutic drugs or light-absorbing chromophores delivered to the tumor site to kill the tumor tissue through photophysical and chemical reactions that occur only when laser light is applied, making phototherapy highly effective and accurate [9, 10]. Self-assembled phototherapy nanodrugs have brought cancer therapy closer to clinical application [11, 12]. However, controlling the self-assembly of light-absorbing chromophores to achieve efficient photophysical and chemical reactions is crucial in this process.

Peptides, widely existing natural compounds composed of amino acids, are an ideal motif for regulating the self-assembly of light-absorbing chromophores to construct supramolecular nanodrugs for precise cancer therapy [13, 14]. The noncovalent intermolecular interactions in the self-assembly process can be easily regulated by designing the peptide molecular structure, increasing the flexibility and diversity of regulation [15, 16]. The supramolecular nanodrugs obtained by the

Peptide Self-Assembly and Engineering: Fundamentals, Structures, and Applications, First Edition.
Edited by Xuehai Yan.

self-assembly process of the light-absorbing chromophore regulated by the peptide have improved structural stability and tumor targeting compared with the light-absorbing chromophore alone [17, 18]. Peptides also have various biological activities, such as enzyme responsiveness, targeting, and immunomodulatory, making them useful as building blocks from biological sources [19, 20]. Therefore, peptides are the ideal motif for regulating the self-assembly of light-absorbing chromophores to construct supramolecular nanodrugs for precise cancer therapy.

This chapter focuses on the self-assembly of peptides and chromophores, including designing theranostic nanodrugs for cancer precision therapy. The molecular design principles followed by peptides and how to self-assemble to prepare theranostic nanodrugs are crucial. Individual phototherapy and other therapies combined with phototherapy are mainly introduced in the application of cancer precision therapy. This chapter provides a comprehensive overview of the self-assembly of peptides and chromophores to design theranostic nanodrugs.

21.2 Molecular Design Principles for Peptides and Chromophores

Peptides and chromophores play distinct roles in cancer therapy, necessitating different design principles. Rational selection and design of these building units can create supramolecular nanodrugs with controlled morphology and properties.

21.2.1 Design Principles of Chromophore

The chromophore molecule follows the Jablonsky diagram (Figure 21.1), with various photophysical and photochemical reactions occurring after photon absorption, such as energy conversion to heat, luminescence, chemical energy, and chemical reactions [21]. The specific process is that when the chromophore molecules capture photons, the electrons of the chromophore molecules are excited from the ground state to the excited state. The chromophore molecules in the excited state are unstable and will release energy back to the ground state through three main processes: emission of photons (fluorescence), nonradiative relaxation (thermal

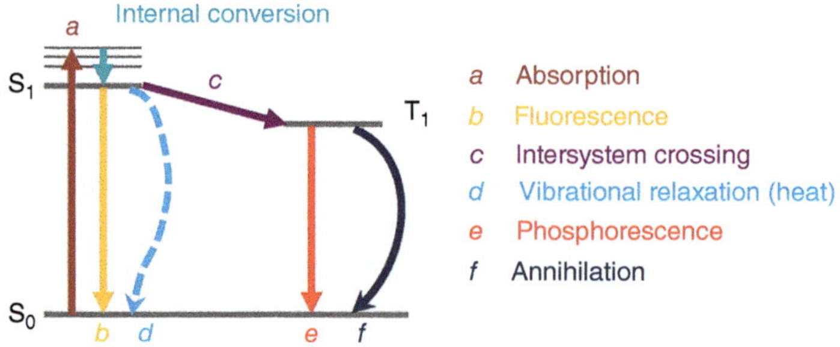

Figure 21.1 Schematic of a Jablonski diagram. Source: Reproduced with permission from Ref. [21]; © 2019, Wiley-VCH Verlag GmbH.

energy), and intersystem crossing (phosphorescent emission and triplet–triplet interaction). Targeted selection and rational design of chromophore molecules based on their reaction upon photon absorption can result in effective tumor treatment. For example, protoporphyrin can be selected as a model molecule for photodynamic therapy (PDT) because it can capture photons and release energy in the path of producing singlet oxygen, which can treat tumors with a photodynamic effect [22]. The biliverdin molecule will capture photons and generate heat energy by nonradiative relaxation, and treat tumors with a photothermal effect, which can be used as a model molecule for photothermal treatment [23].

21.2.2 Design Principles of Peptide

Peptides are commonly used self-assembly units but may also have therapeutic functions, with two categories: bioactive peptides and nonbioactive peptides [24]. Biologically active peptides can be classified based on their activities, such as targeted peptides, immunomodulatory peptides, antigenic peptides, and stimulus-responsive peptides (stimulated by pH or enzymes) [25]. The peptide-based supramolecular assemblies derived from the rational selection and design of active peptide sequences can also have the functions of active peptides [19]. For nonbiologically active peptides, as the interactions of peptides are diverse, in particular the repulsive or attractive electrostatic interactions, directional hydrogen bond interactions, and hydrophobic and van der Waals interactions, peptide sequences can be designed to flexibly regulate the interactions of peptides, which is mainly reflected in the peptide assembly process [26].

However, most chromophores and peptide molecules also have solubility problems, are easy to be degraded by light or enzyme, have short circulation time *in vivo*, are off-target, and decrease efficiency, which limit their further application in tumor therapy [27]. The use of chromophore and peptide molecular self-assembly to form supramolecular nanodrugs has partly solved the challenges of solubility, light/enzyme degradation, short circulation time, and off-target effects. This approach has expanded the application of chromophores and peptides in antitumor therapy through enhanced structural stability and functional integration [28].

21.3 Chromophore and Peptide Self-assembled Theranostic Nanodrugs

Chromophore and peptide self-assembly can integrate their functions, making it an advantageous platform for tumor diagnosis and therapy [16]. Peptides and chromophores are highly versatile in molecular composition and can be combined by covalent and noncovalent bonds. Precisely designed molecular structures and self-assembled peptides possess a variety of unique physical properties and novel functions [13]. This section summarizes the noncovalent self-assembly of peptides and chromophores as well as the self-assembly of peptide–chromophore conjugates.

21.3.1 Noncovalent Assembly of Chromophores and Peptides

The noncovalent combination of chromophores and peptides provides maximum flexibility for each assembly unit in the formation of supramolecular theranostic nanodrugs [15]. The resulting supramolecular theranostic nanodrugs may exhibit different nanostructures, morphology, and properties, which depend on the physical and chemical properties of the two components. In addition, the peptide sequence, the noncovalent binding sites, and the molar ratio between the building blocks can also be used as important factors to regulate the physical and chemical properties of the co-assembled nanodrug structures.

Short peptides with a simple structure containing several residues can be effectively co-assembled with chromophores to form controllable nanomaterials. In the co-assembled nanosystems, the peptide and the chromophore are both building blocks and are combined by noncovalent interactions. Such noncovalent interactions render extremely flexible designs and result in various nanostructures with well-defined morphologies and unique properties. As a typical example, the co-assembly of oppositely charged chlorin e6 (Ce6) and a diphenylalanine derivative (CDP, H-Phe-Phe-NH_2·HCl) leads to a well-defined and uniform spherical structure with diameters of about 200 nm (Figure 21.2a) [29]. Interestingly, the

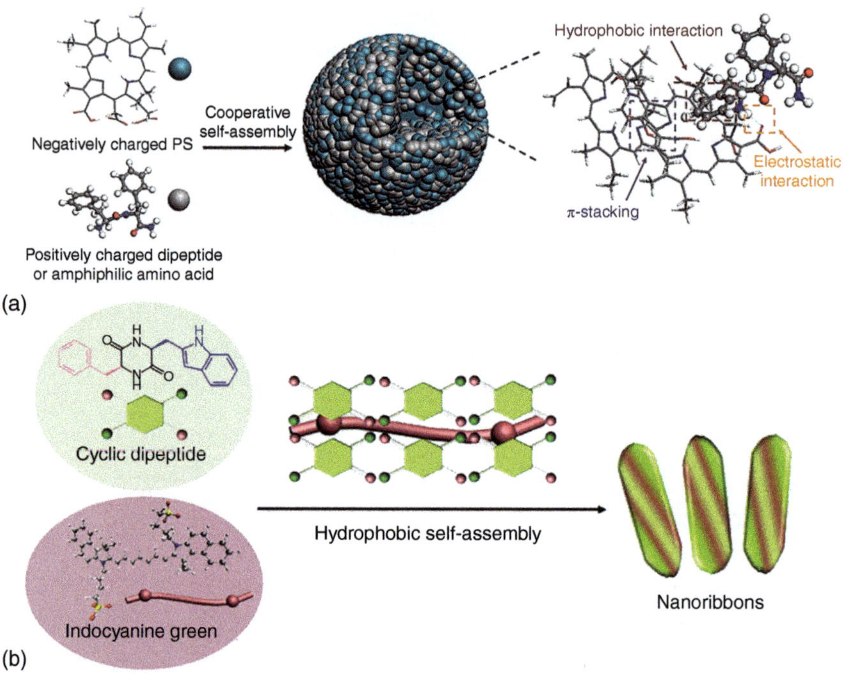

Figure 21.2 (a) Schematic diagram of the preparation of nanoparticles by co-assembly of short peptides and chromophores. Source: Reproduced with permission from Ref. [29]; © 2016, Wiley-VCH Verlag GmbH. (b) Schematic diagram of the preparation of nanoribbons by co-assembly of cyclopeptide and ICG. Source: Reproduced with permission from Ref. [30]; © 2019, Elsevier.

nanoparticle size can be facilely altered by changing the ratio of Ce6 and CDP. Besides, the nanoparticle structures are also affected by pH, surfactant, and even enzymes. The nanoparticles are localized in the cytoplasm and have effective phototoxic killing effects. Of course, in addition to being assembled with Ce6 to form nanospheres, CDP can also be co-assembled with verteporfin, protoporphyrin IX (PPIX), nickel (II) phthalocyanine-tetra sulfonic acid tetrasodium salt (NiPcS), or TPPS to form nanospheres. Similarly, Bai et al. used the short peptide fluorenylmethoxycarbonyl-leucine-leucine-leucine-Ome (Fmoc-L_3-OMe) and the porphyrin derivative meso-tetra(p-hydroxyphenyl) porphine (m-THPP) to co-assemble with a one-step co-assembly method to obtain an enhanced two-photon absorption capacity nanoparticle for cancer photodynamic therapy [31]. Following the above, it is easy to conclude that the molar ratio between the chromophore and the peptide has a vital impact on the morphology and photophysics of the assemblies.

Inspired by the fact that metalloprotein in the organism realizes its function in a self-organized form through three substances including polypeptides, metal ions, and pigments, Yan and coworkers utilize short peptides, photosensitizers, and metal ions to construct a multicomponent coordination assembly, which improved blood circulation and targeted burst release during cancer treatment [32]. Since metal coordination belongs to a kind of chemical bond with directivity and reversibility, its strength is stronger than noncovalent interaction and weaker than most covalent bonds. Therefore, the assemblies formed by metal coordination have special properties that the assemblies formed by nonmetal coordination do not possess.

In addition to linear peptides, cyclic dipeptides, as the smallest naturally occurring cyclic peptides, are also very important in the nanosystem due to their outstanding properties such as structural rigidity and excellent hydrogen bond-forming ability. Yan et al. reported that the cyclic dipeptide cyclo (Phe-Trp) (CFW) and the amphiphilic dye indocyanine green (ICG) jointly assembled to form a nanobelt-like assembly (Figure 21.2b) [30]. The morphology of the assembly can be flexibly changed by increasing the concentration of ICG. The strong hydrophobic interaction and electrostatic repulsion in the assemblies make them stable. The chromophore allows the nanobelt to have an adjustable shape and size under the action of ultrasound, which leads to enhanced chemotherapy efficacy.

21.3.2 Self-assembly of Molecular Peptide–Chromophore Conjugates

Peptide–chromophore conjugates, obtained by covalent interaction conjugation, are another type of building block designed for their clear components and proportions, simple structure, and easy synthesis [16, 33]. Moreover, chromophore–peptide conjugates can be divided into directly connected conjugates and conjugates with connecting groups, which can assemble into supramolecular theranostic nanodrugs.

21.3.2.1 Directly Connected Peptide–Chromophore Conjugates

Mono-L-aspartyl dihydroporphyrin (NPe6), one of the simplest peptide–chromophore molecules (Figure 21.3a), is used as a photodynamic drug for PDT in

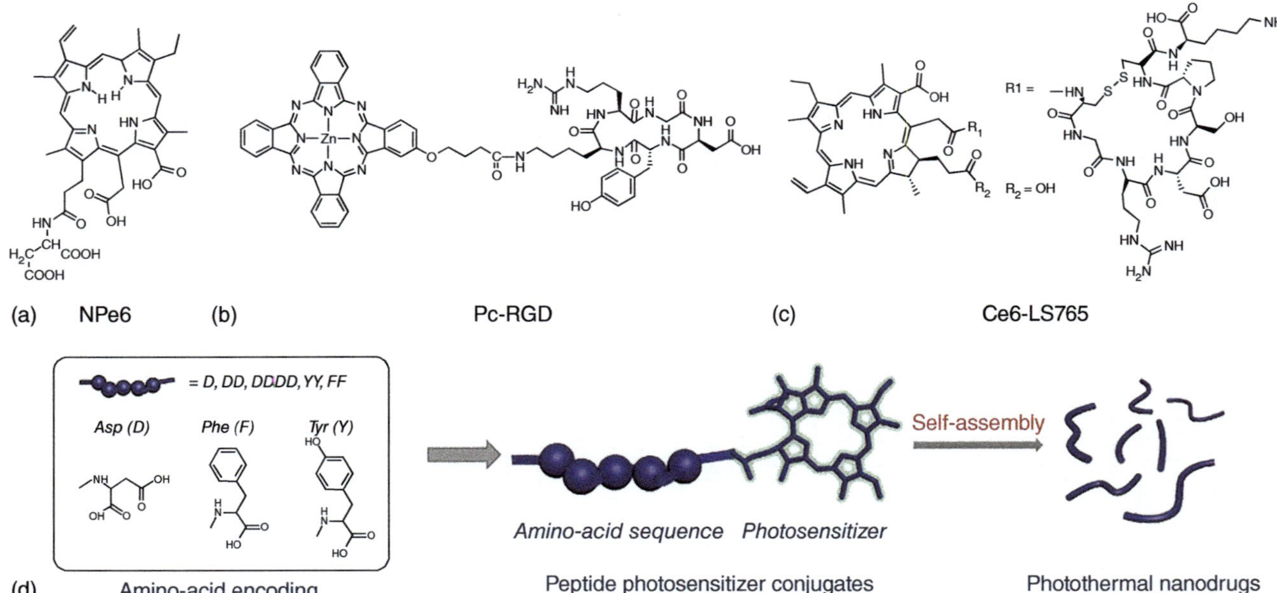

Figure 21.3 The molecular structure of directly connected peptide–chromophore conjugates: (a) NPe6, (b) Pc–RGD, and (c) Ce6–LS765. (d) A series of conjugates through amino-acid coding peptide sequence and their self-assembly to prepare nanodrugs. Source: Reproduced with permission from Ref. [34]; © 2022, Wiley-VCH Verlag GmbH.

mice [35]. Experimental results show that NPe6 can effectively target the tumor and selectively degrade the tumor tissue after irradiation. At the dose of NPe6 as low as 8 $mg\,kg^{-1}$, a 100% cure rate can be achieved. Animals exposed to NPe6 (10 $mg\,kg^{-1}$) and 100–1000 $J\,cm^{-2}$ of light show no harmful side effects, while animals exposed to hematoporphyrin derivative (HpD) suffer adverse skin reactions, such as blistering, followed by skin decay and necrosis. A molecule obtained by simple modification can significantly reduce its phototoxicity. In addition, peptides are directly conjugated to chromophore molecules to obtain conjugates, which can significantly improve the solubility of the chromophore and provide special biological functions such as targeting and therapeutic. For example, cyclic RGD (RGDyK) and phthalocyanine (Pc) are used to obtain Pc–RGD conjugates (Figure 21.3b), which improve the targeting of a chromophore in use [36]. To enhance the targeting of lysosomes, another study reported that LS765 was conjugated with photosensitive chlorin e6 (Ce6) to obtain the peptide–chromophore conjugate (Ce6–LS765, Figure 21.3c) [37]. However, the researchers did not study the self-assembly process of peptide–chromophore conjugates in the above work, which may be limited by the research conditions at that time, and the importance of self-assembly was ignored. In recent years, it has been found that these directly linked peptide–chromophore conjugates self-assembled supramolecular drugs also play an important role in tumor diagnosis and therapy. For example, Yan et al. synthesized a series of conjugates through an amino-acid coding peptide sequence and obtained supramolecular nanodrugs with controllable structure, energy conversion, and therapeutic properties by regulating the self-assembly process (Figure 21.3d) [34].

During the assembly process, the photophysical behavior of the supramolecular assemblies may change greatly with the assembly conditions due to the interaction between the building elements and the surrounding environment. Yan et al. studied the phthalocyanine–diphenylalanine conjugate, which underwent a path-dependent self-assembly process [38]. In less than one second, the assembly unit precipitated rapidly to produce normal nanoparticles with the same absorption maximum as the monomer. By extending the assembly time to several days and adding dimethyl sulfoxide to increase the solubility of the conjugate, the helical nanofibers with an absorption redshift of more than 100 nm were assembled. The change of nanostructure and absorption spectrum is related to the thermodynamically stable supramolecular J-aggregation and dynamic assembly process of phthalocyanine, enabling the conjugate to obtain a stable supramolecular structure.

21.3.2.2 Peptide–Chromophore Conjugates with Connecting Group

Because chromophore and peptide have their functions, to make the newly formed peptide–chromophore conjugate better retain the functions of the two parts and add some new functions, connectors are often added. The commonly used connecting groups are the alkyl chain and polyethene glycol (PEG). For example, the photosensitizer (5-(4-carboxyphenyl)-10,15,20-triphenyl dihydroporphyrin, TPC) was connected to the VEGF receptor-specific heptapeptide (ATWLPPR) through alkyl chain (6-aminocaproic acid, Ahx) to obtain the molecule TPC-Ahx-ATWLPPR [39]. Compared with TPC, TPC-Ahx-ATWLPPR had slightly lower cytotoxicity in the dark and showed enhanced photodynamic activity *in vitro*. However, the assembly structure of the conjugate was not given when it was administered. In addition, the conjugates connected by the alkyl chain can be used as near-infrared fluorescence probes for imaging *in vivo*. Nagano et al. used the near-infrared fluorescence chromophore Cy5 to connect with NIR dark quenching agent BHQ-3 through enzyme response substrate peptide (including PLGLAG sequence) to obtain a conjugate (Cy5-MMP) [40]. The molecule was rapidly internalized through free diffusion and remained in the cell after being activated by extracellular matrix enzyme. Using the fluorophore as the Förster resonance energy transfer (FRET) donor and the dark quencher peptide as the FRET receptor, the molecule can provide a continuous fluorescence signal with a very high signal-to-noise ratio after binding with the peptide substrate enzyme *in vivo*. PEG connecting group is also widely used because its advantages are its high solubility in water and most organic solvents, large hydrodynamic volume, and relatively inert interaction with biomolecules. For example, an antigenic peptide sequence (KVPRNQDWL) that specifically binds to melanoma was linked with the photosensitizer protoporphyrin IX (PpIX) through chemical reaction to form a new conjugate molecule (PpIX-PEG_8-KVPRNQDWL) [41]. This molecule retained the respective functions of photosensitizer and peptide and was used for PDT amplification immunotherapy for malignant melanoma. Similarly, PpIX-PEG_8-RDEVDG-K(TPE)-V-$CONH_2$ conjugate was used for the PDT of caspase-3 enzyme response *in vivo* [42]. However, the above research work has not given whether there is *in situ* self-assembly of the conjugates after they are activated by enzymes *in vivo*, nor has it been studied on their effects on fluorescence imaging and immunotherapy.

The molecular structure of the conjugate affects the obtained supramolecular assemblies by influencing the weak intermolecular interaction during the assembly process. Specifically, Yan and coworkers chose to indirectly link porphyrins and phenylalanine dipeptides using the chemical reaction of glutaric anhydride with the two, synthesizing a porphyrin–phenylalanine dipeptide conjugate (TPP-G-FF, Figure 21.4). The conjugates self-assemble into nanodots, and it was found that the self-assembly property of porphyrin in the conjugate induced the formation of J aggregates and served as the substructure of the nanodots [43]. Thus, nanodots that completely inhibit the fluorescence emission and the production of singlet oxygen can be prepared to achieve a high photothermal conversion efficiency of nanodots. The peptide segments in the conjugates provide not only water supply stability for nanodots through hydrophilic interaction but also a space barrier between porphyrin groups and inhibit the further growth of nanodots through strong π-stacking interaction.

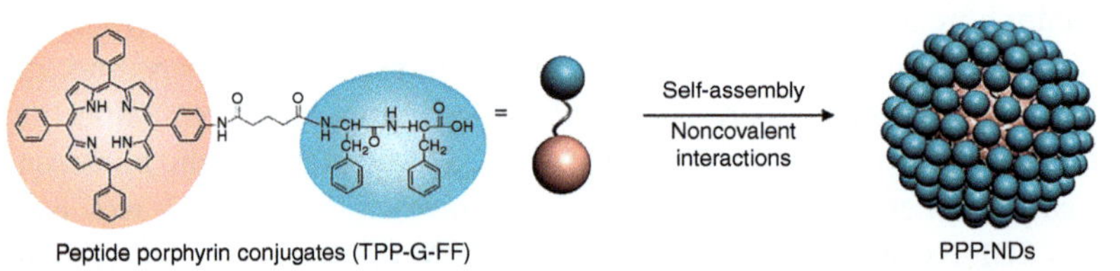

Figure 21.4 Schematic diagram of the nanodots formation by self-assembly of TPP-G-FF. Source: Reproduced with permission from Ref. [43]; © 2017 American Chemical Society.

21.4 Applications for Cancer Precision Therapy

The flexible design of peptide and chromophore self-assembly has great potential in the precise therapy of cancer [20]. Supramolecular assemblies also play an important role in different cancer therapies, such as phototherapy alone and phototherapy combined with other therapies [27].

21.4.1 Phototherapy

Phototherapy is divided into photothermal therapy and photodynamic therapy due to the different ways of energy conversion by phototherapy drugs. Compared with traditional tumor therapy, it has several advantages, such as minimal invasion, convenient operation, rapid recovery, and strong specificity [44]. Generally, phototherapy is carried out through two continuous processes: the first is to transport the phototherapy agent to the lesion area as much as possible, and the second is to irradiate the lesion area with specific light to stimulate the laser therapy agent. The light energy conversion of phototherapeutic agents depends on the intrinsic photophysical behavior and assembly state of chromophores [38]. Therefore, regulating the self-assembly of peptides and chromophores is helpful in controlling the therapeutic properties of phototherapy drugs.

21.4.1.1 Photodynamic Therapy

Photodynamic therapy is a process in which photodynamic drugs absorb photons to the excited state under laser irradiation and generate singlet oxygen from an unstable excited state to release energy and return to the ground state through the intersystem crossing [21]. This process can damage the lesion site with singlet oxygen. In recent years, many studies have made progress in photodynamic antitumor therapy by regulating the self-assembly process of peptides and chromophores to obtain controllable supramolecular nanodrugs [13].

The efficacy of anti-tumor therapy is affected by the size, loading rate, and drug release *in vivo* of self-assembled nanodrugs. Based on this, Yan et al. designed a simple self-assembled nanodrug by selecting cationic diphenylalanine (H-Phe-Phe-NH_2·HCl, CDP) and chromophore chlorin e6 (Ce6) as building blocks [29]. By changing the ratio of the two building elements, the size of nanoparticles and drug-loading rate can be adjusted. Due to their weak intermolecular interaction, nanodrugs exhibit responsive disassembly to pH, surfactants, or enzymes. In addition, the size advantage of nanodrugs also brings excellent cell uptake and biological distribution. Finally, these properties of nanodrugs enhance the antitumor effect of PDT. In addition to this kind of supramolecular nanodrug co-assembled by peptide and chromophore, Xu et al. reported the PDT of tumor initiated by self-assembled nanodots based on pentalysine–phthalocyanine conjugate [45]. The nanoparticles have an inner phthalocyanine hydrophobic shell and a positively charged polypeptide shell exposed on the surface. This inhibits the fluorescence of phthalocyanine molecules and the generation of reactive oxygen species, reducing the photobleaching and targeting effects of photosensitive chromophore molecules in the circulating system. The polypeptide shell of nanoparticles targets the negatively charged

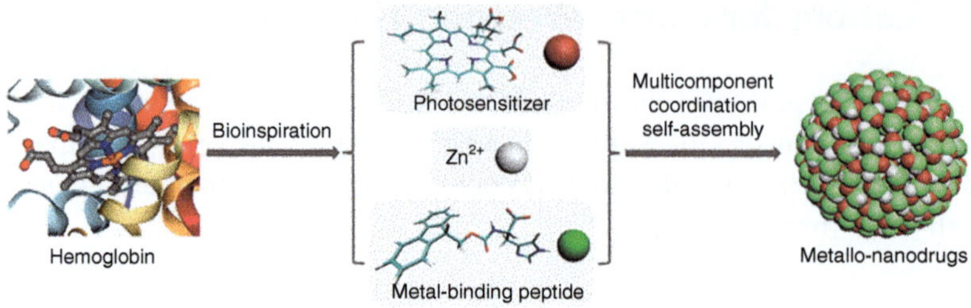

Figure 21.5 Schematic diagram of multicomponent coordination self-assembled metal nanodrug formation. Source: Reproduced with permission from Ref. [32]; © 2018 American Chemical Society.

surface of tumor cells through electrostatic attraction. After contact with tumor cells, the nanodrug was disassembled to obtain the conjugated molecules, showing fluorescence and photodynamic effects.

Some responsive and biomimetic intelligent photodynamic nanodrugs have been designed. For example, inspired by metalloproteins, Yan et al. selected short peptides, photosensitizers, and metal ions to build metal nanodrugs with multicomponent coordination self-assembly (Figure 21.5) [32]. Similarly, inspired by the dynamic changes of molecular assembly morphology in biology, Hest et al. [46], Han et al. [47], and Zhang et al. [48] prepared pH-responsive and morphology-transformable nanomaterials. Another important factor in photodynamic therapy is oxygen, which produces reactive oxygen species that are harmful to cells. Unfortunately, the tumor microenvironment is usually hypoxic, which limits the effect of photodynamic therapy. To solve this problem, Lo et al. designed and developed a catalase-like Fe^{3+}-driven chromophore and amino-acid assembly enzyme with oxygen self-supply capability [49].

As a slow-release system, supramolecular hydrogel also plays a unique role in cancer PDT [50]. Many studies have shown that the hydrogel structure is highly suitable for the treatment of superficial tumors, and it can be locally injected and continuously administered [51, 52]. It was reported that Ce6 was loaded in the hydrogel formed by poly-L-lysine (PLL) and N-fluorenyl methoxycarbonyl diphenylalanine (Fmoc-FF) to obtain assemblies for PDT of a tumor. Due to its excellent rheological properties, such as shear thinning and self-healing, as well as good biocompatibility, the hydrogel can be injected for treatment [53]. In addition, Yan et al. designed a prodrug system, which was prepared from a synthetic bola-dipeptide and the clinically used water-soluble prodrug molecule 5-ALA (Figure 21.6a) [22]. Transmission electron microscopy (TEM) and atomic force microscopy (AFM) results showed that the cross-linked nanofibers were converted into short nanofibers in the presence of glutathione (GSH) due to the presence of disulfide bonds in the hydrogel (Figure 21.6b,c). The prodrug system continuously converted to PpIX after injection at the tumor site and achieved the highest conversion within 6 h, which was selected as the best treatment time point. Finally, because the hydrogel was responsive to trypsin, it can be gradually degraded and metabolized, ensuring biodegradability.

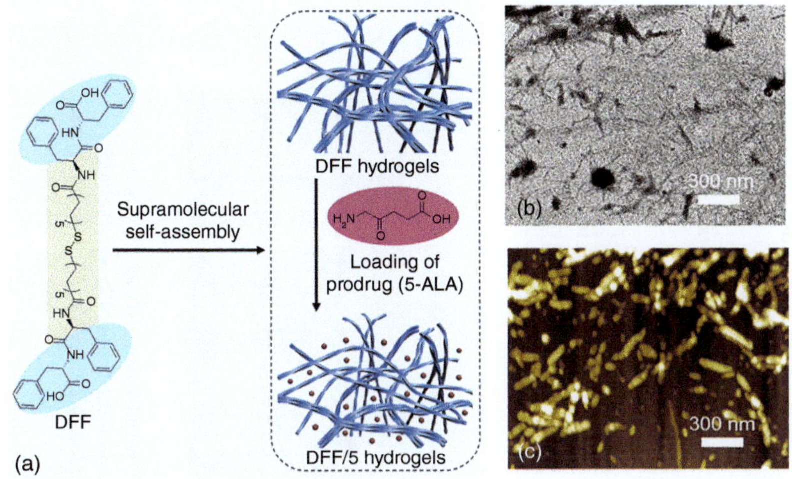

Figure 21.6 (a) Schematic diagram of the formation of the prodrug system. (b) TEM and (c) AFM images of the short nanofibers. Schematic diagram of the preparation of nanoribbons by co-assembly of cyclopeptide and ICG. Source: Reproduced with permission from Ref. [22]; © 2020, Elsevier.

21.4.1.2 Photothermal Therapy (PTT)

PTT is a process in which the photothermal agent reaches the excited state after being irradiated by a specific laser and releases energy in the form of heat when it returns to the ground state, which is helpful to ablate the tumor [13]. Therefore, the goal of effective photothermal therapy is to adjust the chromophore organization mode to promote energy release by heat. However, current nanophotothermal agents have unclear physiological and metabolic mechanisms, which limits their further translation into clinical applications. To address this issue, biliverdin (BV), an endogenous near-infrared absorption chromophore with a clear metabolic pathway in the body, was developed as a photothermal nanoagent [17]. In particular, inspired by the light absorption of hemoglobin, Yan et al. designed and prepared bionic photothermal nanoparticles by selecting BV and Z-Histidine-Obzl (ZHO) as the assembly units [23]. More interestingly, nanoparticles (ZBMn NPs) could also be obtained by co-assembling Mn^{2+} with BV and ZHO, which further improved the stability of nanoparticles and introduced magnetic resonance imaging capabilities (Figure 21.7a). In addition, compared with BV molecules, the absorption spectrum of nanoparticles was broadened to a longer NIR region (Figure 21.7b) due to aggregation, which promoted stability after laser irradiation (Figure 21.7c). Under the guidance of photoacoustic imaging and magnetic resonance imaging of nanoparticles, it was proved that nanoparticles had an effective photothermal therapeutic effect in mice (Figure 21.7d). The nanoparticles obtained in this work use building blocks with clear metabolic mechanism and clinical imaging ability, providing greater hope for further clinical transformation. Peptide-based self-assembled photothermal nanoparticles still face the problem of insufficient penetration caused by short-wavelength absorption. Nanomaterials with near-infrared absorption have a promising future.

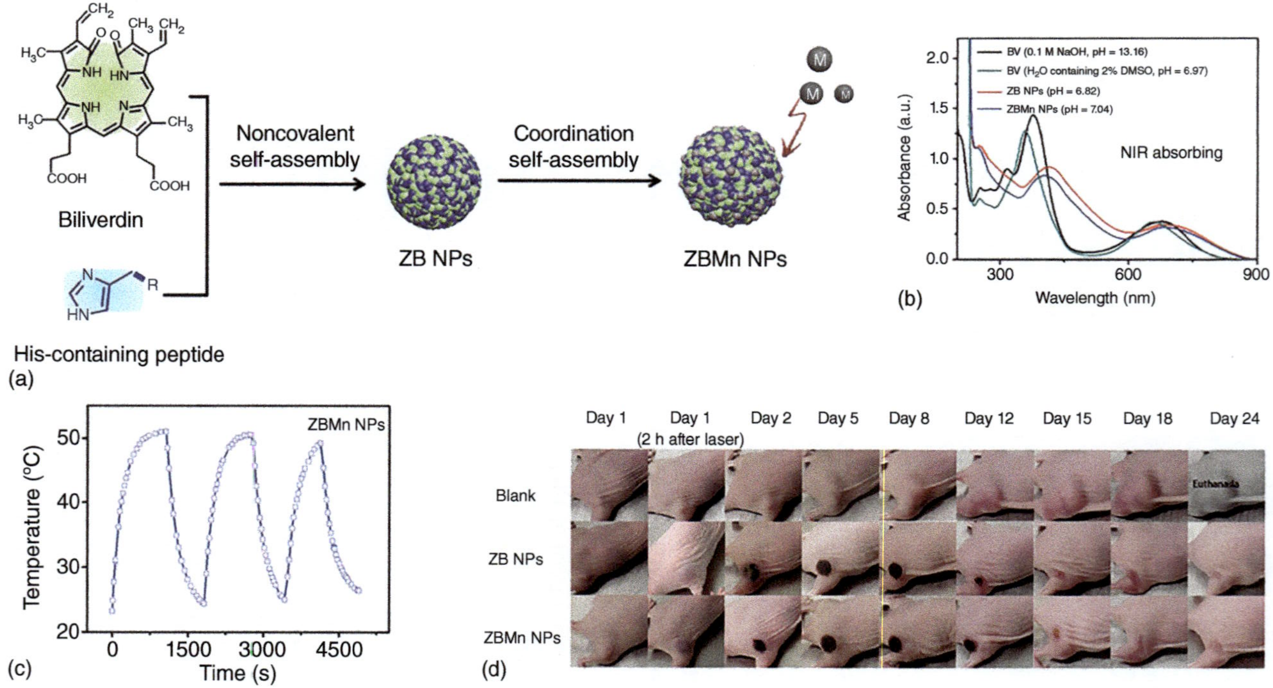

Figure 21.7 (a) Schematic diagram of the preparation of ZBMn NPs by co-assembly of Mn^{2+} with BV and ZHO. (b) UV–vis absorption spectra of different substances. (c) Temperature rise and fall curve of ZBMn NP after three times of laser irradiation. (d) Images of the tumors in different groups. Source: Reproduced with permission from Ref. [23]; © 2019, Wiley-VCH Verlag GmbH.

Similarly, the self-assembly of peptide and chromophore conjugates is also an effective means to prepare photothermal antitumor nanodrugs. For example, Yan et al. linked phenylalanine dipeptide (FF) and porphyrin through glutaric anhydride to obtain a conjugate, which self-assembled in water to form nanodots with strong structural stability and high photothermal conversion efficiency [43]. In addition, to obtain supramolecular nanodrugs with controllable phototherapeutic properties, they synthesized five peptide–chromophore conjugates based on hydrophobic phenylalanine (F), aspartic acid (D), and tyrosine (Y), which can provide hydrophilic and anisotropic hydrogen bond interactions [34]. The experimental results showed that through the design of peptide sequence, the preparation of nanodrugs with controllable assembly structure, energy conversion, and phototherapy performance had been realized.

To solve the drug accumulation problem of PTT in tumor sites, Wang et al. proposed a self-assembly strategy *in vivo*. For example, a near-infrared laser was used to drive the self-assembly *in situ* of the conjugate, wherein the conjugate included a thermal response skeleton polymer (β-Thioester), cytotoxic peptide CGGG $(KLAKLAK)_2$ (KLAK), cell-penetrating peptide CYGRKKRRQRRR (TAT), and ICG [54]. The conjugate first entered the tumors in a molecular state, and then the temperature rose after the near-infrared laser irradiation of the tumor sites, thus triggering the *in situ* self-assembly of the conjugate in the tumors to form nanoparticles. Finally, nanoparticles were effectively internalized into tumor cells and induced cell apoptosis by destroying the mitochondrial membrane. This method has promoted the accumulation of drugs in tumor sites to some extent, but it is impossible to determine the efficiency of *in situ* self-assembly and when to give laser irradiation to ensure the maximum *in situ* self-assembly of conjugated molecules. In addition, self-assembled peptides (ELP) were also used to connect with indocyanine green dye (IR820) through chemical bonds to obtain conjugates [55]. Furthermore, the conjugate was added to the $ZnCl_2$ solution to self-assemble into nanoparticles. This was since the histidine residues contained in ELP could chelate with Zn^{2+} and promote the aggregation of ELP into nanoparticles. Experiments showed that nanoparticles had enhanced drug accumulation in tumors and photothermal effect *in vivo*.

21.4.2 Chemotherapy Combined Phototherapy

Chemotherapy is one of the most effective cancer treatments in clinical use, where chemical drugs are used to kill tumor cells [56]. However, this method has effects on all human cells, which will bring a variety of adverse reactions and side effects to normal cells. To address this, supramolecular nanodrugs self-assembled by peptides and chromophores have been designed and developed as carriers of chemotherapeutic drugs. This has led to a new cancer treatment model, the combination of chemotherapy and phototherapy. Moreover, some peptides and chromophore self-assembled nanodrugs can also achieve the combination of chemotherapy and phototherapy for cancer therapy, given the tumor treatment activity of peptides themselves.

To some extent, this tumor therapy mode incubates certain nanodrug properties of chemotherapy drugs, significantly improving the efficacy and safety of tumor therapy. Kim et al. linked the photodynamic drug Ce6 and the anticancer drug monomethyl auristatin E (MMAE) through an enzyme-responsive peptide sequence (DEVD) to obtain a new conjugate molecule. The nanoparticles formed by self-assembly of these molecules have a diameter of approximately 90 nm, which underwent a cascade reaction *in vivo* [57]. Firstly, the activation of caspase 3 *in vivo* was achieved based on apoptosis of cancer cells triggered by low energy irradiation, thus releasing MMAE from the nanoparticles. Then, the released drug MMAE exerted its chemotherapeutic and anticancer properties without laser irradiation. This work proposed a new therapy of chemotherapy combined with PDT, which overcame the problems of poor drug tissue permeability and rapid oxygen consumption compared with conventional PDT and chemotherapy. The focus of this combined therapy is to improve the accumulation of drugs in tumor tissue. However, the nanodrug platform based on active targeting and intracellular size conversion is rarely developed. Liao et al. designed a peptide and chromophore self-assembly nanoplatform to address this issue [58]. The nanoplatform was based on a hexadecapeptide modified with an indocyanine green derivative (ICGD), three cholic acids (CA), and a 4-carboxyl-3-fluorophenylboric acid (PBA), self-assembling into small nanoparticles with a positive charge and size of less than 30 nm. The small nanoparticles were then wrapped by hyaluronic acid (HA) modified with folic acid and dopamine to form large negatively charged nanoparticles with a size of about 130 nm. The resulting nanoparticles prolonged the blood circulation time, reduced the drug release rate, and effectively reduced drug leakage in advance. Under cell uptake mediated by folic acid, the charge and size of nanoparticles changed, promoting drug release. These nanoplatforms realized the synergy of chemotherapy and phototherapy, promoting the antitumor effect.

Doxorubicin (DOX), a model chemotherapeutic drug, is often loaded into supramolecular nanodrugs self-assembled by peptides and chromophores. For instance, Li et al. developed a liposome vesicle structural material with programmed stimulus response by incorporating photoresponsive pheophorbide a (PPa), heptapeptide spacer (GPLGLAG), PEG chain, and temperature-sensitive liposome (TSL) [59]. They loaded the lipophilic oxaliplatin prodrug with hexadecyl oxaliplatin carboxylic acid and hydrophilic doxorubicin hydrochloride to achieve thermally induced drug release under laser irradiation. Similarly, Lo et al. synthesized two peptide–chromophore molecules (Figure 21.8a) that self-assembled into nanoparticles (Figure 21.8b) by the weak interaction of their respective molecules to load DOX [60].

Recently, melittin has drawn significant attention for its antitumor effect similar to chemotherapeutic drugs [61]. However, its side effects, including hemolysis and nonspecific cytotoxicity, limit its clinical application. Researchers proposed that self-assembling peptides and chromophores into supramolecular nanodrugs might alleviate these serious side effects. Wu et al. obtained stable supramolecular nanomaterials by co-assembling melittin and Ce6 and coated the surface with hyaluronic acid to improve the tumor accumulation of drugs [62]. The experimental results showed that the introduction of chromophore Ce6 promoted the formation of

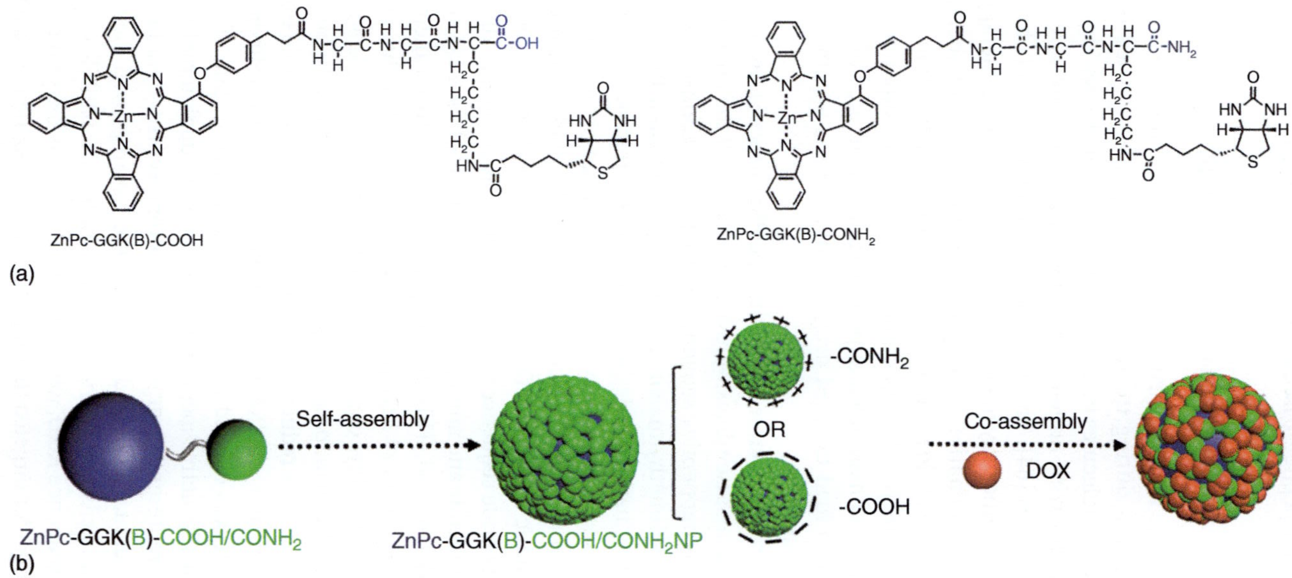

Figure 21.8 (a) The molecular structure of peptide–chromophore molecules. (b) Schematic diagram of the conjugates self-assembled into nanoparticles and their use for loading DOX. Source: Reproduced with permission from Ref. [60]; © 2020 American Chemical Society.

nanomaterials and reduced the hemolysis of melittin, attributed to the moderate hydrophilicity/hydrophobicity and negative charge of Ce6. This work realized the combination of melittin and PDT and improved the delivery efficiency of melittin, providing a new idea for peptide-based tumor therapy drugs.

21.4.3 Targeted Therapy Combined with Phototherapy

Targeted therapy refers to reducing drug use and accurately treating the lesion area by targeting specific sites during treatment [63]. In cancer-targeted therapy, the target is usually protein molecules in tumor tissue. With the deepening of research, some peptide sequences with targeted functions have also been screened out in addition to antibody drugs [64]. The self-assembly of peptides and chromophores has also contributed significantly to the combination of targeted therapy and phototherapy [27]. The combination of targeted therapy and phototherapy can be achieved by selecting a peptide sequence with a targeted function, designing it rationally, and self-assembling it with chromophore to form supramolecular nanodrugs. Furthermore, self-assembled supramolecular structures of peptides and chromophores can also load targeted drugs to enhance the accuracy of targeted drugs reaching tumor sites.

Tumor organelles are often targeted for therapeutic purposes. In one approach, peptide and chromophore assemblies were designed to target the nucleus. Han et al. used the nuclear targeting peptide sequence PKKKRKV to connect with protoporphyrin (PpIX) and 2,3-dimethylmaleic anhydride (DMA) via a PEG connector to create a self-assembling nanoparticle [65]. In the tumor microenvironment, DMA in the nanoparticle responds to acidity, causing its surface charge to change from negative to positive, promoting drug accumulation and reducing the toxic and side effects of photodynamic therapy (PDT). Similarly, Zhang et al. used the same nuclear positioning peptide sequence to connect with a hydrophobic alkyl chain for targeting the plasma membrane and PpIX through a hydrophilic PEG chain to create a self-assembling nanorod. This dual targeting of the plasma membrane and nucleus improved the efficacy of PDT [66]. By removing the PEG chain of the molecule and engineering the alkyl chain through exosomes, they were able to create nanovesicles with good biocompatibility and dual targeting ability of the plasma membrane and nucleus, thus reducing immunogenicity and systemic toxicity [67]. Another self-assembling nanoparticle was developed to target the mitochondria and plasma membranes. It was created by self-assembling a conjugate of PEG-linked PpIX and a biologically active peptide sequence with dual targeting function (rFxrFxrFxr, where r represents D-arginine, and Fx represents L-cyclohexylalanine) [68]. Although this dual-target drug delivery system has improved the therapeutic effect of drugs, it still needs improvement in terms of biocompatibility.

Targeting peptide sequence RGD, which specifically targets integrin receptors, is a common research target for targeted therapy. Wang et al. designed an RGD-modified purpurin 18 (P18) precursor molecule linked by an enzyme-responsive peptide sequence (PLGVRG), which self-assembled into nanofibers *in situ* of tumors, playing a targeted role in photothermal therapy (PTT) [69]. The introduction of this small-molecule targeted peptide enhanced the enrichment of drugs in tumor sites. Xu et al. used iRGD peptide (internalized RGD, CRGDKGPDC), hydrophilic Arg, hydrophobic alkyl chain, and Pro sequence to construct molecules that could self-assemble into nanovesicles [70]. They then loaded hypocrellin B (HB) into nanovesicles to achieve improved photosensitizer accumulation and PDT. Kim et al. obtained a monomer (Ppa-iRGDC-BK01) by linking pyrophoride-a (Ppa) and a quencher (BK01) with iRGD peptide [71]. This monomer promotes the completion of assembly through cascade reactions at the injection site: targeting, penetration, reactivation, and body heat. The result is supramolecular storage to realize the long-term release of drugs.

The targeted research on tumor vessels also shows potential at present [63]. In addition to vascular targeting antibody drugs, some tumor vascular targeting peptides have specific targeting effects on vascular endothelial growth factor and its receptor. Some researchers have tried to connect tumor vascular targeting peptides with chromophores and obtained peptide–chromophore conjugates for cancer therapy, which have been proven to play a certain role in anticancer therapy in experiments [39, 72, 73]. At present, there are few reports on the self-assembly of tumor vascular targeting peptides and chromophores. However, this will be a very attractive research field, especially the combination of this vascular targeted therapy mode and PTT. Since PTT can play its role without entering the tumor cells, it will greatly improve the drug utilization rate.

21.4.4 Immunotherapy Combined Phototherapy

Immunotherapy refers to a therapeutic method that artificially enhances or suppresses the immune function of the body to achieve the purpose of curing diseases. However, immunotherapy also has its problems, such as tumor heterogeneity, insufficient immunogenicity, low efficiency of antigen presentation, and insufficient targeting ability, which all reduce the effect of immunotherapy [74]. In recent years, research reports have found that phototherapy not only kills tumors but also stimulates the body to release immunogenic cell death-related antigens to further improve immunogenicity [20]. Therefore, researchers try to combine immunotherapy with phototherapy to improve the therapeutic effect of tumors. Peptide and chromophore self-assembled nanodrugs have been studied in this combined therapy because they can be used as carriers and have immune activity in some peptides.

Functional peptides such as immunomodulators or antigenic peptides and chromophore self-assembled nanodrugs promote the therapeutic effect of immunotherapy combined with phototherapy. Yan et al. prepared nanofibers (Figure 21.9a) using the co-assembly of clinically approved thymopentin TP5 (RKDVY) and chromophore indocyanine green (ICG) [75]. The formation of nanofibers was dominated by hydrogen bonding, which effectively avoided the oxidation of ICG olefins, so the nanofibers showed improved photostability. After the nanofibers were injected into the tumor sites, PTT was carried out, which effectively activated the cytotoxic T-lymphocyte-mediated immune responses (Figure 21.9b). The therapeutic results *in vivo* also showed that after photothermal immunotherapy, the main

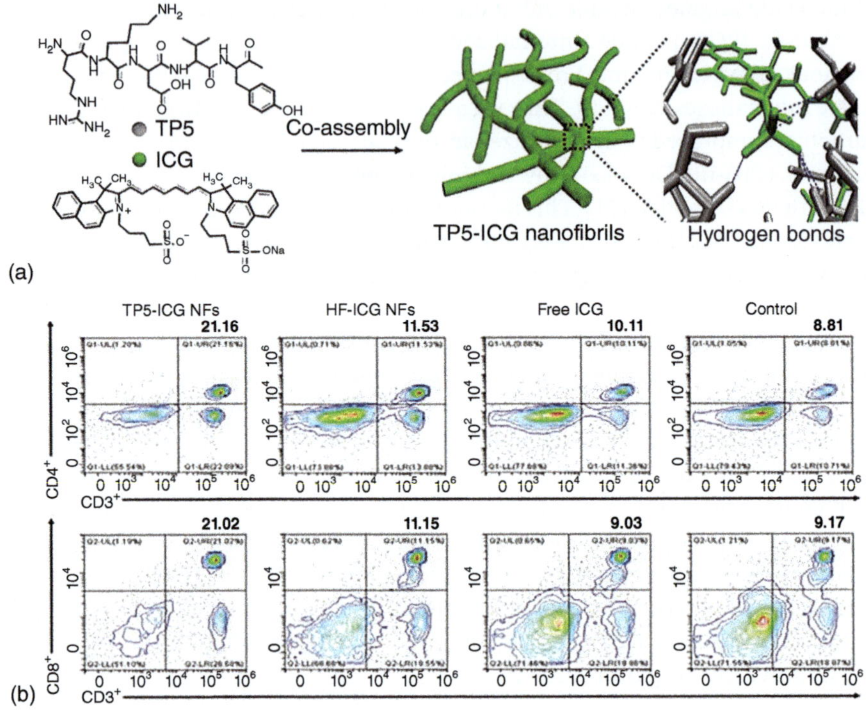

Figure 21.9 (a) Schematic diagram of the preparation of nanofibers by the co-assembly of thymopentin TP5 and ICG. (b) Frequencies of $CD3^{+}CD4^{+}$ and $CD3^{+}CD8^{+}$ T cells in different groups of mice obtained by flow cytometry. Source: Reproduced with permission from Ref. [75]; © 2021, Wiley-VCH Verlag GmbH.

pancreatic solid tumors *in situ* were ablated, and the activated immune response effectively inhibited tumor growth and metastasis. The work selected clinically approved immunoregulatory peptides and chromophore drugs, which provided a reference for promoting the development of photothermal immunotherapy drugs for further clinical transformation. Through design, the combination of immunotherapy and phototherapy can also be achieved by the self-assembly of antigenic peptides and chromophores to form nanoparticles. Li et al. designed a chimeric peptide, including melanin-specific antigen peptide (KVPRNQDWL), PEG chain, and PpIX, which can self-assemble into spherical nanoparticles [41]. First of all, under laser irradiation, the nanoparticles produced singlet oxygen to induce tumor cell necrosis or apoptosis. Then, under the stimulation of antigen peptide, specific cytotoxic T cells were activated to produce immune responses. In addition, PDT can also enhance immunogenicity and improve the efficiency of antigen cross-presentation. Therefore, the designed nanoparticles can inhibit the growth of melanoma under combined photodynamic immunotherapy.

The therapeutic method for blocking immune checkpoints has shown a very good effect on cancer therapy. However, some antibodies, such as PD-L1 antibodies, have low stability and cannot accurately control the drug load of the antibody. Based on this, Luan et al. selected an anti-PD-L1 peptide (APP, NYSKPTDRQYHF-NH_2) to replace the antibody and connected APP with chromophore IR780 through the peptide segment to obtain a new molecule (IR780-M-APP) [76]. Importantly, the molecule has a precise loading capacity (48.4 wt%) and the ability to self-assemble into nanoparticles. IR780 in nanoparticles completed PDT *in vivo* and caused immunogenic cell death (ICD), while APP blocked the PD-1/PD-L1 pathway, and finally realized the immunotherapy of photodynamic therapy synergy. This kind of assembly designed with peptide sequences that can block immune checkpoints provides a way to solve the problems of antibody instability and drug loading. With the help of computer simulation, it is the trend of future development to screen out the peptide sequence that plays a role in the antibody and then realize the replacement of the antibody with a peptide sequence through design. In addition, phototherapy and immunotherapy can be carried out separately. Zhang et al. selected a plasma membrane-targeted K-Ras-derived peptide (KKKKKSKTKC-OMe) to form a new molecule (PpIX-C_6-PEG_8-KKKKKSKTKC-OMe) with PEG chain, hydrophobic C_6 alkyl chain, and PpIX [77]. The self-assembled nanoparticles were driven by intracellular enzymes and fixed on the plasma membrane. Then, under laser irradiation, the nanoparticles produced toxicity to cells and destroyed the plasma membrane structure, further triggering ICD. Combined with anti-PD-1 immune checkpoint blocking immunotherapy, it showed high antitumor potential.

Functional peptides and chromophores can also be co-assembled with immune drugs to supramolecular assemblies. Indoleamine-2,3-dioxygenase (IDO) inhibition as an immune checkpoint-blocking therapy has great potential in cancer therapy. However, there are some problems in the clinical use of IDO inhibitors, such as limited bioavailability and insufficient intratumoral drug exposure. Ma et al. chose to solve this problem using PEG-based IDO inhibitors (IDOi, Epacadostat) and ICG to co-assemble into nanoparticles with core–shell nanostructures [78]. Because this structure contained an enzyme-responsive peptide sequence, when entering the tumor microenvironment, the size of the PEG layer of the core–shell structure stripped by the enzyme became smaller, thus increasing cell uptake. Under laser irradiation, the nanocore–shell converted light energy into heat, thereby ablating tumor cells with heat, further inducing the release of tumor-related antigens to trigger immune responses. The subsequent release of IDO inhibitors can further regulate the immune responses. *In vivo*, experimental results showed that this photothermal immunotherapy effectively inhibited the growth of irradiated tumors and distal tumors. In addition, Zhang et al. conjugated another IDO inhibitor 1-methyltryptophan (1MT) with the enzyme response peptide sequence DEVD and PpIX to obtain chimeric peptides, which further formed nanoparticles in PBS [79]. Nanoparticles produced reactive oxygen under laser irradiation to induce tumor cell death and then promoted the continuous release of 1MT under the action of enzymes released by tumor cells, thus inhibiting the IDO pathway to activate the immune response.

21.5 Conclusions

In summary, we have highlighted the latest research on the design of theranostic nanodrugs based on peptide and chromophore self-assembly and their application in precision cancer therapy. Our focus has been on the molecular design principles of peptides and chromophores and how they self-assemble, including noncovalent self-assembly and the self-assembly of peptide–chromophore conjugates. Self-assembled nanodrugs based on peptides and chromophores offer several benefits for precision cancer therapy, such as enhanced cumulative efficiency of tumor targeting, reduced drug toxicity, and side effects. Regarding therapeutic methods, phototherapy is a precise therapeutic approach that can further improve the curative effects of cancer therapy when combined with other therapeutic methods. By leveraging computer simulations to screen peptide sequences that can block immune checkpoints, it is possible to design assemblies that can overcome the instability and drug-loading problems associated with antibodies. Overall, peptide and chromophore self-assembled nanodrugs offer a promising strategy for cancer therapy, with great potential for clinical translation.

Acknowledgments

This work was funded by the National Science Fund for Distinguished Young Scholars of China (no. 22025207), the National Natural Science Foundation of China (nos. 22072154 and 22232006), the Innovation Research Community Science Fund of China (no. 21821005), and the Youth Innovation Promotion Association of Chinese Academy of Sciences (no. 2021048).

References

1 Zhang, L., Jing, D., Jiang, N. et al. (2020). Transformable peptide nanoparticles arrest HER2 signalling and cause cancer cell death in vivo. *Nat. Nanotechnol.* 15: 145–153.

2 Whrtesides, G.M., Mathias, J.P., and Seto, C.T. (1991). Molecular Self-Assembly and Nanochemistry: a Chemical Strategy for the Synthesis of Nanostructures. *Science* 254: 1312–1319.

3 Wang, J., Liu, K., Xing, R., and Yan, X. (2016). Peptide self-assembly: thermodynamics and kinetics. *Chem. Soc. Rev.* 45: 5589–5604.

4 Yuan, C., Ji, W., Xing, R. et al. (2019). Hierarchically oriented organization in supramolecular peptide crystals. *Nat. Rev. Chem.* 3: 567–588.

5 Zhao, W., Zhang, X., Zhang, R. et al. (2020). Self-Assembled Herbal Medicine Encapsulated by an Oxidation-Sensitive Supramolecular Hydrogel for Chronic Wound Treatment. *ACS Appl. Mater. Interfaces* 12: 56898–56907.

6 Zhang, X., Gong, C., Akakuru, O.U. et al. (2019). The design and biomedical applications of self-assembled two-dimensional organic biomaterials. *Chem. Soc. Rev.* 48: 5564–5595.

7 Qin, L., Cao, J., Shao, K. et al. (2020). A tumor-to-lymph procedure navigated versatile gel system for combinatorial therapy against tumor recurrence and metastasis. *Sci. Adv.* 6: eabb3116.

8 Keller, L. and Pantel, K. (2019). Unravelling tumour heterogeneity by single-cell profiling of circulating tumour cells. *Nat. Rev. Cancer* 19: 553–567.

9 Deng, X., Shao, Z., and Zhao, Y. (2021). Solutions to the Drawbacks of Photothermal and Photodynamic Cancer Therapy. *Adv. Sci.* 8: 2002504.

10 Jiang, B.P., Zhou, B., Lin, Z. et al. (2019). Recent Advances in Carbon Nanomaterials for Cancer Phototherapy. *Chem. A Eur. J.* 25: 3993–4004.

11 Ng, K.K., Lovell, J.F., Vedadi, A. et al. (2013). Self-Assembled Porphyrin Nanodiscs with Structure-Dependent Activation for Phototherapy and Photodiagnostic Applications. *ACS Nano* 7: 3484–3490.

12 Li, X., Schumann, C., Albarqi, H.A. et al. (2018). A Tumor-Activatable Theranostic Nanomedicine Platform for NIR Fluorescence-Guided Surgery and Combinatorial Phototherapy. *Theranostics* 8: 767–784.

13 Abbas, M., Zou, Q., Li, S., and Yan, X. (2017). Self-Assembled Peptide- and Protein-Based Nanomaterials for Antitumor Photodynamic and Photothermal Therapy. *Adv. Mater.* 29: 1605021.

14 Frederix, P.W., Scott, G.G., Abul-Haija, Y.M. et al. (2015). Exploring the sequence space for (tri-)peptide self-assembly to design and discover new hydrogels. *Nat. Chem.* 7: 30–37.

15 Zhao, L., Liu, Y., Xing, R., and Yan, X. (2020). Supramolecular photothermal effects: A promising mechanism for efficient thermal conversion. *Angew. Chem. Int. Ed.* 59: 3793–3801.

16 Li, S., Zou, Q., Xing, R. et al. (2019). Peptide-modulated self-assembly as a versatile strategy for tumor supramolecular nanotheranostics. *Theranostics* 9: 3249–3261.

17 Chen, K., Xing, R., and Yan, X. (2021). Self-assembling bile pigments for cancer diagnosis and therapy. *Aggregate* 2: 84–94.

18 Zou, Q., Bao, J., and Yan, X. (2022). Functional Nanomaterials Based on Self-Assembly of Endogenic NIR-Absorbing Pigments for Diagnostic and Therapeutic Applications. *Small Methods* 6: 2101359.

19 Li, M., Zhao, X., Dai, J., and Yu, Z. (2019). Peptide therapeutics and assemblies for cancer immunotherapy. *Sci. China Mater.* 62: 1759–1781.

20 Chang, R. and Yan, X. (2020). Supramolecular Immunotherapy of Cancer Based on the Self-Assembling Peptide Design. *Small Struct.* 1: 2000068.

21 Zhao, L., Liu, Y., Chang, R. et al. (2018). Supramolecular Photothermal Nanomaterials as an Emerging Paradigm toward Precision Cancer Therapy. *Adv. Funct. Mater.* 29: 1806877.

22 Zou, Q., Chang, R., Xing, R. et al. (2020). Injectable self-assembled bola-dipeptide hydrogels for sustained photodynamic prodrug delivery and enhanced tumor therapy. *J. Control. Release* 319: 344–351.

23 Xing, R., Zou, Q., Yuan, C. et al. (2019). Self-Assembling Endogenous Biliverdin as a Versatile Near-Infrared Photothermal Nanoagent for Cancer Theranostics. *Adv. Mater.* 31: 1900822.

24 Zhang, C., Wu, W., Li, R.Q. et al. (2018). Peptide-Based Multifunctional Nanomaterials for Tumor Imaging and Therapy. *Adv. Funct. Mater.* 28: 1804492.

25 Li, S., Zhang, W., Xue, H. et al. (2020). Tumor microenvironment-oriented adaptive nanodrugs based on peptide self-assembly. *Chem. Sci.* 11: 8644–8656.

26 Li, S., Xing, R., Chang, R. et al. (2018). Nanodrugs based on peptide-modulated self-assembly: Design, delivery and tumor therapy. *Curr. Opin. Colloid Interface Sci.* 35: 17–25.

27 Chang, R., Zou, Q., Xing, R., and Yan, X. (2019). Peptide-Based Supramolecular Nanodrugs as a New Generation of Therapeutic Toolboxes against Cancer. *Adv. Therap.* 2: 1900048.

28 Li, S., Xing, R., van Hest, J.C.M., and Yan, X. (2022). Peptide-based supramolecular assembly drugs toward cancer theranostics. *Expert Opin. Drug Deliv.* 19: 847–860.

29 Liu, K., Xing, R., Zou, Q. et al. (2016). Simple Peptide-Tuned Self-Assembly of Photosensitizers towards Anticancer Photodynamic Therapy. *Angew. Chem. Int. Ed.* 55: 3036–3039.

30 Yang, M., Yuan, C., Shen, G. et al. (2019). Cyclic dipeptide nanoribbons formed by dye-mediated hydrophobic self-assembly for cancer chemotherapy. *J. Colloid Interface Sci.* 557: 458–464.

31 Li, J., Wang, A., Zhao, L. et al. (2018). Self-Assembly of Monomeric Hydrophobic Photosensitizers with Short Peptides Forming Photodynamic Nanoparticles with Real-Time Tracking Property and without the Need of Release in Vivo. *ACS Appl. Mater. Interfaces* 10: 28420–28427.

32 Li, S., Zou, Q., Li, Y. et al. (2018). Smart Peptide-Based Supramolecular Photodynamic Metallo-Nanodrugs Designed by Multicomponent Coordination Self-Assembly. *J. Am. Chem. Soc.* 140: 10794–10802.

33 Falanga, A., Galdiero, M., Morelli, G., and Galdiero, S. (2018). Membranotropic peptides mediating viral entry. *Pept. Sci.* 110: e24040.

34 Chang, R., Zou, Q., Zhao, L. et al. (2022). Amino-Acid-Encoded Supramolecular Photothermal Nanomedicine for Enhanced Cancer Therapy. *Adv. Mater.* 34: 2200139.

35 Nelson, J.S., Roberts, W., and Berns, M.W. (1987). In Vivo Studies on the Utilization of Mono-L-Aspartyl Chlorin (NPe6) for Photodynamic Therapy. *Cancer Res.* 47: 4681–4685.

36 Luan, L., Fang, W., Liu, W. et al. (2016). Phthalocyanine-cRGD conjugate: synthesis, photophysical properties and in vitro biological activity for targeting photodynamic therapy. *Org. Biomol. Chem.* 14: 2985–2992.

37 Gilson, R.C., Tang, R., Gautam, K.S. et al. (2019). Trafficking of a Single Photosensitizing Molecule to Different Intracellular Organelles Demonstrates Effective Hydroxyl Radical-Mediated Photodynamic Therapy in the Endoplasmic Reticulum. *Bioconjug. Chem.* 30: 1451–1458.

38 Zhao, L., Li, S., Liu, Y. et al. (2019). Kinetically Controlled Self-Assembly of Phthalocyanine–Peptide Conjugate Nanofibrils Enabling Superlarge Redshifted Absorption. *CCS Chem.* 1: 173–180.

39 Tirand, L., Frochot, C., Vanderesse, R. et al. (2006). A peptide competing with $VEGF_{165}$ binding on neuropilin-1 mediates targeting of a chlorin-type photosensitizer and potentiates its photodynamic activity in human endothelial cells. *J. Control. Release* 111: 153–164.

40 Myochin, T., Hanaoka, K., Komatsu, T. et al. (2012). Design strategy for a near-infrared fluorescence probe for matrix metalloproteinase utilizing highly cell permeable boron dipyrromethene. *J. Am. Chem. Soc.* 134: 13730–13737.

41 Cheng, H., Fan, G.L., Fan, J.H. et al. (2019). A Self-Delivery Chimeric Peptide for Photodynamic Therapy Amplified Immunotherapy. *Macromol. Biosci.* 19: 1800410.

42 Han, K., Zhang, W.Y., Ma, Z.Y. et al. (2017). Acidity-Triggered Tumor Retention/Internalization of Chimeric Peptide for Enhanced Photodynamic Therapy and Real-Time Monitoring of Therapeutic Effects. *ACS Appl. Mater. Interfaces* 9: 16043–16053.

43 Zou, Q., Abbas, M., Zhao, L. et al. (2017). Biological Photothermal Nanodots Based on Self-Assembly of Peptide-Porphyrin Conjugates for Antitumor Therapy. *J. Am. Chem. Soc.* 139: 1921–1927.

44 Cheng, L., Wang, C., Feng, L. et al. (2014). Functional nanomaterials for phototherapies of cancer. *Chem. Rev.* 114: 10869–10939.

45 Jia, Y., Li, J., Chen, J. et al. (2018). Smart Photosensitizer: Tumor-Triggered Oncotherapy by Self-Assembly Photodynamic Nanodots. *ACS Appl. Mater. Interfaces* 10: 15369–15380.

46 Sun, B., Chang, R., Cao, S. et al. (2020). Acid-Activatable Transmorphic Peptide-Based Nanomaterials for Photodynamic Therapy. *Angew. Chem. Int. Ed.* 59: 20582–20588.

47 Han, K., Zhang, J., Zhang, W. et al. (2017). Tumor-Triggered Geometrical Shape Switch of Chimeric Peptide for Enhanced in Vivo Tumor Internalization and Photodynamic Therapy. *ACS Nano* 11: 3178–3188.

48 Luo, G.F., Chen, W.H., Hong, S. et al. (2017). A Self-Transformable pH-Driven Membrane-Anchoring Photosensitizer for Effective Photodynamic Therapy to Inhibit Tumor Growth and Metastasis. *Adv. Funct. Mater.* 27: 1702122.

49 Li, Y., Sun, P., Zhao, L. et al. (2020). Ferric Ion Driven Assembly of Catalase-Like Supramolecular Photosensitizing Nanozymes for Combating Hypoxic Tumor. *Angew. Chem. Int. Ed.* 59: 23228–23238.

50 Xing, R., Liu, K., Jiao, T. et al. (2016). An Injectable Self-Assembling Collagen-Gold Hybrid Hydrogel for Combinatorial Antitumor Photothermal/Photodynamic Therapy. *Adv. Mater.* 28: 3669–3676.

51 Qi, Y., Min, H., Mujeeb, A. et al. (2018). Injectable Hexapeptide Hydrogel for Localized Chemotherapy Prevents Breast Cancer Recurrence. *ACS Appl. Mater. Interfaces* 10: 6972–6981.

52 Jiang, T., Wang, T., Li, T. et al. (2018). Enhanced Transdermal Drug Delivery by Transfersome-Embedded Oligopeptide Hydrogel for Topical Chemotherapy of Melanoma. *ACS Nano* 12: 9693–9701.

53 Abbas, M., Xing, R., Zhang, N. et al. (2018). Antitumor Photodynamic Therapy Based on Dipeptide Fibrous Hydrogels with Incorporation of Photosensitive Drugs. *ACS Biomater Sci. Eng.* 4: 2046–2052.

54 Liu, F.H., Cong, Y., Qi, G.B. et al. (2018). Near-Infrared Laser-Driven in Situ Self-Assembly as a General Strategy for Deep Tumor Therapy. *Nano Lett.* 18: 6577–6584.

55 Huang, K., Gao, M., Fan, L. et al. (2018). IR820 covalently linked with self-assembled polypeptide for photothermal therapy applications in cancer. *Biomater. Sci.* 6: 2925–2931.

56 Cheng, Y., Qin, S., Liu, W. et al. (2020). Dual-Targeting Photosensitizer-Peptide Amphiphile Conjugate for Enzyme-Triggered Drug Delivery and Synergistic Chemo-Photodynamic Tumor Therapy. *Adv. Mater. Interfaces* 7: 2000935.

57 Um, W., Park, J., Ko, H. et al. (2019). Visible light-induced apoptosis activatable nanoparticles of photosensitizer-DEVD-anticancer drug conjugate for targeted cancer therapy. *Biomaterials* 224: 119494.

58 Cong, Z., Zhang, L., Ma, S.Q. et al. (2020). Size-Transformable Hyaluronan Stacked Self-Assembling Peptide Nanoparticles for Improved Transcellular Tumor Penetration and Photo-Chemo Combination Therapy. *ACS Nano* 14: 1958–1970.

59 Zhou, F., Feng, B., Wang, T. et al. (2017). Programmed Multiresponsive Vesicles for Enhanced Tumor Penetration and Combination Therapy of Triple-Negative Breast Cancer. *Adv. Funct. Mater.* 27: 1606530.

60 Li, Y., Wong, R.C.H., Yan, X. et al. (2020). Self-Assembled Nanophotosensitizing Systems with Zinc(II) Phthalocyanine-Peptide Conjugates as Building Blocks for Targeted Chemo-Photodynamic Therapy. *ACS Appl. Bio Mater.* 3: 5463–5473.

61 Liu, H., Hu, Y., Sun, Y. et al. (2019). Co-delivery of Bee Venom Melittin and a Photosensitizer with an Organic-Inorganic Hybrid Nanocarrier for Photodynamic Therapy and Immunotherapy. *ACS Nano* 13: 12638–12652.

62 Jia, H.R., Zhu, Y.X., Xu, K.F., and Wu, F.G. (2018). Turning Toxicants into Safe Therapeutic Drugs: Cytolytic Peptide-Photosensitizer Assemblies for Optimized In Vivo Delivery of Melittin. *Adv. Healthc. Mater.* 7: 1800380.

63 Ellis, L.M. and Hicklin, D.J. (2008). VEGF-targeted therapy: mechanisms of anti-tumour activity. *Nat. Rev. Cancer* 8: 579–591.

64 Zhang, X., Zhao, Y., Xu, Y. et al. (2014). In situ self-assembly of peptides in glucan particles for macrophage-targeted oral delivery. *J. Mater. Chem. B* 2: 5882–5890.

65 Han, K., Zhang, W., Zhang, J. et al. (2016). Acidity-Triggered Tumor-Targeted Chimeric Peptide for Enhanced Intra-Nuclear Photodynamic Therapy. *Adv. Funct. Mater.* 26: 4351–4361.

66 Cheng, H., Yuan, P., Fan, G. et al. (2019). Chimeric peptide nanorods for plasma membrane and nuclear targeted photosensitizer delivery and enhanced photodynamic therapy. *Appl. Mater. Today* 16: 120–131.

67 Cheng, H., Fan, J.H., Zhao, L.P. et al. (2019). Chimeric peptide engineered exosomes for dual-stage light guided plasma membrane and nucleus targeted photodynamic therapy. *Biomaterials* 211: 14–24.

68 Cheng, H., Zheng, R.R., Fan, G.L. et al. (2019). Mitochondria and plasma membrane dual-targeted chimeric peptide for single-agent synergistic photodynamic therapy. *Biomaterials* 188: 1–11.

69 Zhang, D., Qi, G.B., Zhao, Y.X. et al. (2015). In Situ Formation of Nanofibers from Purpurin18-Peptide Conjugates and the Assembly Induced Retention Effect in Tumor Sites. *Adv. Mater.* 27: 6125–6130.

70 Jiang, Y., Pang, X., Liu, R. et al. (2018). Design of an Amphiphilic iRGD Peptide and Self-Assembling Nanovesicles for Improving Tumor Accumulation and Penetration and the Photodynamic Efficacy of the Photosensitizer. *ACS Appl. Mater. Interfaces* 10: 31674–31685.

71 Cho, H.J., Park, S.J., Jung, W.H. et al. (2020). Injectable Single-Component Peptide Depot: Autonomously Rechargeable Tumor Photosensitization for Repeated Photodynamic Therapy. *ACS Nano* 14: 15793–15805.

72 Tirand, L., Thomas, N., Dodeller, M. et al. (2007). Metabolic profile of a peptide-conjugated chlorin-type photosensitizer targeting neuropilin-1: an in vivo and in vitro study. *Drug Metab. Dispos.* 35: 806–813.

73 Thomas, N., Tirand, L., Chatelut, E. et al. (2008). Tissue distribution and pharmacokinetics of an ATWLPPR-conjugated chlorin-type photosensitizer targeting neuropilin-1 in glioma-bearing nude mice. *Photochem. Photobiol. Sci.* 7: 433–441.

74 Liu, Y., Zhang, L., Chang, R., and Yan, X. (2022). Supramolecular cancer photoimmunotherapy based on precise peptide self-assembly design. *Chem. Commun.* 58: 2247–2258.

75 Li, S., Zhang, W., Xing, R. et al. (2021). Supramolecular Nanofibrils Formed by Coassembly of Clinically Approved Drugs for Tumor Photothermal Immunotherapy. *Adv. Mater.* 33: 2100595.

76 Wang, N., Zhou, Y., Xu, Y. et al. (2020). Molecular engineering of anti-PD-L1 peptide and photosensitizer for immune checkpoint blockade photodynamic-immunotherapy. *Chem. Eng. J.* 400: 125995.

77 Zhang, C., Gao, F., Wu, W. et al. (2019). Enzyme-Driven Membrane-Targeted Chimeric Peptide for Enhanced Tumor Photodynamic Immunotherapy. *ACS Nano* 13: 11249–11262.

78 Liu, Y., Lu, Y., Zhu, X. et al. (2020). Tumor microenvironment-responsive prodrug nanoplatform via co-self-assembly of photothermal agent and IDO inhibitor for enhanced tumor penetration and cancer immunotherapy. *Biomaterials* 242: 119933.

79 Song, W., Kuang, J., Li, C.X. et al. (2018). Enhanced Immunotherapy Based on Photodynamic Therapy for Both Primary and Lung Metastasis Tumor Eradication. *ACS Nano* 12: 1978–1989.

22

Self-assembling Bioactive Peptides for Supramolecular Cancer Immunotherapy

Shukun Li[1,2], Xuehai Yan[1], and Jan van Hest[2]

[1] *State Key Laboratory of Biochemical Engineering, Institute of Process Engineering, Chinese Academy of Sciences, Beijing, China*
[2] *Bio-Organic Chemistry, Institute for Complex Molecular Systems, Eindhoven University of Technology, Eindhoven, The Netherlands*

22.1 Introduction

Cancer immunotherapy, a promising alternative approach to traditional therapies, has radically transformed the landscape of clinical cancer treatment [1, 2]. The aim of cancer immunotherapy is to activate the host immune system to resist or eliminate cancer cells. In several cancer types, particularly malignant melanoma and lung cancer, it has outperformed standard-of-care therapy and has achieved unprecedented outcomes in a number of cases, such as complete regression of metastasized tumors and prolonging of long-term disease-free survival [3].

Supramolecular chemistry explores synergistic or reciprocal intermolecular noncovalent interactions involving the hydrophobic interaction, van der Waals force, π-stacking, hydrogen bond, electrostatic force, and metal coordinative interaction and offers the possibility to fabricate nanomaterials [4, 5]. Peptide-based self-assembly, utilizing bioactive peptides as building blocks, has particularly been demonstrated to be suitable for *de novo* nanoformulations for applications in a biomedical context such as immunotherapy. First of all, the bioactive peptides have variable functions that particularly benefit application in cancer immunotherapy, such as antigenic and adjuvant features, checkpoint blockade, and immunomodulation properties [6–8]. Second, the precise and simple structure makes them interesting candidates for preparation of nanodrugs as well as templates for engineering building blocks that integrate multiple functions [9–11]. Last but not least, bioactive peptides show superior biocompatibility and higher tumor penetration than large proteins or antibodies, which is of utmost importance in the biomedical field [12–14]. Besides these intrinsic features of the peptide building blocks, their

Peptide Self-Assembly and Engineering: Fundamentals, Structures, and Applications, First Edition.
Edited by Xuehai Yan.

formulation into supramolecular nanostructures further provides bioactive peptides with optimized efficacy and safety. That is, manipulating noncovalent interactions endows bioactive peptide-based nanodrugs with favorable biological effects including increased stability, optimized drug pharmacokinetics, and enhanced tumoral selectivity and targetability, which were proven by an increasing number of preclinical and clinical data [15–17]. Because of these highly tunable features, bioactive peptide-based supramolecular nanodrugs have much potential in the field of cancer immunotherapy.

In this chapter, we focus on the design and modification of bioactive peptide building blocks, then introduce the effect of kinetics and dynamics on self-assembling nanodrugs, and finally illustrate how these nanodrugs elicit antitumor immune responses and optimize treatment outcomes. Four kinds of approaches with different immune therapeutic emphasis will be discussed: (I) supramolecular tumor vaccines, (II) immune checkpoint blockade agents, (III) immune cell regulation, and (IV) combination therapy. We describe how in-depth knowledge on bioactive peptide self-assembly leads to efficient usage in tumor immunotherapy, by discussing a series of representative examples related to different therapeutic approaches. Finally, challenges and perspectives regarding self-assembling bioactive peptides toward clinical cancer immunotherapy will be highlighted as well.

22.2 Bioactive Peptides

Bioactive peptides are molecules usually composed of 2–50 amino acids, which exhibit a spectrum of pharmacological effects [18]. In cancer immunotherapy, the targets of interest when applying bioactive peptides are multifaceted. These include antigenic/adjuvant peptide-based vaccines for trigging specific antitumor immune responses, immune checkpoint blockade (ICB) peptides for reversing the immune-suppressive microenvironment, immunomodulator peptides with different mechanisms to regulate immune cells, and combination therapy to enhance therapeutic outcome [19]. With the development of synthetic chemistry and nanotechnology, the possibilities to modify bioactive peptides and further regulate their self-assembly to obtain versatile functional nanodrugs have been greatly extended in recent years [20].

22.2.1 Antigenic Peptides

Peptide epitopes, also called antigenic determinants, are the minimal units of antigens and capable of being recognized by the host immune system for triggering an immune response [21]. In the cancer-immunity cycle, epitopes play the key role in the activation of T cells. Antigen proteins are processed and degraded into epitopes by antigen presentation cells (APCs) and are bound to major histocompatibility complex (MHC) molecules to form MHC–epitope complexes. Normally, two classes of MHC molecules, MHC-I and MHC-II, can present epitopes and enable these complexes to be recognized by T cells via their T-cell receptors (TCRs). For MHC-I, it binds with peptide epitopes with 8–11 amino acids for promoting the production of $CD8^+$ T cells, while the MHC-II complex associates with peptide epitopes of 12–16 amino acids that initiate $CD4^+$ T-cell activation [22]. Here, antigenic peptides are defined as sequences that contain at least one peptide epitope. Using antigenic peptides rather than full-length antigens has advantages regarding structural control, facile production, and ease of modification. Over the past decade, combining antigenic peptides with supramolecular chemistry, mostly in the design of tumor vaccines, has become a research focus in the field of cancer immunotherapy [23].

22.2.2 Adjuvant Peptides

The adjuvant concept has been often employed in tumor vaccine design, where the aim of using adjuvants is to enhance the immunogenicity of the target antigen [24]. The functions of the adjuvant include attracting immune cells to the site of injection, promoting lymphatic drainage of vaccines, and inducing the activation of APCs. Traditionally, adjuvants based on oil emulsions and Toll-like receptors (TLRs) are used [25]; in this chapter, we focus on peptide-based adjuvants, predominately in the form of supramolecular assemblies. Such supramolecular self-adjuvants show a collective effect because of the capability of displaying multivalent antigens on the surface of the nanostructure and as such have gained increasing attention [26].

22.2.3 Checkpoint Blockade Peptides

Immune checkpoints, such as the extensively studied programmed cell death protein 1 (PD-1), PD-programmed cell death protein ligand 1 (PD-L1), and cytotoxic T-lymphocyte antigen 4 (CTLA-4), are accessory molecules that inhibit T-cell activation [27, 28]. That is, these immune checkpoints participate in the immune escape process of tumor cells. Therefore, using immune checkpoint blockade (ICB) inhibitors to block these signaling pathways is an efficient approach to reverse the immune-suppressive microenvironment and induce an antitumor immune response. Distinct with antibodies targeting CTLA-4, PD 1, and PD-L1 and used in the clinic, peptide-based immune checkpoint blockade inhibitors, such as AUNP-12 [7] and ^{D}PPA-1 [29], possess superior features regarding higher tumor tissue penetration and lower manufacturing cost, which turn them into promising candidates for ICB.

22.2.4 Immunomodulatory Peptides

Immunomodulatory peptides possess a broad spectrum of bioactivities toward different immune-related cells encompassing APCs, effector T cells, macrophages, and so on [30]. Also, these immunomodulator peptides can target some signaling pathways or tumor-suppressive microenvironment-related molecules. Combined with the ease of chemical modification, immunomodulatory peptides can be exploited as functional building blocks for combinational therapies in which different mechanisms are integrated toward immune therapy [31].

22.3 Immunotherapy Approaches

When cancer cells start to interact with the immune system, cascades of immune-related responses occur. In the cancer-immunity cycle, seven steps are involved [32]. Briefly, released cancer cell antigens are taken up by APCs, followed by their localization into draining lymphoid tissues where the APCs prime and activate T cells, leading finally to activated T cells that infiltrate and kill tumor cells. Bioactive peptide building blocks have been developed that modulate these different steps. Herein, we classify therapeutic approaches into four main categories: (I) supramolecular tumor vaccines; (II) immune checkpoint blockade agents; (III) immune cell regulation, and (IV) combination therapy.

22.3.1 Supramolecular Tumor Vaccines

Peptide-based supramolecular tumor vaccines are based on antigen peptides that stimulate $CD8^+$ T cells or $CD4^+$ T cells to target tumor-associated antigens (TAAs) or tumor-specific antigens (TSAs). Furthermore, other bioactive molecules or the nanomaterial itself can be incorporated as adjuvant to optimize the potency of the immune response. Peptide-based supramolecular tumor vaccines have been widely studied in tumor immunotherapy because of their advantages in terms of safety, ease of manufacture, and precise immune targeting [33].

22.3.1.1 OVA-based Antigen Peptide Co-assembly

Peptide epitopes from ovalbumin (OVA) have been demonstrated their efficacy and clear stimulation pathway; hence, they are widely used as antigen models [34]. The $OVA_{257-264}$ octapeptide with amino-acid sequence SIINFEKL and the elongated $OVA_{253-266}$ sequence of EQLESIINFEKLTE can bind with MHC-I molecules and then stimulate the activation of $CD8^+$ T cells, while $OVA_{323-339}$ with the sequence of ISQAVHAAHAEINEAGR binds with MHC-II molecules and triggers the specific $CD4^+$ T-cell immune response. Co-assembling OVA antigens into nanomaterials is a simple but versatile approach to construct tumor vaccines. Singh [35] et al. developed a nanogel platform to deliver OVA antigens. A poly(hydroxyethyl methacrylate) (pHEMA) backbone with pyridine included as functionalized hydrophobic side chain was used as the building block. The OVA was chosen as model antigen to complex with pHEMA. Driven by electrostatic interactions and hydrogen bonding, combined with the displacement of OVA molecules from the aqueous medium to the insoluble pHEMA-pyridine at pH 7.4 that is responsible for minimizing the interfacial energy, the nanogel vaccine was obtained (Figure 22.1). Such complexed nanogel induced robust DCs activation and T-cell response at lower antigen doses than soluble OVA molecules, thereby making it a safer and simple tumor vaccine candidate. Lv et al. developed genipin-cross-linked polyethyleneimine (PEI)-OVA nanoparticles (OVA NPs) for nanovaccine fabrication. The OVA NPs were prepared by a cross-linking reaction with genipin between the amino groups of OVA and PEI. The presence of PEI rendered OVA NPs surface with positive charge, which can adsorb negatively charged molecules. Free OVA was adsorbed on the surface of

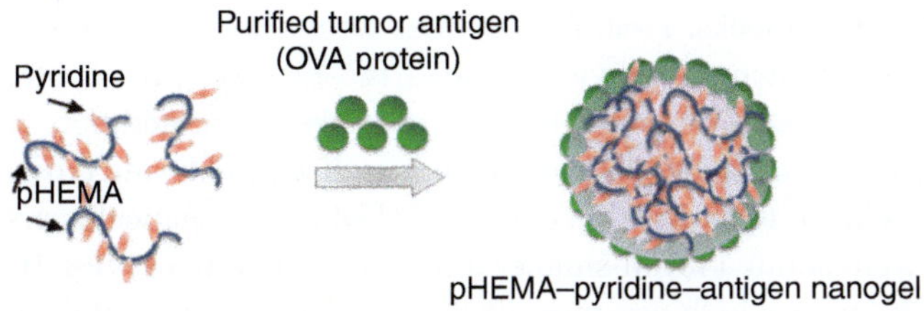

Figure 22.1 The fabrication of nanogel vaccine: A poly(hydroxyethyl methacrylate) (pHEMA) backbone with hydrophobic pyridine side chain was used as the building block. The OVA was chosen as model antigen to co-assemble with pHEMA to form nanogel vaccine. Source: Ref. [35]. Reproduced with permission of 2016 WILEY-VCH Verlag GmbH & Co. KGaA, Weinheim.

OVA NPs by electrostatic interaction, resulting in combination OVA NPs with both inner and outer antigens [36]. The results indicated that the outer antigen of these OVA NPs exerted a fast delivery to induce the initial antigen exposure, while the inner antigen showed persistent delivery. Upon this adequate antigen exposure, DCs effectively matured to activate T cells for immune response. Alternatively, the authors [37] combined the adjuvant of cytosine-phosphate-guanine (CpG) to evoke an immunostimulatory cascade through Toll-like receptor (TLR) binding and activation. After yielding self-cross-linked OVA nanoparticles (ONPs), CpG molecules were adsorbed on the outer layer of ONPs via electrostatic interactions, resulting in nanovaccine ONPs-CpG. *In vitro* and *in vivo* results demonstrated that the ONPs-CpG showed remarkable antitumor effects including DC maturity, T-cell activation, and IFN-γ production.

22.3.1.2 Other Antigen Peptides Assembly

Human epidermal growth factor receptor-2 (HER2) is overexpressed in approximately 20–30% of breast cancer patients and thereby serves as one TAA for fabricating tumor vaccines [38]. Fukase and coworkers [39] co-assembled a lipophilic adjuvant and a lipidated HER2-derived antigenic CH401 peptide (N:163–182, YQDTILWKDIFHKNNQLALT, abbreviated as Pam-CH401) from the HER2 extracellular domain to yield a tumor vaccine. By comparing three co-assembled vaccines with different adjuvants, Pam-CH401+Pam_3CSK_4 (fibril, d = 425 nm), Pam-CH401+α-GalCer (particle, d = 67 nm), and lipid A 506 (short fibril, d = 228 nm), vaccines co-assembled from CH401 and α-GalCer showed the most significant immune activation not only due to the multivalent antigen presentation and suitable immune response but also possibly because of the smaller size, which enhanced lymphatic delivery and uptake. In another example [40], oncofetal antigen (OFA), an immature laminin receptor protein (iLRP) expressed by many hematologic cancer cells, was included in the design of a tumor vaccine. Three peptide sequences with distinct recognition regions were selected: OFA 1 (OFA-$iLRP_{58-66}$: LLLAARAIV), OFA 2 (OFA-$iLRP_{146-154}$: ALCNTDSPL), and OFA 3 (OFA-$iLRP_{177-185}$: MLAREVLRM). Then, one cysteine was introduced onto the C-terminus of OFA 1 and OFA 3, respectively, and two cysteines were added to OFA 2, yielding OFA 1C,

OFA 2C, and OFA 3C building blocks. First, the peptides were dissolved into hexafluoroisopropanol (HFIP), and then trimethylolpropane tris(3-mercaptopropionate) (trithiol) was added to cross-link thiol groups in cysteine. Subsequent addition of diethyl ether (DEE), as nonsolvent, dropwise promoted the self-assembly and cross-linking of the building blocks for the formation of cross-linked peptide nanoclusters (PNCs). OFA 2C PNCs were about 148 nm smaller and more stable than OFA 1C (232 nm) and 3C PNCs (261 nm), which was most likely because OFA 2C contained two cysteines that increased the extent of cross-linking. Additionally, the sterically smaller side groups and the presence of carboxyl and amide groups on OFA 2C promoted their proximity and enhanced hydrogen-bonding forces. Owing to the suitable size for DCs internalization and passive diffusion to regional lymph nodes (LNs), OFA 2C PNCs displayed high retention at the intradermal injection site, allowing more time to interact with DCs in an area of increased DC activity. With its properties of maximizing antigen delivery with minimal off-target effects, OFA 2C PNCs were effective tumor vaccines. Recent advances in the convergence of immune-oncology, bioinformatics, and oncogenomics have led to the identification of tumor neoantigens, which are exclusively present in cancer cells and are excellent candidates for therapeutic vaccine design [41, 42]. Together with binary adjuvants, Chen et al. [43] fabricated a neoantigen-based nanovaccine (banNV), where the neoantigen Adpgk with the sequence of ASMTNMELM was obtained from mouse MC38 tumor cells. Specifically, banNVs were prepared by the following procedure. Conjugating thiolated DNA primer to the maleimide-decorated poly(ethylene oxide)-block-poly (D,L-lactic acid) (MAL-PEG-b-PLA) micelle is the first step. Then, by hybridization method, a circularized CpG template was immobilized on the surface of above nanoparticles, followed by rolling circle amplification (RCA) *in situ* to create self-assembled CpG microparticles (CpG MPs) with the core–shell structure; the hydrophobic resiquimod (R848) was loaded into the obtained microparticles. Finally, the cationic PEG-grafted polypeptide (PPT-g-PEG), which was composed of 45 repetitive units of modified glutamic acid with 90 primary amines and grafted via a Schiff base reaction with PEG, interacted with the negatively charged CpG via electrostatic interactions to cause particle size shrinkage; meanwhile, the hydrophobic PPTs were used for encapsulating hydrophobic peptide neoantigens to yield banNVs (171 ± 22 nm). Interestingly, banNVs realized the simultaneous delivery of neoantigens and adjuvants (CpG and R848) to LN and LN-residing APCs, which promoted antigen presentation on APCs, and augmented cytotoxic T-cell responses. In combination with immune checkpoint blockade, aPD-1, banNVs led to complete regression of 70% neoantigen-specific tumors without recurrence.

22.3.1.3 Antigen Peptide-based Conjugate Assembly

Modification of antigen peptide structures leads to flexible regulation of the assembly kinetics and dynamics of the building blocks, which has been widely studied for constructing supramolecular vaccines [44]. Tirrell et al. [45] conjugated a dialkyl tail with two palmitic (C_{16}) chains to an elongated antigen peptide sequence of EQLESIINFEKLTE, which was termed diC_{16}-OVA. The peptide sequence was composed of a prolonged OVA epitope, $OVA_{253-266}$, and also encompassed more hydrophilic amino acids. The diC$_{16}$-OVA amphiphiles self-assembled into cylindrical micelles with a diameter of 8.0 ± 2.3 nm and length of 50–300 nm, which imparted their properties including antigen depot and self-adjuvant effects of vaccines when applying them *in vivo* (Figure 22.2). In another example, He and coworkers [46] reported EGFRvIII-based peptide conjugates. EGFRvIII is an extracellular domain deletion mutant of EGFR with amino-acid residues 6–273 and possesses an N-terminal epitope with sequence of LEEKKGNYVVTDH. To this antigen epitope, two parts including a hydrophobic cholesterol and a T-cell helper epitope were sequentially conjugated to its N-terminus, generating the Chol-V2 building block. Such amphiphilic Chol-V2 self-assembled into stable micelles with an average diameter of 105.1 ± 28.3 nm. The integrated T-cell helper epitope and antigen epitope were responsible for eliciting humoral and cellular immune responses, respectively. In the B16-EGFRvIII melanoma cells xenograft mice model, the self-assembled vaccine micelles prevented tumor growth and tumorigenesis in either therapeutic or preventive manner. In a recent study, Seder and coworkers [47] conjugated antigen and adjuvant molecules together and regulated their self-assembly for formation of a supramolecular vaccine. In the study, they fabricated a supramolecular vaccine that is based on charge-decorated peptide-TLR-7/8a conjugates. Irrespective of the peptide antigen composition, these chemically programmed conjugates were able to self-assemble into nanoparticles with the average size around 20 nm, which provided a precise platform for loading different peptide neoantigens by linking them to TLR-7/8a adjuvant. Such design can increase antigen uptake and presentation by APCs, subsequently promoting T-cell immunity.

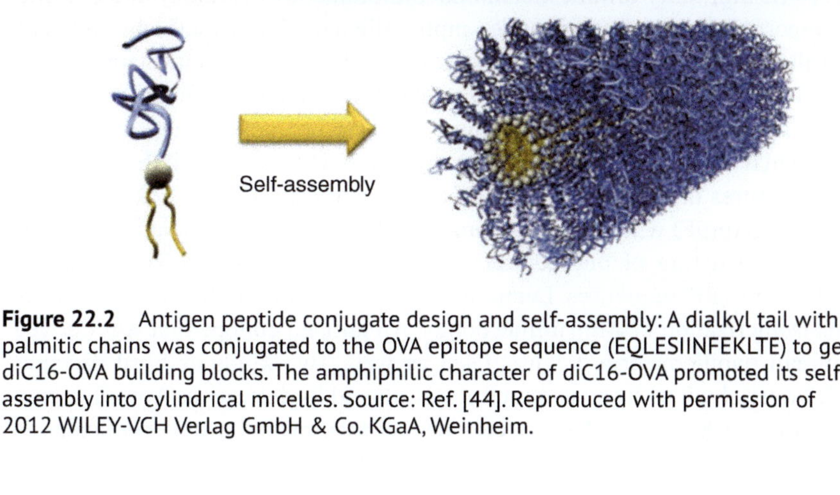

Figure 22.2 Antigen peptide conjugate design and self-assembly: A dialkyl tail with two palmitic chains was conjugated to the OVA epitope sequence (EQLESIINFEKLTE) to get diC16-OVA building blocks. The amphiphilic character of diC16-OVA promoted its self-assembly into cylindrical micelles. Source: Ref. [44]. Reproduced with permission of 2012 WILEY-VCH Verlag GmbH & Co. KGaA, Weinheim.

22.3.1.4 Supramolecular Self-adjuvant Assembly

Self-adjuvanticity has been verified as an intrinsic feature of supramolecular assemblies of peptide-based building blocks [48]. Collier and coworkers conducted the pioneering work. They [49] conjugated antigen OVA to a self-assembling peptide, Q11 (QQKFQFQFEQQ). The conjugated OVA-Q11 self-assembled into nanofibers without any adjuvant molecules. These nanofibers increased the IgG titer against the tumor. Importantly, the self-adjuvant mechanism was elucidated as a result of the conjugation of OVA and Q11. In a more detailed work, they [50] investigated factors accounting for the immunogenicity of OVA-Q11 assemblies. The results suggested that the strong antibody responses were T-cell dependent. By deleting epitope regions recognized by T cells, immunogenicity of OVA-Q11 assemblies was diminished. Additionally, mutating key residues in the self-assembling domain also attenuated their immunogenicity, which proved that the supramolecular structure itself possesses a self-adjuvant effect. Utilizing a Q11 self-assembling template, Li and coworkers [51] conjugated B-cell epitope (HGVTSAPDTRPAPGSTAPPA) via a flexible spacer; the B-cell epitope was derived from the variable number of tandem repeats (VNTR) of MUC1 protein. By manipulation of Thr residue in the peptide motifs PDTRP and PGST, four kinds of building blocks with different glycosylation patterns were obtained. After self-assembly, four MUC1 glycopeptide vaccine candidates with fibril nanostructures were obtained. The results showed that the vaccines with glycosylation in the PDTRP domain elicited the most significant immune response without any adjuvant and induced antibodies that recognized human breast tumor cells. Also, these vaccines showed a T-cell-independent pathway to initiate immune response and were associated with the activation of $CD8^+$ T cells. Besides Q11, other peptide-based self-adjuvant tumor vaccines were reported as well. Wang and coworkers [52] conjugated tyrosinase-related protein 2 (TRP2) epitope (SVYDFFVWL) to self-assembling peptide (KKFKFEFEF) via a disulfide linkage to produce epitope-conjugated peptide amphiphile, abbreviated as KKEF-TRP2. Owing to the amphiphilic nature, the KKEF-TRP2 self-assembled into supramolecular hydrogels (Figure 22.3). The hydrogels not only increased epitope stability but also effectively stimulated the maturation of DCs and potentiated the epitope-specific T-cell immunity toward melanoma. Simultaneously, Tekinay and coworkers [53] reported a biotinylated peptide amphiphile nanofiber as self-adjuvant. The amphiphilic building block biotin-PA was composed of a hydrophobic lauryl group and a biotinylated hydrophilic peptide sequence VVAGKK, which enabled the self-assembly. The OVA-based antigen epitope was furthered incorporated to yield supramolecular self-adjuvant vaccines. Yu's group [54] exploited the favorable structural features of supramolecular self-adjuvant vaccines using a pentapeptide FF-AmpF-FF (AmpF) with cis/trans-isomerization character. In detail, AmpF has the chemical structure of one central 4-aminoproline (Amp) flanked with two diphenylalanine (FF) sequences. Decreasing pH value from 7.4 to 6.5 can trigger the cis/trans-isomerization of Amp amide bonds. An antigen epitope that was derived from human papillomavirus E7 was used as well. Two kinds of fibril vaccines AmpF-E7 were obtained by co-assembling AmpF and its derivatives AmpFE7, conjugated with the $E7_{49-57}$ or $E7_{44-57}$ epitope. As a comparison, the pentapeptide

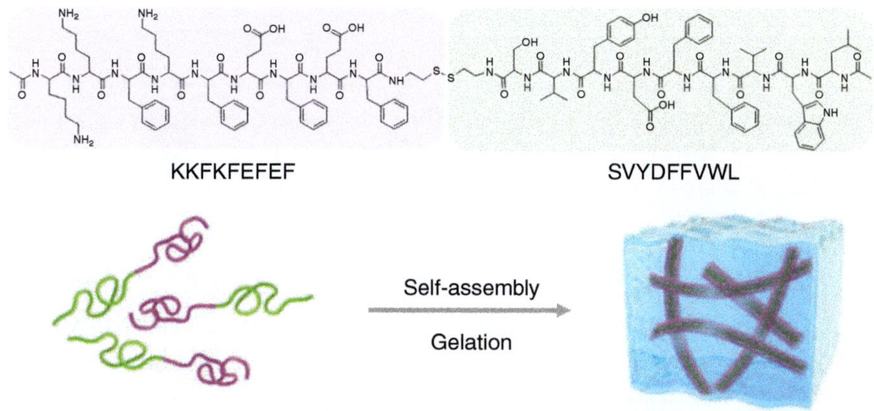

Figure 22.3 The design and self-assembly of self-adjuvant vaccine: Tyrosinase-related protein 2 (TRP2) epitope (SVYDFFVWL) conjugated to self-assembling peptide (KKFKFEFEF) via a disulfide linkage to produce amphiphilic building block, which can self-assemble into supramolecular hydrogels with self-adjuvant effect. Source: Ref. [52]. Reproduced with permission of 2019 WILEY-VCH Verlag GmbH & Co. KGaA, Weinheim.

FFPFF (PF) with a natural-charged proline was used, which can lead to form two kinds of particle vaccines PF-E7 when using the above co-assembly method. The results indicated that the AmpF-E7 fibril vaccines showed enhanced cellular internalization and retention. Therefore, they promoted the maturation of dendritic cells (DCs), accumulation in lymph node, and infiltration of cytotoxic T lymphocytes against tumor.

22.3.2 Immune Checkpoint Blockade

Tumor progression occurs mostly because the immunosuppressive microenvironment aids the tumor to avoid therapeutic eradication [55, 56]. In the past decade, ICBs, such as antibodies including PD-1, PD-L1, and CTLA-4, which can reverse the immune-suppressive microenvironment, have revolutionized oncology and become a top priority to retrigger potent antitumor immunotherapy [57]. Peptides are strong candidates to help blocking immune checkpoints as they show feasible synthesis, ease of modification, deep penetration, and possess capability of binding to and inducing responses from targets on a highly specific level, features that are more difficult to achieve with large proteins.

22.3.2.1 ICB Peptide-based Assembly

Bioactive peptides with ICB function are extensively exploited to construct supramolecular assemblies. ^{D}PPA-1 with a D-type sequence of $^{D}N^{D}Y^{D}S^{D}K^{D}P^{D}T^{D}D^{D}R^{D}Q^{D}Y^{D}H^{D}F$ was the first hydrolysis-resistant peptide antagonist to target the PD-1/PD-L1 pathway, and it could bind PD-L1 at an affinity of 0.51 μM *in vitro* [29]. Based on ^{D}PPA-1, some supramolecular nanodrugs have been developed. For instance, Nie and colleagues [58] utilized a conjugated peptide to co-assemble with the immunosuppressive indoleamine 2,3-dioxygenase (IDO) inhibitor NLG919, to constructing a nanodrug, where the

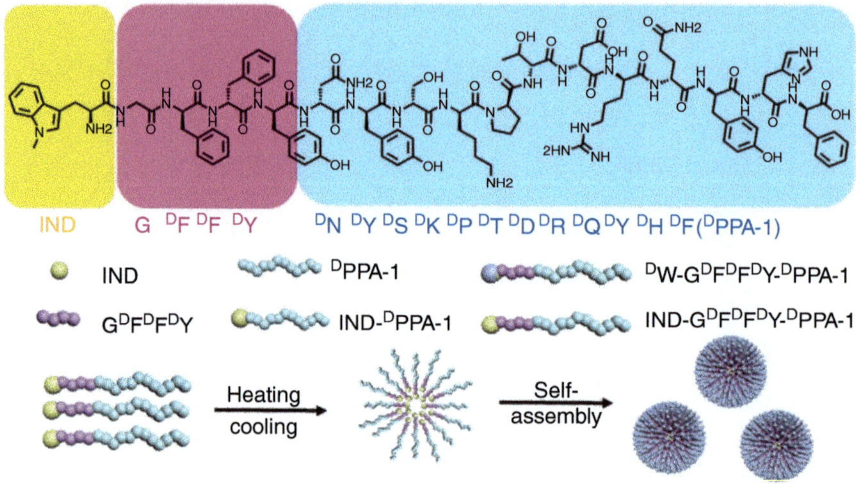

Figure 22.4 The design and self-assembly of IND-G^{D}F^{D}F^{D}Y-^{D}PPA-1 conjugate: By a heating–cooling protocol, IND-G^{D}F^{D}F^{D}Y-^{D}PPA-1 peptide conjugate self-assembled into amorphous spherical aggregates. Source: Ref. [59]. Reproduced with permission of 2021 Wiley-VCH GmbH.

conjugated peptide contains three parts: ^{D}PPA-1, a 3-diethylaminopropyl isothiocyanate (DEAP) segment, and a peptide sequence PLGLAG that can be cleaved by matrix metalloproteinase-2 (MMP-2). The resulting particle nanodrugs accumulated in the tumor microenvironment, where they responded to the increased acidity and presence of MMP-2 to promote DEAP protonation and PLGLAG cleavage, leading to release of ^{D}PPA-1 and NLG919. By blocking the PD-1/PD-L1 pathway and suppressing IDO, a combinational immune response was integrated. In Yang's group, a supramolecular trident was fabricated [59] (Figure 22.4). The peptide conjugate building block consisted of ^{D}PPA-1, indoximod (IND, an IDO inhibitor), and a D-tetrapeptide G^{D}F^{D}F^{D}Y with self-adjuvant function. After self-assembly by a heating–cooling protocol, IND-G^{D}F^{D}F^{D}Y-^{D}PPA-1 formed discrete amorphous aggregates with a hydrodynamic diameter around 110 nm, which were capable of simultaneously binding to PD-L1 and inhibiting the IDO-1 pathway. Hence, immunotherapeutic effects involving recruited cytotoxic CD8$^+$ T lymphocytes, upregulated cytokines, and downregulated immunosuppressive Foxp3$^+$ T cells were demonstrated.

22.3.2.2 Peptide Assembly Synergizing ICB

Fabricating supramolecular nanodrugs that synergize the ICB potency is of significance to activate the immune system against tumorous tissue. To this end, Lou and colleagues [60] designed a peptide-conjugated aggregation-induced emission luminogen (AIEgen) probe (GCP) to downregulate PD-L1. In this design, GCP consisted of three sections: caged GO203 peptide with mucin 1 (MUC1) targeting ability, a Cathepsin B enzyme cleavage peptide, and photosensitizer PyTPA (Figure 22.5).

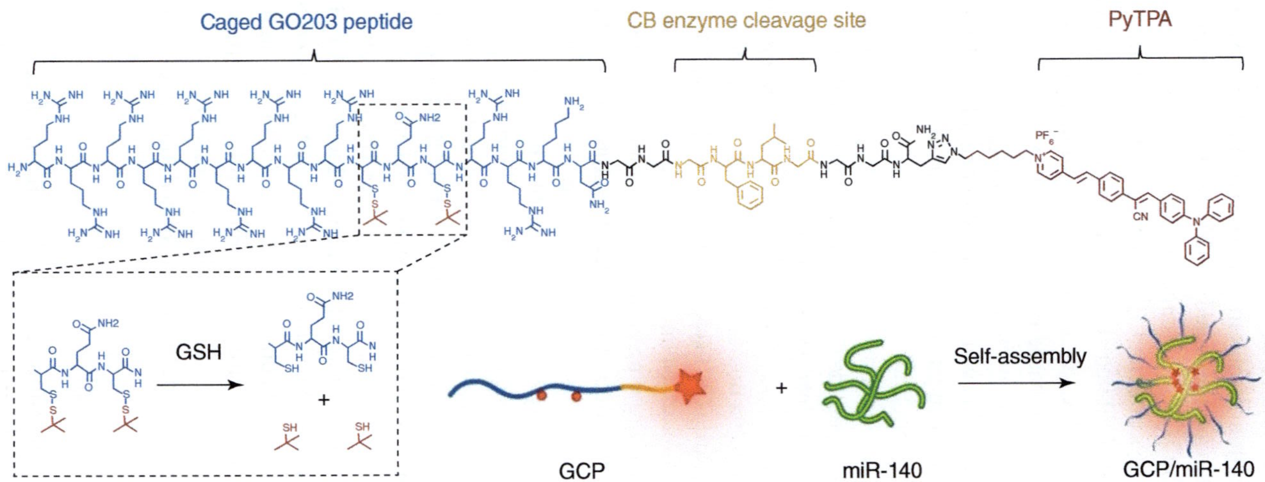

Figure 22.5 The structure of caged peptide-AIEgen probe GCP and its self-assembly: GCP is composed of three sections including caged GO203 peptide, a Cathepsin B enzyme cleavage peptide, and PyTPA. Together with the hydrophobic interactions, the positively charged GCP interacts with the negatively charged miR-140 to form GCP/miR-140 nanoparticles. Source: Ref. [60]. Reproduced with permission of 2022 Wiley-VCH GmbH.

The positively charged side chains of GCP, together with the hydrophobic aromatic groups, enabled GCP to co-assemble with negatively charged microRNA (miR-140) to get nanoparticles (GCP/miR-140). In the presence of Cathepsin B inside the cells, GCP/miR-140 disassembled and released the caged GO203 peptide and miR-140. Then, the high concentration of glutathione (GSH) further cleaved the capping group *tert*-butyl mercaptan of the caged GO203 peptide, allowing its active site exposure that inhibited the MUC1's homodimerization, hence downregulating the expression of PD-L1. At the same time, the released miR-140 bound to PD-L1 messenger RNA (mRNA) and inhibited the PD-L1's translation. Combined with the photodynamic effect of PyTPA, an enhanced immune response was realized. Alternatively, designing peptide-based building blocks with ICB targeting and further regulating their self-assembly is a potent strategy to augment therapeutic effects. For example, Wang and coworkers [61] screened a PD-L1 targeting peptide KYNETWRSED, which has been suggested that it can be coupled with functional molecules and applied for combinational therapy. As another method, Wang and coworkers [62] designed a bifunctional PD-1/PD-L1 peptide antagonist named as PCP, where a PD-1 targeting peptide GADYKPITVKVN (PL120131) was conjugated with ^{D}PPA-1 via a fibroblast activation protein-α (FAP-α)-responsive peptide GPAK linker; the side chains of the two lysine residues of PCP were modified with alkyl chains to form the hydrophobic domain. By co-assembly with doxorubicin (DOX) and R848, a multiagent prodrug (PCP@R848/DOX) was obtained. Upon exposure to FAP-α, R848 and DOX were released and performed their therapeutic action, while the released PD-1 or PD-L1 targeting peptides blockaded the immune-suppressive pathway to reactivate the function of cytotoxic T lymphocytes. Different from the above targeting methods, supramolecular structures aiming for MDM2/MDMX-mediated degradation proved to be a potentially viable therapeutic paradigm to synergize anti-PD-1 immunotherapy, as was shown by Yao and coworkers [63]. An oligomeric Au(I)-peptide precursor with capability of self-assembling into a clustered spherical bionic skeleton was synthesized, where the peptide consisted of an N-terminal ligand which interacted with MDM2/MDMX, a C-terminal ligand bound to an E3 ubiquitin convener and a PEG5 tether. Upon coating with an erythrocyte membrane, an erythrocyte-mimicking nanocell termed Nery-PMIV was fabricated. *In vitro* and *in vivo* results showed that Nery-PMIV potently restored the proteins of p53 and p73 by degrading MDM2/MDMX in a ubiquitin-dependent manner. Of note, Nery-PMIV effectively augmented antitumor immunity elicited by anti-PD-1 therapy in a LUAD orthotopic allograft model and a LUAD-patient-derived xenograft (PDX) mice model with humanized immunity remodeling.

22.3.3 Immune Cell Regulation

As shown in the oncology-immunity cycle, defeating tumor cells is dependent on the orchestration of diverse immune cells, especially antigen presentation cells, macrophages, and T cells [64]. Therefore, designing and constructing nanodrugs that target the regulation of immune cells is of utmost significance for tumor immunotherapy.

22.3.3.1 Antigen Presentation Cells

APCs play an essential role in immune activation as they participate in the phagocytosis and presentation of antigens at the tumor tissue and then home to lymph nodes, where they are involved in antigen presentation to naïve T cells, which induces their proliferation and differentiation [65]. Dendritic cells (DCs) are the most professional APCs. Regulation on structure is a common method to increase immunogenicity and optimize APCs' antigen presentation in the context of immunotherapies. For example, Collier and colleagues [66] designed a series of peptides that when mixed form long α-helical nanofibers with precise control over their lengths. Demonstrating their use as immunotherapies, capped nanofibers, with residues mutated into Ser and Thr at the *a* and *d* or *c* and *f* positions of the Coil29 building block to interrupt the linear assembly of Coil29 and limit fiber length, were preferentially cross-presented by DCs compared to the uncapped counterparts, which may be because of their different surface chemistries at the fiber tips and different levels of curvature. The enhanced cross-presentation therefore triggered strong $CD8^+$ T-cell responses. Incorporating targeting groups in building motifs for fabricating DCs nanoagonists is an alternative means for improving cancer immunotherapy, which was demonstrated by Wang et al. [67] (Figure 22.6). The building block PVA-CD40 was engineered, containing a dibenzocyclooctyne (DBCO) moiety modified with a CD40 anchoring peptide (ATYSEFPGNLKPC) responsible for binding with receptors on APCs and an azide group-labeled peptide ((N3) XAPIAQKDELEKLVFFAEC(Cy)), containing a self-assembling motif (KLVFFAE). During application, the preadministrated anchoring peptide first targeted CD40 on DCs, after which the subsequently administered assembling peptide was conjugated via a click reaction. Upon the hydrogen-bonding interaction, along with the extended hydrophobic motif, the formed conjugate rapidly

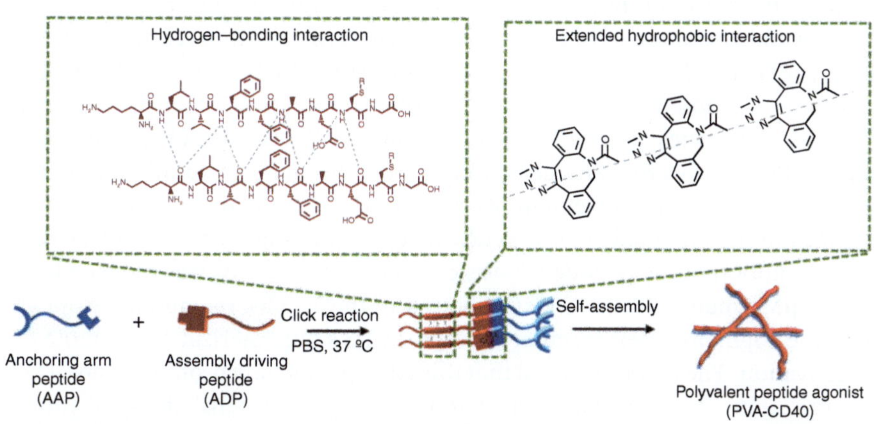

Figure 22.6 Structure and fabrication of PVA-CD40 through click reaction: A CD40 anchoring peptide with CD40 targeting ability and an assembly driving peptide was first conjugated on-site through click reaction, and then the resultant peptide conjugates self-assembled into polyvalent peptide agonist (PVA-CD40) with a fibrous structure. Source: Ref. [67]. Reproduced with permission of 2022 Wiley-VCH GmbH.

self-assembled into a fibrous superstructural network (PVA-CD40), which induced CD40 receptor oligomerization and activated the downstream signaling. Strikingly, one shot administration of PVA-CD40 elicited a maturation period of DCs up to 2.3-fold compared to that of the CD40 antibody, and moreover, the stimulated DCs primed T cells to achieve tumor cell killing. Combined with the anti-PD-1 antibody, PVA-CD40 inhibited the tumor growth in both B16F10 and 4T1 mice tumor models with survival rate up to 37%. As a novel strategy developed by Zhang and coworkers [68], overexpressed tyrosinase in tumor tissue was explored to engineer peptide-based microfibers for promoting antigen presentation. A functional tripeptide DFY was designed and synthesized. When internalized by melanoma cells that overexpress tyrosinase, the DFY tripeptide underwent the reaction of enzymatic polymerization to form pDFY. Meanwhile, tyrosine residues formed quinone-rich intermediates. Then, the intermediates captured immunogenic proteins deriving from the organelles through the Michael addition between sulfhydryl groups and quinone. Similar to necrosis, the capturing process induced quick death of tumor cells. After polymerization and cross-linking, the tripeptide DFY can self-assemble into antigen-contained microfibers. In application, these microfibers could be released from disrupted tumor cells, followed by APCs antigen presentation, and thereafter triggering the potent immune response against tumor.

22.3.3.2 Effector T Cells

Naive T cells are primed to become effector cells, mainly $CD8^+$ T cells and $CD4^+$ T cells, after interacting with APCs that present MHC-antigen complexes and immunogenic signals. Afterward, $CD8^+$ T effector cells could migrate to the tumor tissue, bind with tumor cells by identification of their cognate antigens presented on MHC class I molecules, and finally kill the tumor cells, while $CD4^+$ T helper cells support $CD8^+$ T effector cells by producing cytokines [69]. Nanodrugs with activating effector T-cell function would be very useful for cancer immunotherapy. Wang and coworkers [70] reported the strategy of targeting-recruitment self-assembly (TRA) of peptide conjugate antiCD3-G7-RGD (Figure 22.7). The conjugate is composed of three parts. The soluble peptide G7 (GNNQQNY) that possesses a high critical assembly concentration (CAC) was linked to the targeting tripeptide RGD with capability of binding to integrin $\alpha_V\beta_3$. In addition, the antibody antiCD3 that can interact with its receptor CD3 on the membrane of T cells was linked to the other side of G7, generating the building block of antiCD3-G7-RGD. The motion of the peptide G7 was confined, and its CAC was reduced from 525 to 33 μM when antiCD3-G7-RGD bound to the T cell's membrane. Notably, besides the augmented self-assembly, receptor CD3's oligomerization promoted T cell's activation. The results showed that this strategy not only promoted the CD3's oligomerization and activated T cells but also improved T cells' ability of tumor cytolysis. In a recent publication by Lam et al. [71], a programmable tumor cell/effector T-cell bispecific nanoimmuno engager (NIE) was reported. The NIE was co-assembled from two transformable peptide monomers TPM1 and TPM2. TPM1, LXY30-KLVFFK(*Pa*), comprised three functional domains, an LXY30 cyclic

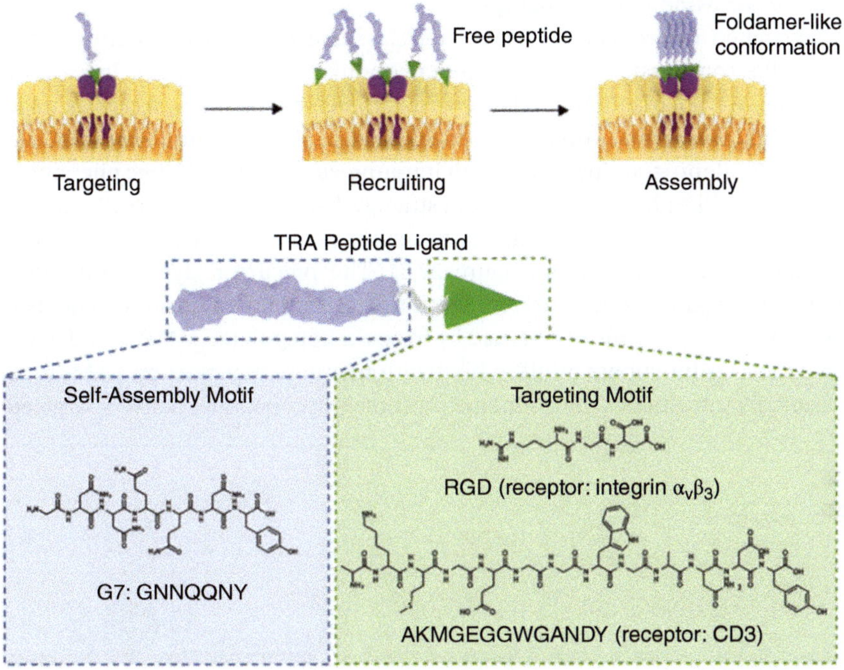

Figure 22.7 The targeting-recruitment self-assembly (TRA) strategy for specific and highly efficient self-assembly: The TRA peptide is composed of the self-assembly motif of G7 and targeting motif to two distinct protein receptors (integrin $\alpha_V\beta_3$ and CD3), which can target T cells. Then, the recruited TRA peptide can self-assemble and mediate receptor oligomerization. Source: Ref. [70]. Reproduced with permission of 2022 Wiley-VCH GmbH.

peptide (cdG-Phe(3,5-diF)-G-HypNcR) ligand that targets the $\alpha_3\beta_1$ integrin (tumor cell membrane), a KLVFF β-sheet-forming peptide, and a pheophorbide a (*Pa*) moiety with fluorescence property that also acted as a hydrophobic core to induce the formation of micellar nanoparticles. TPM2, *pro*LLP2A-KLVFFK(*R848*), also comprised three functional domains: *pro*LLP2A, the "pro-ligand" version of the LLP2A ligand with $\alpha_4\beta_1$ integrin (T-cell membrane)-binding ability of lymphocytes, the same KLVFF β-sheet-forming peptide domain, and the TLRs 7/8 agonist R848 (resiquimod) that was grafted to the main chain of TPM2 via an ester bond. Driven by noncovalent interactions, TPM1 and TPM2 co-assembled into nanoparticles, NIE-NPs, in which KLVFFK(*Pa*) and KLVFFK-(*R848*) hydrophobic domains were in the interior of the NIE-NPs, while relatively hydrophilic LXY30 and *pro*LLP2A ligand peptides were on their surface. NIE-NPs targeted tumor cells. Upon interaction with the $\alpha_3\beta_1$ integrin receptor, the NIE-NPs underwent *in situ* transformation into nanofibers (NIE-NFs) to prolong drug retention. Due to the abundant presence of esterases in TME, *pro*LLP2A was quickly converted to LLP2A to capture $CD8^+$ T cells and facilitate their long-term retention at TME. The large numbers of $CD8^+$ T cells, hence, enhanced ICB therapy.

22.3.3.3 Tumor-associated Macrophages

Tumor-associated macrophages (TAMs) are classified into inflammatory, antitumoral M1-like (or classic), and pro-tumoral M2-like (or alternative). In case of tumor tissue, M1 polarization is related to macrophage-dependent tissue damage and tumor cell killing; however, M2 polarization promotes tumor invasion and metastasis [72]. Reprograming TAMs from immune-suppressive M2-like phenotype to antitumor M1-like phenotype is a potent strategy. Fang and coworkers [73] developed *in situ* activated nanoglycoclusters to realize potent tumor penetration and repolarization of hypoxic TAMs (Figure 22.8). The precursor glycopeptide with three modules, a ligand sequence RGD with tumor targetability, a substrate sequence PLGVRG that can be specifically cleaved by hypoxia-upregulated MMP-2, and a terminal mannose as functional motif to bind with mannose receptors on TAMs, was synthesized. By intravenous injection, the precursor glycopeptides actively targeted

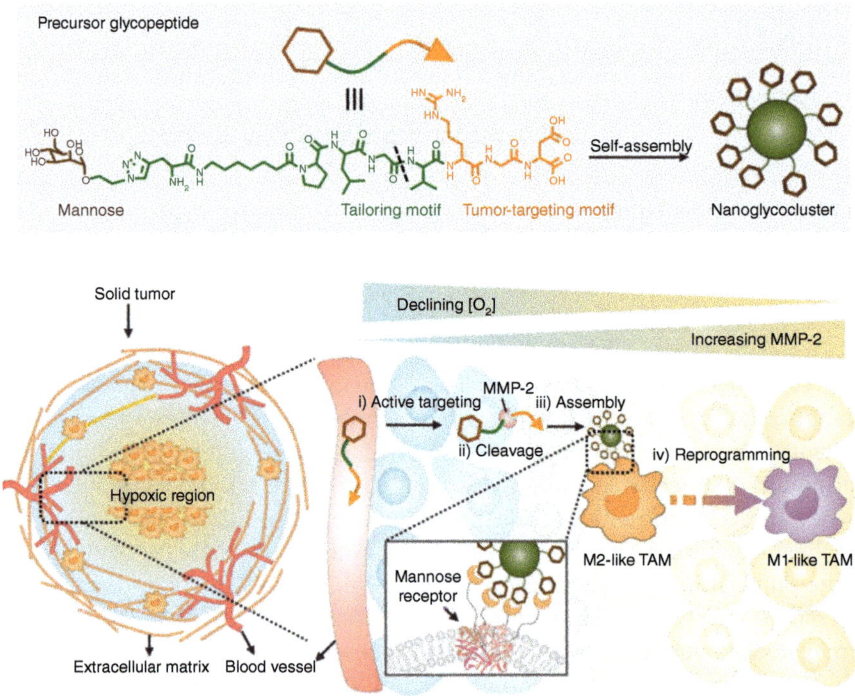

Figure 22.8 The structure and assembly of nanoglycocluster for reprogramming TAMs: The precursor glycopeptide contains three parts of a tumor-targeting motif, an MMP-2-responsive substrate sequence, and a terminal mannose for binding with its receptors that expressed on TAMs. The precursor glycopeptides (i) actively targeted tumor tissue and deeply penetrated through tumor stroma after intravenous injection, (ii) were specifically cleaved by MMP-2, (iii) assembled into nanoglycoclusters in tumor hypoxic regions. The formed nanoglycoclusters displayed densely arrayed mannoses to enable multivalent binding with mannose receptors on M2-like TAMs, and thus iv) efficiently reprogrammed M2-like TAMs into M1-like TAMs. Source: Ref. [73]. Reproduced with permission of 2023 Wiley-VCH GmbH.

tumor tissue and deeply penetrated through tumor stroma, then they were specifically cleaved by MMP-2 whose expression and activity are increasing with the declining oxygen levels, and therefore assembled into nanoglycoclusters throughout the tumor, especially in the hypoxic regions. The size-enlarged nanoglycoclusters retained in the hypoxic regions and displayed densely arrayed mannoses to enable high-affinity and multivalent binding with mannose receptors on M2-like TAMs and thus efficiently polarized them into M1-like TAMs for further activating $CD8^+$ T cells against tumor. Alternatively, Zhang and colleagues [74] used the nanoparticles from cuttlefish ink (CINPs, ~100 nm), which were rich in melanin and contained a variety of amino acids and monosaccharides, for training TAMs and combining this with photothermal therapy (PTT). CINPs can efficiently reprogram immune-suppressive M2-type TAMs to antitumoral M1-type TAMs through the activation of mitogen-activated protein kinase (MAPK) signaling pathway. Additionally, CINPs also convert the absorbed photons to heat, due to the presence of melanin, for PTT. Combined with the released tumor-specific antigens through PTT, the increased proportion of M1-type TAMs, and the fostered recruitment of $CD8^+$ T cells, CINPs could almost completely inhibit tumor growth, lung metastasis, which was accompanied by more active immune responses. TAMs and DCs are all APCs and located in the lymph nodes, of which activation is the first prerequisite for tumor eradication. The Zhang group [75] designed a hybrid cytolytic peptide, α-melittin, in which the N-terminus of melittin was linked to the C-terminus of an amphipathic α-helical peptide (α-peptide) through a GSG linker. The strong α-helical configuration allowed α-melittin to interact with phospholipids, and it self-assembled into lipid nanoparticles (α-melittin-NPs) with an average diameter of 20 nm. Owing to the features of melittin that can induce tumor cell apoptosis or necrosis by releasing TAAs and because of the desirable size for lymphatic drainage, they [76] further evaluated the lymph node-targeting performance of α-melittin-NPs to reshape the immune microenvironment. The results showed that α-melittin-NPs can be drained to inguinal LNs and afterward activated APCs, including TAMs and DCs. In a bilateral flank B16F10 tumor model, locally injected α-melittin-NPs elicited systemic cellular and humoral immune responses, leading to the 70% elimination on primary tumors and 50% elimination on distant tumors.

22.3.3.4 Other Immune Cells

B cells mediate the production of antibodies and are the main cell type in humoral immune response [77]. Liu and colleagues [78] conjugated a B-cell epitope peptide (HGVTSAPDTRPAPGSTAPPA) to a self-assembling peptide Q11 (QQKFQFQFQQQ) via a spacer (SGSG), generating building block MUC1-Q11. MUC1-Q11 formed highly ordered fibril nanostructures by a local mechanical perturbation method, forcing multiple epitopes on the surface and hence leading to effective activation of B cells to produce antitumor antibodies. Distinct with the random interaction between fibrils dispersed in solution and B cells caused by their diffusion, by placing MUC1-Q11 fibrils on mica surfaces, the functional units were arranged in a more defined way than in the solution phase, which facilitated more pronounced B-cell responses and production of higher titer of antitumor antigens. Gao and coworkers [79] showed that the *in situ* assembled peptide nanoblanket extinguished the "fire" of tumor-supportive microenvironment adaption. The MMP2-cleavable self-assembled branched peptide FR17 (FFK(GPLGLAGG-YVDKR)Y) consisted of a self-assembling peptide domain FFKY, a pentapeptide RKDVY with hydrophilic property, and immune modulation effect that was linked to the Lys (K) side chain in the FFKY main chain by an MMP2-responsive peptide linker (GPLGLAGG). When FR17 was cleaved by MMP2, the monomer FG8 (FFK(GPLG)Y) was released, which folded into the peptide nanoblanket with a membrane-like structure, because of the hydrogen bonds and π–π stacking. The *in vivo* results demonstrated that, after R17 subcutaneous administration, the assembled peptide nanoblanket *in situ* in a premetastatic niche (PMN) stromal microenvironment impeded fibroblast activation to retard the prometastatic reconstruction of vessel and stroma, which inhibited the myeloid cells recruitment and metastatic cascades, offering a therapeutic strategy against premetastatic niche formation. In a more comprehensive study, Hartgerink and coworkers [80] assessed the early inflammatory host response to four multidomain peptide hydrogels displaying amines, guanidinium ions, and carboxylates by means of subcutaneous injection. For example, the negatively charged peptides elicited minimal inflammation, while the positively charged peptides showed different performances, such as high infiltration of immune cells and a high degree of collagen deposition. Additionally, the arginine-based hydrogel showed long-time inflammatory response. The work provided the understanding of the immune response to peptide-based nanodrugs and gave the design principle of peptide-based materials for tumor immunotherapy application.

22.3.4 Combination Therapy

Combination therapy, integrating multiple merits of monotherapy into one platform, is of particular interest in immunotherapy for amplifying therapeutic index, which has been found to achieve synergistic effects, promoting tumor ablation and even preventing the recurrence and metastasis of tumors [81]. It has been demonstrated that some treatment modalities, such as photodynamic therapy (PDT), PTT, and chemotherapy, with the character of generation of reactive oxygen species (ROS) and/or endoplasmic reticulum (ER) stress to induce immunogenic cell death (ICD), are the ideal choices to combine with immunotherapy because the immunological tumor state can transfer from cold to hot [82]. In short, after ICD, damage-associated molecular patterns (DAMPs) including heat shock proteins (HSP70 and HSP90), calreticulin (CRT), and high mobility group box 1 (HMGB1) could be induced, which further activate the host immune system against cancer [83, 84].

22.3.4.1 Photodynamic Therapy

PDT uses photosensitizers and light in combination with oxygen to generate cytotoxic ROS that kill tumor cells by necrosis or apoptosis. In the process, generated ROS cause ICD, together with other immune active drug molecules, enabling to achieve an additional effect. For example, Tao and colleagues [85] developed the peptide-based small interfering RNA (siRNA) micelleplexes (P^{A7R}@siPD-L1) for normalizing vascular-immune crosstalk and with the aim to establish a positive feedback loop in potentiating antitumor immunotherapy. The polyethylene glycol (PEG)-R9 peptide conjugated with photosensitizer chlorin e6 (Ce6) was linked with the antiangiogenic peptide A7R via the MMP-2 substrate spacer (GPLGVRG). Then, the obtained peptide conjugate co-assembled with lecithin29 to form P^{A7R} micelleplexes by hydrophobic interaction. Subsequently, siRNA against PD-L1 was bound through electrostatic adsorption to R9, yielding the P^{A7R}@siPD-L1. Upon reaching the MMP-2-rich TME, the P^{A7R}@siPD-L1 was broken down by the hydrolysis of the GPLGVRG peptide. Subsequently, the dissociated antiangiogenic peptide A7R targeted VEGF receptor 2 (VEGFR-2) and neuropilin-1 (NRP-1) on tumor endothelial cells and caused blood-vessel normalization, alleviating hypoxia and promoting immune cells infiltration in TME. Meanwhile, the peptide PEG-R9K(Ce6)-LLGPLG, released simultaneously with siPD-L1, entered tumor cells with the aid of cell-penetrating segment R9. After laser irradiation, Ce6 generated ROS and triggered ICD, while the lysosome was disrupted via the cytotoxic ROS, further facilitating the diffusion of siPD-L1 into the cytoplasm for silencing the PD-L1 expression on tumor cells. Ding and colleagues [86] utilized lysosomal membrane permeabilization (LMP)-induced ICD to effectively convert immunologically cold tumors to hot (Figure 22.9). The LMP inducer named TPE-Py-pYK-(TPP)pY contained three main parts: a protonated TPE-Py as an AIE luminogen (AIEgen) and photosensitizer for imaging and ROS generation, a self-assembling peptide pYKpY (pY = phosphotyrosine) responding to ALP, and a protonated TPP to adjust the charge of the whole molecule. Owing to pY, the inducer TPE-Py-pYK(TPP)pY was a small negatively charged molecule with low fluorescence and ROS generation ability. After ALP-catalyzed dephosphorylation in TME, the molecules transformed into positively charged nanoassemblies with fluorescence turn-on and singlet oxygen turn-on. TPE-Py-pYK(TPP)pY tended to accumulate in ALP-overexpressed cancer cell lysosomes as well as induced LMP and rupture of lysosomal membranes to massively evoke ICD. Such LMP-induced ICD, therefore, promoted abundant $CD8^+$ and $CD4^+$ T cells infiltration into the cold tumors. Li and coworkers also investigated PDT-synergized immunotherapy. One example [87] is that they developed MMP-2-activatable anti-PD-L1 antibody (aPD-L1) nanoparticles, which were first complexed with photosensitizer indocyanine green (ICG) and subsequently stabilized with EGCG dimer (dEGCG) to form the dEGCG-aPD-L1/ICG aggregates which were further compressed by PEG-PLGLAG-dEGCG. The resulting nanoparticles were activated by MMP-2 for sustained release of aPD-L1. Upon laser irradiation, ICG-mediated PDT induced antitumor immunity and promoted the intratumoral infiltration of $CD8^+$ T cells. PDT and aPD-L1-mediated PD-L1 blockade cumulatively suppressed tumor growth and inhibited metastasis. In another example, they [88] recently reported a PDT-motivated PC-Cell@gel, which was fabricated by coating polyethylenimine-conjugated Ce6 (PEI-Ce6) to the oxidized autologous tumor cells in 9-fluorenyl methoxycarbonyl (Fmoc)-KCRGDK-phenylboronic acid (FK-PBA) hydrogels, where the PBA acted as a sialic acid-targeting moiety. PEI-Ce6 was attracted to the cell surface by electrostatic interaction for PDT. The FK-PBA targeted residue tumors

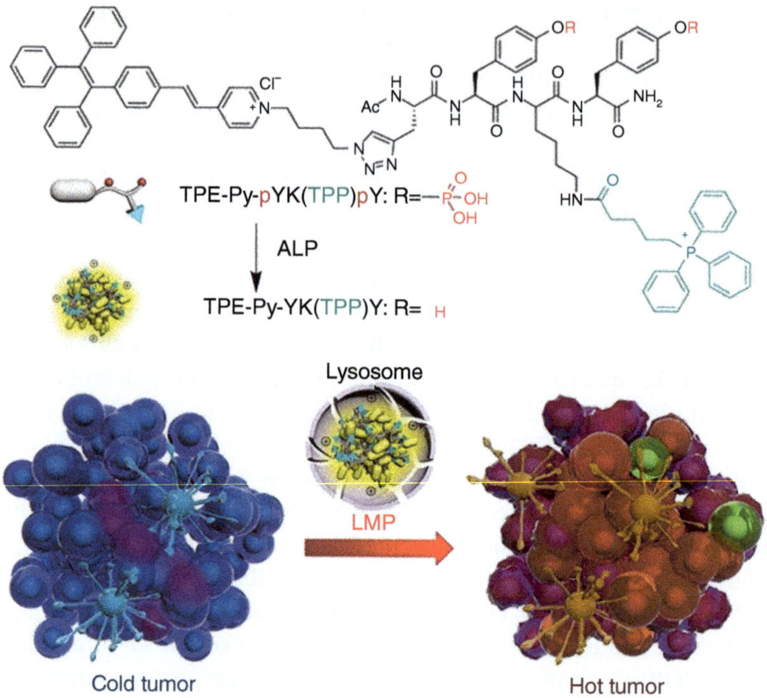

Figure 22.9 The design and application of alkaline phosphatase (ALP)-responsive lysosomal membrane permeabilization (LMP) inducer: TPE-Py-pYK(TPP)pY can be catalyzed into TPE-Py-YK(TPP)Y for formation of nanoassemblies, which can induce LMP and rupture of lysosomal membranes, and therefore can massively evoke ICD and convert cold tumors to hot. Source: Ref. [86]. Reproduced with permission of 2021 Wiley-VCH GmbH.

via the overexpressed sialic acid on tumor cells, while on-demand gelation of FK-PBA was activated by sequentially injected 1 mM Na_2CO_3 solution with dispersion of PEI-Ce6-coated autologous tumor cells (PC-Cell), which can neutralize the residue carboxylic groups to promote hydrogel formation. As such, the antigens can be restricted within residual tumor areas for sustained immune response within the surgical bed. Hence, PC-Cell@gel coupled with PDT resulted in the maturation of DCs, suppression of regulatory T cells, activation of neoepitope-specific $CD8^+$ T-cells, and inhibition of tumor relapse in colorectal and melanoma mouse models.

22.3.4.2 Photothermal Therapy

PTT agents used in PTT are able to convert light into heat through laser irradiation, without limitation on oxygen compared to PDT [89]. The locally generated hyperpyrexia not only ablates tumor tissue but also simultaneously triggers ER stress. Thereafter, the ICD of tumor cells occurs, which is also widely studied in combination with immunotherapy [90]. Injectable supramolecular peptide hydrogels have been designed as promising platforms for encapsulating photothermal and immune agents. Yan and coworkers [91] fabricated collagen polypeptide hydrogels with incorporation of a photothermal drug methylene blue (MB) and immunological agent imiquimod (R837) for combinatorial photothermal and immunotumor therapy. Collagen/alginate hydrogel (Gel) with shear-thinning and self-healing properties was readily constructed by co-assembly of positively charged collagen and negatively charged alginate. In addition, integrating MB and R837 into the hybrid hydrogel (Gel-MB-R837) did not influence their initial injectability. After intratumoral injection of Gel-MB-R837, the high temperature caused by MB effectively ablated the primary tumor and further produced TAAs upon mild laser irradiation. Subsequently, TAAs, together with R837 released from Gel-MB-R837, triggered the immune response for inhibiting distal tumor growth. Furthermore, by the utilization of immune activity endowed by peptide building blocks, additional effects can be easily coupled. As a representative work reported by Yan's group [92], a clinically used pentapeptide thymopentin (RKDVY, abbreviated as TP5) was used for fabricating nanodrugs (Figure 22.10), which has been demonstrated their immunomodulatory bioactivity including promoting thymocyte differentiation and modulating mature T-cell function. Photothermal agent ICG was utilized as another building block to co-assemble with TP5 for constructing nanodrugs. Hydrogen bonds that occurred between the amide groups in TP5 and the sulfonate groups in ICG resulted in the formation of long-range ordered nanofibrils (TP5–ICG NFs), which not only alleviated intermolecular aggregation of ICG molecules but also retained their capabilities of fluorescence imaging and photothermal conversion. Importantly, introducing TP5 in these nanodrugs promoted the proliferation and differentiation of

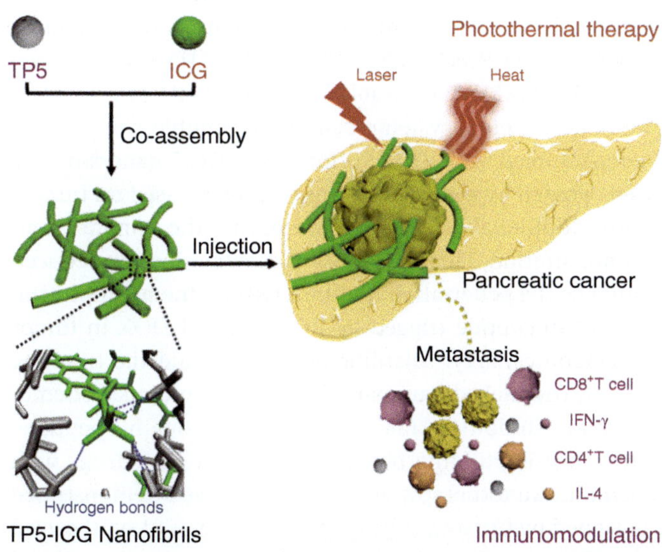

Figure 22.10 The formation and application of thymopentin-based near-infrared photothermal immunomodulatory nanofibrils: Hydrogen bonds promote the co-assembly of TP5 and ICG for the formation of nanofibrils. After localized injection, photothermal and immunomodulatory effects of TP5-ICG nanofibrils inhibit tumor growth and metastasis of pancreatic cancer. Source: Ref. [92]. Reproduced with permission of 2021 Wiley-VCH GmbH.

effector T cells. By this means of integrating rapid tumor ablation and mild systematic immunomodulation after once localized injection and once photoirradiation, the growth and metastasis of pancreatic tumor were inhibited, and the side effects were minimized as well. What is more, as another strategy to fulfill multitherapeutic effects, other drug molecules with specific function can be incorporated to enrich peptide-based nanoplatforms. For example, Qian and coworkers [93] constructed multifunctional nanodrugs with the ability of tumor targeting, penetration enhancement, targeted drug release behavior, and immunomodulation mediated by checkpoint blockade (PD-1/PD-L1). Nanodrugs were co-assembled with chemodrug molecules docetaxel (DTX), photothermal agent IR820, and a predesigned peptide with 27 amino acids (CF27). CF27 functioned as cross-linker in the nanodrugs fabrication to yield high drug loading efficiency. CF27 is responsive to MMP-2 and high GSH levels in the tumor microenvironment. Of note, CF27 contained a peptide sequence for blocking the PD-L1 immunosuppressive signal. The resulting nanodrugs with integrated PTT, chemotherapy, and immunotherapy strikingly inhibited tumor growth and metastasis, thereby enhancing the treatment outcome.

22.3.4.3 Chemotherapy

Chemotherapy is a traditional therapeutic modality in the clinic. Recently, it was demonstrated that chemotherapeutics, such as DOX [94], elicit antitumor immunity by inducing the ICD, and increasing evidence suggests that combining chemotherapy with immunotherapy greatly increases therapeutic effects [95]. For instance, Zhao and coworkers [96] reported a self-assembling selenopeptide that can sensitively respond to enzymes and ROS for augmenting the DOX-based chemotherapy, through the activation of NK cell-mediated immunotherapy by its oxidative metabolite (Figure 22.11). The selenopeptide Sec(Dod)2KGPLGVRGRGD (SeP) comprised a tumor-targeting motif (RGD), an MMP-2-cleavable linker (PLGVR), and an ROS-responsive N-terminal Se-dodecyl-selenocysteine-containing double-chained tail (Sec(Dod)2K). The SeP co-assembled with DOX to form SeP/DOX nanoparticles, which were sequentially recognized by the $\alpha_v\beta_3$ integrins overexpressed on tumors and tumoral neovasculature endothelial cell surfaces to improve the tumoral accumulation after systemic administration. Then, the MMP-2 enzyme cleavage reduced the nanoparticle size to enhance the penetration in tumor tissues, the hydrophilization and decomposition of selenopeptide trigged by ROS released DOX in tumor cells, and the oxidative metabolites, alkyl seleninic acids, activated the immune response of NK cells. The features-packed nanoparticles, finally, enhanced chemo-immunotherapy with a tumor inhibition rate of 86%. Additionally, peptide–chemodrug conjugates are versatile building blocks to construct nanodrugs with regard to combination chemoimmunotherapy, which has been well demonstrated by a variety of prodrugs designed by Cui and colleagues [97]. They [98] synthesized a prodrug hydrogelator, diCPT-PLGLAG-iRGD, and realized its application of local delivering ICBs to trigger antitumor immune response. The hydrophilic peptide iRGD was twice linked to the hydrophobic chemodrug camptothecin (CPT) via an MMP-2 cleavable peptide PLGLAG. The reducible disulfanyl-ethyl carbonate (etcSS) linker was responsible for attaching two CPT molecules to the PLGLAG sequence.

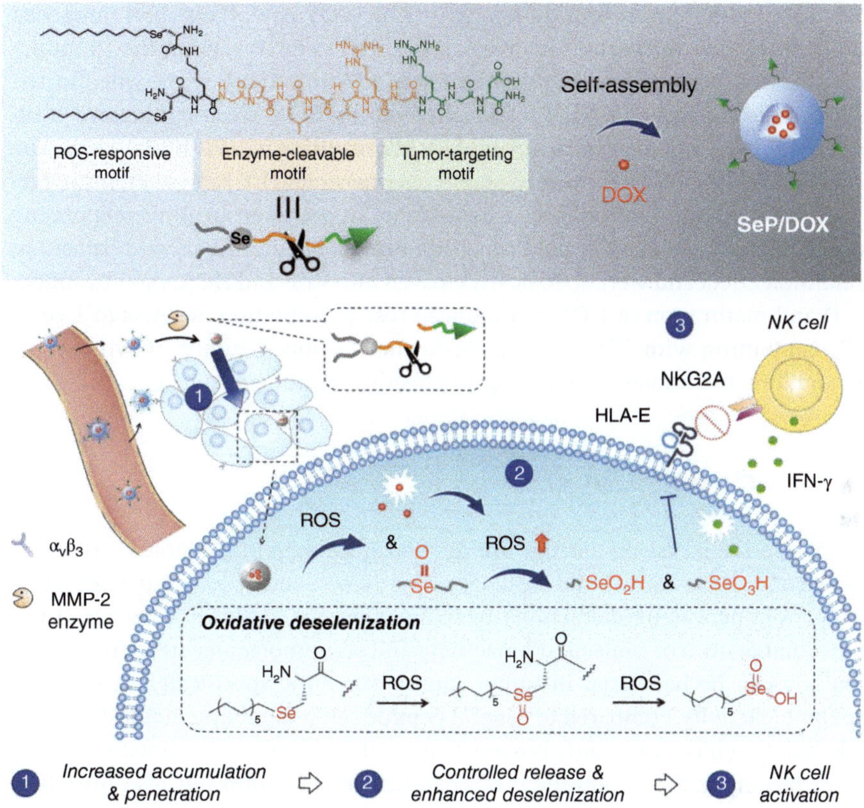

Figure 22.11 The structure and application of the self-assembled selenopeptide nanomedicine: The selenopeptide is composed of three parts including ROS-responsive motif, enzyme-cleavable motif, and tumor-targeting motif, and it can co-assemble with DOX to form SeP/DOX nanoparticles. In the application, the SeP/DOX nanoparticles targeted tumor tissues and were cleaved by MMP-2 enzyme, leading to reduced nanoparticle size for enhancing the penetration within tumor. The encapsulated DOX nanoparticles were released after selenopeptide oxidation, elevating the intracellular ROS levels, which further facilitated the deselenization of the selenopeptide and triggered the activation of NK cells. Source: Ref. [96]. Reproduced with permission of 2022 Wiley-VCH GmbH.

Owing to the highly ordered intermolecular hydrogen bonds, the CPT prodrug self-assembled into ordered nanotubes (P-NTs) with diameters around tens of micrometers. Further, the nanotube can entangle and form the hydrogel by increasing prodrug concentration, in either cell medium or phosphate-buffered saline (PBS), because of the charge-screening effect. By utilization of the sol–gel transition, aPD-1 antibody-loaded P-NT solution was subcutaneously injected into mice tumor tissue for formation of the P-NT-aPD-1 hydrogel. With the assistance of MMP-2 cleavage and later GSH reduction, CPT and aPD1 antibody were extendedly released from the P-NT-aPD-1 hydrogel, which led to the robust antitumor immune response, obvious tumor regression and inhibition on tumor recurrence, and metastasis. Taking advantage of ICD caused by phototherapy, immunochemotherapy could further potentiate tumor immunotherapy. Kim and coworkers [99] proposed visible-light-triggered prodrug nanoparticles (LT-NPs) for reversing the immune-suppressive microenvironment and enhancing ICB immunotherapy, wherein the photosensitizer verteporfin (VPF) and chemodrug DOX were conjugated with the cathepsin B-cleavable peptide linker of FRRG, resulting in VPF-FRRG-DOX. The amphiphilic VPFFRRG-DOX formed stable nanoparticles (LT-NPs) via intermolecular π–π stacking and hydrophobic interactions. In a cathepsin B-overexpressing tumor model, the LT-NPs accumulated within tumors via the enhanced permeation and retention effect and were specifically cleaved into VPF and DOX, thereby inducing ICD and maturation of DCs to stimulate cross-presentation of TAAs to T cells. LT-NPs combining with PD-L1 blockade further inhibited tumor growth, recurrence, and lung metastasis by initiating an effective immune response.

22.4 Conclusion

Bioactive peptide-based nanodrugs are defined here as self-assembled structures composed of peptide-based building blocks with diverse activities. Their assembly is regulated by noncovalent interactions to obtain nanoscale or even macroscale drugs, with the dual feature of molecular bioactivity and supramolecular structure, which particularly can be beneficial in tumor immunotherapy. Specifically, in terms of molecular bioactivity, compared to general peptide self-assembling motifs, bioactive peptide building blocks not only possess features including well-defined structure, excellent biocompatibility, and ease of chemical modification but also introduce inherent immune functions, such as antigen, adjuvant, checkpoint blockade, and immunomodulation. Besides this, supramolecular nanostructures further endow bioactive peptides with optimized efficacy and safety by means of increased stability, optimized drug pharmacokinetics, and enhanced tumoral selectivity and targetability. Therefore, bioactive peptides-based supramolecular nanodrugs are promising candidates for cancer immunotherapy. From the molecular design, to self-assembly regulation, and finally to the resultant nanodrugs function, we have summarized four immune approaches in this chapter, which include (I) supramolecular tumor vaccines, (II) immune checkpoint blockade agents, (III) immune cell regulation, and (IV) combination therapy. Based on representative examples elaborated in each part, a deep understanding of the state-of-art of bioactive peptide self-assembly and their current research status in tumor immunotherapy has been provided.

Despite the success in construction of immune-active peptide-based supramolecular nanodrugs, it remains challenging to translate them into the clinical use. First of all, the bioactivity of peptide building blocks used here is the major prerequisite for their applicable performance. Modification of bioactive peptides, such as conjugating targeting groups or other bioactive molecules, is not evitable but sometimes causes performance failure, which poses a potential threat for clinical application. Therefore, with this in mind, it is important to understand how peptides can be modified without affecting their biological function. Additionally, assessing the change of bioactivity of peptide building blocks before and after modification, both as dissolved molecules and supramolecular structures, is of great importance. Second, the discrepancy of physicochemical and pharmacokinetic properties of incorporated functional molecules remains a major obstacle, especially in tumor vaccines design (antigen and adjuvant) and combination therapy (photosensitizer/chemodrug and immune active motif). Regarding this, indicating the optimal performance window by imaging techniques and subsequent *in vivo* routes by metabolomic studies of individual molecules will enable a more flexible on-demand design of supramolecular structures. Last but not least, most recently reported bioactive peptide-based nanodrugs were obtained on laboratory scale, and the performance was evaluated in animal studies. Considering the clinical use, mass production, and quality control of nanodrugs, rather than only lab-scale availability, are needed to be realized. Further, the different physiology and pathology of human beings challenge traditional animal studies; therefore, establishing orthotopic tumor models and expanding tests to primates will provide more precise information to reflect the real status. Overall, collaborations crossing multiple disciplines need to be achieved to finally realize the clinical translation of bioactive peptide-based nanodrugs from bench to bedside.

Acknowledgment

This work was financially supported by the National Natural Science Foundation of China (project nos. 22207109, 22232006, and 22025207) and the International Postdoctoral Exchange Fellowship Program of Chinese Postdoctoral Council (project no. PC2021079).

References

1 Mellman, I., Coukos, G., and Dranoff, G. (2011). Cancer immunotherapy comes of age. *Nature* 480: 480–489.

2 Scheerstra, J.F., Wauters, A.C., Tel, J. et al. (2022). Polymersomes as a potential platform for cancer immunotherapy. *Mater. Today Adv.* 13: 100203.

3 Shi, Y. and Lammers, T. (2019). Combining nanomedicine and immunotherapy. *Acc. Chem. Res.* 52: 1543–1554.

4 Yuan, C.Q., Ji, W., Xing, R.R. et al. (2019). Hierarchically oriented organization in supramolecular peptide crystals. *Nat. Rev. Chem.* 3: 567–588.

5 Wang, J., Liu, K., Xing, R.R., and Yan, X.H. (2016). Peptide self-assembly: thermodynamics and kinetics. *Chem. Soc. Rev.* 45: 5589–5604.

6 Hamley, I.W. (2017). Small bioactive peptides for biomaterials design and therapeutics. *Chem. Rev.* 117: 14015–14041.

7 Chen, T.K., Li, Q., Liu, Z.L. et al. (2019). Peptide-based and small synthetic molecule inhibitors on PD-1/PD-L1 pathway: A new choice for immunotherapy? *Eur. J. Med. Chem.* 161: 378–398.

8 Beck, A., Klinguer-Hamour, C., Bussat, M.C. et al. (2007). Peptides as tools and drugs for immunotherapies. *J. Pept. Sci.* 13: 588–602.

9 Li, S.K., Xing, R.R., van Hest, J.C.M., and Yan, X.H. (2022). Peptide-based supramolecular assembly drugs toward cancer theranostics. *Expert Opin. Drug Deliv.* 19: 847–860.

10 Cai, Y., Zheng, C., Xiong, F.Q. et al. (2021). Recent progress in the design and application of supramolecular peptide hydrogels in cancer therapy. *Adv. Healthc. Mater.* 10: e2001239.

11 Hainline, K.M., Fries, C.N., and Collier, J.H. (2018). Progress toward the clinical translation of bioinspired peptide and protein assemblies. *Adv. Healthc. Mater.* 7: 1700930.

12 Wang, L., Wang, N.X., Zhang, W.P. et al. (2022). Therapeutic peptides: current applications and future directions. *Signal Transduct. Target. Ther.* 7: 48.

13 Zhang, L., Huang, Y.Y., Lindstrom, A.R. et al. (2019). Peptide-based materials for cancer immunotherapy. *Theranostics* 9: 7807–7825.

14 Furukawa, N. and Popel, A.S. (2021). Peptides that immunoactivate the tumor microenvironment. *Biochim. Biophys. Acta Rev. Cancer* 1875: 188486.

15 Irvine, D.J. and Dane, E.L. (2020). Enhancing cancer immunotherapy with nanomedicine. *Nat. Rev. Immunol.* 20: 321–334.

16 Goldberg, M.S. (2019). Improving cancer immunotherapy through nanotechnology. *Nat. Rev. Cancer* 19: 587–602.

17 Shi, J., Kantoff, P.W., Wooster, R., and Farokhzad, O.C. (2017). Cancer nanomedicine: progress, challenges and opportunities. *Nat. Rev. Cancer* 17: 20–37.

18 Akbarian, M., Khani, A., Eghbalpour, S., and Uversky, V.N. (2022). Bioactive peptides: synthesis, sources, applications, and proposed mechanisms of action. *Int. J. Mol. Sci.* 23: 1445.

19 Li, M., Zhao, X., Dai, J., and Yu, Z. (2019). Peptide therapeutics and assemblies for cancer immunotherapy. *Sci. China Mater.* 62: 1759–1781.

20 Li, L.L., Qiao, Z.Y., Wang, L., and Wang, H. (2019). Programmable construction of peptide-based materials in living subjects: from modular design and morphological control to theranostics. *Adv. Mater.* 31: 1804971.

21 Malonis, R.J., Lai, J.R., and Vergnolle, O. (2020). Peptide-based vaccines: current progress and future challenges. *Chem. Rev.* 25 (120): 3210–3229.

22 Wieczorek, M., Abualrous, E.T., Sticht, J. et al. (2017). Major histocompatibility complex (MHC) class I and MHC class II proteins: conformational plasticity in antigen presentation. *Front. Immunol.* 8: 292.

23 O'Neill, C.L., Shrimali, P.C., Clapacs, Z.P. et al. (2021). Peptide-based supramolecular vaccine systems. *Acta Biomater.* 133: 153–167.

24 Coffman, R.L., Sher, A., and Seder, R.A. (2010). Vaccine adjuvants: putting innate immunity to work. *Immunity* 33: 492–503.

25 Pulendran, B., Arunachalam, P.S., and O'Hagan, D.T. (2021). Emerging concepts in the science of vaccine adjuvants. *Nat. Rev. Drug Discov.* 20: 454–475.

26 Song, H., Su, Q., Huang, P. et al. (2021). Self-assembling, self-adjuvanting and fully synthetic peptide nanovaccine for cancer immunotherapy. *Smart Mater. Med.* 2: 237–249.

27 Han, Y., Liu, D., and Li, L. (2020). PD-1/PD-L1 pathway: current researches in cancer. *Am. J. Cancer Res.* 10: 727–742.

28 Chen, L. (2004). Co-inhibitory molecules of the B7-CD28 family in the control of T-cell immunity. *Nat. Rev. Immunol.* 4: 336–347.

29 Chang, H.N., Liu, B.Y., Qi, Y.K. et al. (2015). Blocking of the PD-1/PD-L1 interaction by a D-peptide antagonist for cancer immunotherapy. *Angew. Chem. Int. Ed.* 54: 11760–11764.

30 Pavlicevic, M., Marmiroli, N., and Maestri, E. (2022). Immunomodulatory peptides-A promising source for novel functional food production and drug discovery. *Peptides* 148: 170696.

31 Kraehenbuehl, L., Weng, C.H., Eghbali, S. et al. (2022). Enhancing immunotherapy in cancer by targeting emerging immunomodulatory pathways. *Nat. Rev. Clin. Oncol.* 19: 37–50.

32 Chen, D.S. and Mellman, I. (2013). Oncology meets immunology: the cancer-immunity cycle. *Immunity* 39: 1–10.

33 Roth, G.A., Picece, V., Ou, B.S. et al. (2022). Designing spatial and temporal control of vaccine responses. *Nat. Rev. Mater.* 7: 174–195.

34 Rötzschke, O., Falk, K., Stevanovic, S. et al. (1991). Exact prediction of a natural T cell epitope. *Eur. J. Immunol.* 21: 2891–2894.

35 Purwada, A., Tian, Y.F., Huang, W. et al. (2016). Self-assembly protein nanogels for safer cancer immunotherapy. *Adv. Healthc. Mater.* 5: 1413–1419.

36 Dong, X., Liang, J., Yang, A.F. et al. (2018). In vivo imaging tracking and immune responses to nanovaccines involving combined antigen nanoparticles with a programmed delivery. *ACS Appl. Mater. Interfaces* 10: 21861–21875.

37 Dong, X., Liang, J., Yang, A.F. et al. (2019). A visible codelivery nanovaccine of antigen and adjuvant with self-carrier for cancer immunotherapy. *ACS Appl. Mater. Interfaces* 11: 4876–4888.

38 Mitri, Z., Constantine, T., and O'Regan, R. (2012). The HER2 receptor in breast cancer: pathophysiology, clinical use, and new advances in therapy. *Chemother. Res. Pract.* 2012: 743193.

39 Aiga, T. et al. (2020). Immunological evaluation of co-assembling a lipidated peptide antigen and lipophilic adjuvants: self-adjuvanting anti-breast-cancer vaccine candidates. *Angew. Chem. Int. Ed.* 59: 17705–17711.

40 Tsoras, A.N. and Champion, J.A. (2018). Cross-linked peptide nanoclusters for delivery of oncofetal antigen as a cancer vaccine. *Bioconjug. Chem.* 29: 776–785.

41 Alspach, E., Lussier, D.M., Miceli, A.P. et al. (2019). MHC-II neoantigens shape tumour immunity and response to immunotherapy. *Nature* 574: 696–701.

42 Schumacher, T.N. and Schreiber, R.D. (2015). Neoantigens in cancer immunotherapy. *Science* 348: 69–74.

43 Ni, Q.Q., Zhang, F.W., Liu, Y.J. et al. (2020). A bi-adjuvant nanovaccine that potentiates immunogenicity of neoantigen for combination immunotherapy of colorectal cancer. *Sci. Adv.* 6: eaaw6071.

44 Wang, C., Ye, Y., Hu, Q. et al. (2017). Tailoring biomaterials for cancer immunotherapy: emerging trends and future outlook. *Adv. Mater.* 29: 1606036.

45 Black, M., Trent, A., Kostenko, Y. et al. (2012). Self-assembled peptide amphiphile micelles containing a cytotoxic T-cell epitope promote a protective immune response in vivo. *Adv. Mater.* 24: 3845–3849.

46 Chen, Y.J., Yuan, F.J., Jiang, X. et al. (2018). Discovery of a self-assembling and self-adjuvant lipopeptide as a saccharide-free peptide vaccine targeting EGFRvIII positive cutaneous melanoma. *Biomater. Sci.* 6: 1120–1128.

47 Lynn, G.M., Sedlik, C., Baharom, F. et al. (2020). Peptide-TLR-7/8a conjugate vaccines chemically programmed for nanoparticle self-assembly enhance CD8 T-cell immunity to tumor antigens. *Nat. Biotechnol.* 38: 320–332.

48 Li, S.K., Zhang, W.J., Xue, H.D. et al. (2020). Tumor microenvironment-oriented adaptive nanodrugs based on peptide self-assembly. *Chem. Sci.* 11: 8644–8656.

49 Rudra, J.S., Tian, Y.F., Jung, J.P., and Collier, J.H. (2010). A self-assembling peptide acting as an immune adjuvant. *Proc. Natl. Acad. Sci. U. S. A.* 107: 622–627.

50 Rudra, J.S., Sun, T., Bird, K.C. et al. (2012). Modulating adaptive immune responses to peptide self-assemblies. *ACS Nano* 6: 1557–1564.

51 Huang, Z.H., Shi, L., Ma, J.W. et al. (2012). A totally synthetic, self-assembling, adjuvant-free MUC1 glycopeptide vaccine for cancer therapy. *J. Am. Chem. Soc.* 134: 8730–8733.

52 Yang, P.X., Song, H.J., Feng, Z.J. et al. (2019). Synthetic, supramolecular, and self-adjuvanting CD8+ T-cell epitope vaccine increases the therapeutic antitumor immunity. *Adv. Therap.* 2: 1900010.

53 Demircan, M.B., Tohumeken, S., Gunduz, N. et al. (2020). Biotin functionalized self-assembled peptide nanofiber as an adjuvant for immunomodulatory response. *Biotechnol. J.* 15: e2000100.

54 Song, Y.Q., Su, Q., Shi, X.G. et al. (2021). Precisely shaped self-adjuvanting peptide vaccines with enhanced immune responses for HPV-associated cancer therapy. *ACS Appl. Mater. Interfaces* 13: 49737–49753.

55 Trac, N.T. and Chung, E.J. (2020). Peptide-based targeting of immunosuppressive cells in cancer. *Bioact. Mater.* 5: 92–101.

56 Motz, G.T. and Coukos, G. (2013). Deciphering and reversing tumor immune suppression. *Immunity* 39: 61–73.

57 Wieder, T., Eigentler, T., Brenner, E., and Röcken, M. (2018). Immune checkpoint blockade therapy. *J. Allergy Clin. Immunol.* 142: 1403–1414.

58 Cheng, K.M., Ding, Y.P., Zhao, Y. et al. (2018). Sequentially responsive therapeutic peptide assembling nanoparticles for dual-targeted cancer immunotherapy. *Nano Lett.* 18: 3250–3258.

59 Li, X.X., Wang, Y.H., Zhang, Y.M. et al. (2021). A supramolecular "trident" for cancer immunotherapy. *Adv. Funct. Mater.* 31: 2100729.

60 Dai, J., Dai, J., Hu, J.J. et al. (2022). Deep downregulation of PD-L1 by caged peptide-conjugated AIEgen/miR-140 nanoparticles for enhanced immunotherapy. *Angew. Chem. Int. Ed.* 61: e202117798.

61 Fu, L.P., Zhang, J.H., Wu, C.C. et al. (2022). A novel PD-L1 targeting peptide self-assembled nanofibers for sensitive tumor imaging and photothermal immunotherapy in vivo. *Nano Res.* 15: 7286–7294.

62 Sun, M.Q., Yao, S.B., Fan, L.Y. et al. (2022). Fibroblast activation protein-alpha responsive peptide assembling prodrug nanoparticles for remodeling the immunosuppressive microenvironment and boosting cancer immunotherapy. *Small* 18: e2106296.

63 Zheng, X.Q., Yan, J., You, W.M. et al. (2021). Novo nano-erythrocyte structurally braced by biomimetic Au(I)-peptide skeleton for MDM2/MDMX predation toward augmented pulmonary adenocarcinoma immunotherapy. *Small* 17: e2100394.

64 Gajewski, T.F., Schreiber, H., and Fu, Y.X. (2013). Innate and adaptive immune cells in the tumor microenvironment. *Nat. Immunol.* 14: 1014–1022.

65 Skwarczynski, M. and Toth, I. (2016). Peptide-based synthetic vaccines. *Chem. Sci.* 7: 842–854.

66 Fries, C.N., Wu, Y.Y., Kelly, S.H. et al. (2020). Controlled lengthwise assembly of helical peptide nanofibers to modulate CD8(+) T-cell responses. *Adv. Mater.* 32: e2003310.

67 Mamuti, M., Wang, Y., Zhao, Y.D. et al. (2022). A polyvalent peptide CD40 nanoagonist for targeted modulation of dendritic cells and amplified cancer immunotherapy. *Adv. Mater.* 34: e2109432.

68 Zhang, Q.L., Zheng, D.W., Dong, X. et al. (2021). A Strategy based on the enzyme-catalyzed polymerization reaction of Asp-Phe-Tyr tripeptide for cancer immunotherapy. *J. Am. Chem. Soc.* 143: 5127–5140.

69 Horowitz, M.C., Friedlaender, G.E., and Qian, H.Y. (1996). The immune response: the efferent arm. *Clin. Orthop. Relat. Res.* 326: 25–34.

70 Wang, M.D., Lv, G.T., An, H.W. et al. (2022). In situ self-assembly of bispecific peptide for cancer immunotherapy. *Angew. Chem. Int. Ed.* 61: e202113649.

71 Zhang, L., Bo, R.N., Wu, Y. et al. (2022). Programmable bispecific nano-immunoengager that captures T cells and reprograms tumor microenvironment. *Nano Lett.* 22: 6866–6876.

72 Mantovani, A., Allavena, P., Marchesi, F., and Garlanda, C. (2022). Macrophages as tools and targets in cancer therapy. *Nat. Rev. Drug Discov.* 21: 799–820.

73 Zhao, Y.D., An, H.W., Mamuti, M. et al. (2023). Reprogramming hypoxic tumor-associated macrophages by nanoglycoclusters for boosted cancer immunotherapy. *Adv. Mater.* 35: 2211332.

74 Deng, R.H., Zou, M.Z., Zheng, D. et al. (2019). Nanoparticles from cuttlefish ink inhibit tumor growth by synergizing immunotherapy and photothermal therapy. *ACS Nano* 13: 8618–8629.

75 Huang, C., Jin, H.L., Qian, Y. et al. (2013). Hybrid melittin cytolytic Peptide-driven ultrasmall lipid nanoparticles block melanoma growth in vivo. *ACS Nano* 7: 5791–5800.

76 Yu, X., Dai, Y.F., Zhao, Y.F. et al. (2020). Melittin-lipid nanoparticles target to lymph nodes and elicit a systemic anti-tumor immune response. *Nat. Commun.* 11: 1110.

77 Nothelfer, K., Sansonetti, P.J., and Phalipon, A. (2015). Pathogen manipulation of B cells: the best defence is a good offence. *Nat. Rev. Microbiol.* 13: 173–184.

78 Karsai, A., Slack, T.J., Malekan, H. et al. (2016). Local mechanical perturbation provides an effective means to regulate the growth and assembly of functional peptide fibrils. *Small* 12: 6407–6415.

79 Zhou, Y., Ke, P., Bao, X.Y. et al. (2022). Peptide nano-blanket impedes fibroblasts activation and subsequent formation of pre-metastatic niche. *Nat. Commun.* 13: 2906.

80 Lopez-Silva, T.L., Leach, D.G., Azares, A. et al. (2020). Chemical functionality of multidomain peptide hydrogels governs early host immune response. *Biomaterials* 231: 119667.

81 Zhang, P.S., Meng, J.L., Li, Y.Y. et al. (2021). Nanotechnology-enhanced immunotherapy for metastatic cancer. *Innovation (Camb)* 2: 100174.

82 Liu, Y.M., Chang, R., Xing, R.R., and Yan, X.H. (2023). Bioactive peptide nanodrugs based on supramolecular assembly for boosting immunogenic cell death-induced cancer immunotherapy. *Small Methods* 7: 2201708.

83 Castano, A.P., Mroz, P., and Hamblin, M.R. (2006). Photodynamic therapy and anti-tumour immunity. *Nat. Rev. Cancer* 6: 535–545.

84 Ng, C.W., Li, J.C., and Pu, K.Y. (2018). Recent progresses in phototherapy-synergized cancer immunotherapy. *Adv. Funct. Mater.* 28: 1804688.

85 Yi, Y.F., Yu, M., Feng, C. et al. (2022). Transforming "cold" tumors into "hot" ones via tumor-microenvironment-responsive siRNA micelleplexes for enhanced immunotherapy. *Matter* 5: 2285–2305.

86 Ji, S.L., Li, J., Duan, X.C. et al. (2021). Targeted enrichment of enzyme-instructed assemblies in cancer cell lysosomes turns immunologically cold tumors hot. *Angew. Chem. Int. Ed.* 60: 26994–27004.

87 Wang, D.G., Wang, T.T., Yu, H.J. et al. (2019). Engineering nanoparticles to locally activate T cells in the tumor microenvironment. *Sci. Immunol.* 4: eaau6584.

88 Fang, L., Zhao, Z.T., Wang, J. et al. (2020). Engineering autologous tumor cell vaccine to locally mobilize antitumor immunity in tumor surgical bed. *Sci. Adv.* 6: eaba4024.

89 Zhao, L.Y., Liu, Y.M., Chang, R. et al. (2019). Supramolecular photothermal nanomaterials as an emerging paradigm toward precision cancer therapy. *Adv. Funct. Mater.* 29: 1806877.

90 Chu, K.F. and Dupuy, D.E. (2014). Thermal ablation of tumours: biological mechanisms and advances in therapy. *Nat. Rev. Cancer* 14: 199–208.

91 Mei, E.C., Li, S.K., Song, J.W. et al. (2019). Self-assembling collagen/alginate hybrid hydrogels for combinatorial photothermal and immuno tumor therapy. *Colloids Surf. A Physicochem. Eng. Asp.* 577: 570–575.

92 Li, S.K., Zhang, W.J., Xing, R.R. et al. (2021). Supramolecular nanofibrils formed by coassembly of clinically approved drugs for tumor photothermal immunotherapy. *Adv. Mater.* 33: e2100595.

93 Peng, J.R., Yang, Q., Xiao, Y. et al. (2019). Tumor microenvironment responsive drug-dye-peptide nanoassembly for enhanced tumor-targeting, penetration, and photo-chemo-immunotherapy. *Adv. Funct. Mater.* 29: 1900004.

94 Krysko, D.V., Kaczmarek, A., Krysko, O. et al. (2011). TLR-2 and TLR-9 are sensors of apoptosis in a mouse model of doxorubicin-induced acute inflammation. *Cell Death Differ.* 18: 1316–1325.

95 Kuai, R., Yuan, W.M., Son, S.J. et al. (2018). Elimination of established tumors with nanodisc-based combination chemoimmunotherapy. *Sci. Adv.* 4: eaao1736.

96 Wei, Z.Y., Yi, Y., Luo, Z. et al. (2022). Selenopeptide nanomedicine activates natural killer cells for enhanced tumor chemoimmunotherapy. *Adv. Mater.* 34: e2108167.

97 Wang, H., Monroe, M., Leslie, F. et al. (2022). Supramolecular nanomedicines through rational design of self-assembling prodrugs. *Trends Pharmacol. Sci.* 43: 510–521.

98 Wang, F.H., Xu, D.Q., Su, H. et al. (2020). Supramolecular prodrug hydrogelator as an immune booster for checkpoint blocker-based immunotherapy. *Sci. Adv.* 6: eaaz8985.

99 Choi, J., Shim, M.K., Yang, S. et al. (2021). Visible-light-triggered prodrug nanoparticles combine chemotherapy and photodynamic therapy to potentiate checkpoint blockade cancer immunotherapy. *ACS Nano* 15: 12086–12098.

23

Self-assembled Stimuli-responsive Nanomaterials Using Peptide Amphiphiles for Targeting Delivery of Drugs

Nayeong Jeon, Ilhyung Choi, and Eunji Lee

School of Materials Science and Engineering, Gwangju Institute of Science and Technology (GIST), 61005 Gwangju, Republic of Korea

23.1 Introduction

Advances in biomedicine and pharmaceutical science have accelerated the development of numerous therapeutic agents for the treatment of various diseases [1–3]. Although therapeutic agents have intriguing potential in health care, many traditional therapeutic agents have failed to overcome the high barriers of preclinical and clinical studies. This failure arises from several reasons, including poor drug stability [4–6], high cytotoxicity [7, 8], poor water solubility [9–12], short circulation time [13, 14], uncontrolled pharmacokinetic rate [15], and inefficient site-specific targeting [16, 17]. During the past few decades, nanoscience and nanotechnology have contributed to the development of biomaterials with applications in drug delivery [18, 19], biomedicine [20], biosensor [21–24], bioimaging [25–28], diagnostics [29, 30], tissue engineering [31–34], and therapy [35, 36]. Nanoscale drug delivery enables new classes of therapeutics and can enhance therapeutic efficacy while decreasing the side effects and difficulties associated with the delivery of conventional drugs [37, 38]. In addition, it can endow biologically active molecules that are previously considered unusable or undevelopable the potential to be considered as pharmaceutically agents. In the 1960s, liposomes were first described by Bangham and proposed as drug or protein carriers for disease treatment [39]. In the 1970s, a viral vector, developed using a virus to inject genetic materials such as deoxyribonucleic acid (DNA) or ribonucleic acid (RNA) into cells or living organisms, was developed to transfer external DNA into cells [40]. Thereafter, cell-derived extracellular vesicles have been utilized to deliver various therapeutics such as proteins [41], lipids [42], genetic materials [43], carbon dots [44], quantum dots [45], graphene [46], plasmonic nanoparticles (NPs) [47], or

Peptide Self-Assembly and Engineering: Fundamentals, Structures, and Applications, First Edition.
Edited by Xuehai Yan.

gold nanoclusters [48] to target cells or organs. However, the applications of these therapeutics have been limited by biological barriers such as enzymatic degradation [49], uptake by the reticuloendothelial system [50], kidney filtration [51], and limited intracellular entry [52]. In order to overcome these barriers, the therapeutic agent was encapsulated and accurately delivered to the disordered area. Nanomaterials for drug delivery based on virus-based NPs [53], liposomes [54], lysosomes [55], polymeric micelles [42, 56], dendrimers [57], solid lipid NPs [58, 59], and organic/inorganic hybrid NPs [60, 61] have been suggested to efficiently encapsulate and deliver therapeutics. Nanocarriers have been designed to modulate multiple pharmaceutical properties, such as pharmacokinetics and pharmacodynamics [62–64]. However, poor recognition, insolubility, deficient biodegradability, low permeability, undesired rapid clearance from blood vessels, unexpected degradation, and immunogenicity of nanomaterials are yet to be solved to target drug delivery [65]. For example, inorganic nanomaterials such as metal NPs and quantum dots cause safety problems due to their high cytotoxicity [66]. Synthetic polymers are hardly biocompatible or biodegradable with poor solubility [67], and virus-based NPs are limited to the delivery of short DNAs [68]. Oligonucleotides and proteins are difficult to penetrate the cells and susceptible to being unexpectedly degraded by nucleases and proteases, such as siRNA, aptamers, and DNA enzymes [69]. On the other hand, peptides have been widely used as building blocks in the field of biomaterials for drug delivery, because of their excellent biocompatibility and ability to encapsulate drugs owing to their self-assembled nanostructures [70–73].

Peptides, which are conjugations of amino acids by amide bonds, are extensively present in living organisms and have important biological functions [74]. In general, numerous peptide sequences can be designed, which can create a great number of opportunities for nanomaterial construction. These peptide sequences, as fundamental assembly units, can not only be self-assembled into stable biomaterials of various morphologies and sizes from zero to multiple dimensions but also have dynamic functions derived from side groups [75, 76]. Consequently, these properties enable peptide-based nanomaterials to function as scaffolds with the necessary conditions for drug delivery, opening a new methodology for the design of nanoscale drug delivery carriers [77]. Especially, the peptide amphiphiles (PAs) have been of particular interest as a building block for drug delivery carriers owing to their unique assembly structure. After the PA composed of either hydrophilic amino acids and hydrophobic polymers or hydrophobic amino acids and hydrophilic polymers was first described [78, 79], self-assembly of PAs via intermolecular noncovalent interactions has been extensively investigated [80–83]. Different types of amino acids and alkyl chains consisting of PAs not only have a critical effect on the spontaneous self-assembly behavior for hierarchical morphologies of nanostructures [84] but also allow hydrophobic drugs and genes to be encapsulated in the core [70, 85].

Anticancer drugs are well known for their side effects limiting their aggressive use, as these cytotoxic anticancer drugs activate DNA replication and cell cycle progression, killing cancer cells while adversely affecting normal proliferating cells [86]. Radiation therapy can lead to an effective reduction in cancerous cells, but the surrounding normal tissue would be unexpectedly damaged [87]. In this regard, PA nanomaterials take advantage of the stimuli-responsive ability as therapeutic platforms in various physiological environments to overcome pharmacological limitations [70, 73, 88]. Stimuli-responsive PA drug carriers can change their biochemical and physicochemical properties and structures in response to stimuli, thereby facilitating the controlled release of drugs at the lesion sites. Pathological lesion sites including cancer cells, tumors, and inflammations present around normal cells or tissues mostly have a distinctive pathophysiology, which is likely to be abnormal pH, temperature environment, disordered redox potential, and overexpressed concentrations of specific enzymes [72, 89–91]. Thus, the manipulated release and selective accumulation of drugs in target cells or tissues can be accomplished by considering the peculiar environmental differences between normal cells and lesions [3]. For example, cancerous cells have been reported to differ from normal cells with respect to several aspects of the cellular environment. They often express glycans that are generally not found in normal cells [92]. Moreover, intracellular glutathione (GSH) levels and concentrations of some enzymes are more than twice as high as extracellular levels [90, 91, 93]. Because abnormal tissues in a tumor promote the formation of hypoxic cells, tumor tissues have a lower pH than normal tissues [94]. Thus, the pH difference of pathological lesions can trigger the release of loaded drugs from pH-sensitive carriers that have entered the cytoplasm of cells whose pH is different from that of normal cells. The structural transformation of PA nanomaterials according to the surrounding environment amplifies the therapeutic effects of drugs, and their small size allows drug carriers to extravasate through the vascular endothelial junctions, enhancing permeability and retention (EPR) effects [70, 72, 95]. Furthermore, peptide sequences that allow penetration or target specific cells or enzymes can easily distinguish lesion sites and help PA drug carriers selectively deliver drugs, and the efficacy of the drug can be greatly enhanced [93, 96].

Consequently, understanding the self-assembly behavior of rationally designed PAs, the resulting hierarchical nanostructures, and their stimuli responsiveness provides many opportunities to customize enhanced therapeutic and biomedical applications. Stimuli-responsive PA drug nanocarrier systems respond not only to physiological internal stimuli in cells and tissues such as pH, temperature, redox potential, oxidative stress, and enzymes but also to external stimuli such as light, ultrasound, electric field, and magnetic field [70, 97]. Among these various stimuli, a stimulus that distinctly changes and selectively triggers the structures of drug carriers in a specific lesion not only induces remarkable drug release but also avoids damage to normal cells and tissues. In recent years, a number of intriguing multimodal stimuli-responsive PA drug carriers that respond to combinations of stimuli have also been reported to have higher therapeutic efficacy [73, 98]. In addition to the investigation and utilization of stimuli for facilitating drug release, methodologies for fabricating stimuli-responsive drug release carriers that enable self-assembled structures to disassemble, phase change, and undergo linker cleavage by stimuli have also been developed. PAs can be used to engineer various nanostructures that respond to complex physiological environments, and the biological functions of specific peptides enable PA drug carriers to detect lesions [99]. Stable PA nanostructures formed by self-assembly can circulate *in vivo* for a long time before releasing the cargo until they are exposed to specific stimuli [70]. In addition, PA biomaterials with active targeting ability and sensitivity to the environments have been used in various fields

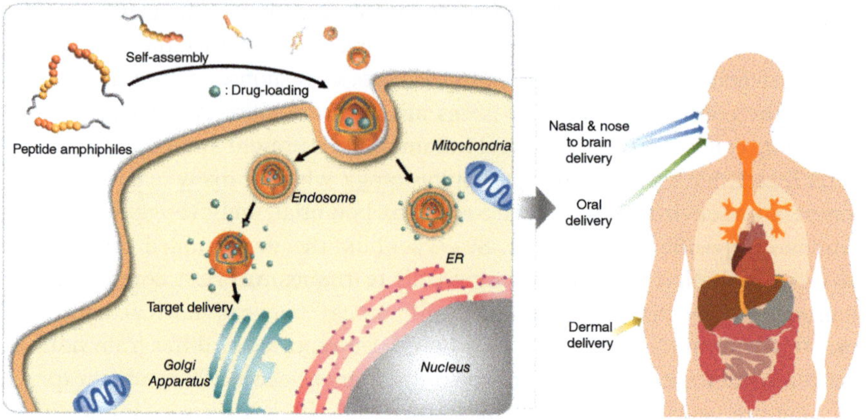

Figure 23.1 Schematic representation of the self-assembled PA vesicles containing drug molecules.

such as antimicrobial theranostic nanocarriers [100, 101], therapeutic gas transmitters [102, 103], photothermal therapeutic agents [104], and cellular cryopreserved agents [105, 106]. This chapter mainly focuses on the recent research progress in stimuli-responsive drug nanocarriers using PAs as building blocks, with an emphasis on the relationship between the PA structure and environmental response or other characteristics. Furthermore, the recent biomedical applications that take advantage of PAs and related supramolecular structures to contribute to the overall therapeutics for human beings are reviewed and discussed (Figure 23.1).

23.2 Design of the PAs for Drug Nanocarriers

23.2.1 Self-assembly Building Blocks and Driving Forces

PAs are an essential family of peptides capable of producing well-defined nanostructures with biological functionality. Lipidated peptides corresponding to the earlier form of currently established PAs were reported in the 1980s through solution reaction synthesis [78, 79]. Subsequently, Tirrell and coworkers devised a highly efficient method for synthesizing PAs via solid-phase peptide synthesis (SPPS) [107, 108]. In addition, it was found that most of the synthesized PAs can form stable bilayer membrane systems by lipid tails acting as an anchor of the functional head group to the lipid assembly. Further, studies have been conducted on the bioactivity of PAs with protein-like structural motifs incorporating sequences of biological interest in an environment mimicking cell membranes [82, 109]. In 2001, Stupp and coworkers demonstrated that PA nanofibers are reminiscent of an extracellular matrix (ECM) capable of displaying biological signals on their surface [80]. This nanomaterial is capable of reversible cross-linking through the oxidative coupling of cysteine residues in the peptide sequence, and this study has inspired advanced studies on the supramolecular assembly of PAs. The fibrillization properties of PAs have received the most interest as biomaterials, owing to their ability to form gels by fibril entanglement at low millimolar concentrations. Such materials have been extensively studied as 3D substrates for cell culture and matrices for regenerative medicine. Thus, the molecular structure of PAs, particularly how the peptide sequence and alkyl tail influence the secondary structure character, morphology, surface chemistry, and potential bioactivity of the resulting nanostructures, is being actively studied [110]. Investigating assembly mechanisms under various concentrations, pH values, or the presence of charged residues is required to elucidate natural self-assembly processes such as the folding of peptide chains into natural protein structures [81, 110, 111].

As shown in Figure 23.2, PAs are multidomain peptides with a hydrophobic, lipid-like tail linked to a hydrophilic peptide headgroup. Amino acids constituting PAs with different kinds of side chains and alkyl tails have a critical effect on the self-assembly behavior of hierarchical morphologies of nanostructures through non-covalent intermolecular interactions such as hydrogen bonding, hydrophobic interactions, π–π stacking, and electrostatic interaction. Synthetic PAs can adopt secondary structures such as α-helices, β-sheets, β-hairpins, or coiled-coils [112–115], and the pitch length of β-sheet tapes influences the final structures because of lateral stacking in parallel with other interactions. Subsequently, PAs self-assemble into supramolecular nanostructures such as 1D fibers, micelles, ribbons, aligned fibers, tubes, and vesicles above the critical micelle concentration (CMC).

The self-assembly pathway of PAs is highly dependent on the thermodynamic and kinetic energy, as depicted in the energy landscape (Figure 23.3a) [116, 117]. The most stable structures without the intervention of environmental conditions would grow into thermodynamically preferred states with high stability for biological applications. However, most supramolecular structures are dynamically stable, rather than thermodynamically stable [118]. This implies that controlled dynamic parameters such as pH and temperature allow the structure to be trapped in a dynamically stable state and further grow to a thermodynamically preferred state. The lipid tail and hydrophobic side chains of PA get an energy penalty upon exposure to water, and electrostatic repulsion between the charged head groups creates

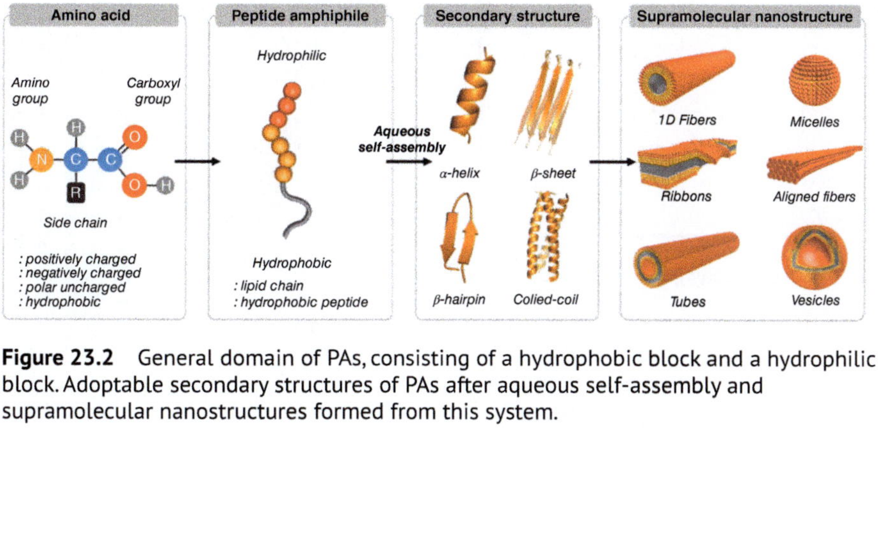

Figure 23.2 General domain of PAs, consisting of a hydrophobic block and a hydrophilic block. Adoptable secondary structures of PAs after aqueous self-assembly and supramolecular nanostructures formed from this system.

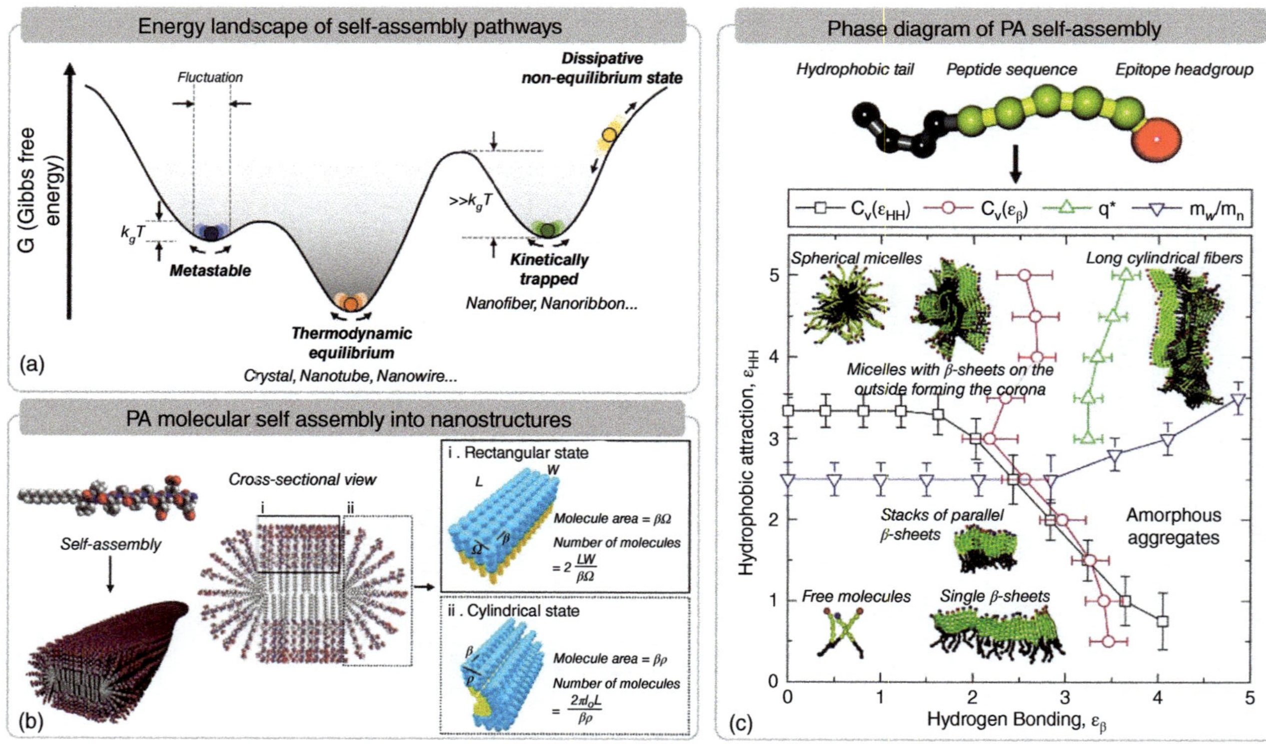

Figure 23.3 (a) Peptide self-assembly pathways under thermodynamic and kinetic control. The final structures are in the state of minimum free energy, while the metastable structures can be formed under kinetic control. (b) Molecular self-assembly of PA into nanostructures consisting of rectangularly packed center domains and cylindrical edges. Source: Ref. [119]. Reproduced with permission of American Chemical Society. (c) Schematic phase diagram of PA assemblies according to hydrogen bonding and hydrophobic attraction, implied by simulation results. Source: Ref. [120]. Reproduced with permission of American Chemical Society.

steric hindrance of adjacent β-sheets (Figure 23.3b) [119]. Thus, the supramolecular structure of PAs is formed by the elaborately modulated balance between hydrophilic and hydrophobic blocks or intermolecular interactions (Figure 23.3c) [81, 110, 120]. Based on these physicochemical properties, self-assembled PA nanomaterials can be designed as controllable and stable nanocarriers for drug delivery. The physical performances of drug nanocarriers such as loading capacity or sustained drug release can be controlled according to the structure of nanocarriers [121, 122] or coarseness of the nanoscale network composed of PAs [85].

23.2.2 Programmed, Self-assembled System for Drug Nanocarriers

Numerous PA-based drug nanocarriers have been constructed and optimized to mediate cell penetration, target tumor microenvironment, respond to tumor-specific enzymes for controlled drug release, and regulate cellular signaling transduction pathways. As PAs are multidomain peptides, modularized concepts for nanocarrier construction have been suggested (Figure 23.4a,b) [72]. Each block can be regarded as a module for system construction for the efficient design and implementation of drug delivery, controlled release, and targeting as well as regulation of the tumor microenvironment. The hydrophilic head of the PA building block is composed of a peptide sequence that can directly participate in drug delivery and release. It often contains peptides with functionalities such as being cell penetrating, stimuli responsive, organelle targeting, and therapeutic (Figure 23.4a), whereas the hydrophobic tail is usually composed of lipophilic compounds such as lipids, alkyl chains, cholesterol, polymers, and cholesterol (Figure 23.4b). Drug molecules are chemically bound or

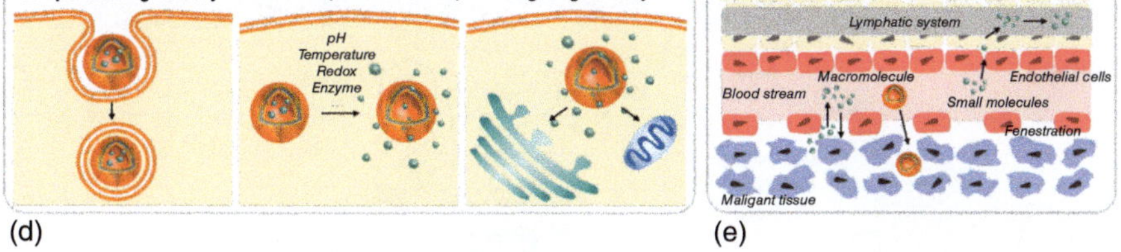

Figure 23.4 Construction of PA-based drug nanocarriers. (a) A hydrophilic block and (b) a hydrophobic block are based on various modules with functionalities. (c) PA self-assembles into nanostructures such as nanofiber, vesicles, and micelle or forms into a hydrogel in response to intermolecular interactions. (d) Schematic illustrations showing drug delivery through cell penetrating, stimuli response, and targeting according to the function of each block constituting the PA. (e) Schematic illustration showing EPR effect of nanocarrier in malignant tissue. Macromolecules with nanosize accumulate in tumor tissues through fenestrations in the blood vessel's endothelial layer and reduce lymphatic drainage.

physically encapsulated in nanocarriers with various supramolecular structures to protect their therapeutic activity while mitigating toxicity and other side effects during transport and eventually controlling their release in the presence of specific stimuli (Figure 23.4c). PA nanocarriers loaded with drug molecules can produce therapeutic effects by cell penetration, responding to specific stimuli, or delivering drugs targeting desired organelles according to the function of the peptide block (Figure 23.4d) [123, 124]. They exhibit certain effects and functions *in vivo* such as the EPR effect while interacting with tissues and cells according to their architecture, size, and structure [70, 125]. Nanocarriers, having the EPR effect, passively accumulate in tumor tissues through fenestrations in the blood vessel's endothelial layer and show significantly reduced lymphatic drainage (Figure 23.4e) [126].

23.2.3 Cellular Uptake and Intracellular Delivery

To accurately display a therapeutic effect in a localized area such as a specific cell or organelle, it is essential to understand how to design the PA molecule to enable penetration of cells and delivery of the drug. Two primary methods of delivering drugs into cells are known: membrane-disruption- and carrier-mediated delivery (Figure 23.5) [127, 128]. Membrane-disruption methods are largely physical, inducing brief discontinuities in the plasma membrane using mechanical, electrical, thermal, optical, or chemical methods, which can be categorized as permeabilization or direct penetration (Figure 23.5a). Drug delivery strategies utilizing PA nanocarriers are closely related to carrier-mediated delivery (Figure 23.5b). Different biological assemblies, molecular or supramolecular structures, are included to build a nanocarrier that can undergo carrier-mediated delivery. Nanocarriers allow cargo to be bound so that it does not deteriorate, access the desired intracellular compartments, and release the loaded drug using appropriate spatiotemporal dynamics [128].

Because of the intrinsic characteristics of the peptide and the variety of cell membranes it interacts with, the cell-penetrating peptide (CPP) and cell membrane properties alter the nature of the interactions, control internalization routes, and let the

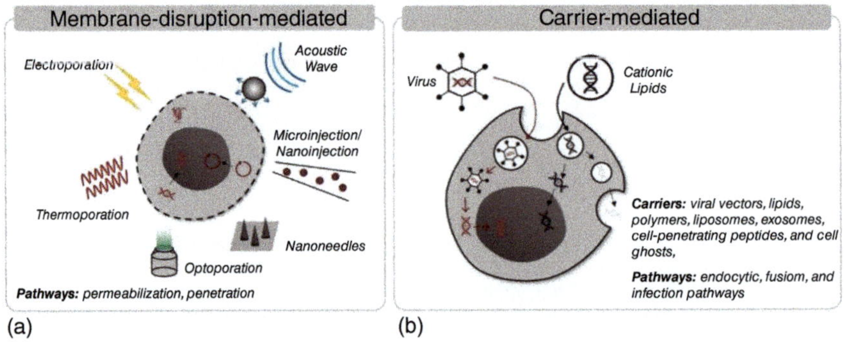

Figure 23.5 Strategies for intracellular delivering drugs. (a) Membrane-disruption-mediated delivery includes permeabilization and penetration. (b) Carrier-mediated delivery includes endocytosis and fusion. *Source:* Ref. [127]. John Wiley & Sons/CC BY 4.0.

nanocarriers deliver drugs intracellular. As shown in Figure 23.6a, internalization mechanisms may be classified into energy-independent (direct translocation), and energy-dependent (endocytosis) mechanisms [129]. Most carriers enter the body through endocytosis, and some may have the ability to fuse with the target membrane owing to their fusogenic potential [131]. Energy-independent or direct translocation occurs at low temperatures in the presence of endocytosis inhibitors when electrostatic interactions exist between the peptide and the negatively charged phospholipid bilayer [132]. Temporary or permanent membrane destabilization occurs following this interaction, allowing the peptide to enter the cytoplasm. This includes mechanisms such as pore formation, inverted micelle formation, and carpet models [129]. Energy-dependent mechanisms or endocytosis include the formation of endosomes, by which the internalization of peptides or macromolecules occurs at the expense of energy. A region of the cell membrane that surrounds the substance to be internalized buds off inside the cell to create an endosome containing the peptides to be internalized [128]. Endocytosis may occur in a clathrin-dependent or -independent manner. The endocytosis pathway is affected by the cell type, development, and physicochemical characteristics of the interacting peptides and the attached cargo. For example, the cellular uptake of arginine-rich CPPs is mediated by macropinocytosis [133–135]. Proline-rich CPPs are internalized in the cells via caveolae-mediated endocytosis [136]. If a PA nanocarrier containing the drug molecule penetrates the cell through endocytosis, an endosomal escape process is required to deliver the drug. After destabilization of the endosomal membrane, therapeutics are released through pore formation, endosomal rupture, or membrane fusion. Residues such as tryptophan and phenylalanine are known to destabilize cellular membranes by burying their hydrophobic side chains in the lipid bilayer [137]. Therefore, a peptide domain could be designed to enhance endosomal escape, as shown in Figure 23.6b [138]. The CPPs containing endosomal escape peptide domains bind to the lipid bilayer of the cell membrane and escape from the endosome. There are multiple proposed explanations for how peptides can escape from endosomes. These include the proton sponge effect, pore formation, membrane disruption, and membrane budding (Figure 23.6c) [130].

23.3 Cell-penetrating PAs for Drug Nanocarriers

23.3.1 PAs with Cell-penetrating Peptide Building Blocks

Drug nanocarriers with cell-permeating ability enhance the selectivity of drug delivery carriers, followed by the creation of efficient anticancer drug transporters, management of stimuli-responsive drug delivery, and mitigation of side effects. In this regard, chemical conjugation of CPPs to PA enables intracellular access and efficient drug delivery [139]. Well-known CPPs can be classified into the following categories on the basis of their physicochemical characteristics: Cationic peptides with an overall positive charge because of arginine and lysine residues; hydrophobic peptides containing amino acids such as alanine, valine, or methionine; and amphiphilic peptides made of both hydrophobic and hydrophilic amino acids. Examples

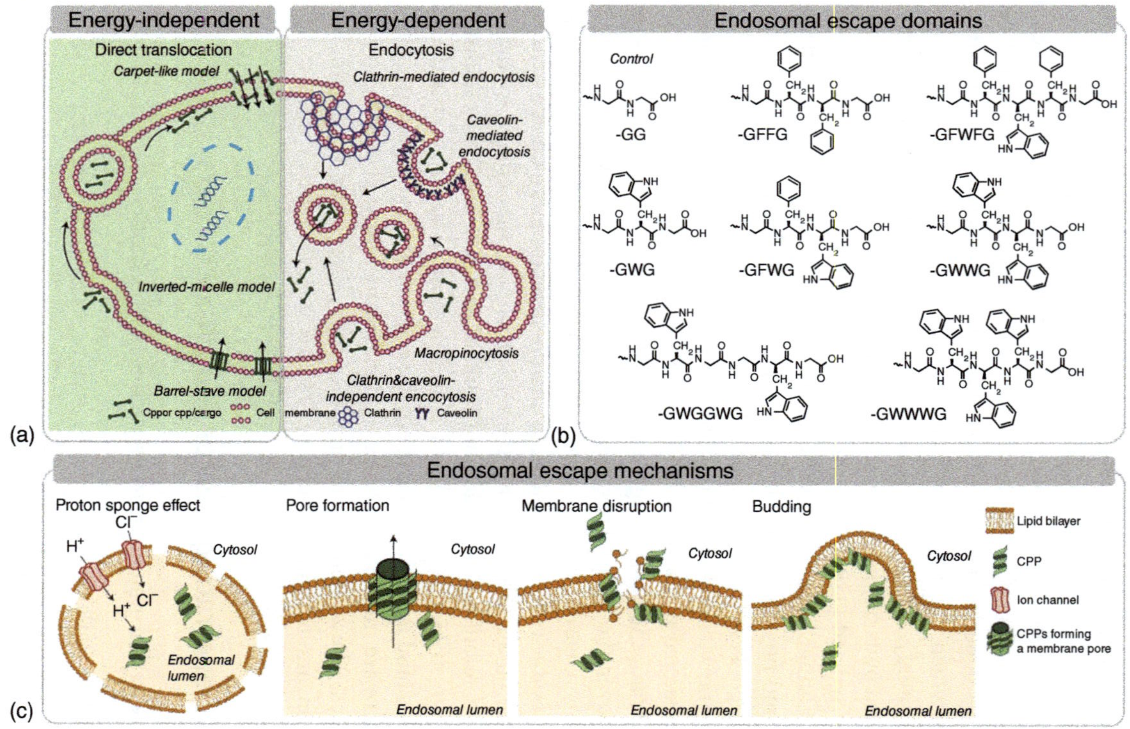

Figure 23.6 (a) Schematic illustration of energy-dependent and -independent internalization pathways of CPPs. Source: Ref. [129]. Frontiers Media SA/CC BY 4.0. (b) Peptide sequences known as endosomal escape domains. (c) Proposed endosomal escape mechanisms of CPPs. Source: Ref. [130]. Reproduced with permission of John Wiley & Sons.

of the CPPs are listed in Table 23.1. Most naturally occurring CPPs are cationic, and this is best represented by the TAT from human immunodeficiency virus (HIV) [140, 141]. Artificial cationic CPPs include polyarginine and polylysine peptides [153]. Amphiphilic CPPs contain both polar and nonpolar areas. Hydrophilic and hydrophobic amino acids are concentrated on different sides of a secondary structure, where the hydrophilic portion is accessible and interacts with the surrounding solvent, while the hydrophobic section is enclosed [154]. TAT peptide was conjugated with octanoic acid tails for effective drug transportation [155]. The PA was self-assembled into nanofiber with encapsulated paclitaxel. Tekinay and coworkers designed a PA nanosphere delivery system decorated with CPPs containing polyarginine residues and a cell surface-binding peptide, Lys-Arg-Ser-Arg (KRSR), for oligonucleotide delivery [139]. Stupp and coworkers enhanced the permeability and retention effects of PA on cells by including a charged amino-acid sequence and high aspect ratio morphology [156]. This drug delivery carrier encapsulated camptothecin, a naturally occurring hydrophobic chemotherapeutic agent, and showed improved drug uptake *in vivo*. Drugs were effectively delivered into cells using PA assemblies containing stimuli-responsive or targeting peptides along with CPP.

23.4 Stimuli-responsive PA Drug Nanocarriers

The physicochemical properties of well-designed drug nanocarriers are stimuli responsive [157–160]. Their nanostructure is changed by the stimuli, promoting the controlled release of the encapsulated drug at the lesion site in a specific environment. In general, low pH, high temperature, abnormal redox environment, and overexpressed enzymes are pathological phenomena that appear mostly in lesions such as cancer cells, tumors, and inflammation that exist around normal cells [161]. Ultimately, drug carriers capable of noticing the environmental differences between normal cells and diseased cells or tissues can realize customized release and accumulation of drugs into targeted cells or tissues [70, 71, 73, 88, 162–164]. Stimuli that can be used to trigger drug release from drug nanocarriers can be divided into internal and external stimuli [99]. Internal stimuli refer to differences in the natural pathological environments of lesions and normal cells or targets. External stimuli such as light, ultrasound, electric field, and magnetic field refer to stimuli artificially applied from outside the biological system [165–168]. External stimuli-responsive materials provide precise temporal and spatial control of drug release [169, 170]. Examples of internal and external stimuli that can be used to trigger drug release are shown in Figure 23.7a. The physiological characteristics of the disease must be studied to understand the cause and aggravation process of the disease and to develop effective drugs. In addition, the understanding of specific pathological phenomena has enabled the development of stimuli-responsive carriers that can selectively deliver drugs to diseased cells or tissues [88, 161, 171]. For example, the pH of most normal cells, tissue, and blood are approximately 7.4, which tends to be neutral, whereas the pH of lesion sites is more acidic [72, 172]. Drug nanocarriers first reach the cytoplasm after passing through the cell membrane. At this time, the

Table 23.1 Examples of common cationic, hydrophobic, or amphipathic CPPs, sequences, and characteristics.

Protein group	Examples	Sequence	Characteristics	Ref
Cationic	TAT	GRKKRRQRRRPPQ	Transcriptional regulator of HIV-1 tat protein	[140, 141]
	Penetratin	RQIKIWFQNRRMKWKK	Natural peptide from Antennapedia *Drosophila melanogaster*	[142, 143]
	Polyarginine	R_n (n = 8, 9, 10, 12)	Synthetic peptide	[144]
	Polylysine	K_n (n = 8)	Synthetic peptide	[145]
Hydrophobic	VP22	DAATATRGRSAASRPTERPRAPARSASRPRRVD	Natural peptide from capsid of HSV-1 virus	[146]
	Pep-7	SDLWEMMMVSLACQY	Natural peptide from CHL8	[147]
Amphipathic	VT5	DPKGDPKGVTVTVTVTVTGKGDPKPD	Capsid protein of rotaviruses	[148]
	Pep-1	KETWWETWWTEWSQPKKKRKV	Chimeric peptide from HIV-reverse transcriptase and SV40 T antigen	[147]
	MPG	GALFLGFLGAAGSTMGAWSQPKKKRKV	Chimeric peptide from HIV-gp41 and SV40 T antigen	[149]
	Transportan	GWTLNSAGYLLGKINLKALAALAKKIL	Synthetic peptide	[150, 151]
	MAP	KLALKLALKALKAALKLA	Synthetic peptide	[152]

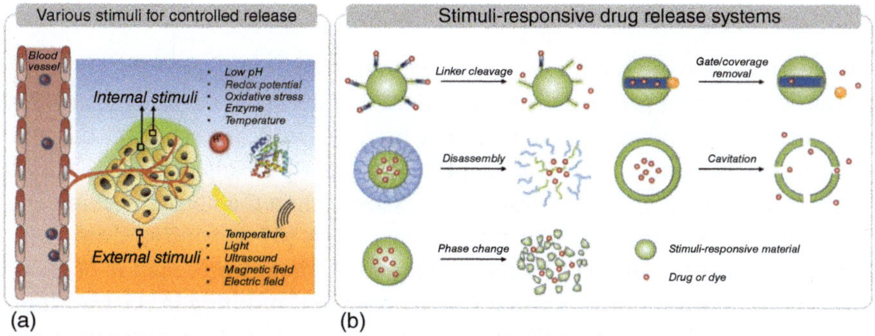

Figure 23.7 (a) Examples of various stimuli used for controlled release of therapeutic agents. The release of therapeutic agents can be selectively triggered by internal stimuli, including low pH, redox potential, oxidative stress, enzyme, and temperature, or external stimuli, including temperature, light, ultrasound, magnetic field, and electronic field. (b) The major strategies for fabricating stimuli-responsive drug release systems are summarized in schematic illustrations. Source: Ref. [99]. Reproduced with permission of Wiley-VCH.

pH-responsive drug nanocarrier recognizes the difference in pH, followed by the release of drugs in the cytoplasm by degradation of the nanostructure of drug nanocarriers or cleavage of the pH-responsive linker conjugated to the drugs. As the temperature of an inflamed area generally rises, it also rises when a pathological issue occurs in cells or tissues [173, 174]. Thus, drugs can be released under a specific temperature range using the phenomenon in which the nanostructure of the drug nanocarriers is decomposed when the temperature increases. Because the redox potential of the cytoplasm is abnormal compared to the extracellular environment, the difference in redox potential is another internal stimulus that promotes intracellular drug delivery [175, 176]. The nanostructures of redox-responsive drug nanocarriers are not destroyed in the extracellular environment. Redox-responsive drug nanocarriers release drugs after degradation in the cytoplasm, which has an abnormal redox potential. In addition, because abnormal redox potentials due to the generation of reactive oxygen species (ROS) have been observed in diseases, high levels of ROS can also trigger drug release [177, 178]. Lastly, certain enzymes that are highly expressed in diseased cells can also be used as triggers for drug release [179, 180]. As shown in Figure 23.7b, drug nanocarriers have been developed in which the self-assembled structure can be disassembled, the phase can be changed, and the linker can be cleaved by stimuli. The drug or dye can be directly conjugated to the drug carrier via a cleavable linkage that is susceptible to stimuli. Stimuli-responsive drug carriers can release drugs through the disassembly of drug-loaded carriers owing to the weakening of the intermolecular noncovalent interactions that construct the drug carrier or the change in the molecular structure inside the carrier. The physically loaded drugs can be released owing to the phase change of the carrier by a stimulus, and hollow drug carriers capped with polymers or NPs by stimuli-responsive cleavable linkers can release drugs by stimuli. In addition, a recent system allows the release of encapsulated drugs through the pores of carrier shells. Encapsulated molecules that can generate bubbles form pores in the shell under a certain stimulus, which triggers the rapid release of the loaded drugs.

23.4.1 pH-responsive Nanocarriers

An abnormal pH environment has been used to trigger drug release via the structural transformation of pH-responsive materials. Deviation from normal pH results in changes in noncovalent interactions that have a significant effect on the self-assembled structure, because a specific pH range greatly affects the charge across the peptide. In general, the pH of lesion sites is lower than the normal pH, making them suitable targets for inducing drug release from pH-responsive drug carriers [181]. Thus, pH-responsive PAs undergo protonation or deprotonation of ionizable chemical groups in this abnormal pH environment, resulting in the transition or degradation of self-assembled PA nanostructures [182, 183]. Consequently, drugs or genes are released after the transition or degradation of self-assembled PAs nanostructures. In general, ionizable amino acids include arginine, histidine, and lysine, which have a positive charge at neutral pH, and aspartic acid and glutamic acid, which have a negative charge at pH 7.0. Although different amino acids have the same charge in a specific pH range, peptide self-assembly and disassembly behaviors are different, and many peptide sequences prepared from these various amino acids can create myriad pH-responsive drug release systems. In addition to using ionizable functional groups to impart pH responsiveness to drug nanocarriers, pH-cleavable linkages can be a new option [184, 185]. These linkages are stable at normal physiological pH, whereas pH-responsive linkages are susceptible to breakage under acidic or basic conditions. Consequently, the loaded drugs are released when the acid- or base-labile bonds are cleaved, or the self-assembled PA structure decomposes or undergoes a phase transition.

Chen and coworkers designed a pH-responsive drug delivery carrier using a PA with a CPP (stearyl-H16R8-OH, NP1) [189]. This PA consisted of one hydrophobic chain (stearic acid), a histidine-rich pH-responsive component (16 histidine amino acids, H16), and an arginine-rich cell-penetrating component (8 arginine amino acids, R8). The pH-responsive component (H16) was deprotonated above pH 6, and hydrogen bonding was formed between peptides, resulting in self-assembled nanostructures. At pH value below 6, the protonated H16 caused the disassembly of the carrier owing to strong repulsive forces between the imidazole side groups. Owing to the guanidino group on arginine, the arginine-rich cell-penetrating component is positively charged, facilitating cell penetration via electrostatic interactions with the negatively charged plasma membrane. Furthermore, the nanostructure growth is limited, and the formation of spherical structures instead of fibers is promoted by R8. Ellipticine (EPT), an anticancer drug, was successfully encapsulated into the micelle nanostructures due to the hydrophobic stearic acid tail and released inside cancer cells at different pH values through disassembly of the micelles. The NP1-EPT drug delivery system destroyed more than 85% of the cancer cells, which was four times higher than the same amount of EPT alone according to the *in vitro* experiments on A549 cells and CHO-K1 cells.

Quan and coworkers developed a pH-responsive drug carrier using a PA composed of a mimicking peptide and stearic acid. The mimicking peptide derived from the antennapedia homeodomain consists of basic 17 amino acids (DRQIKIWFQNRRMKWKK) (Figure 23.8a) [186]. Because this peptide contains arginine and lysine, which can be protonated under acidic pH, it exhibited a conformational transition of the secondary structure from β-sheet at pH 7.4 to α-helix at pH 5.0 (Figure 23.8b). The conformational transition of the secondary structure caused the transformation of the self-assembled PA structure from the nanosphere to the nanofiber, which allowed drugs to be released into the cytoplasm of tumor cells whose pH was out of the normal state because of the electrostatic repulsions between doxorubicin (DOX) and the primary amine groups. *In vitro* experiments showed that

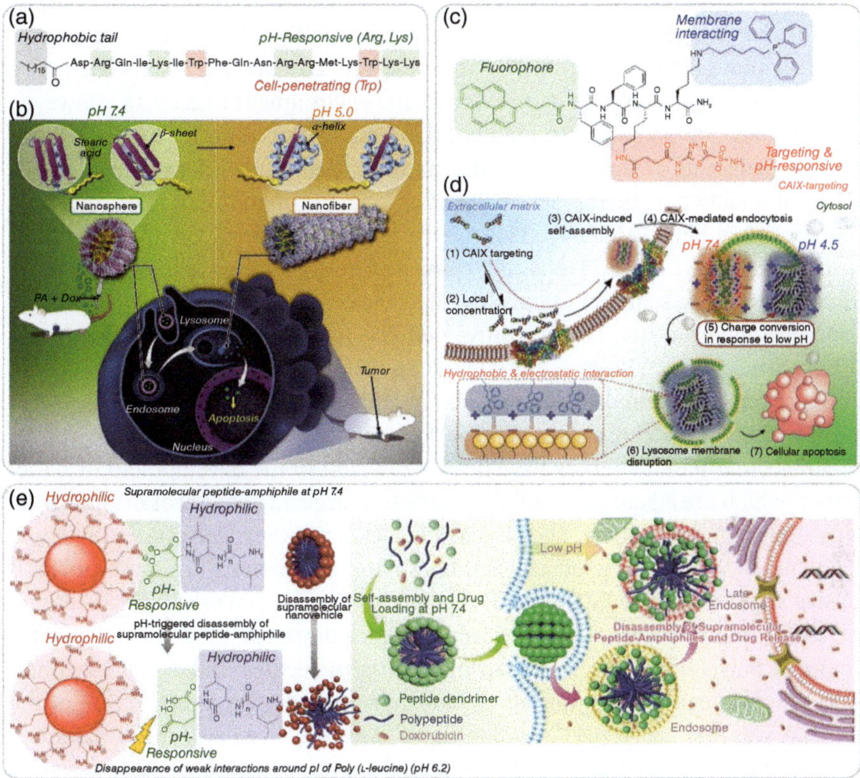

Figure 23.8 (a) Molecular structure of PA composed of a pH-responsive peptide with cell-penetration ability and stearic acid. (b) Schematic illustration of pH-triggered secondary structure transformation of mimicking PA in an acidic environment (pH 5.0) of tumor cell for controlled drug release and cell apoptosis. Source: Ref. [186]. Reproduced with permission of Elsevier. (c) Molecular structure of carbonic anhydrase IX (CAIX)-targeting PA which was functionalized by membrane interaction moiety (triphenylphosphonium, TPP) and CAIX targeting moiety. (d) Schematic illustration of the mechanism of Pep-AT. Pep-AT easily approaches the cancerous membrane owing to the strong binding affinity between acetazolamide and CAIX. The nanofiber formed by the CAIX-induced self-assembly is internalized via CAIX-mediated endocytosis and results in cellular apoptosis. Source: Ref. [187]. Reproduced with permission of American Chemical Society. (e) Molecular structure of supramolecular PA and schematic illustrations of pH-triggered disassembly of peptide amphiphile and self-assembled nanovehicle at low pH. DOX-loaded nanovehicles could respond to different pH, which triggers the disassembly of peptide amphiphiles and releases hydrophobic drugs in the cell. Source: Ref. [188] Reproduced with permission of Wiley-VCH.

the Dox-loaded PA NP (PA@DOX) readily penetrated the cell owing to the penetration capability of the peptide mimicking the membrane. The released Dox then caused apoptosis of murine colon carcinoma CT26 (MCCC) cells, suggesting that this pH-responsive PA-based drug nanocarrier can be used for cancer therapy.

Recently, drug carriers that are disassembled by a certain intracellular pH and can release drugs have received significant attention as therapeutic agents, but PAs with the potential to kill cancer cells when they are self-assembled at a specific pH have also been developed. Ryu and coworkers designed a carbonic anhydrase IX (CAIX)-targeting PA (Pep-AT) self-assembly system which is pH responsive to control cellular fate by modulating the charge based on pH change and lipophilic TPP for enhanced membrane interaction (Figure 23.8c) [187]. The designed PAs are self-assembled into a nanofiber with a negative charge in an extracellular environment with CAIX. However, the surface charge of the nanofiber changed to a positive charge owing to the protonation of acetazolamide at the lysosome during endocytosis. The membrane was disrupted by interaction with the positively charged TPP of the nanofiber, inducing cellular apoptosis (Figure 23.8d). They revealed concentration-dependent cellular cytotoxicity for Pep-AT toward HeLa cells compared to NIH/3T3 cells, which suggested the importance of the spatiotemporal control of the controllable peptide. In addition, they demonstrated that the CAIX-positive cell line had lower IC50 values than the CAIX-negative cell line. These results suggest that Pep-AT could be used for a cancer cell or tumor therapy by modulating the cellular fate with pH-responsive self-assembly behavior, molecular-packing change, and surface charge conversion.

Supramolecular nanomaterials have been significant in the development of nanomedicines, which are advantageous for the effective targeted delivery of drugs, genes, proteins, and diagnostic agents. The targeted delivery and controlled release system of hydrophobic DOX into targeted cells using smart nanocarriers composed of pH-responsive supramolecular PAs were developed by Gu and coworkers [188] (Figure 23.8e). These pH-responsive supramolecular PAs composed of dendritic poly(*L*-leucine) and poly(*L*-leucine) can encapsulate drug molecules under neutral conditions. DOX was encapsulated into self-assembled NPs, and approximately 80% of the loaded DOX was retained at pH 7.4 and released at pH 6.2 because of the disassembly of self-assembled PAs structure, which resulted from the weakening of non-covalent interactions (electrostatic interactions) within supramolecular PAs around the isoelectric point of poly (*L*-leucine). Controlled release of DOX was achieved by taking advantage of intracellular pH as a trigger. *In vitro* release profiles and confocal laser scanning microscopy images of HepG2 cells demonstrated that lower pH values can induce the disassembly of nanocarriers and intracellular DOX delivery.

23.4.2 Temperature-sensitive Nanocarriers

In addition to pH value as a trigger to release drugs, temperature responsiveness has been widely investigated as another strategy to induce controlled drug release [190, 191]. Most cells are highly susceptible to temperature changes since cell activities are diminished when temperature increases, which results in enzyme deactivation and metabolic abnormalities. However, when a lesion occurs in a human organism, the temperature slightly increases [173]. In particular, the temperature of a tumor or an inflammatory region is higher than that in a normal state. Thus, the elevated temperature of cells or tissues can be used to trigger the release of drugs from temperature-responsive PA nanocarriers. Temperature change in temperature-responsive materials leads to a phase transition [162]. Self-assembly and dissociation, as well as phase transition, depend on the noncovalent interactions, especially molecular hydrophobicity and charge distribution. In this case, there are two temperature-response mechanisms: the lower critical solution temperature (LCST) and the upper critical solution temperature (UCST) [192]. These two mechanisms can be adopted when temperature-responsive drug carriers are designed to modulate drug release profiles. Temperature-responsive drug carriers of the LCST type aggregate when the temperature is higher than a certain critical temperature, which depends on the component of the carriers, and then the drugs can be encapsulated. When the phase transition temperature is lower than the normal temperature, the drug carriers can circulate intact in the blood without being released. When the drug carriers approach cells or tissues exhibiting higher temperatures compared to normal cells or tissues, the carriers accumulate, and the drugs are sustainably released. In contrast, in the case of temperature-responsive drug nanocarriers of the UCST type, upon elevation above the critical temperature, the nanocarrier decomposes through a phase transition, bursting the loaded drugs. A number of components of temperature-responsive drug nanocarriers have been employed, including elastin-like peptides (ELPs) [193–196], poly(ethylene glycol) (PEG) [197], and poly(N-isopropyl acrylamide) (pNIPAAm) [198]. As mentioned above, incorporating an ELP into the building blocks constituting self-assembled structures is a well-established and efficient way to endow them with temperature responsiveness. ELP contains a repetitive sequence motif composed of Val-Pro-Gly-X-Gly (VPGXG), where X represents any amino acid excluding proline. Depending on the temperature, the conformation of the ELP changes, and ELP undergoes a phase transition.

Jeong and coworkers reported temperature-responsive elastin-like PA (ELPAs) (Figure 23.9a) [194]. They derived the temperature responsiveness of PAs by substituting a single N-terminal amino acid with different nonpolar amino acids (tryptophan, phenylalanine, tyrosine, leucine, valine, and alanine) at the final stage of peptide synthesis. Furthermore, the terminal hydrophobic peptide sequence was responsible for the formation of a hydrophobic core to encapsulate hydrophobic drugs. The temperature-responsive behavior between ELPAs changed according to the varied hydrophobic amino-acid sequences or the number of aromatic phenylalanine residues. They then studied whether these peptides could be used as platforms for the development of temperature-responsive ELPAs with various bioactive peptide sequences. The ELP platform conjugated with a short linear RGD peptide exhibited rapid aggregation (coacervation) upon heating and slower disaggregation upon cooling (Figure 23.9a(1)). An ELP platform conjugated with an α-helical guest peptide with a lariat-type structure was also prepared. As the temperature was increased to 43 °C, the ELPAs disintegrated faster than those without α-helical guest peptides (Figure 23.9a(2)). The dynamic disintegration of the ELPAs resulted from steric hindrance induced by the temperature-dependent conformational change, which led to the destabilization of the supramolecular structure. They demonstrated that the encapsulated pyrene fluorophores as hydrophobic small

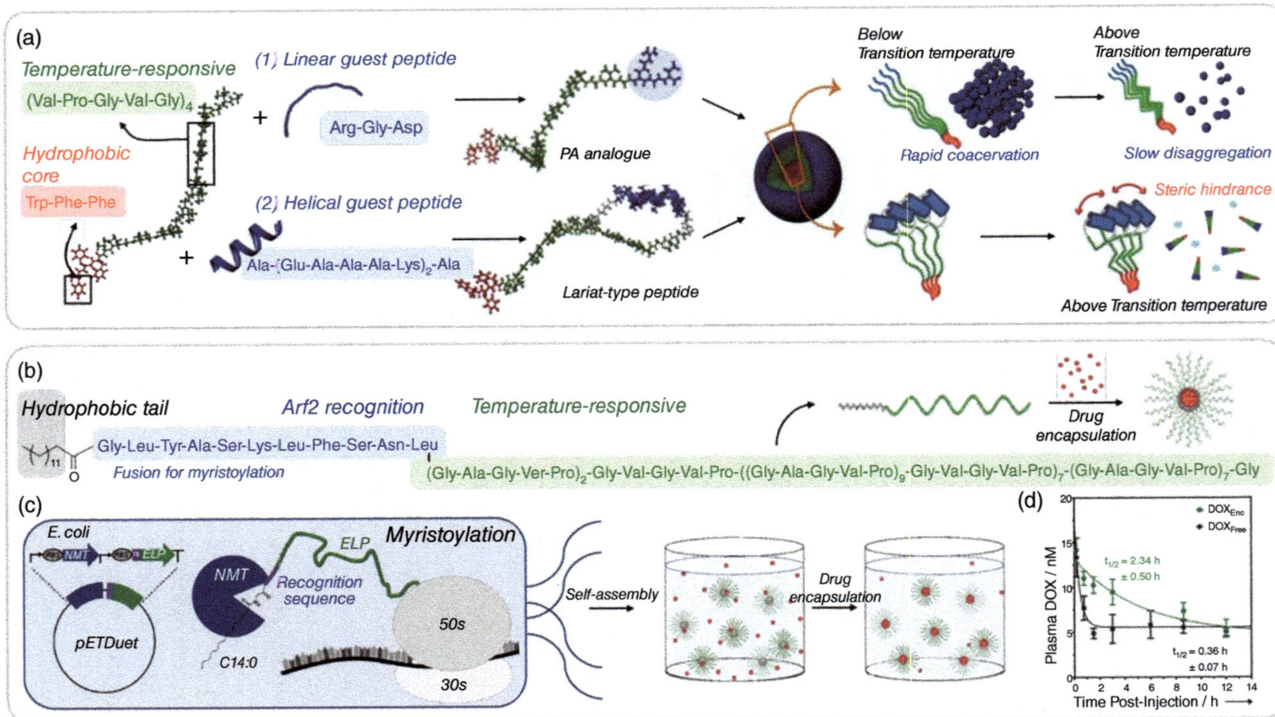

Figure 23.9 (a) Chemical structure of the peptide based on an ELP for developing ELPAs with a controlled temperature responsiveness by modulating the conjugated guest peptides (linear guest peptide (1) and helical guest peptide (2)) and N-terminal amino-acid residues. Source: [194]. Reproduced with permission of Wiley-VCH. (b) Sequence and functions of myristoylated ELP (M-ELP). (c) M-ELPs were self-assembled into spherical or rod-like micelles because of the amphiphilic nature induced by myristoylation. Hydrophobic drugs can be easily loaded into the hydrophobic core of the micelle. (d) Plasma concentration of DOX over postinjection time, which showed that encapsulated DOX has a longer plasma half-life. Source: Ref. [195]. Reproduced with permission of Wiley-VCH.

molecular payloads can be released from the micelle core of ELPAs to the aqueous environment owing to the temperature-responsive disassembly. They suggested that these temperature-responsive ELPA platforms have the potential to be used for temperature-responsive drug delivery systems.

Luginbuhl and coworkers studied the combination of ELP NPs with fatty acids (myristic acids) by genetically encoded posttranslational modifications of the ELP for the delivery of hydrophobic drugs such as Dox and paclitaxel (Figure 23.9b) [195]. In this study, the pETDuet-1 plasmid was used to ligate the DNA sequence encoding the fusion protein polymer of ELP with N-myristoyl transferase (NMT), and NMT was expressed in *Escherichia coli* (*E. coli*). Myristic acid in myristoylated ELP (M-ELP) facilitated the self-assembly of lipoproteins into spherical micelles whose hydrophobic lipid core was suitable for loading Dox and paclitaxel without chemical linkage (Figure 23.9c). DOX was physically encapsulated into the hydrophobic core of the micelles and the Dox-loaded myristoylated micelles which were internalized by cancer cells that exhibited high cytotoxicity against 4T1 and PC-3 cells. Moreover, the intravenous injection of DOX-loaded M-ELP micelles into mice showed a longer circulation half-life than DOX itself (Figure 23.9d). These lipid–peptide hybrids were self-assembled into nanoscale drug carriers that could physically encapsulate and release hydrophobic anticancer drugs such as DOX and paclitaxel. They used this method to demonstrate that the biotechnological utility of repetitive peptide polymers associated with temperature-dependent phase transitions can be extended to stimuli-responsive drug carriers.

Aluri and coworkers reported an inverse phase transition of ELPAs prepared by dipalmitoylation of a nonionic polypeptide derived from human tropoelastin [196]. The addition of two saturated 16-carbon chains enabled ELPAs to phase separate at certain temperatures and provided a driving force for the hydrophobic assembly of fiber-like structures. The length and cellular uptake of fiber-like ELPAs assemblies were controlled by changing the number of amino acids or the type of aliphatic chain. Additionally, the phase inversion temperature was modulated by adjusting the concentration of ELPAs. Paclitaxel was encapsulated into nanofibers, and the construct demonstrated anticancer effects. In general, these UCST-type temperature-responsive PA carriers can be assembled into nanofibers with high efficiency for drug encapsulation and cellular uptake. They demonstrated that the designed elastin-like biopolymers can be used to engineer stimuli-responsive materials for drug and cell delivery applications owing to their temperature-responsive phase separation, charge neutrality, and controllable aspect ratio.

PA assemblies composed of block copolymers that serve as carriers for small-molecule drugs were developed by Huang and coworkers. Block copolymers composed of PEG and an oligo(tyrosine) block were synthesized with different compositions by N-carboxyanhydride (NCA) polymerization [197]. PAs were assembled into nanofibers and formed temperature-responsive hydrogels at a low concentration range of 0.25–3.0 wt% within a temperature range of 25–50 °C. Cryogenic-transmission electron microscopy (TEM) images of the hydrogels showed a continuous network of fibers. They demonstrated that hydrogel formation was affected by the amphiphilic balance between PEG and oligo(tyrosine) blocks, hydrogen bonding via β-sheet conformation, and phenolic groups. Circular dichroism results confirmed that better packing of the β-sheet tyrosine blocks at increasing temperatures caused reverse thermogelation. Desferrioxamine was chosen as a small-molecule drug for the entrapment and release experiment. Desferrioxamine was rapidly released within the first 24 h, followed by a sustained release over seven days. They suggested its potential as an injectable temperature-responsive drug carrier because the hydrogel was noncytotoxic, biodegradable, and able to release a small-molecule drug for an extended period.

As another example of using ELP for targeted drug delivery with enhanced cellular uptake, MacEwan and Chilkoti reported efficient cellular uptake by modulating the function of CPPs with thermally toggled self-assembly of a genetically encoded polypeptide NP [199]. They synthesized diblock copolymer ELPs that can be self-assembled into temperature-responsive micelles in a narrow temperature range between 37 and 42 °C (the highest temperature approved for mild clinical hyperthermia). They turned on the CPP function of ELP by modulating the density of arginine residues through the temperature-responsive assembly of diblock copolymer ELPs. Micelles were assembled by diblock ELPs composed of hydrophilic and hydrophobic ELPs, resulting in micelles with high arginine density that exhibited LCST transitions at 39 and 56 °C. At 37 °C (systemic physiological temperature), the diblock ELPs were in a soluble unimer state with low arginine density. Thus, local hyperthermia was able to turn on/off the cell penetration function of diblock ELPs. The experimental results showed that micelles with high arginine density induced by the temperature-responsive phase transition of diblock ELPs enhanced the cellular uptake of HeLa cells eight times greater than that of the same diblock copolymer of ELPs in which it is a soluble unimer state. Because cellular uptake is a very important factor in drug delivery systems, this approach has the potential to enhance the efficiency of targeted drug delivery by temperature-controllable CPP activation of self-assembled NPs.

23.4.3 Redox-sensitive Nanocarriers

Redox-triggered drug delivery systems that can induce drug release through differences in the redox environment between normal and diseased cells have gained considerable attention in recent years [200–202]. For example, intracellular (2–10 mM) and extracellular (2–20 μM) concentrations of GSH are maintained at constant levels by reducing enzymes (GSH reductase) to maintain reductive conditions inside the cell [99]. However, since the concentration of GSH in diseased cells is several orders of magnitude higher than that in normal cells, this unusual environment can be used as a novel stimulus for drug release [176]. This concentration difference allows the redox-responsive drug carriers to release drugs by introducing disulfide (S–S) bonds, which can be reduced by intracellular GSH [73]. As the concentration of extracellular GSH is generally lower here than that of intracellular GSH, drug carriers can be successfully transported and accumulated into cells with abnormal GSH concentrations without disruption. ROS can also be used as an additional stimulus in redox-responsive drug release systems [203]. The levels of ROS, such as hydrogen peroxide (H_2O_2) and hydroxyl radicals (HO•), in lesions are usually elevated by pathological processes, such as immune responses, because of cellular inflammation [200]. Thus, abnormal level of ROS in lesions acts as a trigger to release drugs into the targeted cells or tissues.

Kim and coworkers reported a redox-responsive PAs vesicle that could release anticancer drugs triggered by GSH. Various PAs containing the CPP peptide TAT (RKKRRQRRR) were synthesized by varying the position and number of disulfide linkages in the PAs (Figure 23.10a) [93]. The location of the amino acid cysteine (C) within the molecular structure has an impact on the self-assembly behavior of PAs followed by the resulting morphology. A vesicle was formed when a C residue was present at the N-terminus of the hydrophilic peptide segment, whereas 2D sheets were formed when a C residue was present between the pyrenyl group and the alkyl chain of the hydrophobic portion. All PAs formed vesicles only when disulfide bonds were formed. In addition, the location of the disulfide bond affected the loading capacity of the hydrophobic drug in the nanostructure by controlling the degree of packing between the PAs. Sustained release of anticancer drugs to specific tumors upon exposure to GSH was demonstrated as a result of an increase in the number of disulfide bonds between PAs (Figure 23.10b). In this study, biocompatible PAs for efficient drug-delivery vehicles were designed, and all vesicles exhibited a ability to deliver anticancer drugs to specific cancer cells alone, which could serve as a solid foundation for further nanocarrier development for biomedical applications.

Since enzymes such as esterase or matrix metalloproteinase (MMP) are overproduced in cancer cells compared to normal cells, improved anticancer drug delivery can be accomplished with protease-cleavable linkers. Yoo and coworkers developed a protease-activatable CPP containing ROS-responsive methionine, cell-penetrating lysine, and MMP-2 cleavable linker (Figure 23.10c) [96]. They formulated a poly (*L*-methionine-block-*L*-lysine)-PLGLAG-PEG (MLMP) micelle by connecting poly (*L*-methionine-b-*L*-lysine) (ML) with PEG using an MMP-2 cleavable linker, in which PLGLAG served as the substrate of MMP-2/9. In addition, poly-*L*-lysine chains promoted cellular penetration of micelles via electrostatic interactions. As shown in Figure 23.10d, the excess MMP-2 enzyme cleaved the MMP-responsive linkers when the DOX-loaded MLMP micelles reached the tumors, causing the PEG corona to shed from the micelles. The exposed lysine strongly absorbed the cells via electrostatic interactions. The methionine groups in the core were oxidized to hydrophilic sulfoxides owing to the high ROS level inside the cancer cell and triggered an amplified release of DOX. Approximately 56% of NCI-H460 cells died after 24 h of incubation with DOX-loaded MLMP micelles, which was higher than the 27% for those treated with free DOX. The biodistribution study of IR-780 dye-encapsulated MLMP demonstrated enhanced tumor targetability with long retention, and DOX-loaded micelles effectively decreased tumor size.

As an example of redox-responsive reversible self-assembly, Gao, Lu, and their colleagues (2021) synthesized a brush-like peptide-selenopolypeptide (pSe-NapFFC-Glu) conjugate for the delivery of anticancer drugs [204]. The conjugate consisted of a polypeptide backbone to which a redox-responsive selenoether moiety and a short peptide (NapFFC) were attached. Under native/reduced conditions, the backbone of the conjugate showed a robust and rigid α-helical conformation that prevented

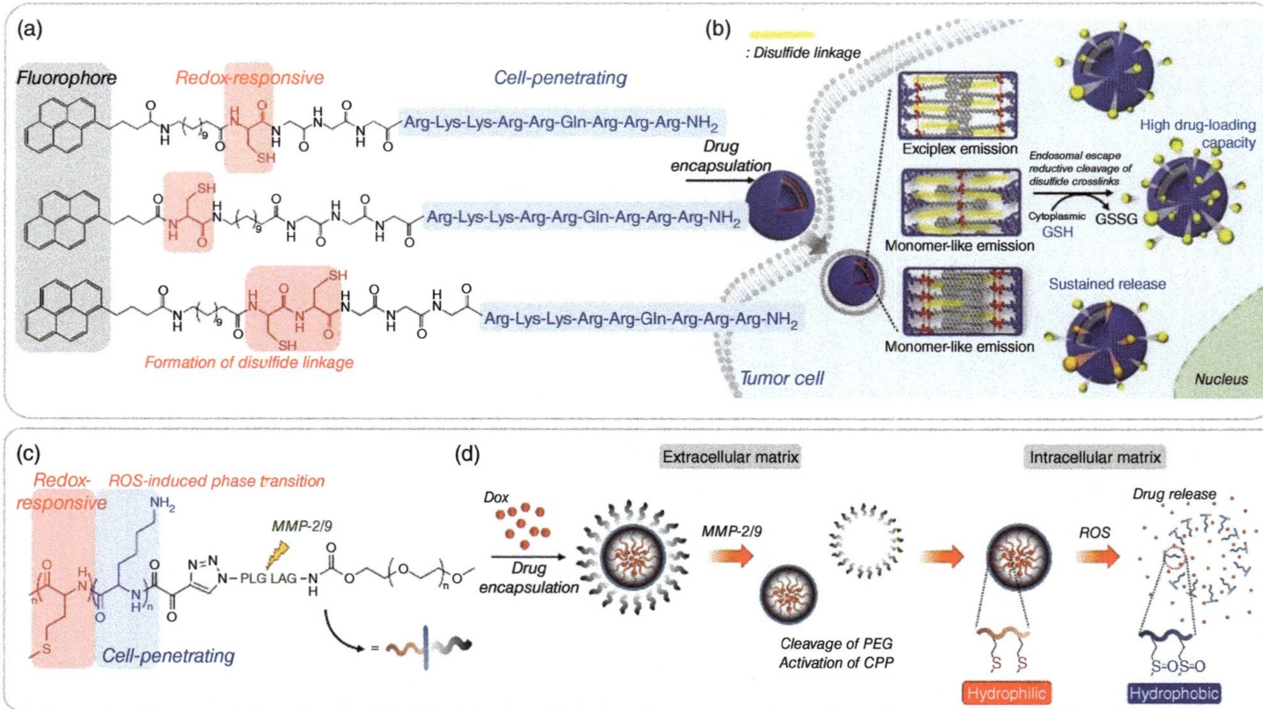

Figure 23.10 (a) Molecular structures of PAs with C moiety participating in the disulfide bridge. (b) Self-assembled peptide vesicles with mono- or disulfide bridges within the wall, which had different drug-loading capacities and release behavior in tumor cells. Although DOX-loaded 1-ss, 2-ss, and 1-1-ss formed vesicles, their capacity for loading drugs and reductive cleavable drug release behavior can be adjusted according to the position and the number of disulfide cross-links in the PA structure. Source: [93]. Reproduced with permission of Royal Society of Chemistry. (c) Molecular structure of CPP possessing ROS-triggered phase transition for enhanced cancer therapy. (d) Schematic illustration of the DOX delivery procedure. In the ECM of cancer cells, the MMP-sensitive linker of MLMP can be broken. Thus, PEG chains were cleaved enzymatically, and then exposed poly-*L*-lysine chains penetrate cells owing to their cell-penetrating ability. After that, the ROS in the intracellular matrix converted the hydrophobic thioether groups of the poly-*L*-methionine chains into hydrophilic sulfoxide groups. Consequently, the DOX-loaded micelle was disrupted by the polypeptide chain conversions, and the encapsulated DOX was subsequently released into the cells. Source: Ref. [96]. Reproduced with permission of Elsevier.

supramolecular assembly of the short peptide, resulting in irregular aggregation morphology. The α-helical conformation of the polypeptide backbone changed into a flexible and disordered conformation with hydrophilic properties upon oxidation to selenoxide. By adopting a β-sheet conformation, the converted selenoxide allowed the supramolecular assembly of NapFFC to transform nanofibrils. Irregular aggregates were transformed into micelles through micellization to load the drugs into the pSe-NapFFC-Glu conjugate. High levels of ROS caused the conversion of selenoether to selenoxide and the transformation from micelles to nanofibers, facilitating drug release when drug-loaded micelles interact with cancer cells.

23.4.4 Enzyme-sensitive Nanocarriers

Recently, enzyme-responsive materials have been widely developed for drug delivery [205, 206]. Enzymes, essential catalysts in metabolic processes, play an important role in biomedicine because of their selectivity, sensing ability, and catalytic reactivity [73]. As in previous cases, enzyme responsiveness can be advantageous for controlled drug release, since enzymes can be overexpressed in cells or tissues by many disease-related pathological processes such as progression, metastasis, and angiogenesis [179]. Enzyme-responsive drug carriers rely primarily on the cleavage of esters or specific peptide sequences, which is vulnerable to esterase or protease such as Cathepsin B and MMP, which is a kind of hydrolase that consumes water to break noncovalent peptide bonds [158, 183]. Thus, controlled drug release to the lesions can be achieved by disassembly or degradation of drug carriers, which is triggered by enzymes considering that proteases are generated in excess by tumor cells or other cells present at the diseased site. This means that the reaction mechanism of enzymatic reactive systems requires an enzyme-responsive component that is responsible for changing the interaction inside the structure of the drug carriers. According to this strategy, by incorporating unique molecules that can change the self-assembled PAs structure triggered by enzymes into the PA sequence constituting the drug carriers, drugs can be released at the desired sites [183].

In enzyme-responsive drug release systems, photosensitizers are useful in chemophotodynamic synergistic therapy for enhanced tumor treatment. Zhang and coworkers combined a chemotherapeutic drug, photosensitizer, and PA to fabricate a dual-targeted photosensitizer–PA conjugate (PpIX-GGGK(TPP)GG-GFLG-R7-RGD or pPAC), designed to encapsulate DOX for chemophotodynamic therapy (Figure 23.11a) [207]. The amphiphilic nature and π–π interactions of pPAC resulted in the formation of core–shell-structured micelles in aqueous media, where DOX was loaded into the nucleus to form DOX@pPAC. The DOX@pPAC micelles exhibited efficient tumor cellular uptake through integrin receptor-mediated endocytosis owing to the tumor-targeting RGD peptide. The membrane-penetrating R8 peptide enhanced cellular internalization, and DOX@pPAC rapidly released DOX into the tumor microenvironment due to Cathepsin B-triggered hydrolysis of the GFLG linker. Simultaneously, the TPP cation of the PA conjugate side chain allowed the photosensitizer PpIX to accumulate in subcellular mitochondria, followed by *in situ* photocatalytic generations of phototoxic ROS under

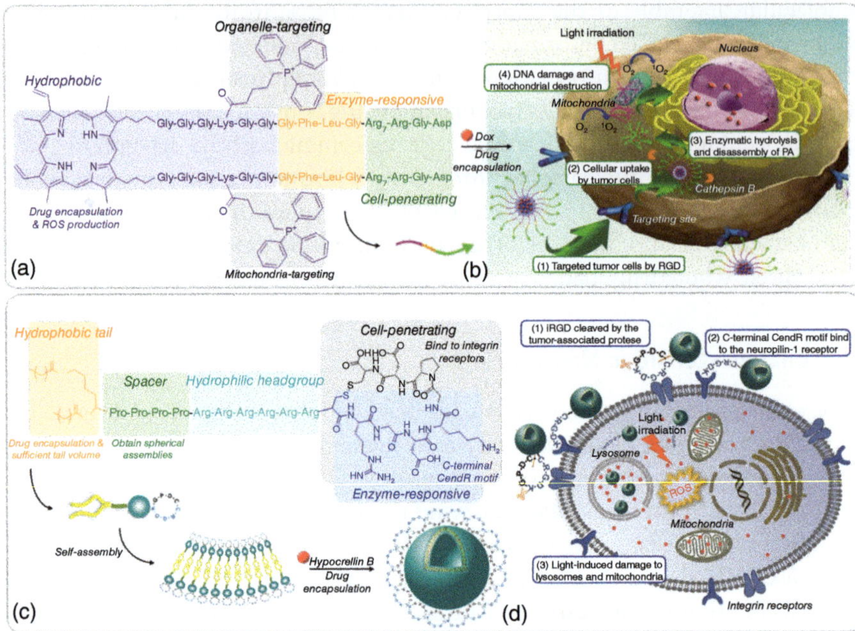

Figure 23.11 (a) Molecular structure and the bioactive peptide sequence of dual-targeting photosensitizer-PA conjugate (pPAC). (b) Schematic illustration of the self-assembly of pPACs to encapsulate DOX for Cathepsin B-responsive drug release and synergistic chemophotodynamic therapy. ((1) DOX-loaded micelles easily reached tumor cells because of the tumor-targeting peptide in micelles, (2) cellular uptake into tumor cells, (3) overexpressed Cathepsin B in endosomes and lysosomes caused the disintegration of pPAC through enzymatic hydrolysis of GFLG linker, and (4) selective delivery of DOX to nucleus and PpIX to mitochondria, which in turn damaged DNA and destructed mitochondria under 680 nm light irradiation.) Source: [207]. Reproduced with permission of Wiley-VCH. (c) Schematic illustration of the iRGD-based PA composed of cell-penetrating and targeting peptide and the encapsulation of HB into self-assembled spherical nanovesicles. (d) Schematic illustration of HB-loaded iRGD-based PA nanovesicles with enhanced tumor-targeted accumulation, and photoactivation, that promoted the generation of ROS used for image-guided photodynamic anticancer efficacy of the photosensitizer. ((1) After binding to the membrane, iRGD is cleaved by the protease, which exposes its C-terminal CendR motif (CRGDK/R). (2) This motif binds to the neuropilin-1 receptor, and then penetration into the interior of tumors occurs. (3) iRGD-peptide-based nanoplatform exhibits effective photodynamic therapy.) Source: Ref. [208]. Reproduced with permission of American Chemical Society.

light irradiation. This resulted in significant tumor death (Figure 23.11b). *In vitro* studies demonstrated that the chemophotodynamic synergistic therapy of developed micelles significantly enhanced the therapeutic effect against tumor cells with the least off-target cytotoxicity.

Similarly, the photosensitizer hypocrellin B (HB) has also been used as an efficient theranostic agent. For instance, Xu and coworkers designed an iRGD (internalizing RGD, CRGDKGPDC)-based PA with a novel off–on mode to form spherical nanovesicles via self-assembly. In this PA, iRGD, a nine-unit cyclic tumor-homing and tissue-penetrating peptide, was adopted to bind to integrin receptors, and HB as a photosensitizer was loaded into PA vesicles (Figure 23.11c) [208]. The iRGD tissue-targeting motif was chemically modified with a hydrophilic arginine-rich sequence and a hydrophobic alkyl chain to induce self-assembly. HB in PA vesicles was inactivated by quenching resulting from aggregation. However, after transfer to tumor tissues the assemblies were dissociated by tumor proteases such as cathepsin B, and the encapsulated HB was released, restoring HB fluorescence activity. The production of ROS, which plays an important role in photodynamic therapy-induced apoptosis, was also evaluated by flow cytometry. The HB-PA/photodynamic therapy treatment group showed a higher ROS count, indicating that HB-PA could generate more ROS after delivery into the cells. As a result, the self-assembled HB-loaded PA vesicles with tumor-targeted activation, preferable tumor accumulation, and deep tumor penetration exhibited excellent fluorescence-image-guided photodynamic therapy (Figure 23.11d).

Peptide dendrimer drug conjugate-based NPs are also candidate drug delivery vehicles. Gu and coworkers developed an enzyme-responsive amphiphilic mPEGylated peptide dendron-Gly-Phe-Leu-Gly (GFLG)-DOX conjugate for breast tumor treatments [209]. DOX was conjugated to the terminals of the mPEGylated peptide dendrons via GFLG oligopeptides using a click reaction. The TEM and dynamic light scattering (DLS) studies showed that the conjugate of mPEGylated dendron-GFLG-DOX was self-assembled into compact NPs with a negatively charged surface. The NPs with 9.62 wt% DOX exhibited enzyme responsiveness in drug release tests. The mPEGylated dendron-GFLG-DOX conjugate exhibited cytotoxicity toward 4T1 murine breast cancer cell lines *in vitro* tests, and the IC50 was reported to be 0.76 mg/mL, which was 1.9-fold higher than plain DOX (0.41 mg/mL), demonstrating efficient tumor cell death. The accumulation of NPs inside the tumor, 6 h after intravenous administration, was revealed using fluorescent images. *In vivo* tests using female BALB/c mice bearing 4T1 murine breast cancer cells revealed higher tumor growth inhibition of approximately 80.3% and lower toxicity compared to free DOX (57.3%) when the formulation was intravenously injected. *In vivo* tests in which the formulation was intravenously injected into female BALB/c mice bearing 4T1 murine breast cancer cells revealed elevated tumor growth inhibition of approximately 80.3% and decreased toxicity in comparison to free DOX (57.3%). Consequently, they suggested that mPEGylated dendron-GFLG-DOX conjugate-based NPs could be potential drug delivery vehicles for breast cancer therapy.

23.4.5 Other Stimuli-responsive Carriers

In addition to the above mentioned stimuli, other stimuli can trigger drug release. Although most of the previously reported drug carriers could release the drugs by changing assembled structures under unique environments (pH, temperature, redox, and enzyme), stimuli-responsive drug carriers in response to an electrical field, magnetic field, light irradiation, and ultrasound have also been reported [70, 99]. However, there are not many reports to date on PA-based systems that practically deliver loaded drugs by these stimuli. As an external stimulus, light has been exploited to induce the transformation of assembled structures and release drugs. By combining photochromic molecules such as azobenzene, and its derivatives with spiropyran and coumarin, light responsiveness can be derived [210–212]. The structure of the light-responsive molecules changes via light-induced isomerization, cleavage of covalent bonds, and dimerization [213]. Among several stimuli that induce drug release, the advantages of stimuli using light include the ability to accurately adjust the intensity of light, control the exposure duration and irradiation location, and turn the light on and off in real time. Hao and coworkers prepared PA assemblies by the coupling of cinnamic acid and glycylglycine and then demonstrated that the assembled PA vesicles were responsive to light irradiation [214]. Due to the cis–trans transition of the cinnamoyl functional groups, most of the vesicles were disassembled upon UV light irradiation for a while. This PA carrier could achieve a controlled drug release with high efficacy for the encapsulation of hydrophobic drugs. Das and coworkers described the formation of supramolecular vesicles from cucurbit[8]uril (CB[8])-based ternary complex [215]. A CT complex involving a peptide containing an azobenzene moiety as a terminal group and a methyl viologen derivative composed of a long aliphatic chain as two amphiphilic guest molecules was formed inside the host cavity to produce a CB8-based supramolecular amphiphile, which self-assembled into vesicles in solution. Upon photoirradiation, the azobenzene units were subjected to trans to cis isomerization, resulting in vesicle rupture, because the space inside the CB8 cavity was insufficient to accept the cis-isomer. Furthermore, the vesicles exhibited reversible responses to a competitive binder such as 1-adamantylamine, resulting in the disruption of vesicles by displacing both guest molecules from the CB8 host. In contrast, when 2,6-dihydroxynaphthalene was utilized as a competitive binder, it substituted the peptide unit from the CB8 cavity and was also a part of the host cavity, forming a new ternary complex. Although peptide units were released from the original vesicles, the vesicle structure remained unchanged. The authors suggested that these reversible formation–deformation systems using stimuli-responsive vesicles could be used for applications including drug delivery, sensors, and molecular switches.

The PA carrier that can be used to treat cancer cells or malignant tumors upon light irradiation by encapsulating photosensitizers instead of conventional hydrophobic drugs has also been developed. Huang and coworkers reported a supramolecular peptide that showed programmable self-assembly for photodynamic therapy [216]. The peptide sequence (G7CCERGDS) was designed as follows: Because hydrogen-bonded hydrophobic cores are important for constructing nanostructures via self-assembly, glycine moieties were used to form strong multiple hydrogen bonds. Cysteine units were introduced because they are easily oxidized and form a cross-linked structure by disulfide bonds. The ERGDS heading group facilitated the cellular uptake of self-assembled NPs into cancer cells overexpressing αvβ3 integrin via receptor-mediated endocytosis. The self-assembled supramolecular morphology could be easily controlled by adding a water-soluble pillar [5] arene bearing 10 tri(ethyleneoxide) groups (P5) and heating (NPs were formed above LCST). Self-assembled NPs served as nanocarriers to encapsulate a hydrophobic species such as tetrakis(4-hydroxyphenyl)porphyrin, enhancing the photosensitizing effect to ablate the tumors. In addition, the disulfide cross-linked shell was formed by the oxidation of the cysteine unit on the pyridinium cation (PyP), preventing the collapse of NP when the temperature decreased. Disulfide bonds respond to GSH and may consume intracellular GSH to boost the efficacy of photodynamic therapy. Owing to the outer targeting ligand (ERGDS) and self-assembly of hydrophobic cores, supramolecular peptide NPs can be utilized as desirable carriers of a hydrophobic photosensitizer to enhance the efficacy of photodynamic therapy.

23.4.6 Multimodal-responsive Nanocarriers

Owing to the complex physiological fluids and the lesion environment, which hinder the intended effect of traditional nanomedicines against cancers, stimuli-responsive drug delivery systems have become significant instruments for cancer treatment. However, still there are difficulties and challenges in engineering evolutionarily improved drug delivery systems. Hence, many dual-stimuli-responsive materials that respond to combinations of stimuli such as pH–temperature [217], pH–enzyme [218], pH–redox [219], pH–light [220], pH–ultrasound [221], temperature–redox [222], temperature–electric [223], temperature–light [224], redox–light [225], and enzyme–redox [226] have been reported. Thus, drug nanocarriers that can overcome physiological and pathological obstacles to transport therapeutic agents cotriggered by multiple stimuli in targeted destinations, such as tumor tissue and cancer cells, have been developed [227].

Yuan and coworkers reported multi-stimuli-responsive 3-mercaptopropionic acid-modified poly(*L*-cysteine) (P(Cys-SS-CH2CH2COOH)) PA derivatives with different alkyl tails and S–S bonds for controlled drug delivery, in which PA1 (alkyl chain length 6), PA2 (alkyl chain length 12), and PA3 (alkyl chain length 18) were prepared [228]. In the solid state, these three PAs mainly adopted a β-sheet secondary structure, and their molecular weight distribution was relatively narrow. The three PAs are self-assembled into micelles or nanofibrous hydrogels for drug delivery because of their amphiphilic nature. Cisplatin (CDDP) was loaded into PA3 micelles, which were stable at pH 7.4, and had a spherical morphology. When the CDDP-loaded PA3 micelles reached the tumor cells, low pH (5.5) and high levels of GSH (10 mM) induced the targeted delivery of cisplatin at the tumor sites, demonstrating that the PA3 micelles had pH/reduction dual responsiveness and exhibited a controlled release of CDDP. The three PAs were also able to self-assemble into nanofibrous hydrogels at pH values in the range of 5.6–6.0. The addition of metal ions, such as Ca^{2+} to CDDP-loaded nanofibers, enabled a change in the secondary structure from α-helix to β-sheet with excellent dynamic reversibility. The CDDP-loaded PA3 hydrogel showed a sustained release profile and nearly linear release over 48 h. Consequently, they designed a dual stimuli-responsive drug delivery system using PAs, which showed potential for both the systemic and localized delivery of therapeutics.

The appropriate size of multifunctional nanomedicines has a considerable influence on their physicochemical features and biological functions, such as prolonged blood circulation time, efficient tumor accumulation, and deep tumor penetration. Zhu and coworkers developed size-transformed multifunctional peptide NPs with an acidic tumor microenvironment, and near-infrared laser irradiation-triggered size shrinkage, enhancing efficient photo–chemo combined antitumor therapy with tumor penetration capability (Figure 23.12) [98]. This multifunctional bicomponent self-assembled NP was constructed by electrostatic interaction of negatively charged PA C12-K(Dye)EEEGRGDS (PA1) and positively charged GSH-responsive peptide prodrug CKKK-SS-DOX (PA2) (Figure 23.12a). PA1 consisted of four components:

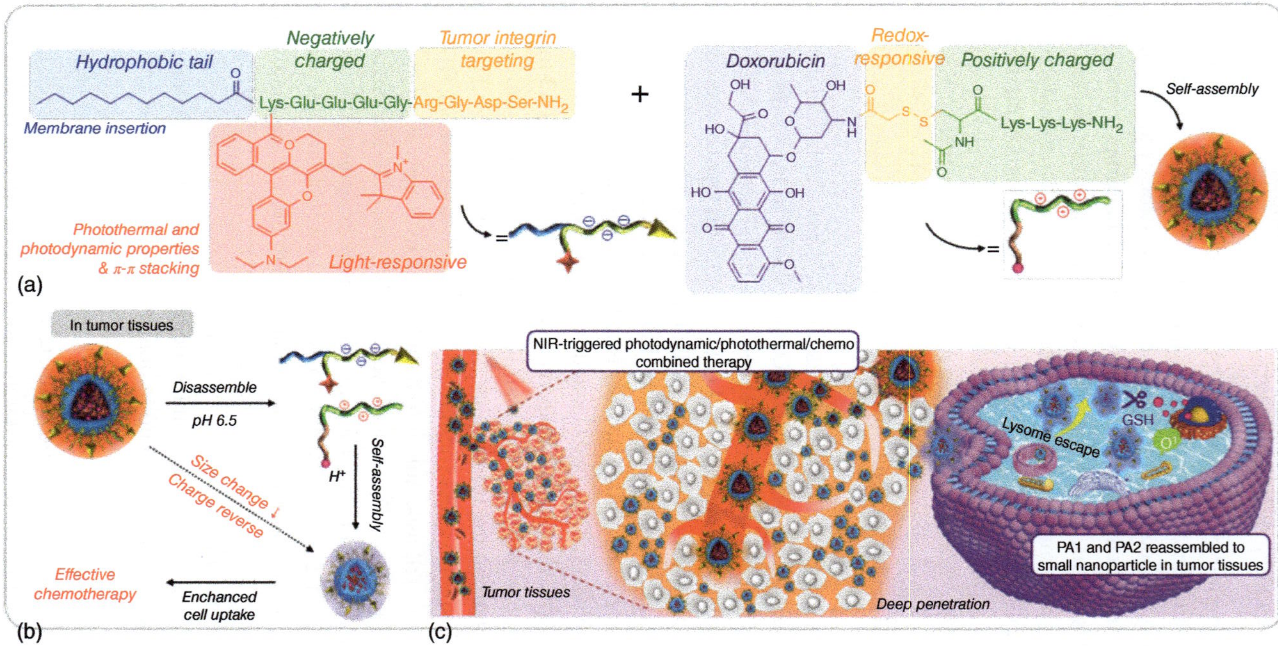

Figure 23.12 a) Molecular structures and the charged states of PA1 and PA2. b) Schematic illustration of the formation of the multifunctional biocomponent peptide NPs mediated by electrostatic interaction between negatively charged PA1 and positively charged PA2. c) Schematic illustration of tumor-targetable and size-transformable multifunctional biocomponent NPs for deep tumor penetration and efficient photo–chemo combined antitumor therapy. Source: Ref. [98]. Reproduced with permission of Wiley-VCH.

(1) RGD peptide for tumor integrin binding, (2) glutamic acids with negative charges, (3) near-infrared (NIR) dye as a photosensitizer-reinforced π–π stacking interaction with DOX, and (4) lauric acid as a lipophilic component for membrane insertion. The GSH responsiveness of PA2 resulted from disulfide bonds. Once NPs reached tumor tissues, they were reassembled into small NPs by responding to both acidic microenvironment and near-infrared laser irradiation, which endowed them with deep tumor penetration ability and enhanced cellular internalization (Figure 23.12b). Both *in vitro* and *in vivo* studies demonstrated that a synergistic therapeutic effect was induced by integrating significant ROS generation, temperature elevation upon NIR laser irradiation, and GSH-triggered drug release in the presence of overexpressed GSH in the tumor (Figure 23.12c). This combined photo–chemotherapy using tumor-microenvironment-induced size-transformable bicomponent NPs exhibited excellent *in vivo* antitumor efficacy and provided insight into combined antitumor therapy with efficient tumor penetration.

23.4.7 Stimuli-responsive Hydrogel Nanocarriers

Stimuli-responsive hydrogels have advanced significantly in recent years owing to the demand for hydrogels in nanotechnology and biomedical applications [229]. Supramolecular hydrogels with good biocompatibility and biodegradability are constituted by noncovalent interactions that form supramolecular structures and encapsulate water through the self-assembly of small molecules in water. Supramolecular hydrogels based on therapeutic agents have been investigated because of their potential use in drug delivery systems [230]. For medical applications, adjustable release rates can be achieved through the controlled transition between gel–sol states. In addition, stimuli-responsive hydrogel systems that release drugs triggered by various stimuli have been reported to enhance drug-release systems [198, 231]. Unfortunately, there are not many studies on PA-based hydrogel that release drugs via structural transformation by these stimuli.

Xu and Yang prepared UV-responsive supramolecular hydrogels consisting of a PA Nap-Nitrob-GFFYGE and a diselenide-containing polymer for drug delivery of naproxen [232]. Entangled nanofibers and hydrogels were formed by electrostatic and hydrogen-bonding interactions between the negatively charged peptide and positively charged polymers. The hydrogel was degraded when it was exposed to γ-irradiation because the produced oxidative species such as hydroxyl radicals and hydrogen peroxide oxidized the diselenide bonds inside the polymers. Furthermore, photocleavage of O-nitrobenzyl groups also led to gel–sol transformation and induced the release of naproxen under light irradiation.

23.5 Targeting Delivery of PA-based Nanoscaffolds

23.5.1 Cell-targeted Delivery

The immune system consists of specialized cells, tissues, and organs that function as a unit to protect the body from a variety of diseases and injuries. In addition to the stimulus-responsive delivery strategy, by targeting these specific properties, a therapeutic effect with low toxicity of infection-related tissue damage, malignant tumors, or infection can be expected [72]. Targeted drug delivery has become important for improving the therapeutic benefits of drugs and lowering their side effects in the management of various medical conditions. For cell-based therapies, synthetic cell delivery scaffolds based on polymers or peptides have created EPR effect at the treatment site [42, 126]. Epitopes for cellular interactions, particularly patterns that encourage cell adhesion, have been included as a result of attempts to introduce signal transduction capabilities into nonbioactive materials [232]. The binding of integrin proteins on the cell surface to certain epitopes found on ECM proteins is one of the mechanisms by which biological adhesion to the ECM occurs. This process results in focal adhesions, which anchor cells and allow communication with the environment [233]. One of the ECM proteins involved in biological adhesion, fibronectin, binds to integrins via a domain composed of Arg-Gly-Asp-Ser (RGDS). To encourage cellular contact and adhesion, cell-adherable sequences have been introduced into many PA-based drug nanocarriers.

The RGDS epitope spacing on nanofibers has been determined to be crucial for detecting and responding to cells [234, 235]. For example, an RGDS spacing of 140 nm is appropriate to focal contact and form stress fiber, and a spacing of 440 nm is sufficient for integrin αVβ3-mediated fibroblast spreading [236]. Stupp and coworkers investigated RGDS sequence-introduced PA nanostructures as potential bioactive mediators for targeting bone marrow mononuclear cells [237]. PA molecules containing RGDS (10%) were co-assembled with nonbioactive dilute PA molecules (90%) to change the epitope density, leading to optimized cell signaling. Bone-marrow mononuclear cells were successfully cultured with excellent adherent on surfaces coated with co-assembled PAs. RGDS and Gly-His-Lys (GHK), a well-known pleiotropic regulator of cellular activity, were conjugated to alkyl chains to enhance the anticancer effects of a medication formulation on epithelial and endothelial tumor cells [239]. The dual targeting system using RGD and GHK acted synergistically on the cellular uptake of the liposomal formulation in integrin-overexpressing cancer and endothelial cells. By loading DOX or paclitaxel, the system induced oxidative stress and mitochondria defunctionalization in the targeted cells.

Alternatively, motifs capable of targeting the tumor microenvironment have been introduced into PAs to improve tumor treatment [125]. Tumor cells, including various stromal cells, ECM, soluble cytokines, and tumor vasculature, have a specific microenvironment distinct from that of other normal cells [72, 90]. Interactions between tumor cells and their surrounding microenvironment occur at all stages of tumor progression. For example, hypoxia activates tumor vascular endothelial cells with aberrant expression of cell surface and secreted proteins, including integrins and MMPs, which promote the formation of blood vessels that are malformed and dysfunctional [240]. Cancer-associated fibroblasts (CAFs) are highly prevalent features of the tumor microenvironment and remodel ECM to promote tumor growth [241]. In malignant solid tumors, tumor-associated macrophages predominate as inflammatory cells, which are immunosuppressive and

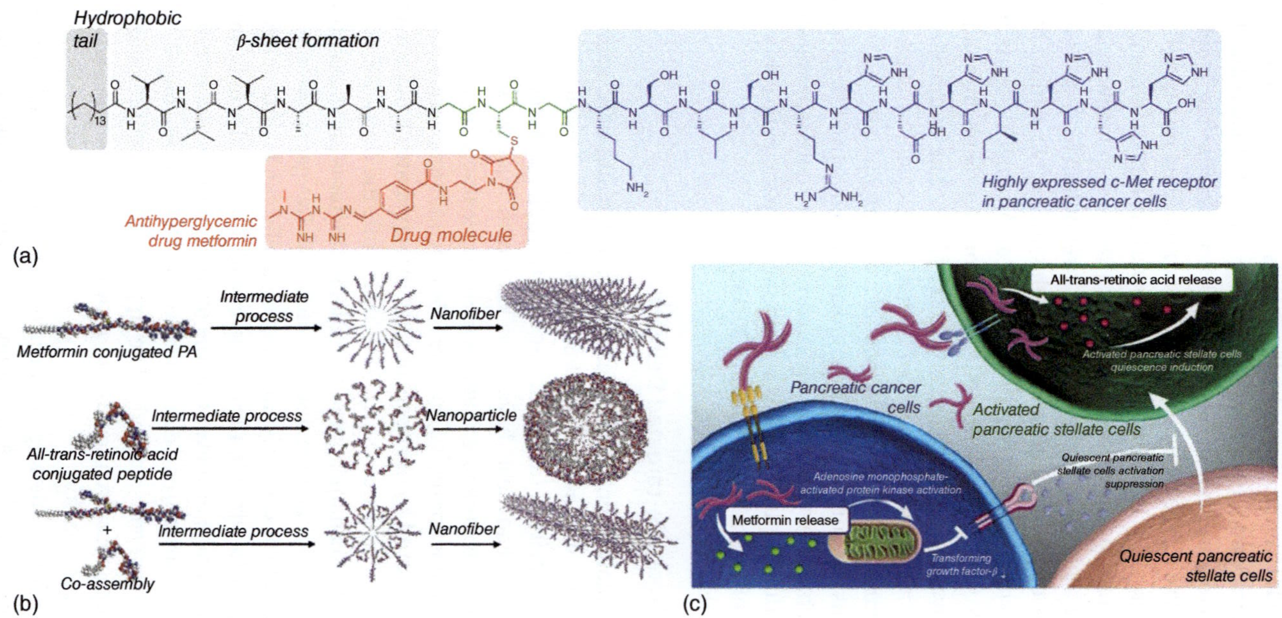

Figure 23.13 (a) Chemical structure of PA including the targeting peptide to highly expressed c-Met receptor in pancreatic cancer cells. (b) Schematic illustration of self-assembly and co-assembly strategies of PA molecules into the stable nanostructures through the intermediate process. (c) Schematic illustration of drug delivery strategy to suppress pancreatic cancer. Source: Ref. [238]. Reproduced with permission of Wiley-VCH.

crucial for angiogenesis. A physiological barrier that protects tumor cells and promotes drug resistance can also be formed by stromal cells and ECM in the tumor microenvironment [242]. Therefore, PA nanocarriers targeting the folate receptor [243], xenografts [244], antibody-producing B cells [245], etc. have been proposed to achieve therapeutic effects by targeting the characteristic tumor microenvironment. Tirrell and coworkers designed a PA containing a cytotoxic T-cell epitope [245]. These molecules self-assemble into micelles, enabling them to target antibody-producing B cells. Maruyama and coworkers exploited the fact that tyrosine kinases are overexpressed in cancer cells [246]. PA phosphorylated in response to kinases self-assembled in the endoplasmic reticulum (ER) and induced the apoptosis of cancer cells. In addition, to target the microenvironment of pancreatic cancer cells in which c-Met is highly expressed, a PA molecule containing a peptide moiety capable of targeting the c-Met receptor and metformin, an antihyperglycemic drug, was designed (Figure 23.13a) [238]. The synthesized PA conjugated with metformin was co-assembled with a peptide conjugated with all-trans-retinoic acid (Figure 23.13b), which is used for cancer treatment, and released the drug into target cells, forming stable and compact 1D nanostructure. The drug delivery system, which has a very stable nanostructure with two therapeutic agents, effectively released metformin and all-trans-retinoic acid to pancreatic cancer cells, showing a suppressive effect on cancer (Figure 23.13c).

23.5.2 Subcellular Organelle-targeted Delivery

Subcellular compartmentalization is a key feature of eukaryotic cells. Each organelle plays a unique role within the cell but causes disease when disordered (Table 23.2) [262]. The majority of therapeutic agents, including anticancer medications, genes, free radicals, and heat, have been known to interact with the cell nucleus [247]. Diseases, such as cancer, diabetes mellitus, deafness, and cardiomyopathy, can be caused by mitochondrial disorders [250]. In addition, various diseases such as Alzheimer's are caused by disorders of the Golgi apparatus [252] and cystic fibrosis of the endoplasmic reticulum (ER) [254–256], while the Golgi–ER network can activate both recovery mechanisms and cell suicide programs [263]. Peroxisome disorder can also cause serious genetic diseases such as Zellweger syndrome [257]. Therefore, a moiety capable of precisely targeting organelle can be introduced into the PA molecule to deliver the drug to the organelle with the disorder to be treated. This method has the advantage of preventing the overuse of drugs and minimizing side effects. PA drug nanocarriers can carry medications directly into target certain cells using intracellular delivery methods. The appropriate bioactive moiety can be added to the PA molecular architecture to provide organelle-targeting ability intended for functional modularity.

One of the well-known organelle-targeted drug nanocarrier strategies is to deliver drugs by targeting the mitochondria. Mitochondria play an important role in apoptosis and may be involved in the development of chemoresistance in most human cancers [250]. In addition, oxidative phosphorylation can be performed to remove ROS, mitochondrial disorder is a phenomenon found in several adult diseases.

Table 23.2 Examples of diseases that can be caused by the disorder of each subcellular organelle and moiety targeting that organelle.

Subcellular organelles	Organelle disorder	Examples	Ref
Nucleus	Progeria, ED muscular distrophy	Polylysine Trans-activator of transactivating (TAT peptide) Short sequence of arginine	[247–249]
Mitochondria	Cardiomyopathy, cancer, diabetes mellitus, and deafness	SS31 (Szeto-Schiller peptides) Triphenyl phosphonium	[250, 251]
Golgi apparatus	Alzheimer's, congenital disorders of glycosylation syndrome	Hydrogen sulfide	[252, 253]
ER	Cystic fibrosis, ERSDs	Carboxyl group Pardaxin peptides *p*-toluene sulfonamide	[254–256]
Peroxisome	Zellweger syndrome, rhizomelic chondrodysplasia punctata	Ser-Lys-Leu (SKL) tripeptide	[257, 258]
Lysosome-related organelles	LSD (Tay-sachs disease), autoimmune diseases	RGD (cyclic Arg-Gly-Asp-Tyr-Cys) Triethylenediamine	[259–261]

Ryu and coworkers designed a PA that specifically accumulates and self-assembles in the mitochondria (Figure 23.14a-c) [264]. PA successfully accumulated in the mitochondria and formed a fibril structure above the CMC (Figure 23.14b), resulting in tumor cell death (Figure 23.14c). Since peroxisomes also have various metabolic functions such as lipid synthesis, fatty acid oxidation, and genetically inherited diseases such as peroxisome biogenesis disorders and peroxisomal enzyme deficiency, it is important to target peroxisomes and deliver therapeutics [257]. We presented a supramolecular nanostructure based on the self-assembly of PAs with a peroxisome-targeting moiety (Figure 23.14d,e). In addition, because *D*-amino acids, a mirror form of *L*-amino acids in nature, possess enduring stability due to their high resistance to endogenous proteases [267], heterochiral self-assembly of mitochondria-targeting PAs induced enhanced mitochondrial destruction [268]. PA was also designed to include the peroxisome-targeting tripeptide, Ser-Lys-Leu (SKL), and a fluorophore (Figure 23.14d) [265]. The α-helical nature of the peptide blocks owing to the carboxyl-terminal group in the SKL of PA and the fibrillar morphology of the nanoassemblies enhanced the targeting efficiency of the PA supramolecular nanoprobe (Figure 23.14e). The ER synthesizes, folds, and modifies proteins within the cell and transports them to the Golgi apparatus [252, 263].

The Golgi apparatus is an organelle that allows the collected proteins to be secreted extracellularly or used intracellularly. The two organelles work organically with each other, and the simultaneous targeting of these two organelles can be a very effective strategy to promote organelle dysfunction and cell death. Yu and coworkers designed and generated a self-sorting assembly of two GSH-responsive peptides in cancer cells for simultaneous organelle targeting (Figure 23.14f,g) [266]. A Golgi target group and an ER target group were introduced to the surface of the assembly, leading to combined organelle dysfunction and cell death (Figure 23.14f). The peptides responded to GSH within HeLa cells to form twisted or flat nanoribbons driven by interdigitated or parallel configurations (Figure 23.14g).

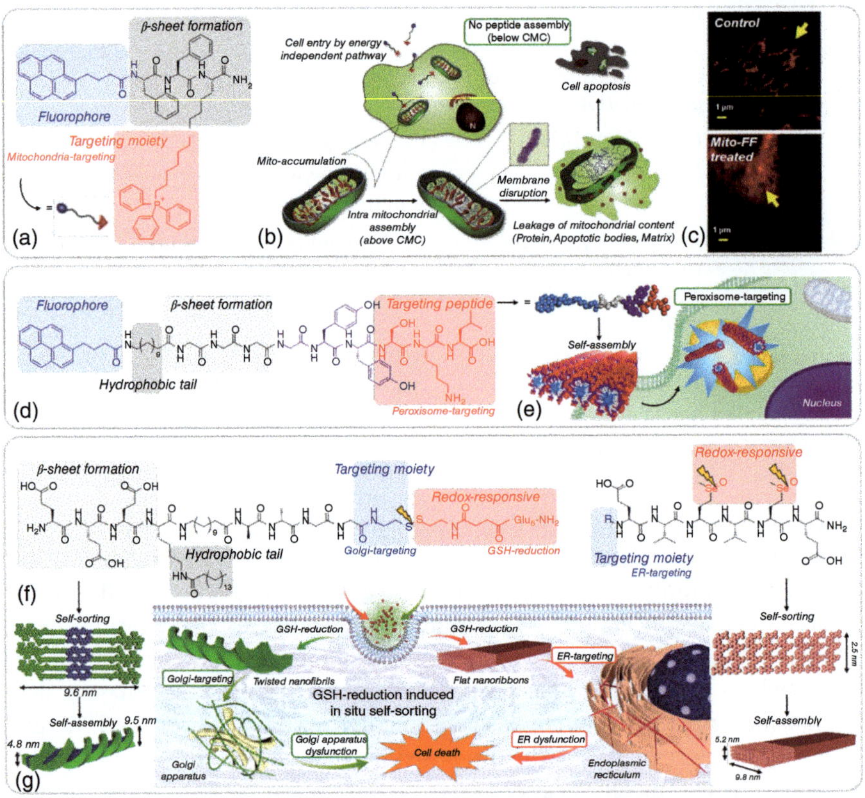

Figure 23.14 (a) Chemical structure of PA molecule including mitochondria-targeting moiety. (b) Schematic illustration of cell apoptosis strategy using the intramitochondrial assembly of PAs, driven by the accumulation of PAs in mitochondria. (c) Confocal images showing mitochondrial shrinkage after mitochondria-targeting PA treatment on HeLa cells (bottom), compared to control (top). Source: Ref. [264]. Springer Nature/CC BY 4.0. (d) Chemical structure of PA molecule including peroxisome-targeting peptide. (e) The PA self-assembled into nanofibers to target peroxisome. Source: Ref. [265]. Reproduced with permission of Wiley-VCH. (f) The chemical structure of PA includes Golgi-targeting and redox-responsive PA and ER-targeting peptides. (g) Both GSH-responsive peptides are self-sorted and assembled endowing their simultaneous targeting of the ER and Golgi apparatus. Source: Ref. [266]. Reproduced with permission of American Chemical Society.

23.5.3 Cardiovascular System and Brain-targeted Delivery

Controlling the formation of new blood vessels or showing therapeutic effects by targeting blood vessels is crucial for regenerative medicine, cancer treatment, and cardiovascular disease treatment. Angiogenesis, a phenomenon in which new blood vessels are formed in existing blood vessels, is a very important process for wound healing, but angiogenesis in cancer cells means the expansion of cancer [269]. Therefore, antiangiogenic molecules that can inhibit the expansion of blood vessels in cancer cells are advantageous for the treatment of cancer cells [270]. Enhanced angiogenesis through 3D scaffolds based on PA assembly with basic fibroblast growth factor suspension could improve tissue regeneration [271]. Heparin is known to bind to many angiogenic growth factors, including vascular endothelial growth factor [272], and the PA self-assembled nanostructure nucleated by heparin yielded rigid nanofibers that display heparin chains outermost, thus promoting the growth of blood vessels [273]. In addition, cardiovascular interventions have a high failure rate due to restenosis [274]. If the drug can be delivered using PA having the moiety that can bind to the collagen of blood vessels, it can be delivered without the long-term existence of a foreign substance such as a stent, and side effects can be avoided by delivering multiple doses of the drug very locally. The targeting ability of vascular intervention according to the PA nanostructures was investigated after balloon angioplasty (Figure 23.15a-d) [275]. As shown in Figure 23.15a, PAs including collagen-binding peptides were designed to be assembled into nanosphere and nanofiber (Figure 23.15b), and using fluorescence, selective binding to the site of vascular intervention was confirmed (Figure 23.15c). Cylindrical nanostructures are observed to target the site of arterial injury, while spherical nanostructures with an equivalent diameter display no binding (Figure 23.15d). Abdominal aortic aneurysm (AAA) carries a serious risk of death when the aorta in the abdomen is locally dilated and ruptures; however, the causes are not fully understood [276]. Stupp and coworkers reported the development of injectable supramolecular nanofibers using PA molecules designed to localize AAA by targeting matrix metalloproteinase 2 (MMP-2) and membrane type 1 matrix metalloproteinases [277]. After co-assembling the target and diluent PAs in different molar ratios, the morphology of nanofibers was confirmed using transmission electron microscopy and successfully localized in the AAA of male and female Sprague–Dawley rats with high organ distribution in the kidney. Furthermore, PA molecules designed to target tissue factors could be developed into injectable targeted supramolecular nanotherapeutics and, therefore, selectively localize to sites of liver injury to slow hemorrhage [278].

The development of efficient neuropharmaceuticals continues to face difficulties in the delivery of therapeutic PAs to the central nervous system because it is challenging for big hydrophilic molecules to penetrate the blood–brain barrier (BBB), which separates the blood from the brain [279]. To illustrate the idea of using an amphiphilic derivative of a peptide to enhance its delivery to the brain, Tirrell and coworkers used the model peptide moiety (Tyr-*D*-Ala-Gly-Phe-Leu-Arg) [280]. This peptide is an opioid receptor agonist that shows specificity for mu-opioid receptors and is typically excluded from the central nervous system. The PA molecules self-assembled into a nanofiber structure and successfully targeted red blood cells in the brain tissue.

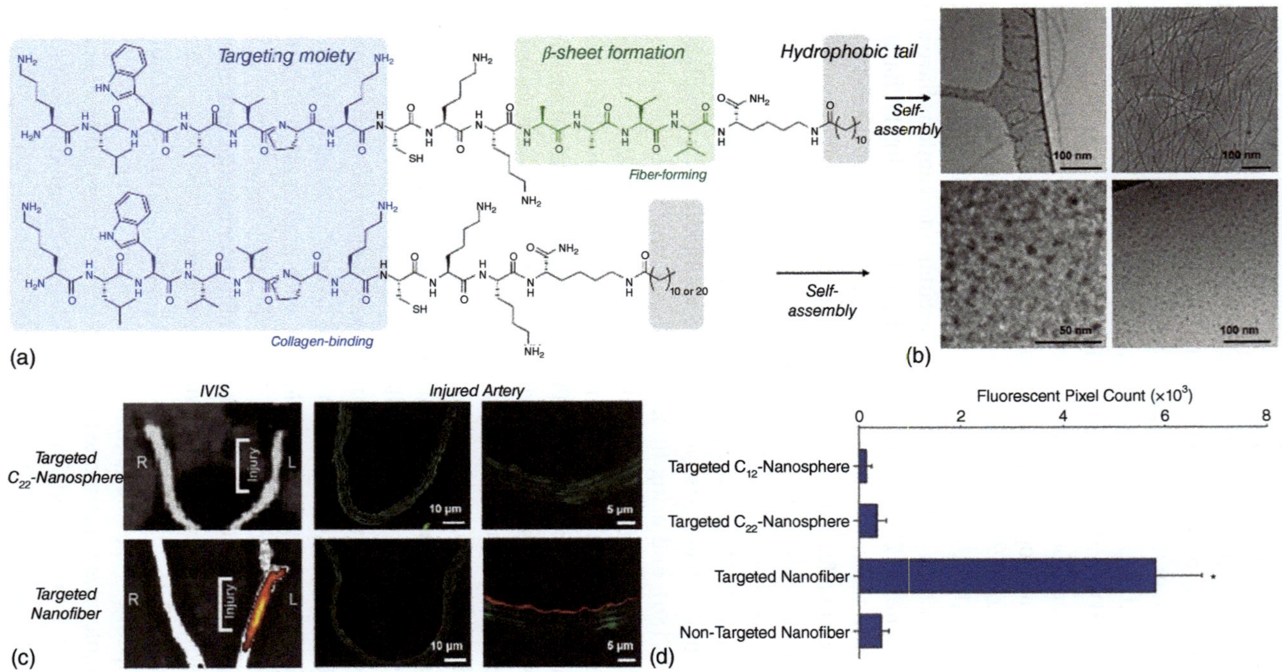

Figure 23.15 (a) Chemical structure of blood vessels-targeting PA including collagen-binding peptide. (b) TEM images of self-assembled PAs with blood vessels-targeting ability. (c) Fluorescent images of gross injured carotid arteries (left) and arterial cross sections of injured left carotid artery treated with targeted C22-nanospheres and targeted nanofibers. (d) Graph showing the quantification of positive fluorescent signal from the arterial cross sections. Source: Ref. [275]. Reproduced with permission of Wiley VCH.

Because fibrin deposition in and around tumor sites is a hallmark of both primary and metastatic brain tumors, the targeting ability of micellar NPs functionalized with the coagulation-binding peptide (Cys-Arg-Glu-Lys-Ala) was investigated [281]. Micelles, an assembly of PA, accumulated in glioblastoma through enhanced permeability and retention effects and exhibited enhanced tumor homing.

23.6 Supramolecular Theranostic Nanocarriers

23.6.1 Theranostic Nanocarriers

As mentioned above, the utilization of organic, inorganic, or hybrid materials at the nanoscale has advanced medicine, which encompasses a wide range of applications including therapeutics, diagnosis and imaging tools, tissue engineering, and drug delivery [2, 86]. Due to the characteristics such as biocompatibility, biodegradability, simple synthesis, adaptability, and bioactivity (penetration and targeting ability), peptides with the ability to self-assemble have been actively used to develop therapy and diagnosis of diseases. The development of chemical synthesis and understanding of self-assembly behavior allows the incorporation of various bioactive moieties and functional groups at the desired position in the peptide sequence and enables control of the structure, dimension, and surface area of the self-assemblies [83]. In this section, theranostics (*in vivo* integrated therapeutic and diagnostic applications for the simultaneous monitoring and treatment of diseases) using supramolecular self-assembled peptide nanostructures are discussed.

We developed multifunctional theranostic agents as supramolecular nanoplatforms for application in customized medicine [282]. These theranostic agents were prepared by co-assembly of two PEGylated peptides, both of which consisted of common motifs and an octreotide [somatostatin (SST) analogue] for tumor-targeting motifs or a 1,4,7,10-tetraazacyclododecane-1,4,7,10-tetraacetic acid (DOTA) motif for magnetic resonance (MR) imaging. The common motif consisted of hydrophobic amino acids (phenylalanine, Phe, or cyclo-hexylalanine, Cha) alternated with four lysine residues and a PEG linker with four ethoxylic units (Figure 23.16a). Co-assembled nanofibers were prepared by combining Cha-DOTA and C-Cha at molar ratios of 2:8, 5:5, and 8:2 (Figure 23.16b). PAs tagged with octreotide self-assembled into nanofibrils in an aqueous solution and exhibited target-specific intracellular delivery of DOX to human breast adenocarcinoma cells overexpressing SST receptor (Figure 23.16c). They exhibited a proton relaxivity (r_1) between 17.1 and 19.5 mM^{-1} s^{-1}, which were related to the size of each nanostructure, and larger nanofibers had the highest r_1 value (Figure 23.16c). For nanofibrils co-assembled with Cha-DOTA and C-Cha, the fluorescence intensity of DOX was calculated to be around 8.5 times higher than that of the control (Figure 23.16d).

As a novel multimodality imaging probe, integrated NIR fluorescent and MR dual-imaging nanoprobes were designed for trypsin-responsive targeted drug delivery against malignant tumors by Dou and coworkers (Figure 23.16e) [284]. These nanoprobes are composed of Fe_3O_4 magnetic NPs surface-decorated with poly acrylic acid and Cy5.5-modified poly-L-lysine (PLL-g-Cy5.5) enabling MR

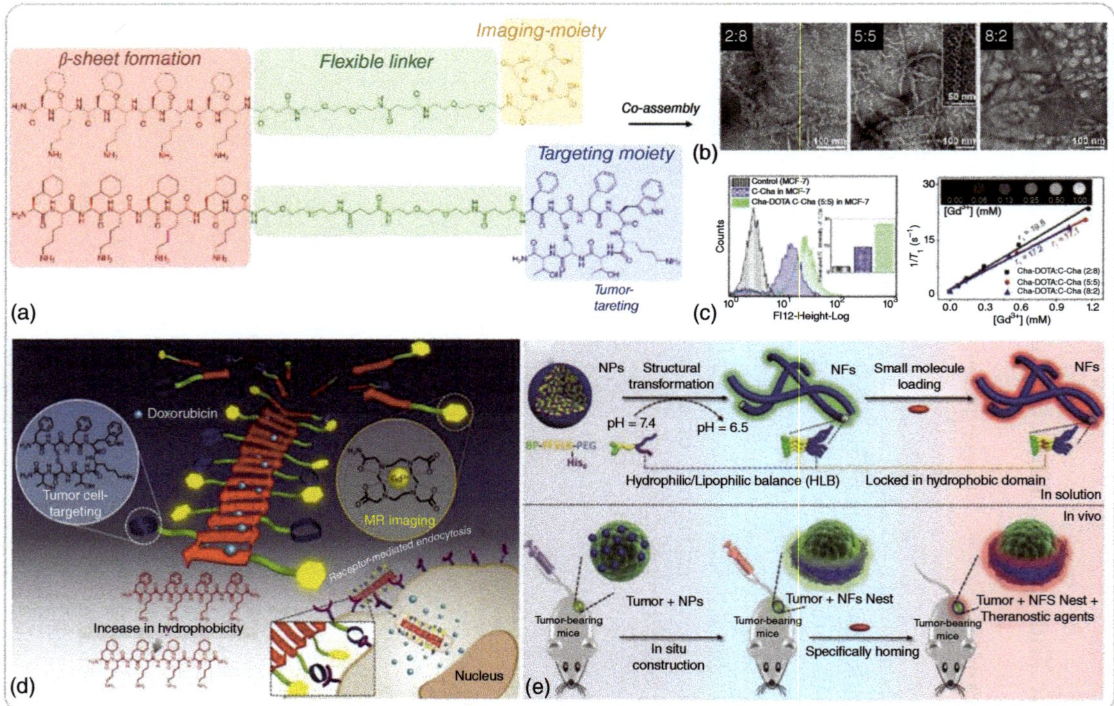

Figure 23.16 (a) Molecular structures and various functions of PAs (Cha-DOTA and C-Cha) used in this study. They were co-assembled into one-dimensional nanofibrils with the tumor-targeting ability and MR imaging for theranostics. (b) TEM images of negatively stained co-assembled nanostructures of Cha-DOTA and C-Cha with the molar ratios of 2:8, 5:5, and 8:2 in aqueous solution. (c) (Left) Flow cytometry histogram of MCF-7 cells incubated with DOX-loaded nanofibrils of C-Cha and Cha-DOTA:C-Cha with 5:5 molar ratio and fluorescence intensity of DOX in MCF-7 cell (inset). (Right) T_1 relaxivity plots of Gd^{3+}-chelating nanofibrils of Cha-DOTA:C-Cha with different molar ratios (2:8, 5:5, and 8:2) as a function of concentration of Gd^{3+} and T_1-weighted MR images of 5:5 Cha-DOTA:C-Cha (inset). (d) Schematic illustration of 1D supramolecular nanofibril prepared by co-assembly of PAs for theranostics. *Source:* Ref. [282]. Reproduced with permission of American Chemical Society. (e) Schematic illustration of pH-triggered morphological transformation from peptide-based self-assembled nanoparticles to nanofibrils and nest-like hosts in tumor for homing theranostics. In solution, monomers self-assemble into nanoparticles in neutral condition and transformed to β-sheet nanofibrils in acidic condition. The nanofibrils captured small molecules via hydrophobic interactions. In vivo, NPs-1 were accumulated in tumor via passive accumulation mechanisms, followed by nanoparticles transformed into nanofibrils and constructed the nest-like host in acidic condition. Theranostic small molecules were gathered in the tumor nest-like host. *Source:* Ref. [283]. Reproduced with permission of Wiley-VCH.

imaging and trypsin-responsive substrate/NIR fluorescent agents, respectively. The PLL-g-Cy5.5 was self-quenched after the construction of the nanoprobes due to the close distances between the Cy5.5 molecules. The nanoprobes were disrupted after trypsin-triggered hydrolysis of PLL peptide inside the tumor cells. This resulted in 18 times increase in NIR fluorescent intensity compared to that of the initial nanopeptide and a significant improvement in the MR imaging. *In vitro* and *in vivo* studies demonstrated that the prepared nanoprobes exhibited enhanced trypsin-responsive NIR fluorescent and MR dual-imaging abilities to recognize lesions where trypsin was overexpressed.

The development of host materials that are transformable from nanoparticle to nanofibril in the tumor microenvironment for theranostics was reported by Wang and coworkers [283] (Figure 23.16e). They designed and synthesized host materials that can undergo controlled transformations in response to the specific conditions in tumor microenvironments. These host materials were designed to target tumors and deliver therapeutic small molecules while simultaneously providing diagnostic information. The *in vivo* studies showed that the host materials were effectively accumulated in the tumors via passive targeting mechanisms. Once inside the tumor, the host materials transformed from nanoparticles to nanofibrils, constructing a nest-like structure that could effectively capture small molecules following intravenous injection. This homing theranostic agent allowed for the targeted delivery of therapeutic agents to the tumor site while providing imaging information for monitoring the therapeutic response. The transformable host materials exhibited enhanced therapeutic efficacy, as well as imaging ability for tumor detection and monitoring.

Recently, to synthesize a therapeutic nanosystem while taking advantage of dual-imaging nanoprobes, tumor-triggered targeting dual-mode NIR fluorescent/MR imaging and photodynamic therapy system was developed through the self-assembly by Zou and coworkers [285]. The prepared NPs exhibited biocompatibility and tumor-triggered targeting ability and delivered the insoluble photosensitizer therapeutic agent chlorin e6 (Ce6) into tumor cells, leading to cancer cell death. The designed theranostic nanosystem could be used for tumor-targeted dual-mode NIR fluorescent/MR imaging and photodynamic when the MMP2-cleavable short peptide (PLGVR), agent Ce6, and chelating Gd ions coexisted at the same time. Specifically, NPs were actively internalized into tumor cells via Arg-Gly-Asp (RGD) peptide-mediated cellular uptake after PLGVR was hydrolyzed in the tumor microenvironment by MMP2. The targeted NPs displayed an elevated therapeutic ability to promote cancer cell apoptosis with high accumulation in tumors after laser irradiation. Thus, they demonstrated the potential of these NPs for accurate clinical tumor diagnosis and photodynamic therapy with minimal side effects.

23.6.2 Antimicrobial Theranostic Nanocarriers

In the process of fabricating artificially self-assembled nanomaterials, the natural self-assembly process has been studied, and novel self-assembled nanomaterials inspired by assembled organisms found in nature have also been created. Artificial nanomaterials that surpass those found in nature have been designed and have led to the development of improved biomedical nanomaterials for human beings.

Specifically, a lot of building blocks and driving forces to prepare antimicrobial self-assembled nanostructures have been studied. These self-assembled materials have well-organized multilayer nanostructures that can directly kill bacteria and have good antifouling, antibiofilm, and bacteriostatic properties [286, 287]. Self-assembled nanostructures constructed from PAs, polypeptides, cyclic peptides, short peptides, and peptide hydrogels have been exploited for antimicrobial therapy and diagnosis [288]. In addition, hybrid inorganic self-assembled nanomaterial also exhibited antimicrobial effects and low toxicity [289]. We prepared two pyrene-labeled peptide nanofibrils for "light-off" and "light-up" fluorescence detection of Cu^{2+} and Ag^{+}, respectively [100]. The peptides consisted of a hydrophobic linear- or branched-alkyl chain (for PA1 and PA2, respectively) and a hydrophilic histidine-rich peptide (HGGGHGHGGGHG). Subsequently, PA2 nanofibrils were formed through the self-assembly of PAs (Figure 23.17a). The emission spectra of the pyrene showed that the supramolecular assemblies of PA1 and PA2 could have a significant effect on the binding affinity to Cu^{2+} or Ag^{+}. Histidine-coated PA1 nanofibrils exhibited a high binding affinity to Cu^{2+} as a fluorescent "light-off" sensor (Figure 23.17b). The incubation of PA2 with silver nitrate and the subsequent

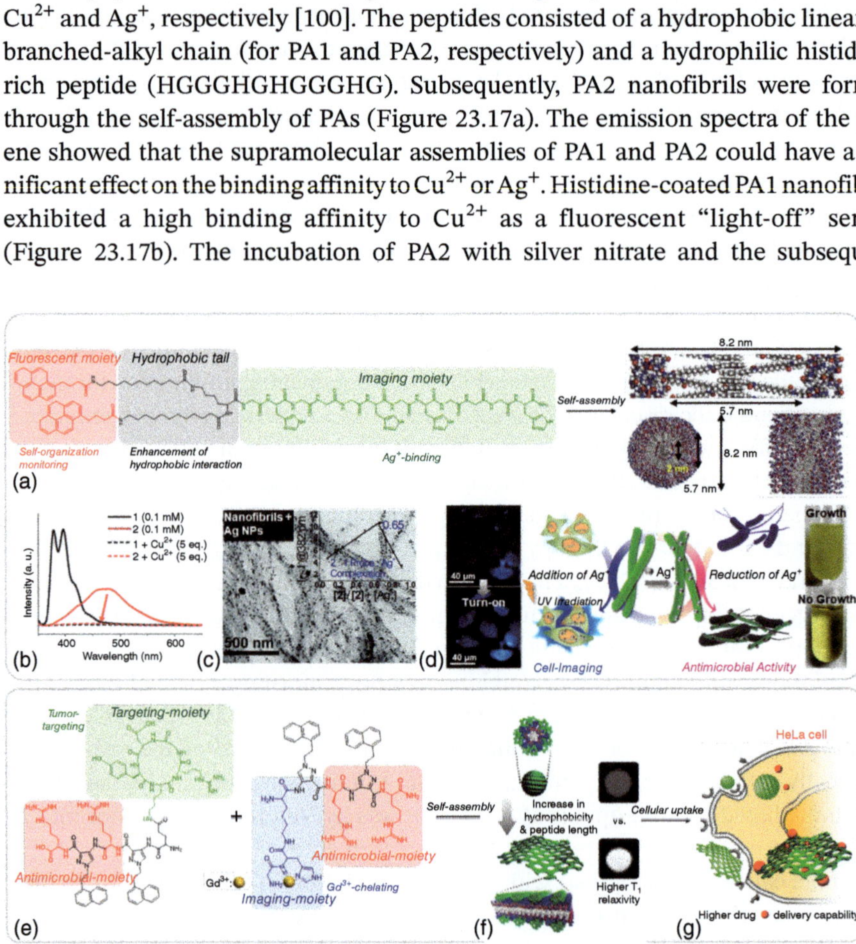

Figure 23.17 (a) Molecular structure and bioactive molecules of PA2 which self-assembled into peptide nanofibrils. (b) Emission spectra before and after the addition of Cu^{2+} to PA1 and PA2 (λ_{ex} = 340 nm). (c) TEM image of PA2 NFs after AgNPs generation (inset, fluorescence Job's plot for the determination of the stoichiometry of the NF-Ag^{+} complex). (d) Schematic illustration of dual-functional hybrid PA nanofibrils for cell imaging (left) and antimicrobial effects (right). Source: Ref. [100]. Reproduced with permission of Royal Society of Chemistry. (e) Molecular structures and multiple functions of AMPs with metal-chelating moieties G3 and with cell-targeting moieties R3. (f) Controllable MR relaxivity via morphology transformation of the self-assembled nanoaggregates by modulating hydrophobicity and peptide length. (g) Schematic illustration of delivery of a theranostic agent using Co-AMPs. Source: Ref. [101]. Reproduced with permission of American Chemical Society.

reduction nucleated Ag NPs along with the nanofibrils (Figure 23.17c). "Light-up" fluorescent Ag^+ detection of PA2 nanofibrils through inhibition of photoinduced electron transfer (PET) was observed. These nanofibrils incorporated with AgNPs displayed highly effective and long-term antibacterial activity against both Gram-negative and -positive bacteria (Figure 23.17d).

The supramolecular theranostic nanoagent with antimicrobial activities was also developed by us [101]. These theranostic nanoagents, based on the self-assembly of antimicrobial peptide (AMP), can conjugate gadolinium(III) (Gd^{3+}) and target tumors in an aqueous solution. Specifically, a series of AMPs (G1, G2, and G3) composed of N-alkyl/aryl pyrazole (Py) amino acids and arginine (Arg) were designed (Figure 23.17e). The hydrophobicity and positive charge of the peptides resulted from the presence of Py and Arg. Then, the AMPs were covalently decorated with the tripeptide glycine–histidine–lysine (GHK) for the coordination of Gd^{3+} or cyclic arginine–glycine–aspartic acid (cRGD) (R1, R3) for the identification of $\alpha v\beta 3$ and $\alpha v\beta 5$ integrin receptors in tumor cells. Different kinds of Gd-complexed AMPs were co-assembled (Co-AMPs, G1R1, G2R1, G3R1, G1R3, G2R3, and G3R3) by mixing GHK-AMP and cRGD-AMP peptides which were obtained by repeating Py-Arg building units to form a molecular structure with various peptide lengths, which resulted in the formation of micelles, fibrils, vesicles, sheets, and planar networks. The two-dimensional (2D) networks formed by robust hydrophobic interactions of C0-AMPs exhibited higher longitudinal (T_1) relaxivity of water protons (Figure 23.17f) and lesser antimicrobial activity and tumor-cell cytotoxicity with higher DOX loading/delivery capability owing to the larger hydrophobic capacity and receptor-binding areas (Figure 23.17g).

23.7 Other Applications of Stimuli-responsive Nanomaterials

23.7.1 Therapeutic Gas Transmitters

In mammalian physiology, carbon monoxide (CO) has been shown to have anti-inflammatory, antiapoptotic, vasodilatory, antihypertensive, and cytoprotective effects [290]. However, a high level of CO in the blood can provoke tissue hypoxia due to the exceptional affinity of CO for hemoglobin, which deteriorates the oxygen-delivery capacity of the blood [291]. CO-Releasing molecules (CORMs) based on metal–carbonyl complexes have been utilized for convenient and safer delivery of therapeutic CO instead of using pure CO gas for inhalation therapy [292]. The water-soluble tricarbonylchloro(glycinato)ruthenium(II) (CORM-3, Ru(CO)3Cl(glycinate)) is one of the most potent CORMs. CO can be dissociated from CORM-3 at a short half-life in human plasma, reducing therapeutic efficacy due to the release of CO before it reaches the target sites. In order to handle this problem, CORM was incorporated into nanostructured scaffolds composed of organic small molecules, polymers, and NPs for sustained release of CO [293]. Schatzchneider and coworkers first suggested inherently biocompatible and biodegradable peptide scaffold conjugated with CORM [294]. However, since ultraviolet (UV) irradiation was requisite to induce CO release, nonspecific CO release could occur. To deal with this problem, a

CO-releasing supramolecular hydrogel based on the self-assembly of PAs conjugated with the water-soluble CORM-3 was reported by Stupp and coworkers [295]. When compared to the small CORM, the half-life of the CO release of CORM with peptide hydrogel was more than eight times longer. This was due to the slow water–gas ligand exchange of CORM-3 located onto nanofibrils of the hydrogel.

We prepared a supramolecular CO-releasing injectable peptide hydrogel (COH) and a corresponding adhesive hydrogel patch (COHP) based on the self-assembly of a diphenylalanine (FF)-peptide derivative (P2-CORM) (Figure 23.18d) [102]. The most potent water-soluble CO-releasable molecule, CORM-3, was coupled to the peptide based on FF, followed by co-assembly with fluorenylmethyloxycarbonyl (Fmoc)-FF, resulting in the formation of a supramolecular hydrogel constructed from CO-releasing fiber (Figure 23.18a). TEM revealed that P2-CORM self-assembled into fibrillar structures in aqueous solution (Figure 23.18b). Fibrillar structure was formed by the π–π interaction between phenyl rings and hydrogen bonds among neighboring peptides. The prepared CO-releasing peptide-based hydrogel showed cytoprotective and anti-inflammatory effects in H2O2-stimulated cardiomyocytes (Figure 23.18c). In addition, the adhesive ability was introduced to their hydrogel patch to apply on desired sites in the tissues or organs regardless of the surface condition, which can be used for implantable CO therapeutic agent (Figure 23.18d). Fmoc-serine (S) and catechol-FF were used to impart mechanical stiffness and tissue adhesion to the hydrogel, so that adhesive hydrogel patch was fabricated upon exposure to divalent cation Ca^{2+} (Figure 23.18e). Since catechol-FF has a high binding affinity to various nucleophiles such as amine, thiol, and imidazole, it can endow COHP with the adhesive ability (Figure 23.18f). Although torsional stress was externally applied, the formulation of COHP remained intact without separating from the substrate. They demonstrated that both COH and COHP can realize the localization of therapeutic CO gas by injection or implantation into targeted sites, which showed a new direction for the therapeutic gas transmitter using peptide-based materials.

23.7.2 Photothermal Therapeutic Nanoagents

Photothermal therapy, which converts light (most often in infrared wavelengths) energy to heat energy, has been developed for the treatment of various diseases [296]. Photothermal therapy was derived from photodynamic therapy, where the incorporated photosensitizer is excited by externally irradiated light with a specific wavelength. Light irradiation enables the activation of the photosensitizer to an excited state and then generates vibrational energy (heat), leading to the death of targeted cells or tissues. Additionally, photothermal therapy does not require oxygen to interact with the target cells or tissues compared to photodynamic therapy. Although there are many ways to improve the efficiency of tumor heat ablation to treat cancer, it is still important to reduce side effects and severe damage to normal tissue [297]. Peptides and their derivatives with the aforementioned advantages have also been utilized for photothermal therapy [298].

A method of preventing the spread of antibiotic-resistant germs is to use smart antibacterial systems that release antimicrobials in a highly controlled manner.

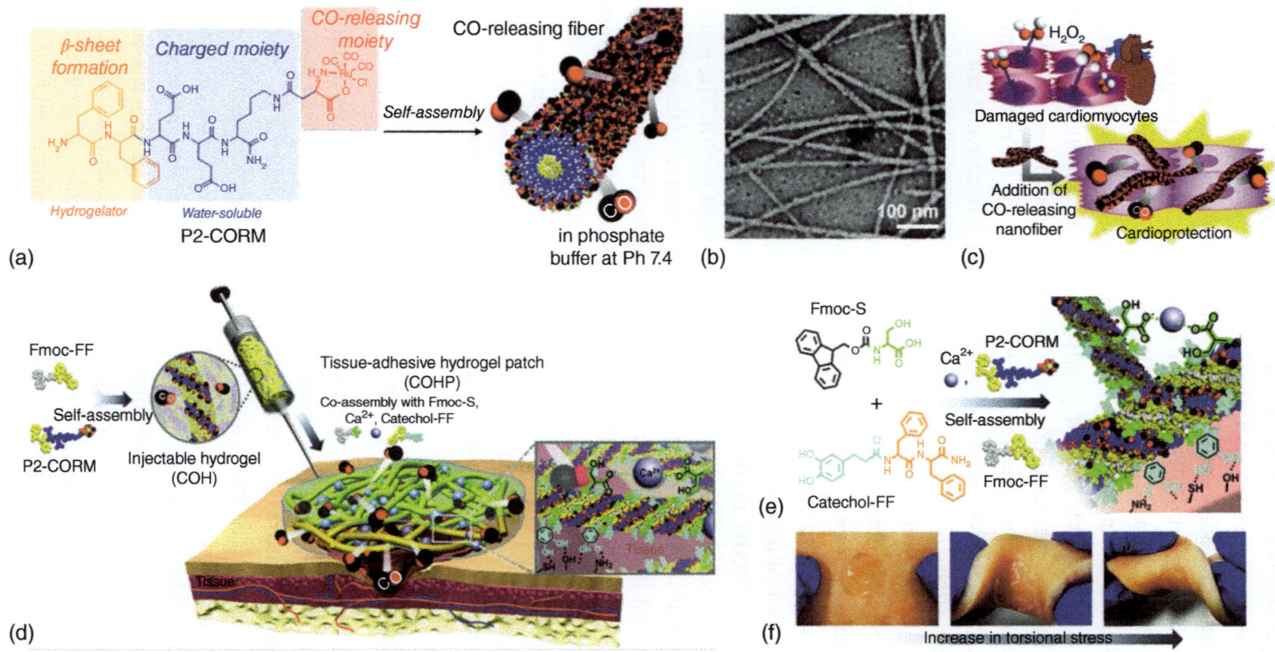

Figure 23.18 (a) Molecular structures and synthesis of P1-CORM and P2-CORM. P2-CORM only can be self-assembled into a nanofiber that releases CO in phosphate buffer at pH 7.4. (b) Negatively stained TEM image of self-assembled P2-CORM nanofibrils. (c) Schematic representation of the cardioprotective activity of nanofibrils formed by P2-CORM for oxidatively stressed cardiomyocytes (H9C2 cells). (d) Schematic illustration of supramolecular injectable hydrogel and tissue-adhesive hydrogel patch. (e) Chemical structures of Fmoc-S and Catechol-FF, and schematic representation of their co-assembly with P2-CORM to construct COHP. (f) Photographs of COHP adhering to porcine skin under torsional stress. Source: Ref. [102]. Reproduced with permission of Wiley-VCH.

Kraatz and coworkers reported a light-responsive antimicrobial nanocomposite hydrogel platform for the controlled and sustained release of a hydrophobic drug by combining a myristyl-Phe-Phe-OH (C14-FF) peptide gelator to entrap rifampicin in the hydrophilic hydrogel matrix and photothermally active polydopamine NPs [299]. They demonstrated that the direct interaction of rifampicin with both the PA and PDNP resulted in a greater drug-loading capacity and a significantly slower rate of passive release. The incorporation of PDNP made laser-induced drug release possible. The hybrid hydrogel combining C14-FF, PDNP, and rifampicin exhibited a thick and dense fiber network with heterogeneous fiber bundles. The C14-FF hydrogel without polydopamine NP exhibited a low passive release of rifampicin, and the addition of PDNP to the hydrogel resulted in a much lower rate of passive release. Upon NIR laser irradiation, photothermal heating led to the release of more rifampicin from the gel, which prevented the growth of Gram-negative *E. coli*.

If natural approaches such as light and sound without side effects are used to remove cancerous lesions, noninvasive treatment with improved medical efficacy can be realized, and the death rate would be reduced. Liu and coworkers fabricated composite PA-indocyanine green (ICG) micelles (C18GR7RGDS-ICG micelles) through self-assembly of PAs incorporation with ICG encapsulation for sonodynamic, photodynamic, and photothermal combination therapy [300]. Using both light and sound can be an effective method for eliminating cancer cells, allowing for a noninvasive treatment to reduce mortality and improve patient health. The results demonstrated that this multimodal treatment was efficient *in vitro* cell targeting and *in vivo* treatments of breast tumors. Routine blood examinations, pro-inflammatory cytokine analysis, and histological HE-TUNEL staining demonstrated an immune response activation mechanism and enhanced tumor elimination capability without side effects on normal cells. Consequently, this multifunctional nanomaterial combining phototherapy with sonodynamic therapy or chemiluminescence excitation was a potential method to enhance the efficacy of therapy against cancer.

23.7.3 Cellular Cryopreserved Nanoagents

Self-assembled peptides can be utilized as material candidates for the cryostorage and transport of drugs, organs, cells, or tissues by mimicking ice-binding proteins (IBPs) in nature [301–303]. Natural IBPs show the periodic distance of ice-binding moieties, similar to the ice crystal lattice, and their structural properties induce ice recrystallization inhibition (IRI) activity and thermal hysteresis [304, 305]. Self-assembled systems of peptides can arrange ice-binding moieties relatively regularly through intermolecular interactions and form microcurvature at the ice–water interface, and through this, the IRI activity of IBP can be artificially emulated [303, 306]. In particular, since the biocompatibility and low cytotoxicity of peptides are great advantages for use as cryopreservatives, mimicking IBPs using peptide assemblies has received attention.

Representative ice-binding amino acids were introduced into the main scaffold of Fmoc-FF, which forms robust, self-assembled fibrillar nanoaggregates with enhanced colloidal stability due to π–π stacking (Figure 23.19) [106]. The outermost

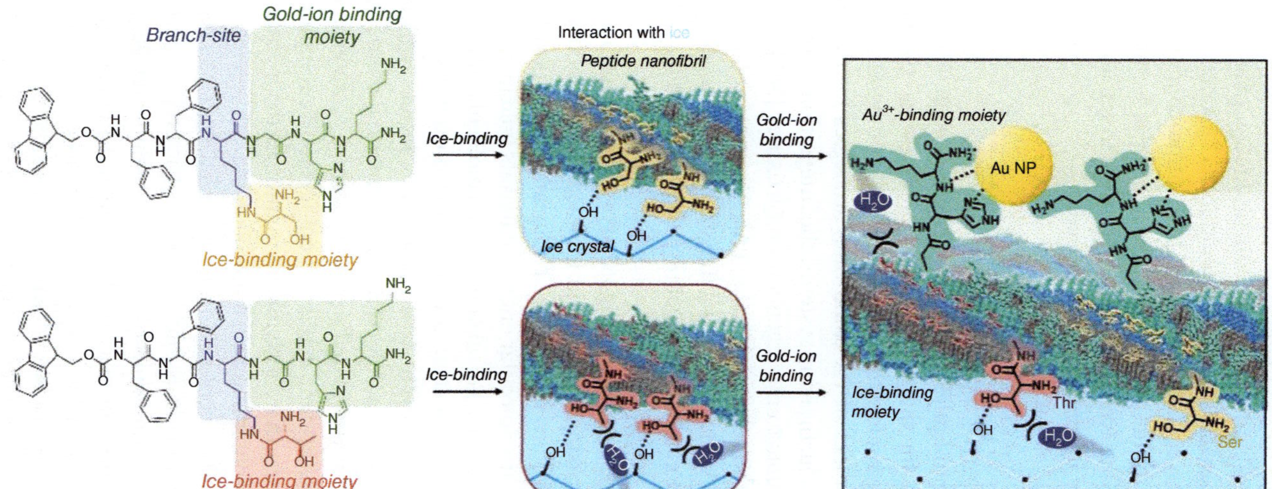

Figure 23.19 Molecular structures of Fmoc-FF-based peptides that can chelate with gold ions. With Fmoc-FF as a scaffold, lysine (K) was used as a branch site for coupling ice-binding moieties, and the GHK tripeptide was used as an Au ion-chelating site. Serine (S) and threonine (T) were used as ice-binding moieties; S only has a hydroxyl group, while T has both hydroxyl and methyl groups. Source: [106]. Reproduced with permission of American Chemical Society.

ice-binding pendant of peptide fibrils induced the IRI activity. Peptide nanoscaffolds containing a Gly–His–Lys (GHK) tripeptide are capable of tethering with gold NPs that can readily monitor IRI activity. This could be confirmed through a colorimetric assay based on the dispersion of gold NPs confined in peptide nanofibrils. The adsorbing process to the ice-binding surface could be directly visualized through enhanced scattering caused by gold NPs. Peptide nanoribbons based on naphthalene-FF were also used as cellular cryopreservatives [105]. By introducing threonine (T), known as an ice-binding moiety, into the peptide molecule, the structural characteristics of natural IBPs with regular ice-binding moieties were imitated, and through this, the IRI effect and thermal hysteresis were induced.

23.7.4 Others

The self-assembled PA supramolecules can display bioactive signals on their surface, which can be exploited for many biomedical applications, by introducing epitopes or controlling the intermolecular interactions in assembly. Supramolecular assemblies and covalent networks of PA could offer strategies for the bottom-up design to mimic living organisms. In living systems, the integration of supramolecular structures and PA contributes to the regeneration of tissues [307], ECM [308], and membranes [309]. Using the collagen-binding PAs, filamentous nanostructures with suitable structural stability and yielding solid hydrogel with excellent rheological properties were formed to exhibit the capability of therapy using atomization and nebulization [310].

Emulating the alignment and assembly of light-harvesting protein machinery in plants based on self-assembly using noncovalent interactions could offer the functional correlation among molecules to optimize photocatalysis, photovoltaics, and energy storage [311]. Thus, supramolecular energy materials hold great potential in the design of photovoltaic systems. For example, intermolecular interactions in porphyrins-doped PA self-assembled structures maximized exciton diffusion, and also induced the formation of excimers between adjacent molecules, which serve as exciton traps [312]. Light-responsive soft materials are composed of self-assembled PAs chemically bonded to spiropyran-based networks that expel water in response to visible light [313]. Thus, the supramolecular system formed a reversibly deformable and water-draining skeleton that mechanically reinforces the hybrid, enabling faster bending and flattening actuation like a nanorobot.

In addition, PA is considered a very promising material owing to its complex supramolecular structure and properties, such as biomimetic properties. Therefore, grafting bioinspired structures or biomolecules into PA could be fertile ground for discovery in the future. Integration of machine learning and atomistic simulations and supramolecular materials in which structure, dynamics, and function will emerge by self-assembly will be discovered without experimental process [314]. Metallurgical supramolecular materials will allow alloys to exhibit unique photophysical and mechanical properties and morphologies [315].

References

1 Min, Y., Caster, J.M., Eblan, M.J., and Wang, A.Z. (2015). Clinical translation of nanomedicine. *Chem. Rev.* 115: 11147–11190.

2 Pelaz, B., Alexiou, C., Alvarez-Puebla, R.A. et al. (2017). Diverse applications of nanomedicine. *ACS Nano* 11: 2313–2381.

3 Mitchell, M.J., Billingsley, M.M., Haley, R.M. et al. (2021). Engineering precision nanoparticles for drug delivery. *Nat. Rev. Drug Discov.* 20: 101–124.

4 Fitzpatrick, S., McCabe, J.F., Petts, C.R., and Booth, S.W. (2002). Effect of moisture on polyvinylpyrrolidone in accelerated stability testing. *Int. J. Pharm.* 246: 143–151.

5 Li, S., Wei, B., Fleres, S. et al. (2004). Correlation and prediction of moisture-mediated dissolution stability for benazepril hydrochloride tablets. *Pharm. Res.* 21: 617–624.

6 Veronica, N., Heng, P.W.S., and Liew, C.V. (2023). Relative humidity cycling: implications on the stability of moisture-sensitive drugs in solid pharmaceutical products. *Mol. Pharm.* 20: 1072–1085.

7 Nicholson, J.K., Connelly, J., Lindon, J.C., and Holmes, E. (2002). Metabonomics: A platform for studying drug toxicity and gene function. *Nat. Rev. Drug Discov.* 1: 153–161.

8 Hu, J.J., Xiao, D., and Zhang, X.Z. (2016). Advances in peptide functionalization on mesoporous silica nanoparticles for controlled drug release. *Small* 12: 3344–3359.

9 Cioffi, N., Torsi, L., Ditaranto, N. et al. (2005). Copper nanoparticle/polymer composites with antifungal and bacteriostatic properties. *Chem. Mater.* 17: 5255–5262.

10 Luan, L., Meng, Q., Xu, L. et al. (2015). Peptide amphiphiles with multifunctional fragments promoting cellular uptake and endosomal escape as efficient gene vectors. *J. Mater. Chem. B* 3: 1068–1078.

11 Sun, Y., Kaplan, J.A., Shieh, A. et al. (2016). Self-assembly of a 5-fluorouracil-dipeptide hydrogel. *Chem. Commun.* 52: 5254–5257.

12 Elzoghby, A.O., Samy, W.M., and Elgindy, N.A. (2012). Albumin-based nanoparticles as potential controlled release drug delivery systems. *J. Control. Release* 157: 168–182.

13 Yokoyama, M., Kwon, G.S., Okano, T. et al. (1993). Composition-dependent in vivo antitumor activity of adriamycin-conjugated polymeric micelle against murine colon adenocarcinoma 26. *Drug Deliv.* 1: 11–19.

14 Ma, W., Cheetham, A.G., and Cui, H. (2016). Building nanostructures with drugs. *Nano Today* 11: 13–30.

15 Din, F.U., Aman, W., Ullah, I. et al. (2017). Effective use of nanocarriers as drug delivery systems for the treatment of selected tumors. *Int. J. Nanomedicine* 12: 7291–7309.

16 Hansel, D.E., Platt, E., Orloff, M. et al. (2010). Mammalian target of rapamycin (mTOR) regulates cellular proliferation and tumor growth in urothelial carcinoma. *Am. J. Pathol.* 176: 3062–3072.

17 Jin, J., Sui, B., Gou, J. et al. (2014). PSMA ligand conjugated PCL-PEG polymeric micelles targeted to prostate cancer cells. *PloS One* 9: e112200.

18 Sun, Q., Sun, X., Ma, X. et al. (2014). Integration of nanoassembly functions for an effective delivery cascade for cancer drugs. *Adv. Mater.* 26: 7615–7621.

19 Gregoriadis, G. and Ryman, B.E. (2003). Liposomes as carriers of enzymes or drugs: a new approach to the treatment of storage diseases. *Biochem. Soc.* 238: 761–762.

20 Fang, F., Li, M., Zhang, J., and Lee, C.S. (2020). Different strategies for organic nanoparticle preparation in biomedicine. *ACS Mater. Lett.* 2: 531–549.

21 Akhavan, O., Ghaderi, E., and Rahighi, R. (2012). Toward single-DNA electrochemical biosensing by graphene nanowalls. *ACS Nano* 6: 2904–2916.

22 Freeman, R., Willner, B., and Willner, I. (2011). Integrated biomolecule-quantum dot hybrid systems for bioanalytical applications. *J. Phys. Chem. Lett.* 2: 2667–2677.

23 Endo, T., Kerman, K., Nagatani, N. et al. (2006). Multiple label-free detection of antigen-antibody reaction using localized surface plasmon resonance-based core-shell structured nanoparticle layer nanochip. *Anal. Chem.* 78: 6465–6475.

24 Kim, S., Kim, J.H., Lee, J.S., and Park, C.B. (2015). Beta-sheet-forming, self-assembled peptide nanomaterials towards optical, energy, and healthcare applications. *Small* 11: 3623–3640.

25 Ding, D., Li, K., Liu, B., and Tang, B.Z. (2013). Bioprobes based on AIE fluorogens. *Acc. Chem. Res.* 46: 2441–2453.

26 Escudero, A., Carrillo-Carrión, C., Zyuzin, M.V. et al. (2016). Synthesis and functionalization of monodisperse near-ultraviolet and visible excitable multifunctional Eu3+, Bi3+:REVO4 nanophosphors for bioimaging and biosensing applications. *Nanoscale* 8: 12221–12236.

27 Diaferia, C., Gianolio, E., Palladino, P. et al. (2015). Peptide materials obtained by aggregation of polyphenylalanine conjugates as gadolinium-based magnetic resonance imaging contrast agents. *Adv. Funct. Mater.* 25: 7003–7016.

28 Preslar, A.T., Tantakitti, F., Park, K. et al. (2016). 19F Magnetic resonance imaging signals from peptide amphiphile nanostructures are strongly affected by their shape. *ACS Nano* 10: 7376–7384.

29 Tassa, C., Shaw, S.Y., and Weissleder, R. (2011). Dextran-coated iron oxide nanoparticles: A versatile platform for targeted molecular imaging, molecular diagnostics, and therapy. *Acc. Chem. Res.* 44: 842–852.

30 Li, S., Xu, L., Ma, W. et al. (2016). Dual-mode ultrasensitive quantification of microRNA in living cells by chiroplasmonic nanopyramids self-assembled from gold and upconversion nanoparticles. *J. Am. Chem. Soc.* 138: 306–312.

31 Ku, S.H., Lee, M., and Park, C.B. (2013). Carbon-based nanomaterials for tissue engineering. *Adv. Healthc. Mater.* 2: 244–260.

32 Lewitus, D.Y., Landers, J., Branch, J.R. et al. (2011). Biohybrid carbon nanotube/agarose fibers for neural tissue engineering. *Adv. Funct. Mater.* 21: 2624–2632.

33 Matsuura, K., Utoh, R., Nagase, K., and Okano, T. (2014). Cell sheet approach for tissue engineering and regenerative medicine. *J. Control. Release* 190: 228–239.

34 Hao, Z., Song, Z., Huang, J. et al. (2017). The scaffold microenvironment for stem cell based bone tissue engineering. *Biomater. Sci.* 5: 1382–1392.

35 Huang, P., Lin, J., Wang, X. et al. (2012). Light-triggered theranostics based on photosensitizer-conjugated carbon dots for simultaneous enhanced-fluorescence imaging and photodynamic therapy. *Adv. Mater.* 24: 5104–5110.

36 Zhang, Z., Wang, J., Nie, X. et al. (2014). Near infrared laser-induced targeted cancer therapy using thermoresponsive polymer encapsulated gold nanorods. *J. Am. Chem. Soc.* 136: 7317–7326.

37 Milligan, C.J., Li, J., Sukumar, P. et al. (2009). Robotic multiwell planar patch-clamp for native and primary mammalian cells. *Nat. Protoc.* 4: 244–255.

38 Ali, H., Weigmann, B., Neurath, M.F. et al. (2014). Budesonide loaded nanoparticles with pH-sensitive coating for improved mucosal targeting in mouse models of inflammatory bowel diseases. *J. Control. Release* 183: 167–177.

39 Bangham, A.D. (2005). Liposomes and the physico-chemical basis of unconsciousness. *FASEB J.* 19: 1766–1768.

40 Goff, S.P. and Berg, P. (1976). Construction of hybrid viruses containing SV40 and λ phage DNA segments and their propagation in cultured monkey cells. *Cell* 9: 695–705.

41 Lee, Y., Fukushima, S., Bae, Y. et al. (2007). A protein nanocarrier from charge-conversion polymer in response to endosomal pH. *J. Am. Chem. Soc.* 129: 5362–5363.

42 Torchilin, V.P. (2007). Micellar nanocarriers: pharmaceutical perspectives. *Pharm. Res.* 24: 1–16.

43 Guo, P. (2010). The emerging field of RNA nanotechnology. *Nat. Nanotechnol.* 5: 833–842.

44 Baker, S.N. and Baker, G.A. (2010). Luminescent carbon nanodots: emergent nanolights. *Angew. Chem. Int. Ed.* 49: 6726–6744.

45 Parak, W.J., Pellegrino, T., and Plank, C. (2005). Labelling of cells with quantum dots. *Nanotechnology* 16: 9–25.

46 Nurunnabi, M., Khatun, Z., Reeck, G.R. et al. (2014). Photoluminescent graphene nanoparticles for cancer phototherapy and imaging. *ACS Appl. Mater. Interfaces* 6: 12413–12421.

47 Sperling, R.A., Rivera Gil, P., Zhang, F. et al. (2008). Biological applications of gold nanoparticles. *Chem. Soc. Rev.* 37: 1896–1908.

48 Lin, C.A.J., Yang, T.Y., Lee, C.H. et al. (2009). Synthesis, characterization, and bioconjugation of fluorescent gold nanoclusters toward biological labeling applications. *ACS Nano* 3: 395–401.

49 Van Haute, D., Longmate, J.M., and Berlin, J.M. (2015). Controlled assembly of biocompatible metallic nanoaggregates using a small molecule crosslinker. *Adv. Mater.* 27: 5158–5164.

50 Wang, Y. and Grainger, D.W. (2014). Barriers to advancing nanotechnology to better improve and translate nanomedicines. *Front. Chem. Sci. Eng.* 8: 265–275.

51 Kolosnjaj-Tabi, J., Javed, Y., Lartigue, L. et al. (2015). The one year fate of iron oxide coated gold nanoparticles in mice. *ACS Nano* 9: 7925–7939.

52 Talmadge, J.E. (1993). The pharmaceutics and delivery of therapeutic polypeptides and proteins. *Adv. Drug Deliv. Rev.* 10: 247–299.

53 Berardi, A., Evans, D.J., Baldelli Bombelli, F., and Lomonossoff, G.P. (2018). Stability of plant virus-based nanocarriers in gastrointestinal fluids. *Nanoscale* 10: 1667–1679.

54 Allen, T.M. and Cullis, P.R. (2013). Liposomal drug delivery systems: From concept to clinical applications. *Adv. Drug Deliv. Rev.* 65: 36–48.

55 Lloyd, J.B. (2000). Lysosome membrane permeability: implications for drug delivery. *Adv. Drug Deliv. Rev.* 41: 189–200.

56 Ahmad, Z., Shah, A., Siddiq, M., and Kraatz, H.B. (2014). Polymeric micelles as drug delivery vehicles. *RSC Adv.* 4: 17028–17038.

57 Caminade, A.M. and Turrin, C.O. (2014). Dendrimers for drug delivery. *J. Mater. Chem. B* 2: 4055–4066.

58 Blasi, P., Giovagnoli, S., Schoubben, A. et al. (2007). Solid lipid nanoparticles for targeted brain drug delivery. *Adv. Drug Deliv. Rev.* 59: 454–477.

59 Neves, A.R., Queiroz, J.F., Lima, S.A.C., and Reis, S. (2017). Apo E-functionalization of solid lipid nanoparticles enhances brain drug delivery: Uptake mechanism and transport pathways. *Bioconjug. Chem.* 28: 995–1004.

60 Di Martino, A., Guselnikova, O.A., Trusova, M.E. et al. (2017). Organic-inorganic hybrid nanoparticles controlled delivery system for anticancer drugs. *Int. J. Pharm.* 526: 380–390.

61 Manatunga, D.C., Godakanda, V.U., de Silva, R.M., and de Silva, K.M.N. (2020). Recent developments in the use of organic–inorganic nanohybrids for drug delivery. *Wiley Interdiscip. Rev. Nanomed. Nanobiotechnol.* 12: 1–29.

62 Cai, X., Jin, M., Yao, L. et al. (2023). Physicochemical properties, pharmacokinetics, toxicology and application of nanocarriers. *J. Mater. Chem. B* 11: 716–733.

63 Griffin, B.T., Guo, J., Presas, E. et al. (2016). Pharmacokinetic, pharmacodynamic and biodistribution following oral administration of nanocarriers containing peptide and protein drugs. *Adv. Drug Deliv. Rev.* 106: 367–380.

64 Askarizadeh, A., Butler, A.E., Badiee, A., and Sahebkar, A. (2019). Liposomal nanocarriers for statins: a pharmacokinetic and pharmacodynamics appraisal. *J. Cell. Physiol.* 234: 1219–1229.

65 Rabinow, B.E. (2004). Nanosuspensions in drug delivery. *Nat. Rev. Drug Discov.* 3: 785–796.

66 Zhou, X., Dorn, M., Vogt, J. et al. (2014). A quantitative study of the intracellular concentration of graphene/noble metal nanoparticle composites and their cytotoxicity. *Nanoscale* 6: 8535–8542.

67 Englert, C., Brendel, J.C., Majdanski, T.C. et al. (2018). Pharmapolymers in the 21st century: Synthetic polymers in drug delivery applications. *Prog. Polym. Sci.* 87: 107–164.

68 Giacca, M. and Zacchigna, S. (2012). Virus-mediated gene delivery for human gene therapy. *J. Control. Release* 161: 377–388.

69 Dowdy, S.F. (2017). Overcoming cellular barriers for RNA therapeutics. *Nat. Biotechnol.* 35: 222–229.

70 Song, Z., Chen, X., You, X. et al. (2017). Self-assembly of peptide amphiphiles for drug delivery: the role of peptide primary and secondary structures. *Biomater. Sci.* 5: 2369–2380.

71 Zhao, C., Chen, H., Wang, F., and Zhang, X. (2021). Amphiphilic self-assembly peptides: rational strategies to design and delivery for drugs in biomedical applications. *Colloids Surf. B Biointerfaces* 208: 112040.

72 Qin, H., Ding, Y., Mujeeb, A. et al. (2017). Tumor microenvironment targeting and responsive peptide-based nanoformulations for improved tumor therapy. *Mol. Pharmacol.* 92: 219–231.

73 Devika, V., Sreelekshmi, P.J., Rajeev, N. et al. (2022). Recent advances in peptides-based stimuli-responsive materials for biomedical and therapeutic applications: A review. *Mol. Pharm.* 19: 1999–2021.

74 Levin, A., Hakala, T.A., Schnaider, L. et al. (2020). Biomimetic peptide self-assembly for functional materials. *Nature Rev. Chem.* 4: 615–634.

75 Yuan, C., Ji, W., Xing, R. et al. (2019). Hierarchically oriented organization in supramolecular peptide crystals. *Nature Rev. Chem.* 3: 567–588.

76 Ulijn, R.V. and Smith, A.M. (2008). Designing peptide based nanomaterials. *Chem. Soc. Rev.* 37: 664–675.

77 Muttenthaler, M., King, G.F., Adams, D.J., and Alewood, P.F. (2021). Trends in peptide drug discovery. *Nat. Rev. Drug Discov.* 20: 309–325.

78 Jain, R.K., Gupta, C.M., and Anand, N. (1981). Synthesis of peptidylglycophospholipids, novel derivatives of muramyl-dipeptide. *Tetrahedron Lett.* 22: 2317–2320.

79 Thompson, N.L., Brian, A.A., and McConnell, H.M. (1984). Covalent linkage of a synthetic peptide to a fluorescent phospholipid and its incorporation into supported phospholipid monolayers. *Biochim. Biophys. Acta (BBA) - Biomembr.* 772: 10–19.

80 Hartgerink, J.D., Beniash, E., and Stupp, S.I. (2001). Self-assembly and mineralization of peptide-amphiphile nanofibers. *Science* 294: 1684–1688.

81 Hartgerink, J.D., Beniash, E., and Stupp, S.I. (2002). Peptide-amphiphile nanofibers: A versatile scaffold for the preparation of self-assembling materials. *Proc. Natl. Acad. Sci. U. S. A.* 99: 5133–5138.

82 Dori, Y., Bianco-Peled, H., Satija, S.K. et al. (2000). Ligand accessibility as means to control cell response to bioactive bilayer membranes. *J. Biomed. Mater. Res.* 50: 75–81.

83 Hendricks, M.P., Sato, K., Palmer, L.C., and Stupp, S.I. (2017). Supramolecular assembly of peptide amphiphiles. *Acc. Chem. Res.* 50: 2440–2448.

84 Hamley, I.W. (2007). Peptide fibrillization. *Angew. Chem. Int. Ed.* 46: 8128–8147.

85 Liu, Z., Tang, X., Feng, F. et al. (2021). Molecular design of peptide amphiphiles for controlled self-assembly and drug release. *J. Mater. Chem. B* 9: 3326–3334.

86 Wang, J., Li, Y., and Nie, G. (2021). Multifunctional biomolecule nanostructures for cancer therapy. *Nature Rev. Mater.* 6: 766–783.

87 Barker, H.E., Paget, J.T.E., Khan, A.A., and Harrington, K.J. (2015). The tumour microenvironment after radiotherapy: Mechanisms of resistance and recurrence. *Nat. Rev. Cancer* 15: 409–425.

88 Mura, S., Nicolas, J., and Couvreur, P. (2013). Stimuli-responsive nanocarriers for drug delivery. *Nat. Mater.* 12: 991–1003.

89 Rosenblum, D., Joshi, N., Tao, W. et al. (2018). Progress and challenges towards targeted delivery of cancer therapeutics. *Nat. Commun.* 9: 1410.

90 Kao, K.C., Vilbois, S., Tsai, C.H., and Ho, P.C. (2022). Metabolic communication in the tumour–immune microenvironment. *Nat. Cell Biol.* 24: 1574–1583.

91 Peng, J., Yang, Q., Xiao, Y. et al. (2019). Tumor microenvironment responsive drug-dye-peptide nanoassembly for enhanced tumor-targeting, penetration, and photo-chemo-immunotherapy. *Adv. Funct. Mater.* 29: 1900004.

92 Brockhausen, I. (1999). Pathways of O-glycan biosynthesis in cancer cells. *Biochim. Biophys. Acta* 1473: 67–95.

93 Kim, H., Kim, I., Hwang, J.H. et al. (2020). Glutathione-adaptive peptide amphiphile vesicles rationally designed using positionable disulfide-bridges for effective drug transport. *Polym. Chem.* 11: 4547–4556.

94 Parks, S.K., Chiche, J., and Pouyssegur, J. (2011). pH control mechanisms of tumor survival and growth. *J. Cell. Physiol.* 226: 299–308.

95 Trent, A., Marullo, R., Lin, B. et al. (2011). Structural properties of soluble peptide amphiphile micelles. *Soft Matter* 7: 9572–9582.

96 Yoo, J., Sanoj Rejinold, N., Lee, D.Y. et al. (2017). Protease-activatable cell-penetrating peptide possessing ROS-triggered phase transition for enhanced cancer therapy. *J. Control. Release* 264: 89–101.

97 Booth, R., Insua, I., Ahmed, S. et al. (2021). Supramolecular fibrillation of peptide amphiphiles induces environmental responses in aqueous droplets. *Nat. Commun.* 12: 6421.

98 Ma, T., Chen, R., Lv, N. et al. (2022). Size-transformable bicomponent peptide nanoparticles for deep tumor penetration and photo-chemo combined antitumor therapy. *Small* 18: 2106291.

99 Wang, Y., Shim, M.S., Levinson, N.S. et al. (2014). Stimuli-responsive materials for controlled release of theranostic agents. *Adv. Funct. Mater.* 24: 4206–4220.

100 Kim, I., Jeong, H.H., Kim, Y.J. et al. (2014). A "light-up" 1D supramolecular nanoprobe for silver ions based on assembly of pyrene-labeled peptide amphiphiles: Cell-imaging and antimicrobial activity. *J. Mater. Chem. B* 20: 6478–6486.

101 Kim, I., Jin, S.M., Han, E.H. et al. (2017). Structure-dependent antimicrobial theranostic functions of self-assembled short peptide nanoagents. *Biomacromolecules* 18: 3600–3610.

102 Kim, I., Han, E.H., Bang, W.Y. et al. (2018). Supramolecular carbon monoxide-releasing peptide hydrogel patch. *Adv. Funct. Mater.* 28: 1803051.

103 Kim, I., Bang, W.Y., Park, W.H. et al. (2019). Photo-crosslinkable elastomeric protein-derived supramolecular peptide hydrogel with controlled therapeutic CO-release. *Nanoscale* 11: 17327–17333.

104 Kesharwani, K., Kautu, A., Sharma, S. et al. (2022). Short peptide amphiphile nanostructures facilitate sunlight-induced nanowelding of gold nanosheets. *Chem. Commun.* 13815–13818.

105 Xue, B., Zhao, L., Qin, X. et al. (2019). Bioinspired ice growth inhibitors based on self-assembling peptides. *ACS Macro Lett.* 8: 1383–1390.

106 Jeon, N., Choi, I., Lee, P.C.W., and Lee, E. (2022). Gold nanoparticle-tethered peptide nanofibrils for monitoring ice recrystallization inhibition: Implications for cryopreservation. *ACS Appl. Nano Mater.* 5: 15418–15428.

107 Berndt, P., Fields, G.B., and Tirrell, M. (1995). Synthetic lipidation of peptides and amino acids: monolayer structure and properties. *J. Am. Chem. Soc.* 117: 9515–9522.

108 Yu, Y.C., Berndt, P., Tirrell, M., and Fields, G.B. (1996). Self-assembling amphiphiles for construction of protein molecular architecture. *J. Am. Chem. Soc.* 118: 12515–12520.

109 Fields, G.B., Lauer, J.L., Dori, Y. et al. (1998). Proteinlike molecular architecture: Biomaterial applications for inducing cellular receptor binding and signal transduction. *Biopolymers* 47: 143–151.

110 Cui, H., Cheetham, A.G., Pashuck, E.T., and Stupp, S.I. (2014). Amino acid sequence in constitutionally isomeric tetrapeptide amphiphiles dictates architecture of one-dimensional nanostructures. *J. Am. Chem. Soc.* 136: 12461–12468.

111 Pashuck, E.T., Cui, H., and Stupp, S.I. (2010). Tuning supramolecular rigidity of peptide fibers through molecular structure. *J. Am. Chem. Soc.* 132: 6041–6046.

112 Aggeli, A., Bell, M., Boden, N. et al. (1997). Responsive gels formed by the spontaneous self-assembly of peptides into polymeric β-sheet tapes. *Nature* 386: 259–262.

113 Percec, V., Dulcey, A.E., Balagurusamy, V.S.K. et al. (2004). Self-assembly of amphiphilic dendritic dipeptides into helical pores. *Nature* 430: 764–768.

114 Cui, H., Muraoka, T., Cheetham, A.G., and Stupp, S.I. (2009). Self-assembly of giant peptide nanobelts. *Nano Lett.* 9: 945–951.

115 Choi, I., Park, I.S., Ryu, J.H., and Lee, M. (2012). Control of peptide assembly through directional interactions. *Chem. Commun.* 48: 8481–8483.

116 Tantakitti, F., Boekhoven, J., Wang, X. et al. (2016). Energy landscapes and functions of supramolecular systems. *Nat. Mater.* 15: 469–476.

117 Wang, J., Liu, K., Xing, R., and Yan, X. (2016). Peptide self-assembly: Thermodynamics and kinetics. *Chem. Soc. Rev.* 45: 5589–5604.

118 Sorrenti, A., Leira-Iglesias, J., Markvoort, A.J. et al. (2017). Non-equilibrium supramolecular polymerization. *Chem. Soc. Rev.* 46: 5476–5490.

119 Sangji, M.H., Sai, H., Chin, S.M. et al. (2021). Supramolecular interactions and morphology of self-assembling peptide amphiphile nanostructures. *Nano Lett.* 21: 6146–6155.

120 Velichko, Y.S., Stupp, S.I., and De La Cruz, M.O. (2008). Molecular simulation study of peptide amphiphile self-assembly. *J. Phys. Chem. B* 112: 2326–2334.

121 Pandurangan, K., Roy, B., Rajasekhar, K. et al. (2020). Molecular architectonics of cyclic dipeptide amphiphiles and Their application in drug delivery. *ACS Appl. Bio Mater.* 3: 3413–3422.

122 Jin, S.M., Jeon, J., Park, M.K. et al. (2018). Multicompartment vesicles formation by emulsification-induced assembly of poly(ethylene oxide)-block-poly(ε-caprolactone) and their dual-loading capability. *Macromol. Rapid Commun.* 39: 1–5.

123 Yang, J., An, H.W., and Wang, H. (2021). Self-assembled peptide drug delivery systems. *ACS Appl. Bio Mater.* 4: 24–46.

124 Berillo, D., Yeskendir, A., Zharkinbekov, Z. et al. (2021). Peptide-based drug delivery systems. *Medicina* 57: 1209.

125 Wei, G., Wang, Y., Huang, X. et al. (2018). Peptide-based nanocarriers for cancer therapy. *Small Methods* 2: 1–16.

126 Nakamura, Y., Mochida, A., Choyke, P.L., and Kobayashi, H. (2016). Nanodrug delivery: Is the enhanced permeability and retention effect sufficient for curing cancer? *Bioconjug. Chem.* 27: 2225–2238.

127 Hur, J. and Chung, A.J. (2021). Microfluidic and Nanofluidic Intracellular Delivery. *Adv. Sci.* 8: 2004595.

128 Stewart, M.P., Sharei, A., Ding, X. et al. (2016). In vitro and ex vivo strategies for intracellular delivery. *Nature* 538: 183–192.

129 Xie, J., Bi, Y., Zhang, H. et al. (2020). Cell-penetrating peptides in diagnosis and treatment of human diseases: from preclinical research to clinical application. *Front. Pharmacol.* 11: 1–23.

130 Nadal-Bufí, F. and Henriques, S.T. (2020). How to overcome endosomal entrapment of cell-penetrating peptides to release the therapeutic potential of peptides? *Peptide Sci.* 112: e24168.

131 Kube, S., Hersch, N., Naumovska, E. et al. (2017). Fusogenic liposomes as nanocarriers for the delivery of intracellular proteins. *Langmuir* 33: 1051–1059.

132 Lin, J. and Alexander-Katz, A. (2013). Cell membranes open "doors" for cationic nanoparticles/biomolecules: Insights into uptake kinetics. *ACS Nano* 7: 10799–10808.

133 Futaki, S., Suzuki, T., Ohashi, W. et al. (2001). Arginine-rich peptides. An abundant source of membrane-permeable peptides having potential as carriers for intracellular protein delivery. *J. Biol. Chem.* 276: 5836–5840.

134 Futaki, S., Nakase, I., Tadokoro, A. et al. (2007). Arginine-rich peptides and their internalization mechanisms. *Biochem. Soc. Trans.* 35: 784–787.

135 Lättig-Tünnemann, G., Prinz, M., Hoffmann, D. et al. (2011). Backbone rigidity and static presentation of guanidinium groups increases cellular uptake of arginine-rich cell-penetrating peptides. *Nat. Commun.* 2: 453.

136 Pujals, S. and Giralt, E. (2008). Proline-rich, amphipathic cell-penetrating peptides. *Adv. Drug Deliv. Rev.* 60: 473–484.

137 Chen, L., Gan, L., Liu, M. et al. (2011). Destabilization of artificial biomembrane induced by the penetration of tryptophan. *Appl. Surf. Sci.* 257: 5070–5076.

138 Lönn, P., Kacsinta, A.D., Cui, X.S. et al. (2016). Enhancing endosomal escape for intracellular delivery of macromolecular biologic therapeutics. *Sci. Rep.* 6: 1–9.

139 Mumcuoglu, D., Sardan, M., Tekinay, T. et al. (2015). Oligonucleotide delivery with cell surface binding and cell penetrating peptide amphiphile nanospheres. *Mol. Pharm.* 12: 1584–1591.

140 Frankel, A.D. and Pabo, C.O. (1988). Cellular uptake of the tat protein from human immunodeficiency virus. *Cell* 55: 1189–1193.

141 Green, M. and Loewenstein, P.M. (1988). Autonomous functional domains of chemically synthesized human immunodeficiency virus tat trans-activator protein. *Cell* 55: 1179–1188.

142 Derossi, D., Joliot, A.H., Chassaing, G., and Prochiantz, A. (1994). The third helix of the Antennapedia homeodomain translocates through biological membranes. *J. Biol. Chem.* 269: 10444–10450.

143 Milletti, F. (2012). Cell-penetrating peptides: Classes, origin, and current landscape. *Drug Discov. Today* 17: 850–860.

144 Jiang, T., Olson, E.S., Nguyen, Q.T. et al. (2004). Tumor imaging by means of proteolytic activation of cell-penetrating peptides. *Proc. Natl. Acad. Sci. U. S. A.* 101: 17867–17872.

145 Mai, J.C., Shen, H., Watkins, S.C. et al. (2002). Efficiency of protein transduction is cell type-dependent and is enhanced by dextran sulfate. *J. Biol. Chem.* 277: 30208–30218.

146 Zavaglia, D., Favrot, M.C., Eymin, B. et al. (2003). Intercellular trafficking and enhanced in vivo antitumour activity of a non-virally delivered P27-VP22 fusion protein. *Gene Ther.* 10: 314–325.

147 Morris, M.C., Deshayes, S., Heitz, F., and Divita, G. (2008). Cell-penetrating peptides: from molecular mechanisms to therapeutics. *Biol. Cell* 100: 201–217.

148 Oehlke, J., Krause, E., Wiesner, B. et al. (1997). Extensive cellular uptake into endothelial cells of an amphipathic β-sheet forming peptide. *FEBS Lett.* 415: 196–199.

149 Madani, F., Lindberg, S., Langel, Ü. et al. (2011). Mechanisms of cellular uptake of cell-penetrating peptides. *J. Biophys.* 2011: 1–10.

150 Pooga, M., Hällbrink, M., Zorko, M., and Langel, Ü. (1998). Cell penetration by transportan. *FASEB J.* 12: 67–77.

151 Pooga, M., Kut, C., Kihlmark, M. et al. (2001). Cellular translocation of proteins by transportan. *FASEB J.* 15: 1451–1453.

152 Derakhshankhah, H. and Jafari, S. (2018). Cell penetrating peptides: a concise review with emphasis on biomedical applications. *Biomed. Pharmacother.* 108: 1090–1096.

153 Robison, A.D., Sun, S., Poyton, M.F. et al. (2016). Polyarginine interacts more strongly and cooperatively than polylysine with phospholipid bilayers. *J. Phys. Chem. B* 120: 9287–9296.

154 Feger, G., Angelov, B., and Angelova, A. (2020). Prediction of amphiphilic cell-penetrating peptide building blocks from protein-derived amino acid sequences for engineering of drug delivery nanoassemblies. *J. Phys. Chem. B* 124: 4069–4078.

155 Zhang, P., Cheetham, A.G., Lin, Y.A., and Cui, H. (2013). Self-assembled tat nanofibers as effective drug carrier and transporter. *ACS Nano* 7: 5965–5977.

156 Soukasene, S., Toft, D.J., Moyer, T.J. et al. (2011). Antitumor activity of peptide amphiphile nanofiber-encapsulated camptothecin. *ACS Nano* 5: 9113–9121.

157 Shi, Y., Lin, R., Cui, H., and Azevedo, H.S. (2018). Multifunctional self-assembling peptide-based nanostructures for targeted intracellular delivery: Design, physicochemical characterization, and biological assessment. *Methods Mol. Biol.* 1758: 11–26.

158 Zelzer, M., Todd, S.J., Hirst, A.R. et al. (2013). Enzyme responsive materials: Design strategies and future developments. *Biomater. Sci.* 1: 11–39.

159 Swami, A., Reagan, M.R., Basto, P. et al. (2014). Engineered nanomedicine for myeloma and bone microenvironment targeting. *Proc. Natl. Acad. Sci. U. S. A.* 111: 10287–10292.

160 Delfi, M., Sartorius, R., Ashrafizadeh, M. et al. (2021). Self-assembled peptide and protein nanostructures for anti-cancer therapy: Targeted delivery, stimuli-responsive devices and immunotherapy. *Nano Today* 38: 101119.

161 Qu, M., Jiang, X., Zhou, X. et al. (2020). Stimuli-responsive delivery of growth factors for tissue engineering. *Adv. Healthc. Mater.* 9: 1–19.

162 Karimi, M., Ghasemi, A., Sahandi Zangabad, P. et al. (2016). Smart micro/nanoparticles in stimulus-responsive drug/gene delivery systems. *Chem. Soc. Rev.* 45: 1457–1501.

163 Raza, A., Rasheed, T., Nabeel, F. et al. (2019). Endogenous and exogenous stimuli-responsive drug delivery systems for programmed site-specific release. *Molecules* 24: 1–21.

164 Sun, H. and Zhong, Z. (2020). 100th anniversary of macromolecular science viewpoint: Biological stimuli-sensitive polymer prodrugs and nanoparticles for tumor-specific drug delivery. *ACS Macro Lett.* 9: 1292–1302.

165 Du, L., Jin, Y., Zhou, W., and Zhao, J. (2011). Ultrasound-triggered drug release and enhanced anticancer effect of doxorubicin-loaded poly(D,L-lactide-co-glycolide)-methoxy-poly(ethylene glycol) nanodroplets. *Ultrasound Med. Biol.* 37: 1252–1258.

166 Satarkar, N.S. and Hilt, J.Z. (2008). Magnetic hydrogel nanocomposites for remote controlled pulsatile drug release. *J. Control. Release* 130: 246–251.

167 Schmidt, D.J., Moskowitz, J.S., and Hammond, P.T. (2010). Electrically triggered release of a small molecule drug from a polyelectrolyte multilayer coating. *Chem. Mater.* 22: 6416–6425.

168 Wei, P., Cornel, E.J., and Du, J. (2021). Ultrasound-responsive polymer-based drug delivery systems. *Drug Deliv. Transl. Res.* 11: 1323–1339.

169 Hoare, T., Santamaria, J., Goya, G.F. et al. (2009). A magnetically triggered composite membrane for on-demand drug delivery. *Nano Lett.* 9: 3651–3657.

170 Kubota, T., Kurashina, Y., Zhao, J.Y. et al. (2021). Ultrasound-triggered on-demand drug delivery using hydrogel microbeads with release enhancer. *Mater. Des.* 203: 109580.

171 Onaca, O., Enea, R., Hughes, D.W., and Meier, W. (2009). Stimuli-responsive polymersomes as nanocarriers for drug and gene delivery. *Macromol. Biosci.* 9: 129–139.

172 Matsuyama, S., Llopis, J., Deveraux, Q.L. et al. (2000). Changes in intramitochondrial and cytosolic pH: Early events that modulate caspase activation during apoptosis. *Nat. Cell Biol.* 2: 318–325.

173 Power, G., Moore, Z., and O'Connor, T. (2017). Measurement of pH, exudate composition and temperature in wound healing: A systematic review. *J. Wound Care* 26: 381–397.

174 Lavrador, P., Gaspar, V.M., and Mano, J.F. (2018). Stimuli-responsive nanocarriers for delivery of bone therapeutics – Barriers and progresses. *J. Control. Release* 273: 51–67.

175 Saito, G., Swanson, J.A., and Lee, K.D. (2003). Drug delivery strategy utilizing conjugation via reversible disulfide linkages: Role and site of cellular reducing activities. *Adv. Drug Deliv. Rev.* 55: 199–215.

176 Balendiran, G.K., Dabur, R., and Fraser, D. (2004). The role of glutathione in cancer. *Cell Biochem. Funct.* 22: 343–352.

177 Block, M.L., Zecca, L., and Hong, J.-S. (2007). Microglia-mediated neurotoxicity: uncovering the molecular mechanisms. *Nat. Rev. Neurosci.* 8: 57–69.

178 Eltzschig, H.K. and Eckle, T. (2011). Ischemia and reperfusion-from mechanism to translation. *Nat. Med.* 17: 1391–1401.

179 Wen, J., Anderson, S.M., Du, J. et al. (2011). Controlled protein delivery based on enzyme-responsive nanocapsules. *Adv. Mater.* 23: 4549–4553.

180 Parks, W.C., Wilson, C.L., and López-Boado, Y.S. (2004). Matrix metalloproteinases as modulators of inflammation and innate immunity. *Nat. Rev. Immunol.* 4: 617–629.

181 Dharmayanti, C., Gillam, T.A., Klingler-Hoffmann, M. et al. (2021). Strategies for the development of pH-responsive synthetic polypeptides and polymer-peptide hybrids: Recent advancements. *Polymers* 13: 1–17.

182 Gong, Z., Liu, X., Wu, J. et al. (2020). pH-triggered morphological change in a self-assembling amphiphilic peptide used as an antitumor drug carrier. *Nanotechnology* 31: 165601.

183 Cao, Z., Li, W., Liu, R. et al. (2019). pH- and enzyme-triggered drug release as an important process in the design of anti-tumor drug delivery systems. *Biomed. Pharmacother.* 118: 109340.

184 Zhang, J., Lin, W., Yang, L. et al. (2022). Injectable and pH-responsive self-assembled peptide hydrogel for promoted tumor cell uptake and enhanced cancer chemotherapy. *Biomater. Sci.* 10: 854–862.

185 Wang, T.W., Yeh, C.W., Kuan, C.H. et al. (2017). Tailored design of multifunctional and programmable pH-responsive self-assembling polypeptides as drug delivery nanocarrier for cancer therapy. *Acta Biomater.* 58: 54–66.

186 Liang, P., Zheng, J., Dai, S. et al. (2017). pH triggered re-assembly of nanosphere to nanofiber: The role of peptide conformational change for enhanced cancer therapy. *J. Control. Release* 260: 22–31.

187 Kim, D., Kim, S., Park, G. et al. (2022). Spatiotemporal self-assembly of peptide amphiphiles by carbonic anhydrase IX-targeting induces cancer-lysosomal membrane disruption. *JACS Au* 2: 2539–2547.

188 Xu, X., Li, Y., Li, H. et al. (2014). Smart nanovehicles based on pH-triggered disassembly of supramolecular peptide-amphiphiles for efficient intracellular drug delivery. *Small* 10: 1133–1140.

189 Zhang, L., Xu, J., Wang, F. et al. (2019). Histidine-rich cell-penetrating peptide for cancer drug delivery and its uptake mechanism. *Langmuir* 35: 3513–3523.

190 Karimi, M., Zangabad, P.S., Ghasemi, A. et al. (2016). Temperature-fesponsive smart nanocarriers for delivery of therapeutic agents: applications and recent advances. *ACS Appl. Mater. Interfaces* 8: 21107–21133.

191 Akimoto, J., Nakayama, M., and Okano, T. (2014). Temperature-responsive polymeric micelles for optimizing drug targeting to solid tumors. *J. Control. Release* 193: 2–8.

192 Bordat, A., Boissenot, T., Nicolas, J., and Tsapis, N. (2019). Thermoresponsive polymer nanocarriers for biomedical applications. *Adv. Drug Deliv. Rev.* 138: 167–192.

193 Jenkins, I.C., Milligan, J.J., and Chilkoti, A. (2021). Genetically encoded elastin-like polypeptides for drug delivery. *Adv. Healthc. Mater.* 10: 1–18.

194 W. jin Jeong, S. hyun Kwon, Y. beom Lim. (2018). Modular self-assembling peptide platform with a tunable thermoresponsiveness via a single amino acid substitution. *Adv. Funct. Mater.* 28: 1803114.

195 Luginbuhl, K.M., Mozhdehi, D., Dzuricky, M. et al. (2017). Recombinant synthesis of hybrid lipid–peptide polymer fusions that self-assemble and encapsulate hydrophobic drugs. *Angew. Chem. Int. Ed.* 56: 13979–13984.

196 Aluri, S., Pastuszka, M.K., Moses, A.S., and MacKay, J.A. (2012). Elastin-like peptide amphiphiles form nanofibers with tunable length. *Biomacromolecules* 13: 2645–2654.

197 Huang, J., Hastings, C.L., Duffy, G.P. et al. (2013). Supramolecular hydrogels with reverse thermal gelation properties from (oligo)tyrosine containing block copolymers. *Biomacromolecules* 14: 200–206.

198 Han, L., Zhang, Y., Lu, X. et al. (2016). Polydopamine nanoparticles modulating stimuli-responsive PNIPAM hydrogels with cell/tissue adhesiveness. *ACS Appl. Mater. Interfaces* 8: 29088–29100.

199 MacEwan, S.R. and Chilkoti, A. (2012). Digital switching of local arginine density in a genetically encoded self-assembled polypeptide nanoparticle controls cellular uptake. *Nano Lett.* 12: 3322–3328.

200 Hu, B., Lian, Z., Zhou, Z. et al. (2020). Reactive oxygen species-responsive adaptable self-assembly of peptides toward advanced biomaterials. *ACS Appl. Bio Mater.* 3: 5529–5551.

201 Sun, B., Luo, C., Zhang, X. et al. (2019). Probing the impact of sulfur/selenium/carbon linkages on prodrug nanoassemblies for cancer therapy. *Nat. Commun.* 10: 3211.

202 Wang, Y.C., Wang, F., Sun, T.M., and Wang, J. (2011). Redox-responsive nanoparticles from the single disulfide bond-bridged block copolymer as drug carriers for overcoming multidrug resistance in cancer cells. *Bioconjug. Chem.* 22: 1939–1945.

203 Saravanakumar, G., Kim, J., and Kim, W.J. (2017). Reactive-oxygen-species-responsive drug delivery systems: Promises and challenges. *Adv. Sci.* 4: 1600124.

204 Yao, Q., Wu, G., Hao, H. et al. (2021). Redox-mediated reversible supramolecular assemblies driven by switch and interplay of peptide secondary structures. *Biomacromolecules* 22: 2563–2572.

205 Fouladi, F., Steffen, K.J., and Mallik, S. (2017). Enzyme-responsive liposomes for the delivery of anticancer drugs. *Bioconjug. Chem.* 28: 857–868.

206 Li, M., Zhao, G., Su, W.K., and Shuai, Q. (2020). Enzyme-responsive nanoparticles for anti-tumor drug delivery. *Front. Chem.* 8: 1–20.

207 Cheng, Y.J., Qin, S.Y., Liu, W.L. et al. (2020). Dual-targeting photosensitizer-peptide amphiphile conjugate for enzyme-triggered drug delivery and synergistic chemo-photodynamic tumor therapy. *Adv. Mater. Interfaces* 7: 1–9.

208 Jiang, Y., Pang, X., Liu, R. et al. (2018). Design of an amphiphilic iRGD peptide and self-assembling nanovesicles for improving tumor accumulation and penetration and the photodynamic efficacy of the photosensitizer. *ACS Appl. Mater. Interfaces* 10: 31674–31685.

209 Li, N., Li, N., Yi, Q. et al. (2014). Amphiphilic peptide dendritic copolymer-doxorubicin nanoscale conjugate self-assembled to enzyme-responsive anti-cancer agent. *Biomaterials* 35: 9529–9545.

210 Zhu, J., Guo, T., Wang, Z., and Zhao, Y. (2022). Triggered azobenzene-based prodrugs and drug delivery systems. *J. Control. Release* 345: 475–493.

211 Cardano, F., Del Canto, E., and Giordani, S. (2019). Spiropyrans for light-controlled drug delivery. *Dalton Trans.* 48: 15537–15544.

212 Wang, H., Miao, W., Wang, F., and Cheng, Y. (2018). A self-assembled coumarin-anchored dendrimer for efficient gene delivery and light-responsive drug delivery. *Biomacromolecules* 19: 2194–2201.

213 Chivers, P.R.A., Dookie, R.S., Gough, J.E., and Webb, S.J. (2020). Photo-dissociation of self-assembled (anthracene-2-carbonyl)amino acid hydrogels. *Chem. Commun.* 56: 13792–13795.

214 Li, S., Sun, T., Yang, X. et al. (2013). Light-responsive drug carrier vesicles assembled by cinnamic acid-based peptide. *Colloid Polym. Sci.* 291: 2639–2646.

215 Mondal, J.H., Ahmed, S., Ghosh, T., and Das, D. (2015). Reversible deformation-formation of a multistimuli responsive vesicle by a supramolecular peptide amphiphile. *Soft Matter* 11: 4912–4920.

216 Zhu, H., Wang, H., Shi, B. et al. (2019). Supramolecular peptide constructed by molecular lego allowing programmable self-assembly for photodynamic therapy. *Nat. Commun.* 10: 1–10.

217 Hiruta, Y., Kanda, Y., Katsuyama, N., and Kanazawa, H. (2017). Dual temperature- and pH-responsive polymeric micelle for selective and efficient two-step doxorubicin delivery. *RSC Adv.* 7: 29540–29549.

218 Ni, R., Zhu, J., Xu, Z., and Chen, Y. (2020). A self-assembled pH/enzyme dual-responsive prodrug with PEG deshielding for multidrug-resistant tumor therapy. *J. Mater. Chem. B* 8: 1290–1301.

219 Liu, X., Jia, K., Wang, Y. et al. (2017). Dual-responsive bola-type supra-amphiphile constructed from water-soluble pillar[5]arene and naphthalimide-containing amphiphile for intracellular drug delivery. *ACS Appl. Mater. Interfaces* 9: 4843–4850.

220 Reifarth, M., Bekir, M., Bapolisi, A.M. et al. (2022). A dual pH- and light-responsive spiropyran-based surfactant: investigations on its switching behavior and remote control over emulsion stability. *Angew. Chem. Int. Ed.* 61: e202114687.

221 Li, X., Xie, C., Xia, H., and Wang, Z. (2018). pH and ultrasound dual-responsive polydopamine-coated mesoporous silica nanoparticles for controlled drug delivery. *Langmuir* 34: 9974–9981.

222 Xu, J., Li, G., Zhang, Y. et al. (2021). A dual-responsive drug delivery system based on mesoporous silica nanoparticles covered with zipper-type peptide for intracellular transport/release. *Colloids Surf. A Physicochem. Eng. Asp.* 631: 127672.

223 Li, F., Zhu, Y., and Wang, Y. (2014). Dual-responsive drug delivery system with real time tunable release behavior. *Micropor. Mesopor. Mater.* 200: 46–51.

224 Zhu, Y., Zeng, Q., Zhang, Q. et al. (2020). Temperature/near-infrared light-responsive conductive hydrogels for controlled drug release and real-time monitoring. *Nanoscale* 12: 8679–8686.

225 Feng, Q., Zhang, Y., Zhang, W. et al. (2016). Tumor-targeted and multi-stimuli responsive drug delivery system for near-infrared light induced chemo-phototherapy and photoacoustic tomography. *Acta Biomater.* 38: 129–142.

226 Huang, L., Liu, J., Gao, F. et al. (2018). A dual-responsive, hyaluronic acid targeted drug delivery system based on hollow mesoporous silica nanoparticles for cancer therapy. *J. Mater. Chem. B* 6: 4618–4629.

227 Fu, X., Hosta-Rigau, L., Chandrawati, R., and Cui, J. (2018). Multi-stimuli-responsive polymer particles, films, and hydrogels for drug delivery. *Chem* 4: 2084–2107.

228 Dong, L., Chen, H., Liu, T. et al. (2021). Poly(l -cysteine) peptide amphiphile derivatives containing disulfide bonds: Synthesis, self-assembly-induced β-sheet nanostructures, pH/reduction dual response, and drug release. *Biomacromolecules* 22: 5374–5381.

229 Liu, X., Gao, M., Chen, J. et al. (2022). Recent advances in stimuli-responsive shape-morphing hydrogels. *Adv. Funct. Mater.* 32: 2203323.

230 Kass, L.E. and Nguyen, J. (2022). Nanocarrier-hydrogel composite delivery systems for precision drug release. *WIREs Nanomed. Nanobiotechnol.* 14: 1–23.

231 Park, S.Y., Kang, J.H., Kim, H.S. et al. (2022). Electrical and thermal stimulus-responsive nanocarbon-based 3D hydrogel sponge for switchable drug delivery. *Nanoscale* 14: 2367–2382.

232 Hersel, U., Dahmen, C., and Kessler, H. (2003). RGD modified polymers: Biomaterials for stimulated cell adhesion and beyond. *Biomaterials* 24: 4385–4415.

233 Erez, N., Bershadsky, A., and Geiger, B. (2005). Signaling from adherens-type junctions. *Eur. J. Cell Biol.* 84: 235–244.

234 Comisar, W.A., Hsiong, S.X., Kong, H.J. et al. (2006). Multi-scale modeling to predict ligand presentation within RGD nanopatterned hydrogels. *Biomaterials* 27: 2322–2329.

235 Maheshwari, G., Brown, G., Lauffenburger, D.A. et al. (2000). Cell adhesion and motility depend on nanoscale RGD clustering. *J. Cell Sci.* 113: 1677–1686.

236 Massia, S.P. and Hubbell, J.A. (1991). An RGD spacing of 440 nm is sufficient for integrin αvβ3-mediated fibroblast spreading and 140 nm for focal contact and stress fiber formation. *J. Cell Biol.* 114: 1089–1100.

237 Webber, M.J., Tongers, J., Renault, M.A. et al. (2010). Development of bioactive peptide amphiphiles for therapeutic cell delivery. *Acta Biomater.* 6: 3–11.

238 Zhang, W., Zhan, J., Zhao, R. et al. (2022). Parallelism to conquer: binary supramolecular peptide amphiphiles launch synergistic stromal reprogramming to remove the baffle in pancreatic cancer therapy. *Adv. Funct. Mater.* 32: 1–17.

239 Zoughaib, M., Pavlov, R.V., Gaynanova, G.A. et al. (2021). Amphiphilic RGD and GHK peptides synergistically enhance liposomal delivery into cancer and endothelial cells. *Mater. Adv.* 2: 7715–7730.

240 Carmeliet, P. (2000). Mechanisms of angiogenesis and lymphangiogenesis. *Nat. Med.* 6: 389–395.

241 Neri, S., Hashimoto, H., Kii, H. et al. (2016). Cancer cell invasion driven by extracellular matrix remodeling is dependent on the properties of cancer-associated fibroblasts. *J. Cancer Res. Clin. Oncol.* 142: 437–446.

242 Rogers, T.L. and Holen, I. (2011). Tumour macrophages as potential targets of bisphosphonates. *J. Transl. Med.* 9: 1–17.

243 Boekhoven, J., Zha, R.H., Tantakitti, F. et al. (2015). Alginate-peptide amphiphile core-shell microparticles as a targeted drug delivery system. *RSC Adv.* 5: 8753–8756.

244 Arap, W., Pasqualini, R., and Ruoslahti, E. (1998). Cancer treatment by targeted drug delivery to tumor vasculature in a mouse model. *Science* 279: 377–380.

245 Black, M., Trent, A., Kostenko, Y. et al. (2012). Self-assembled peptide amphiphile micelles containing a cytotoxic T-cell epitope promote a protective immune response in vivo. *Adv. Mater.* 24: 3845–3849.

246 Morita, K., Nishimura, K., Yamamoto, S. et al. (2022). In situ synthesis of an anticancer peptide amphiphile using tyrosine kinase overexpressed in cancer cells. *J. Am. Chem. Soc.* 2: 2023–2028.

247 Pan, L., Liu, J., and Shi, J. (2018). Cancer cell nucleus-targeting nanocomposites for advanced tumor therapeutics. *Chem. Soc. Rev.* 47: 6930–6946.

248 Ibrahim, M.X., Sayin, V.I., Akula, M.K. et al. (2013). Targeting isoprenylcysteine methylation ameliorates disease in a mouse model of progeria. *Science* 340: 1330–1333.

249 Maraldi, N.M., Lattanzi, G., Sabatelli, P. et al. (2002). Functional domains of the nucleus: implications for Emery-Dreifuss muscular dystrophy. *Neuromuscul. Disord.* 12: 815–823.

250 Calkins, M.J., Manczak, M., and Hemachandra Reddy, P. (2012). Mitochondria-targeted antioxidant SS31 prevents Amyloid beta-induced mitochondrial abnormalities and synaptic degeneration in Alzheimer's disease. *Pharmaceuticals* 5: 1103–1119.

251 Zielonka, J., Joseph, J., Sikora, A. et al. (2017). Mitochondria-targeted triphenylphosphonium-based compounds: Syntheses, mechanisms of action, and therapeutic and diagnostic applications. *Chem. Rev.* 117: 10043–10120.

252 Greenfield, J.P., Tsai, J., Gouras, G.K. et al. (1999). Endoplasmic reticulum and trans-Golgi network generate distinct populations of Alzheimer β-amyloid peptides. *Proc. Natl. Acad. Sci. U. S. A.* 96: 742–747.

253 Gilbert, A.K. and Pluth, M.D. (2022). Subcellular delivery of hydrogen sulfide using small molecule donors impacts organelle stress. *J. Am. Chem. Soc.* 144: 17651–17660.

254 Wan, J., Sun, L., Wu, P. et al. (2018). Synthesis of indocyanine green functionalized comblike poly(aspartic acid) derivatives for enhanced cancer cell ablation by targeting the endoplasmic reticulum. *Polym. Chem.* 9: 1206–1215.

255 Li, W., Yang, J., Luo, L. et al. (2019). Targeting photodynamic and photothermal therapy to the endoplasmic reticulum enhances immunogenic cancer cell death. *Nat. Commun.* 10: 3349.

256 Li, Y., Zhang, X., Wan, X. et al. (2020). Inducing endoplasmic reticulum stress to expose immunogens: A DNA tetrahedron nanoregulator for enhanced immunotherapy. *Adv. Funct. Mater.* 30: 2000532.

257 Lodhi, I.J. and Semenkovich, C.F. (2014). Peroxisomes: A nexus for lipid metabolism and cellular signaling. *Cell Metab.* 19: 380–392.

258 Miura, S., Kasuya-Arai, I., Mori, H. et al. (1992). Carboxyl-terminal consensus Ser-Lys-Leu-related tripeptide of peroxisomal proteins functions in vitro as a minimal peroxisome-targeting signal. *J. Biol. Chem.* 267: 14405–14411.

259 Gao, W., Cao, W., Zhang, H. et al. (2014). Targeting lysosomal membrane permeabilization to induce and image apoptosis in cancer cells by multifunctional Au-ZnO hybrid nanoparticles. *Chem. Commun.* 50: 8117–8120.

260 Yang, X., Zhang, C., Li, A. et al. (2019). Red fluorescent ZnO nanoparticle grafted with polyglycerol and conjugated RGD peptide as drug delivery vehicles for efficient target cancer therapy. *Mater. Sci. Eng. C* 95: 104–113.

261 Zhao, S., Niu, G., Wu, F. et al. (2017). Lysosome-targetable polythiophene nanoparticles for two-photon excitation photodynamic therapy and deep tissue imaging. *J. Mater. Chem. B* 5: 3651–3657.

262 Zhen, W., An, S., Wang, S. et al. (2021). Precise subcellular organelle targeting for boosting endogenous-stimuli-mediated tumor therapy. *Adv. Mater.* 33: 1–25.

263 Wlodkowic, D., Skommer, J., McGuinness, D. et al. (2009). ER-Golgi network-A future target for anti-cancer therapy. *Leuk. Res.* 33: 1440–1447.

264 Jeena, M.T., Palanikumar, L., Go, E.M. et al. (2017). Mitochondria localization induced self-assembly of peptide amphiphiles for cellular dysfunction. *Nat. Commun.* 8: 26.

265 Kim, I., Bang, W.Y., Kim, S. et al. (2018). Peroxisome-targeted supramolecular nanoprobes assembled with pyrene-labelled peptide amphiphiles. *Chem. Asian J.* 13: 3485–3490.

266 Liu, X., Li, M., Liu, J. et al. (2022). In situ self-sorting peptide assemblies in living cells for simultaneous organelle targeting. *J. Am. Chem. Soc.* 144: 9312–9323.

267 Tugyi, R., Uray, K., Iván, D. et al. (2005). Partial D-amino acid substitution: Improved enzymatic stability and preserved Ab recognition of a MUC2 epitope peptide. *Proc. Natl. Acad. Sci. U. S. A.* 102: 413–418.

268 Jeena, M.T., Jeong, K., Go, E.M. et al. (2019). Heterochiral assembly of amphiphilic peptides inside the mitochondria for supramolecular cancer therapeutics. *ACS Nano* 13: 11022–11033.

269 Khoury, C.C. and Ziyadeh, F.N. (2011). Angiogenic factors. *Contrib. Nephrol.* 170: 83–92.

270 Carmeliet, P. and Jain, R.K. (2000). Angiogenesis in cancer and other diseases. *Nature* 407: 249–257.

271 Hosseinkhani, H., Hosseinkhani, M., Khademhosseini, A. et al. (2006). Enhanced angiogenesis through controlled release of basic fibroblast growth factor from peptide amphiphile for tissue regeneration. *Biomaterials* 27: 5836–5844.

272 Senturk, B., Mercan, S., Delibasi, T. et al. (2016). Angiogenic peptide nanofibers improve wound healing in STZ-induced diabetic rats. *ACS Biomater Sci. Eng.* 2: 1180–1189.

273 Rajangam, K., Behanna, H.A., Hui, M.J. et al. (2006). Heparin binding nanostructures to promote growth of blood vessels. *Nano Lett.* 6: 2086–2090.

274 Gröschel, K., Riecker, A., Schulz, J.B. et al. (2005). Systematic review of early recurrent stenosis after carotid angioplasty and stenting. *Stroke* 36: 367–373.

275 Moyer, T.J., Kassam, H.A., Bahnson, E.S.M. et al. (2015). Shape-dependent targeting of injured blood vessels by peptide amphiphile supramolecular nanostructures. *Small* 11: 2750–2755.

276 Keisler, B. and Carter, C. (2015). Abdominal aortic aneurysm. *Am. Fam. Physician* 91: 538–543.

277 Ledford, B.T., Akerman, A.W., Sun, K. et al. (2022). Peptide amphiphile supramolecular nanofibers designed to target abdominal aortic aneurysms. *ACS Nano* 16: 7309–7322.

278 Klein, M.K., Kassam, H.A., Lee, R.H. et al. (2020). Development of optimized tissue-factor-targeted peptide amphiphile nanofibers to slow noncompressible torso hemorrhage. *ACS Nano* 14: 6649–6662.

279 Chang, S.M., Kuhn, J.G., Ian Robins, H. et al. (2001). A phase II study of paclitaxel in patients with recurrent malignant glioma using different doses depending upon the concomitant use of anticonvulsants: A North American brain tumor consortium report. *Cancer* 91: 417–422.

280 Mazza, M., Notman, R., Anwar, J. et al. (2013). Nanofiber-based delivery of therapeutic peptides to the brain. *ACS Nano* 7: 1016–1026.

281 Chung, E.J., Cheng, Y., Morshed, R. et al. (2014). Fibrin-binding, peptide amphiphile micelles for targeting glioblastoma. *Biomaterials* 35: 1249–1256.

282 Kim, I., Han, E.H., Ryu, J. et al. (2016). One-dimensional supramolecular nanoplatforms for theranostics based on co-assembly of peptide amphiphiles. *Biomacromolecules* 17: 3234–3243.

283 Yang, P.-P., Luo, Q., Qi, G.-B. et al. (2017). Host materials transformable in tumor microenvironment for homing theranostics. *Adv. Mater.* 29: 1605869.

284 Guo, H., Song, S., Dai, T. et al. (2020). Near-infrared fluorescent and magnetic resonance dual-imaging coacervate nanoprobes for trypsin mapping and targeted payload delivery of malignant tumors. *ACS Appl. Mater. Interfaces* 12: 17302–17313.

285 Yang, L., Tang, J., Yin, H. et al. (2022). Self-assembled noparticles for tumor-triggered targeting dual-mode NIRF/MR imaging and photodynamic therapy applications. *ACS Biomater Sci. Eng.* 8: 880–892.

286 Mukherjee, S., Vaishnava, S., and Hooper, L.V. (2008). Multi-layered regulation of intestinal antimicrobial defense. *Cell. Mol. Life Sci.* 65: 3019–3027.

287 Zhu, X. and Jun Loh, X. (2015). Layer-by-layer assemblies for antibacterial applications. *Biomater. Sci.* 3: 1505–1518.

288 Zou, P., Chen, W.T., Sun, T. et al. (2020). Recent advances: peptides and self-assembled Peptide-nanosystems for antimicrobial therapy and diagnosis. *Biomater. Sci.* 8: 4975–4996.

289 Pazos, E., Sleep, E., Pérez, C.M.R. et al. (2016). Nucleation and growth of ordered arrays of silver nanoparticles on peptide nanofibers: Hybrid nanostructures with antimicrobial properties. *J. Am. Chem. Soc.* 138: 5507–5510.

290 Motterlini, R. and Otterbein, L.E. (2010). The therapeutic potential of carbon monoxide. *Nat. Rev. Drug Discov.* 9: 728–743.

291 Huston, C.J. (1996). Carbon monoxide poisoning. *Am. J. Nurs.* 96: 48–49.

292 Lazarus, L.S., Benninghoff, A.D., and Berreau, L.M. (2020). Development of triggerable, trackable, and targetable carbon monoxide releasing molecules. *Acc. Chem. Res.* 53: 2273–2285.

293 Hasegawa, U., Van Der Vlies, A.J., Simeoni, E. et al. (2010). Carbon monoxide-releasing micelles for immunotherapy. *J. Am. Chem. Soc.* 132: 18273–18280.

294 Pfeiffer, H., Rojas, A., Niesel, J., and Schatzschneider, U. (2009). Sonogashira and "Click" reactions for the N-terminal and side-chain functionalization of peptides with [Mn(CO)3(tpm)]+-based CO releasing molecules (tpm = tris(pyrazolyl) methane). *Dalton Trans.* 4292.

295 Matson, J.B., Webber, M.J., Tamboli, V.K. et al. (2012). A peptide-based material for therapeutic carbon monoxide delivery. *Soft Matter* 8: 6689–6692.

296 Li, X., Lovell, J.F., Yoon, J., and Chen, X. (2020). Clinical development and potential of photothermal and photodynamic therapies for cancer. *Nat. Rev. Clin. Oncol.* 17: 657–674.

297 Cao, Y., Ren, Q., Hao, R., and Sun, Z. (2022). Innovative strategies to boost photothermal therapy at mild temperature mediated by functional nanomaterials. *Mater. Des.* 214: 110391.

298 Ma, Z., Zhang, Y., Zhang, J. et al. (2020). Ultrasmall peptide-coated platinum nanoparticles for precise NIR-II photothermal therapy by mitochondrial targeting. *ACS Appl. Mater. Interfaces* 12: 39434–39443.

299 Falcone, N., Andoy, N.M.O., Sullan, R.M.A., and Kraatz, H.B. (2021). Peptide-polydopamine nanocomposite hydrogel for a laser-controlled hydrophobic drug delivery. *ACS Appl. Bio Mater.* 4: 6652–6657.

300 Liu, Z., Li, J., Chen, W. et al. (2020). Light and sound to trigger the Pandora's box against breast cancer: A combination strategy of sonodynamic, photodynamic and photothermal therapies. *Biomaterials* 232: 119685.

301 Qin, Q., Zhao, L., Liu, Z. et al. (2020). Bioinspired l -proline oligomers for the cryopreservation of oocytes via controlling ice growth. *ACS Appl. Mater. Interfaces* 12: 18352–18362.

302 Graham, B., Bailey, T.L., Healey, J.R.J. et al. (2017). Polyproline as a minimal antifreeze protein mimic that enhances the cryopreservation of cell monolayers. *Angew. Chem. Int. Ed.* 56: 15941–15944.

303 Jeon, N., Jeong, I.H., Cho, E. et al. (2023). Microcurvature controllable metal-organic framework nanoagents capable of ice-lattice matching for cellular cryopreservation. *JACS Au* 3: 154–164.

304 Kristiansen, E. and Zachariassen, K.E. (2005). The mechanism by which fish antifreeze proteins cause thermal hysteresis. *Cryobiology* 51: 262–280.

305 Garnham, C.P., Campbell, R.L., and Davies, P.L. (2011). Anchored clathrate waters bind antifreeze proteins to ice. *Proc. Natl. Acad. Sci. U. S. A.* 108: 7363–7367.

306 Liou, Y.C., Tocilj, A., Davies, P.L., and Jia, Z. (2000). Mimicry of ice structure by surface hydroxyls and water of a β-helix antifreeze protein. *Nature* 406: 322–324.

307 Loo, Y., Goktas, M., Tekinay, A.B. et al. (2015). Self-assembled proteins and peptides as scaffolds for tissue regeneration. *Adv. Healthc. Mater.* 4: 2557–2586.

308 Mata, A., Hsu, L., Capito, R. et al. (2009). Micropatterning of bioactive self-assembling gels. *Soft Matter* 5: 1228–1236.

309 Lin, Y., Thomas, M.R., Gelmi, A. et al. (2017). Self-assembled 2D free-standing janus nanosheets with single-layer thickness. *J. Am. Chem. Soc.* 139: 13592–13595.

310 Anderson, C.F., Chakroun, R.W., Grimmett, M.E. et al. (2022). Collagen-binding peptide-enabled supramolecular hydrogel design for improved organ adhesion and sprayable therapeutic delivery. *Nano Lett.* 22: 4182–4191.

311 Dumele, O., Chen, J., Passarelli, J.V., and Stupp, S.I. (2020). Supramolecular energy materials. *Adv. Mater.* 32: 1–32.

312 Solomon, L.A., Sykes, M.E., Wu, Y.A. et al. (2017). Tailorable exciton transport in doped peptide-amphiphile assemblies. *ACS Nano* 11: 9112–9118.

313 Li, C., Iscen, A., Sai, H. et al. (2020). Supramolecular–covalent hybrid polymers for light-activated mechanical actuation. *Nat. Mater.* 19: 900–909.

314 Dijkstra, M. and Luijten, E. (2021). From predictive modelling to machine learning and reverse engineering of colloidal self-assembly. *Nat. Mater.* 20: 762–773.

315 Dannenhoffer, A., Sai, H., Bruckner, E.P. et al. (2022). Metallurgical alloy approach to two-dimensional supramolecular materials. *Chem* 9: 170–180.

Index

Peptide Self-Assembly and Engineering: Fundamentals, Structures, and Applications, First Edition.
Edited by Xuehai Yan.

d

g

h

i

n

o

p

t